III   IV   V   VI   VII   0

He
2

B
5

C
6

N
7

O
8

F
9

Ne
10

Al
13

Si
14

P
15

S
16

Cl
17

Ar
18

Fe
26

Co
27

Ni
28

Cu
29

Zn
30

Ga
31

Ge
32

As
33

Se
34

Br
35

Kr
36

Ru
44

Rh
45

Pd
46

Ag
47

Cd
48

In
49

Sn
50

Sb
51

Te
52

I
53

Xe
54

Os
76

Ir
77

Pt
78

Au
79

Hg
80

Tl
81

Pb
82

Bi
83

Po
84

At
85

Rn
86

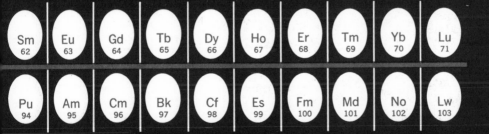

Sm
62

Eu
63

Gd
64

Tb
65

Dy
66

Ho
67

Er
68

Tm
69

Yb
70

Lu
71

Pu
94

Am
95

Cm
96

Bk
97

Cf
98

Es
99

Fm
100

Md
101

No
102

Lw
103

chemistry: principles and properties

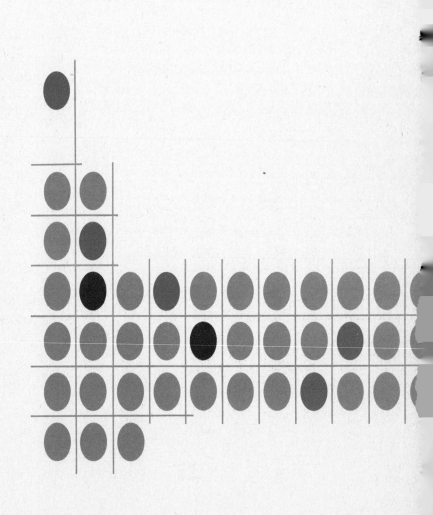

chemistry: principles and properties

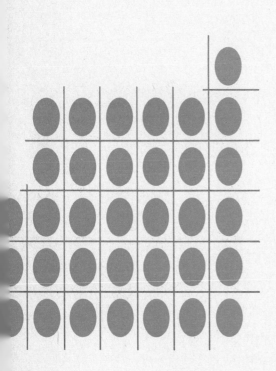

MICHELL J. SIENKO
Professor of Chemistry
Cornell University
ROBERT A. PLANE
Professor of Chemistry
Cornell University

McGRAW-HILL
BOOK COMPANY
New York
St. Louis
San Francisco
Toronto
London
Sydney

chemistry: principles and properties

preface

During the past decade, the level of chemistry instruction has been raised at a rate without parallel in recent history. Although much of the credit belongs to the new high school chemistry programs and the innovators who boldly tried new approaches to the learning process, recognition must be given also to the increasing pressure generated by the logarithmic expansion of scientific discovery. The first-year college chemistry course is now confronted with better prepared students and has an expanded and more complex body of knowledge to present.

In this text, as in our earlier book, the emphasis is on the principles of chemistry. Because of the steadily improving background of today's entering college student, it is possible—in fact, necessary—to increase the depth of coverage in the first-year course. Particularly in the areas of chemical bonding, thermodynamics, mechanisms, and spectroscopic studies, more powerful, though more abstract, concepts are available for increasing the efficiency of the freshman course. Yet chemistry is, above all, an experimental discipline that rests firmly on observed behavior. Consequently, it is imperative that the freshman student be taught its descriptive aspects as well as its theoretical principles. A proper balance of theoretical and experimental aspects produces the best perspective for stimulating the student to the profitable further study of chemistry.

In the present book we have attempted to maintain a suitable ratio of theory and description, while intensifying the treatment so as to capitalize on improved student preparation. We have omitted much of the classical combining-weight approach to atoms in favor of the particle-physics approach, which is closer to the actual mental processes of today's chemists. Once the atomic-structure principles have been developed, bonding and molecule formation are considered in terms of both valence-bond and molecular-orbital theory. Both theories seem to be requisite for any significant further work in chemistry.

As in our earlier book, the material is presented in order of increasing complexity—atoms, molecules, gases, condensed phases, solutions, reactions, descriptive chemistry of the elements. More difficult aspects of chemistry have been embraced than were previously (e.g., nonideal behavior of gases, quantitative aspects of phase changes, spatial restraints in crystal packing, criteria for spontaneous changes). Throughout much of this discussion, the necessity of drawing on the concepts of elementary thermodynamics is developed. Only after the need has been established and some vocabulary has been presented is a unified summary chapter of introductory chemical thermodynamics given. We have found in our classes that a successful approach to thermodynamics requires three stages: establishing the need for the concepts, developing the concepts and their mathematical relations, and solving a variety of computational problems. Computations involving thermodynamic concepts are liberally used throughout the latter part of the book in connection with the descriptive chemistry of specific elements.

Clearly evident in the incoming student is an increasing ability to apply mathematical operations. For this reason we have felt justified in making appreciable use of mathematics. This we have done through numerical descriptions of properties, mathematical equations for interrelating observed behavior, and substitution of derivations for lengthy verbal steps in logic. Problem solving is a key part of our freshman chemistry course, so in this text we have included numerous worked-out examples and lists of exercises. The exercises, or questions at the ends of the chapters, are presented in order of increasing difficulty, culminating with a challenge for even the best of students. Many of the problems are supplied with numerical answers, which provide useful checks for the student without disclosing the method of solution. In those rare cases when it is necessary to use the most elementary fundamentals of calculus (e.g., kinetics and, to a lesser extent, thermodynamics) the symbols and the methods have been defined *ab initio*.

Although considerable descriptive chemistry is used in the first 15 chapters to illustrate the principles discussed, the systematic description of the behavior of the elements is collected in the subsequent chapters with full application of the previously developed principles. After hydrogen and oxygen are treated individually, the other elements are taken up group by group across the periodic table from the alkali metals through the noble-gas compounds. Although the order of presentation is from left to right, almost complete flexibility of order can be exercised by the instructor, because basic principles have previously been covered. Only in a few cases is a fundamentally new concept introduced in the latter part of the book (e.g., nuclear magnetic resonance in the chapter on hydrogen, ligand-field theory in the introductory chapter on transition elements).

The principal aim of the latter part of the book is to present an organized body of systematic inorganic chemistry from which an instructor can select those topics most appropriate to his own students. Organic chemistry is presented as an interesting and unique aspect of the group IV element carbon. Because the descriptive chemistry is organized around the principles, many of the problems at the ends of chapters emphasize the application of the concepts discussed earlier (e.g., stoichiometry, equilibrium, structure, thermodynamics, kinetics, oxidation potentials). Also, in the descriptive part of the text, special sections have been included to cover the qualitative analysis of the more common members of each group of elements. An extensive appendix is included, containing physical concepts and data useful to the student. An instructor's manual useful to the teacher is available from the publisher.

We recognize the truly formidable task confronting colleagues who teach freshman chemistry. This text is presented not as a substitute for, but as an aid to, the development of personalized, effective teaching that will lead to meaningful learning by today's more able student.

In preparing this book, we have received invaluable aid from Dr. William P. Schaefer of the California Institute of Technology.

michell j. sienko
robert a. plane

contents

1 atomic structure

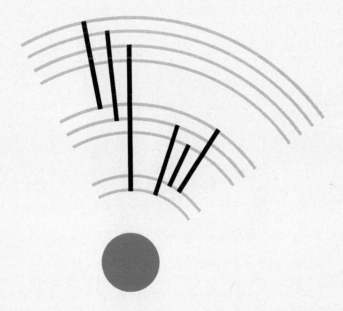

Man has long speculated that matter in its ultimate state of subdivision is atomic, i.e., consists of discrete, indivisible particles. Early in the nineteenth century these ideas were given quantitative expression by the classic work of John Dalton. Working with the law of definite composition and the law of multiple proportions, he assigned a self-consistent set of masses to the atoms of the various elements. However, no sooner was his work achieved than succeeding experimenters, notably Faraday, Crookes, and Goldstein, showed that atoms were indeed divisible and apparently electrical in nature.

It is the purpose of this chapter to consider the classic experiments which cast light on the quantitative properties of the particles from which atoms are composed. Having established this foundation, we shall go on to consider energy states of atoms. In subsequent chapters we shall see how these atomic energy states form the basis for understanding chemical behavior.

1.1 ELECTRONS

If, to a neutral atom of any kind, sufficient energy is added, then the atom can be ionized, i.e., converted to positive and negative fragments. The positive fragment, called an *ion,* differs with the identity of the atom used. However, the negative fragment, called an *electron,* is the same no matter what atoms are ionized. The properties of the electron, specifically its charge and its mass, can be measured by studying the effect on the electron of electrical and magnetic forces. The original experiments were performed by J. J. Thomson in 1897. Figure 1.1 shows an arrangement which could be used for such a study. The negative electrode (cathode) emits electrons, which are accelerated to the right in

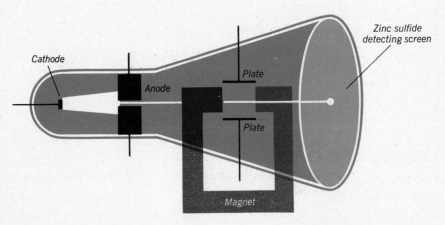

1.1
Deflection of cathode rays by electric and magnetic fields

the evacuated tube. Some electrons pass through the hole in the positive electrode (anode) to give a narrow beam, which falls on the zinc sulfide detecting screen at the face of the tube. Electric plates in the tube, one located above the beam and the other below the beam, can deflect the beam in an up-and-down direction, because the negative plate repels the negative beam and the positive plate attracts it. The amount of deflection depends on the voltage between the plates.

A magnet, which surrounds the tube from the outside, will also cause the beam to be deflected, because moving electric charges are bent into curved paths by a magnetic field. The experiment consists of two parts. In one a deflection is measured with plates uncharged; i.e., the deflection is due to the magnetic field alone. In the other part of the experiment the plates are charged in the proper direction and to the extent required to produce no net deflection; i.e., the electric field and the magnetic field exactly counteract each other.

Figure 1.2 shows the relation of the quantities involved. An electron with charge e moves to the right with velocity v. In passing through

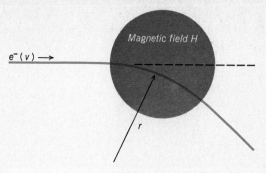

Magnetic field H

$e^-(v) \longrightarrow$

r

magnetic field H, which is perpendicular to the plane of the diagram, the electron is bent into a curved path with radius of curvature r, which can be determined by measuring the displacement of the spot at the end of the tube. The force due to the magnetic field is Hev. This force in turn is equal to the mass of the electron times its acceleration, and for a curving particle is mv^2/r. This gives the equality $Hev = mv^2/r$, from which we see that

$$\frac{e}{m} = \frac{v}{Hr}$$

This relation would give us the charge-to-mass ratio if we knew v, since H and r can be measured. To get v, we proceed to the second part of the experiment and measure E, the electric field strength (voltage between plates divided by distance of separation) needed to restore the electron beam to its original path. When there is no net deflection, the magnetic force Hev is just balanced by the electric force Ee. From this equality, $Hev = Ee$, we see that

$$v = \frac{E}{H}$$

Substituting for v in the earlier equation, we obtain

$$\frac{e}{m} = \frac{E}{H^2 r}$$

The numerical value of e/m so obtained for all electrons is

$$-1.7588 \times 10^8 \text{ coulombs g}^{-1}$$

(The coulomb, a unit for measuring electric charge, is the amount of charge passing a given point in one second when the electric current is one ampere. See Appendix 3.7.)

Once the charge-to-mass ratio has been measured, another experiment has to be performed to get either the charge or the mass separately. If, for example, the charge is measured independently, the mass can be calculated from the value of e/m. The charge of the electron was first measured precisely in a classic experiment by R. A. Millikan in 1909. Figure 1.3 shows the essential features of the experiment. A cloud of oil droplets is sprayed between two charged plates. Because

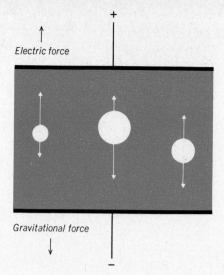

+

Electric force

Gravitational force

−

of gravity the droplets tend to settle, the gravitational force being equal to Mg, where M is the mass of a drop and g is the constant of gravitational acceleration. However, if the droplets carry a negative charge, they will experience an upward force due to the electric field between the charged plates. The magnitude of this electric force is Eq, where E is the electric field strength and q is the total electric charge on a particular drop. Different droplets may carry different charges, owing to the way the experiment is done. For example, irradiation with X rays may be used. The X rays presumably knock electrons off atoms in the air; one or more of these electrons can be picked up by a single oil droplet, thus making it negative.

The rate of motion of a particular oil droplet is measured by observing it in a transverse light beam. By adjusting the voltage on the plates, the droplet can be made stationary. Under this condition, the gravity force Mg (corrected for air buoyancy) just equals the electric force Eq. Since E and g are known, q can be calculated once M is obtained. To evaluate M, the electric field is shut off, and the free fall of the droplet in air is observed. Because of air friction, there will be a drag on the droplet. The amount of drag increases with speed, so that a limiting rate of fall is reached. At this limiting rate the net gravitational pull equals the frictional drag. From a measurement of the limiting rate v of free fall the radius a of the drop can be calculated, since v is proportional to a^2. Once a is determined, the effective mass of the droplet is $(\frac{4}{3})\pi a^3$ times the density of oil, determined in air.

It is observed that, although the charges on different oil droplets vary, the values obtained are always small, whole-numbered multiples of -1.60×10^{-19} coulomb. Apparently, the smallest possible charge that any one oil droplet can pick up is -1.60×10^{-19} coulomb, and this is assumed to be the charge of an individual electron. Combining the charge of the electron (-1.60×10^{-19} coulomb) with its charge-to-mass ratio (-1.76×10^8 coulombs g^{-1}) gives the mass of the electron as 9.1×10^{-28} g.

1.2 DISCOVERY OF THE NUCLEUS

By the beginning of the twentieth century, it was generally accepted that atoms can be fragmented into negatively charged electrons and positive ions. Following his measurement of e/m for electrons, J. J. Thomson, in 1898, proposed that the atom be considered a sphere of positive electricity in which negative electrons are embedded like jelly beans in a ball of cotton. Most of the mass of the atom would have to be associated with the positive electricity, a conclusion drawn from the observation that the positive fragments of atoms are much heavier than the electrons. In 1911, Lord Rutherford performed a classic experiment which tested the Thomson model. He was investigating the scattering of particles produced by radioactive decay, specifically the scattering of alpha particles. An alpha particle carries two units of positive charge (twice the charge of an electron but opposite in sign) and has a mass equal to that of a helium atom from which two electrons have been removed.

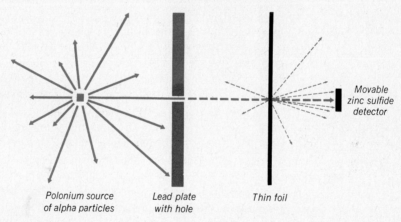

Polonium source
of alpha particles

Lead plate
with hole

Thin foil

Movable
zinc sulfide
detector

1.4
Rutherford's experiment
for studying the scattering
of alpha particles

A beam of alpha particles can be obtained from a radioactive element such as polonium or radium and can be directed onto a metal-foil target through a pinhole in a lead plate. Figure 1.4 shows a possible experimental setup. Since alpha particles are very energetic, they penetrate thin foils readily. On the basis of the Thomson model of the atom, it was thought that a metal consists of atoms which are spheres of positive electricity containing negative electrons; i.e., the metal is essentially a sea of positive electricity containing negative charges. If the positive charge and the mass are distributed uniformly throughout the metal, the alpha particle has little reason to swerve off its original path and should plow right through any metal foil in the path of the beam. A detector in the path of the beam, such as a photographic plate or a screen coated with zinc sulfide, would be expected to show that the particles going through a metal foil suffer at most only slight deflections. On the contrary, it was found that some are deflected at fairly large angles. A few are actually reflected back along their path. To Rutherford this was

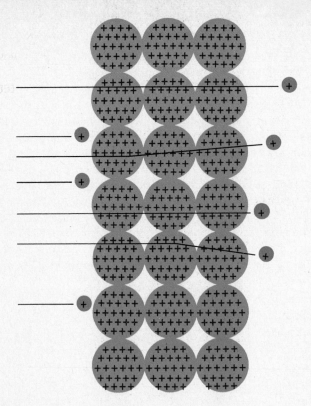

1.5
Penetration of metal foil
as expected from Thomson
model (positive charge
distributed throughout the
atom)

absolutely unbelievable. In his own words, "it was almost as incredible as if you fired a 15-inch shell at a piece of tissue paper and it came back and hit you."

The Thomson model could not account for such large deflections. If mass and positive charge were uniformly spread throughout the metal, a positively charged alpha particle would not encounter a large repulsion or major obstacle anywhere in its path. This is shown in Figure 1.5. According to Rutherford, the only way to account for the large deflection is to say that the positive electricity and mass in the metal foil are concentrated in very small regions. Although, as shown in Figure 1.6, most of the alpha particles can go through without any deflection, occasionally one comes very close to the high concentration of positive charge. This high concentration of positive charge is essentially immovable because of its high mass. As the like charges get closer together, they repel each other, and the repulsion may be great enough to cause the alpha particle to swerve considerably from its original path. So, Rutherford suggested that an atom has a *nucleus*, or center, in which its positive charge and mass are concentrated.

The quantitative results of scattering experiments such as Rutherford's indicate that the nucleus of an atom has a diameter of approximately 10^{-13} cm, which is about 1/100000 of the size ascribed to atoms in solids.

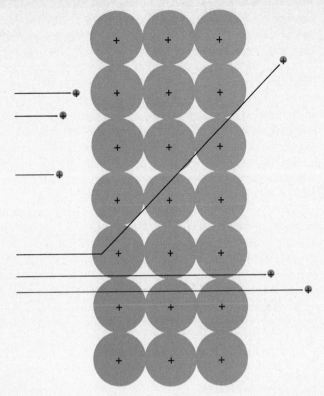

1.6
Deflection of alpha
particles as accounted for
by Rutherford model
(entire positive charge of
atom concentrated at
center)

1.3 ATOMIC NUMBER

About the same time that Rutherford was led to postulate the existence of the nucleus, H. G. J. Moseley was measuring the energies of X rays emitted by various elements. These measurements, which contributed greatly to further characterization of the nuclear atom, can be carried out with an X-ray tube such as the one shown in Figure 1.7. Electrons from the curved cathode on the right are focused to impinge on the replaceable anode on the left, giving rise to the emission of X rays from the target material. It is found that wavelengths emitted are characteristic of the element from which the anode is made.

X rays, like light, are a form of electromagnetic radiation. They move through space with the speed of light, 2.998×10^{10} cm sec^{-1}, and they can be characterized in terms of a wavelength and a frequency. Figure 1.8 illustrates what is meant by wavelength, designated by λ, for the

1.7
An X-ray tube

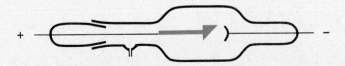

particular case of waves spreading out from a central point on the surface of a liquid. The distance between any pair of corresponding points, such as two adjacent wave crests, is called the *wavelength* and is equal to the velocity at which the train of waves is propagated divided by the frequency of the wave. The *frequency,* designated by v, can be pictured as the number of complete waves or pulses that pass a given point per second. As an illustration, if two wave trains differ in that wave 1 has twice the wavelength of wave 2, it follows that the frequency of the first wave train is half that of the second. The energy E associated with an electromagnetic wave is proportional to its frequency, that is, $E = hv$, where the proportionality constant h, a fundamental constant called the *Planck constant,* has the value 6.6256×10^{-27} erg-sec.

If an X-ray tube has an anode made of copper, the shortest-wavelength X ray emitted has $\lambda = 1.541$ Å (where 1 Å = one angstrom = 1×10^{-8} cm). On the other hand, if the anode is made of molybdenum, the shortest-wavelength X ray emitted has $\lambda = 0.709$ Å. Moseley's experiments, in which he successively substituted different anode materials, showed that there was a systematic relation between the wavelengths of the X rays emitted and the nature of the anode material. Specifically, he obtained a straight line when he plotted the square root

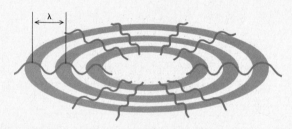

1.8
Wave motion generated on the surface of a liquid

of the X-ray frequency (for the short-wavelength limit) against the order in which the element appeared in the periodic table of the chemical elements.

As shown in Figure 1.9, to get a smooth curve, Moseley found it necessary to leave gaps in a few places (corresponding to then-undiscovered elements) and to use an order based on trends of chemical properties rather than strict adherence to increasing atomic mass. For example, in the case of cobalt [58.93 amu (atomic mass units)] and nickel (58.71 amu), cobalt would come first on the basis of chemical trends but nickel would come first on the basis of its smaller atomic mass. From his X-ray data Moseley was led to choose the order cobalt followed by nickel, thus overturning the notion that atomic mass was most decisive in fixing atomic properties. Instead, there is a characteristic number called the *atomic number,* generally designated as Z, which is believed to be equal to the positive charge of the nucleus and which determines the ordering of the elements by chemical behavior.

1.3 Atomic number

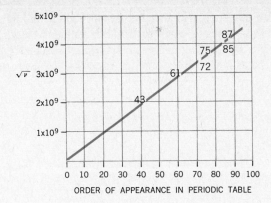

ORDER OF APPEARANCE IN PERIODIC TABLE

1.9
Moseley's plot of X-ray
frequencies for the
elements

1.4 ATOMIC MASS*

Why is it in some cases that chemical properties of the elements do not follow an order based on atomic mass, but instead follow an order based on atomic number? Put another way, why is there not a direct parallel between increasing atomic number and increasing atomic mass? The answer lies in the fact that different atoms of the same element may

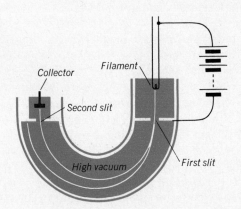

1.10
Mass spectrometer
(magnetic field not shown)

differ in mass. Atoms that have the same atomic number but differ in mass are called *isotopes*.

The existence of isotopes can be shown by use of the mass spectrometer. Figure 1.10 shows some essential features of this device schematically. The filament, on being heated by an electric current, emits electrons which ionize the gas present in the chamber and near the filament. The positive ions are accelerated through the first slit and are bent into a circular path by a magnetic field. Ions having different values of the charge-to-mass ratio follow different paths, as shown by

* Most chemists instinctively use the term *atomic weight* instead of *atomic mass*, and later we may occasionally slip in that direction. However, in this chapter on atomic physics, in which we consider experiments for measuring mass by means other than weighing (using gravity), we shall attempt to use the term *atomic mass* consistently.

the curved lines in the figure. Separation of ion paths occurs for the following reasons. For an accelerating voltage V, a particle with charge q is given an amount of energy equal to qV. This energy is added to the particle as kinetic energy and so equals $\frac{1}{2}mv^2$. From the equality

$$qV = \frac{1}{2}mv^2$$

the particle velocity v can be found to be

$$v = \sqrt{\frac{2qV}{m}}$$

As shown in Section 1.1, the charge-to-mass ratio of a charged particle moving in a magnetic field H is related to the radius of curvature r as follows:

$$\frac{q}{m} = \frac{v}{Hr}$$

Substituting for v, we obtain

$$\frac{q}{m} = \frac{2V}{H^2r^2}$$

This equation indicates that, for fixed values of the voltage V and the magnetic field H, particles of larger charge-to-mass ratio follow paths of smaller radius of curvature. In other words, for unit positive charge, lighter particles are bent more and, therefore, particles of different charge-to-mass ratio can be separated in a mass spectrometer.

In practice, a mass spectrometer operates with a fixed collector to catch only ions of a particular radius of curvature. By varying either V or H, ions of a particular q/m can be focused on the collector. For a particular element it is found that several beams are produced and that the beams differ from each other in q/m value. For example, typical values for neon gas are $+4.81 \times 10^3$, $+9.62 \times 10^3$, and $+4.33 \times 10^3$ coulombs g^{-1}. The second of these values is exactly twice the first. Apparently, some of the atoms have lost two electrons instead of one and hence have twice as large a charge-to-mass ratio. The third value, $+4.33 \times 10^3$, bears no simple relation to the other two and cannot be explained by assuming a loss of a different number of electrons. The fact that the charge-to-mass ratio differs by something other than a whole-number multiple indicates that particles of different mass must be present. In other words, the sample of the element neon contains nonidentical atoms, or isotopes. For every element two or more isotopes are known. The relative abundance of isotopes can vary widely from element to element, as can be determined by measuring the relative intensity of the different isotope beams in the mass spectrometer.

An illustration of isotope abundances is afforded by the element oxygen. A natural mixture of oxygen atoms consists of three isotopes, which can be designated O^{16}, O^{17}, and O^{18}. The superscripts indicate the mass number, which is the whole number closest to the isotopic mass. The masses of these isotopes are 15.9949 amu for O^{16}, 16.9991

1.4 Atomic mass

10

amu for O^{17}, and 17.9991 amu for O^{18}. The relative abundances are 99.759% of O^{16}, 0.037% of O^{17}, and 0.204% of O^{18}. The atomic mass used for calculations involving natural oxygen is not equal to the mass of any single isotope, but is a weighted average of the three. This means that in a representative collection of 100000 oxygen atoms the average mass per atom will be equal to 99759 times 15.9949 amu plus 37 times 16.9991 amu plus 204 times 17.9991 amu all divided by 100000 to give 15.9994 amu.

Because, for many years, oxygen was the standard of reference for setting up atomic-mass scales, a problem arose from differences of definition. On the old scale used by chemists an "average" oxygen atom was assigned a mass of exactly 16 atomic mass units. On the old scale used by physicists an O^{16} atom was assigned a mass of exactly 16 atomic mass units. Thus, there was a difference in the definition of the atomic mass unit. Fortunately, this difference has been done away with, and now there is agreement on a single scale based on the assignment of exactly 12 atomic mass units as the mass of a C^{12} atom. This particular isotope has been chosen as a compromise between the two factions.

Practically all the mass of an atom resides in the nucleus. However, there is not a one-to-one correspondence between the change of mass in going from one nucleus to another and the change in positive charge as determined by Moseley's X-ray method. For example, in the case of carbon, in going from C^{12} to C^{13} the mass changes from 12 to 13.0034 amu, whereas the atomic number is constant at 6. Furthermore, in going from C^{12} to N^{12} the mass change is only from 12 to 12.0187 amu, whereas the atomic number has changed from 6 to 7. The independence of nuclear charge from nuclear mass is accounted for by assuming that in the nucleus there are both protons and neutrons, the former accounting for the positive charge and the two together accounting for the mass. Considering the magnitude of the electron's charge as unity, the proton has a charge of $+1$ (for the same scale on which the electron has a charge of -1). The neutron, as the name implies, is electrically neutral.

The relative masses of isolated protons, neutrons, and electrons are 1.00728, 1.00867, and 0.000549 amu, respectively. These masses apply strictly to isolated particles at rest and are not simply related to masses of atomic nuclei. In the formation of a nucleus from isolated protons and neutrons, some of the mass is converted to energy, as discussed in Section 29.5. However, because the masses of the neutron and proton are so close to unity, the mass number gives directly the total number of neutrons plus protons in the nucleus. It follows, then, that isotopes of the same element have the same number of protons per nucleus but differ in the number of neutrons. Thus, for example, C^{12} has six protons and six neutrons per nucleus, whereas C^{13} has six protons and seven neutrons per nucleus. Similarly, N^{12} has seven protons and five neutrons, whereas N^{13} has seven protons and six neutrons.

Frequently, nuclei are designated by symbols such as $_8O^{18}$. Here the subscript 8 indicates the atomic number Z, which is the nuclear charge, the number of protons in the nucleus, and would also be the number of electrons in the neutral atom. The superscript* 18 indicates the mass number A, which is the total number of neutrons plus protons in the nucleus and is equal approximately to the atomic mass of the nucleus. $A - Z$ gives the number of neutrons in the nucleus, which in this case is 10.

1.5 ATOMIC SPECTROSCOPY

If white light, as from a glowing solid, is dispersed by being passed through a prism, it is observed that the resulting pattern consists of a *continuous spectrum* of colors, a gradual blending from one color to the next. The red end corresponds to lower energy, i.e., lower frequency but longer wavelength; the blue end corresponds to higher energy, i.e., higher frequency but shorter wavelength. Visible light corresponds to energies intermediate between these extremes. Ultraviolet radiation lies to the high-energy side beyond the blue; infrared radiation (or heat waves) lies to the low-energy side beyond the red.

If, instead of white light, the colored light resulting from a heated gaseous sample is dispersed by a prism, the resulting pattern is not continuous, but consists of a series of narrow lines of colors. An example of such a *line spectrum* is shown in Figure 1.11. The actual pattern

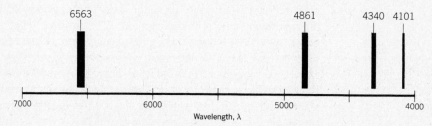

1.11
Hydrogen line spectrum
(wavelengths in angstrom
units)

obtained differs from element to element and is characteristic of the energy levels of the particular atoms present. As a sample absorbs energy, the atoms are raised to discrete energy states from which they can return to lower energy states by the release of light of definite frequencies. These frequencies measure the spacings of the energy levels. For hydrogen, it has been found that the frequencies form a series which, in the visible region of the spectrum, can be represented by the equation

$$ \nu = 3.290 \times 10^{15} \left(\frac{1}{2^2} - \frac{1}{b^2} \right) $$

where b can have values 3, 4, 5, 6, ...   In the ultraviolet region, there is a similar series of spectral lines fitting the equation

$$ \nu = 3.290 \times 10^{15} \left(\frac{1}{1^2} - \frac{1}{b^2} \right) $$

* The superscript seems to jump from upper right to upper left periodically, depending on which group of proponents is most vociferous in the international meeting. Logic appears to favor the left; common sense and esthetic balance favor the right. *De gustibus non est disputandum.*

where now b can have values 2, 3, 4, 5, 6, ... It is clearly evident that a regularity exists for observed atomic spectral lines and hence also for atomic energy levels.

1.6 BOHR ATOM

Major credit for the first workable theory of atomic structure belongs to Niels Bohr, a Danish physicist who proposed his revolutionary model in 1913. He was striving to explain three important sets of observations related to atomic behavior: periodic recurrence of properties when elements are ordered by atomic mass (or, preferably, atomic number); systematic regularity of spectral-line frequencies; apparent contradiction between classical electrodynamics and its application to the problem of electrons in atoms. By this last point is meant the fact that electrically charged particles moving in curved paths are observed to radiate energy to the surroundings (e.g., the bluish glow emitted from a particle accelerator such as a synchrotron). Similarly, if atoms consist of negative electrons surrounding positive nuclei and if these electrons are in motion so as to counteract the attraction into the nucleus, then the atoms would be expected to radiate energy unceasingly. However, such radiation, which would necessarily result in ultimate collapse of all atoms, is certainly not observed. In fact, no atom will radiate energy unless it has previously been excited to a higher energy state.

In setting up Bohr's model of the atom, the force of electrical attraction between nucleus and electron is equated to the centripetal force. The electric attraction between a nucleus of positive charge Ze and an electron of negative charge e separated by a distance r is Ze^2/r^2. The centripetal force for an electron of mass m moving with velocity v along a path with radius of curvature r is mv^2/r. Equating these two terms leads to

$$\frac{Ze^2}{r^2} = \frac{mv^2}{r} \tag{1}$$

where any value of r would seem to be possible. However, Bohr then introduced the additional requirement, which was hard to accept at the time, that the angular momentum of the electron can take on only certain permitted values. This requirement, referred to as the *quantum condition,* can be expressed as

$$mvr = n\frac{h}{2\pi} \tag{2}$$

where mvr is the angular momentum, n is a whole number which can take on values 1, 2, 3, 4, 5, . . . , and h is the Planck constant, 6.6256×10^{-27} erg-sec. Thus, the angular momentum is restricted to taking on values that are integral multiples of $h/2\pi$. Each of these values would correspond to a permitted state of the atom. The corresponding values of r can be obtained by combining Equations (1) and (2) as follows. Equation (2) is solved for v to give $v = nh/(2\pi mr)$ and this result is substituted into Equation (1)

$$\frac{Ze^2}{r^2} = \frac{m}{r}\left(\frac{n^2h^2}{4\pi^2m^2r^2}\right)$$

Canceling m from numerator and denominator and canceling r^2 from the denominator on each side gives a result for r:

$$r = n^2 \frac{h^2}{4\pi^2 m Z e^2} = \frac{n^2}{Z} a_0 \qquad (3)$$

This equation states that the only permitted values for the radius of the electron path are those equal to the square of a whole number times a collection of known constants divided by the atomic number Z. For hydrogen, $Z = 1$, allowed values of r are $1a_0, 4a_0, 9a_0, 16a_0, 25a_0, \ldots$, where a_0, called the Bohr radius, has the value 0.529167 Å. Nuclei with higher Z can also be treated in principle by Equation (3); however, since the derivation does not take into account repulsions between electrons in the same atom, Equation (3) can be used only for the combination of a nucleus and one electron.

Actually, the radius of an electron path in an atom, although interesting, is not an observable quantity. More accessible to experiment are the energy states of an atom, or rather differences between states. In the simple Bohr atom described above, the electron's energy in various states can be calculated. Its total energy is the sum of kinetic and potential terms. The kinetic-energy term is $\frac{1}{2}mv^2$, the same as for any moving body; the potential energy term is $-Ze^2/r$. The reason for the minus sign in the potential term is that, when two opposite charges attract each other, the potential energy decreases (that is, becomes more negative) as the charges come closer together (that is, r decreases). Designating the total energy as E, we write

$$E = \tfrac{1}{2}mv^2 - \frac{Ze^2}{r} \qquad (4)$$

From Equation (1) we see that mv^2 is Ze^2/r. Substituting for mv^2 in Equation (4), we get

$$E = -\frac{Ze^2}{2r}$$

Finally, by putting in the expression for r from Equation (3), we obtain

$$E = -\frac{Ze^2}{2(n^2 a_0/Z)} = -\frac{Z^2 e^2}{2n^2 a_0} \qquad (5)$$

Equation (5) gives the energies for the various states (i.e., various n values) of a one-electron atom. Although it is not possible to measure the energy of individual states, spectral lines correspond to energy differences between states. For calculating energy differences from Equation (5), we can write the energy difference as

$$E_b - E_a = \left(-\frac{Z^2 e^2}{2n_b^2 a_0}\right) - \left(-\frac{Z^2 e^2}{2n_a^2 a_0}\right)$$

$$E_b - E_a = \frac{Z^2 e^2}{2a_0}\left(\frac{1}{n_a^2} - \frac{1}{n_b^2}\right) \qquad (6)$$

where E_b and E_a are the energies of two different states corresponding to quantum numbers n_b and n_a. The lowest energy state of the atom, called the *ground state*, has $n = 1$. If we let E_a be the energy of the ground state, then Equation (6) describes the energy differences between the ground state and more energetic states (i.e., *excited states*). Converting the energy difference to a frequency

$$E_b - E_a = h\nu$$

where h is Planck's constant and ν is the frequency of the light wave emitted by the transition from state E_b to state E_a, we find

$$\nu = \frac{Z^2 e^2}{2h a_0}\left(\frac{1}{1} - \frac{1}{n_b^2}\right)$$

or, on substitution with appropriate units for the various constants,

$$\nu = 3.290 \times 10^{15}\left(\frac{1}{1} - \frac{1}{n_b^2}\right)$$

which is precisely the same as the expression given in Section 1.5 for the observed series of ultraviolet lines in the hydrogen spectrum. In like manner, if E_a represents one of the higher states, it is possible to derive a similar equation for each of the other observed series of spectral lines. Thus, at least for the hydrogen atom, the Bohr theory accurately describes observed atomic spectra. With some modification to approximate the effects due to electron-electron repulsion, the Bohr theory has been satisfactorily extended to a few other elements. However, as will be discussed in the next chapter, there are serious faults in the Bohr model, and they have led to its replacement by a more sophisticated theory of the atom.

QUESTIONS

1.1 *Atomic mass*   Given that gallium consists 60.0% of the Ga^{69} isotope (mass = 68.93 amu) and 40.0% of the Ga^{71} isotope (mass = 70.93 amu), calculate the atomic mass for a sample of normal gallium.

1.2 *Atomic mass*   Chlorine consists of only two isotopes: Cl^{35} of mass 34.969 amu and Cl^{37} of mass 36.966 amu. Calculate the relative abundance of these two isotopes to account for the normal atomic mass of 35.453 amu for the element chlorine.

1.3 *Fundamental particles*   How many neutrons, protons, and electrons are there in each of the following: (*a*) neutral atom $_7N^{14}$, (*b*) positive ion $(_{11}Na^{23})^+$, (*c*) negative ion $(_{17}Cl^{37})^-$, (*d*) positive ion $(_{92}U^{238})^{+3}$?

1.4 *Bohr atom*   (*a*) Referring ahead to Figure 2.3, make clear the distinction between an energy state and the energy observed in a spectral transition. (*b*) On the diagram, show the origin of each series of spectral lines.

1.5 *Law of definite composition*   By showing that (1), (2), and (3) are self-consistent, illustrate the law of definite composition: (1) When magnesium burns in oxygen, 2.43 g of Mg combines with 16.0 g of O. (2) Magnesium oxide analyzes to be 60.4% Mg and 39.6% O by weight. (3) When 1.00 g of Mg and 1.00 g of O are allowed to react with each other, 1.66 g of magnesium oxide is formed and 0.34 g of unreacted oxygen is left.

1.6 Law of multiple proportions (a) What is the law of multiple proportions? (b) Show that the following data illustrate the law of multiple proportions: 2.40 g of element A just reacts with 7.20 g of element B to form 9.60 g of compound I. Under different conditions, 0.600 g of element A just reacts with 2.70 g of element B to form 3.30 g of compound II.

1.7 e/m In the Thomson experiment for measuring the charge-to-mass ratio, with no electric field applied, how would doubling each of the following affect the observed radius of curvature of the electron: (a) doubling the electron velocity, (b) doubling the magnetic field, (c) doubling the mass of the electron, (d) doubling the charge of the electron?

1.8 Nuclear atom The radii of nuclei are given by the expression $1.2 \times 10^{-13} A^{1/3}$, where A is the mass number of the particular nucleus. Calculate what fraction of the atom's volume is occupied by the nucleus in the following cases: (a) $_{13}Al^{27}$, atomic radius 1.25 Å, (b) $_{29}Cu^{64}$, atomic radius 1.17 Å, (c) $_{1}H^{1}$, atomic radius 0.37 Å, (d) $_{52}Te^{125}$, atomic radius 1.37 Å.

1.9 Electromagnetic waves (a) Light having a wavelength of 4500 Å falls in the blue region of the spectrum. Calculate both the frequency and the energy associated with it. (b) A wavelength of 5900 Å corresponds to yellow light. Calculate the frequency and energy. (c) What is the difference in energy between the above blue light and yellow light?

1.10 Moseley's law Given that elements of atomic numbers 20, 30, 40, 50, and 60 have shortest X rays of wavelength 3.35, 1.43, 0.78, 0.49, and 0.33 Å, respectively, construct the following plots: (a) wavelength vs. atomic number, (b) frequency vs. atomic number, (c) square root of frequency vs. atomic number.

1.11 Atomic mass By using the definitions and data given in Section 1.4, calculate what would have been the atomic mass of $_{6}C^{12}$ on the old chemical scale and on the old physical scale.

1.12 Mass spectrometer How would the radius of curvature of a particle of fixed charge-to-mass ratio be affected by each of the following: (a) doubling the magnetic field H at constant accelerating voltage V, (b) doubling the accelerating voltage V with constant magnetic field H, (c) doubling the particle's charge but keeping its mass constant, H and V remaining unchanged?

1.13 Spectral lines By using the equations of Section 1.5, calculate the wavelength of the first three lines observed in the hydrogen spectrum in both the visible and ultraviolet series.

1.14 Oil-drop experiment (a) Suppose in a Millikan-type experiment you observed, for the charges on various oil droplets, the following values: -1.28×10^{-18}, -1.60×10^{-18}, -6.4×10^{-19}, -9.6×10^{-19} coulomb. What should you conclude about the magnitude of the fundamental charge of the electron? (b) Explain why the above conclusion is different from the usual value.

1.15 Wave numbers   Frequently we encounter the term "wave num-ber" used to describe electromagnetic radiation. It is defined as the re-ciprocal of the wavelength and has units cm^{-1}. (*a*) What is the wave number for blue light having wavelength of 4500 Å? (*b*) What is the physical significance of your answer to (*a*)? Refer to Figure 1.8. (*c*) What is the relationship between frequency and wave number?

1.16 X rays and Moseley's law   (*a*) Given that the shortest-wavelength X ray emitted by a molybdenum target is 0.709 Å, calculate both the frequency and energy associated with it. (*b*) By using Moseley's law, predict what would be the wavelength of the shortest X ray emitted by a chromium target.

1.17 Atomic mass   Tell how the atomic mass for an element might be obtained from an experiment that involves weighing and from one that does not.

1.18 Bohr atom   (*a*) Given the ion He^+. Calculate for it the energies of its three lowest (most negative) energy levels. (*b*) In principle there are three possible transitions involving only these levels. Calculate the fre-quencies and the wavelengths corresponding to those transitions.

1.19 Mass spectrometer   (*a*) Given two particles of identical charge with the mass of one 10% greater than the mass of the other. Calcu-late the ratio of their radii of curvature in a spectrometer operating at a fixed accelerating voltage V and a fixed magnetic field H. (*b*) What would happen to the radii and to the ratio of the radii if V and H were each doubled?

1.20 Bohr atom   (*a*) In terms of the equations of Section 1.6, show that the energy levels get progressively closer and converge on a limit corresponding to $E = 0$ (complete removal of the electron from the atom). (*b*) Show for each series of spectral lines that the lines converge to a series limit at some highest frequency.

ANSWERS

1.2 75.8% Cl^{35} *1.11* 12.00045, 12.0038

2 periodic law

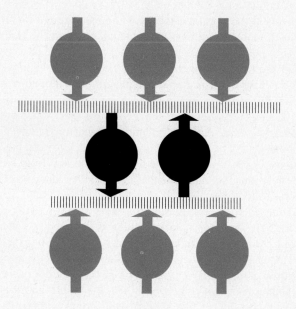

Just as the scientific postulate of atoms rested on the observations of chemistry as embodied in the laws of chemical change, so modern concepts of atomic structure rest at least in part on chemical observations involving systematic differences in the behavior of elements. Even before most of the atomic physics experiments discussed in the preceding chapter, there was an impressive accumulation of the facts of descriptive chemistry which were systematized in the periodic law. Both the periodic law and the experiments of atomic physics contributed in shaping the form of present concepts on the nature of atoms. For example, Moseley was helped by the periodic law in his development of the concept of atomic numbers. Similarly, the extension of the Bohr atomic model to atoms more complex than hydrogen was guided by attempts to account for observed chemical behavior.

2.1 PERIODIC LAW

The periodic law was discovered independently by Lothar Meyer in Germany and Mendeleev in Russia about 1868–1870. In its present form it states that the *properties of elements recur periodically if the elements are arranged in order of increasing atomic number.* To illustrate, we can consider the property of chemical reactivity. Most of the elements react with other elements, but a few, like argon, are substantially inert. Such elements react only under special conditions and then only with fluorine or oxygen. Figure 2.1 is a schematic representation of the distribution of relative inertness among the elements. Those showing low reactivity are helium, neon, argon, krypton, xenon, and radon, having atomic numbers 2, 10, 18, 36, 54, and 86, respectively. Since they are gases under usual conditions, they were called *inert gases* prior to the discovery of their actual reactivity. Although the name "inert gases" is still reasonably descriptive, most people now refer to them as the *noble gases,* the *rare gases,* or even *aerogens.*

The elements which directly follow the noble gases—lithium, sodium, potassium, rubidium, cesium, and francium, with atomic numbers 3, 11, 19, 37, 55, and 87, respectively—are *metals;* i.e., they have a *shiny luster* and are *good conductors of heat and electricity.* As a group they are called the *alkali metals.* In their chemical properties the alkali metals bear strong resemblance to each other. For example, they all react vigorously with water to liberate hydrogen and form basic solutions. If these basic solutions are neutralized with hydrochloric acid and the water is evaporated, a white salt is formed in each case. These salts, e.g., sodium chloride (NaCl) and potassium chloride (KCl), are quite similar to each other; for instance, all dissolve readily in water to give electrically conducting solutions. The salts can also be made by direct reaction between the alkali metals and chlorine gas. All the alkali metals form hydroxy compounds, for example, NaOH, which are basic.

The elements which directly precede the noble gases—fluorine, chlorine, bromine, iodine, and astatine, with atomic numbers 9, 17, 35, 53, and 85, respectively—also resemble each other. As a group, they are called the *halogens.* (The element hydrogen, which directly precedes helium, is not included in this group. As the first of all elements, hydrogen has unique properties, which do not resemble those of the halogens.) Unlike the alkali elements, the halogens are *nonmetals;* i.e., they are *poor conductors of heat and electricity.* Under usual conditions, fluorine and chlorine are gases, bromine is a liquid, and iodine and astatine are solids.

The halogens resemble each other in that all react with hydrogen to form compounds, e.g., hydrogen fluoride (HF) or hydrogen chloride (HCl), which dissolve in water to give acid solutions. Neutralization of these acid solutions with sodium hydroxide, followed by evaporation of the water, leads to the formation of white sodium salts. These salts, e.g., sodium fluoride (NaF) and sodium iodide (NaI), can also be prepared by the direct reaction of the halogens with sodium. With the exception of fluorine, halogens form hydroxy compounds all of which are acidic. An example is HOCl (hypochlorous acid).

The elements that fall between an alkali metal and the next-following halogen show a progressive gradation of properties between the two extremes. For example, the elements magnesium (atomic number 12), aluminum (13), silicon (14), phosphorus (15), and sulfur (16), which lie between sodium (11) and chlorine (17), represent such a gradation. In this sequence there is a decrease in metallic character. Magnesium and aluminum are metals; phosphorus and sulfur are nonmetals; silicon is intermediate. Concurrently, there is a progressive change from basic to acidic character of the hydroxy compounds. The hydroxy compound of magnesium, $Mg(OH)_2$, or magnesium hydroxide, is basic; the hydroxy compounds of sulfur and phosphorus, for example, H_2SO_4 or $(HO)_2SO_2$, sulfuric acid, and H_3PO_4 or $(HO)_3PO$, phosphoric acid, are acidic; the hydroxy compounds of aluminum and silicon are intermediate.

In order to emphasize the periodic reappearance of properties, it is customary to lay out the elements, not in a long straight line as in Figure 2.1, but in what is known as a *periodic table*. There are many

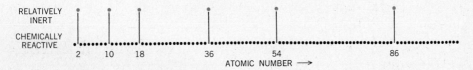

2.1
Periodic occurrence of low
reactivity in the elements

forms of the periodic table, one of which is shown in Figure 2.2. The number beneath the symbol of each element is the atomic number. The asterisk and the dagger represent the elements listed at the bottom.

The basic feature of the periodic table is the arrangement of the elements in order of increasing atomic number, with elements that are similar in properties placed under each other in a vertical column called a *group*. There are eight main groups, designated in Figure 2.2 as I, II, III, IV, V, VI, VII, and 0. Group I includes hydrogen plus the alkali metals; group VII, the halogens; and group 0, the noble gases. The elements intervening between groups II and III are called the *transition elements*. Each short vertical column of transition elements is called a *subgroup* and is named after the head element. Thus, Zn, Cd, and Hg make up the zinc subgroup.

A horizontal sequence of the periodic table is called a *period,* and the periods are numbered from the top down. The first period contains 2 elements (H and He); the second and third, 8 elements; the fourth and fifth, 18 elements. The elements denoted by the asterisk are part of the sixth period; those by the dagger, the seventh period.

Periodic law

21

The periodic table is a useful device for organizing the chemistry of the elements. Furthermore, the fact that the elements can be arranged systematically in such a table indicates a periodic recurrence of detailed structure of individual atoms.

Group	I	II											III	IV	V	VI	VII	0
Period 1	H 1																	He 2
2	Li 3	Be 4											B 5	C 6	N 7	O 8	F 9	Ne 10
3	Na 11	Mg 12			Transition elements								Al 13	Si 14	P 15	S 16	Cl 17	Ar 18
4	K 19	Ca 20	Sc 21	Ti 22	V 23	Cr 24	Mn 25	Fe 26	Co 27	Ni 28	Cu 29	Zn 30	Ga 31	Ge 32	As 33	Se 34	Br 35	Kr 36
5	Rb 37	Sr 38	Y 39	Zr 40	Nb 41	Mo 42	Tc 43	Ru 44	Rh 45	Pd 46	Ag 47	Cd 48	In 49	Sn 50	Sb 51	Te 52	I 53	Xe 54
6	Cs 55	Ba 56	* 57–71	Hf 72	Ta 73	W 74	Re 75	Os 76	Ir 77	Pt 78	Au 79	Hg 80	Tl 81	Pb 82	Bi 83	Po 84	At 85	Rn 86
7	Fr 87	Ra 88	† 89–103															

*	La 57	Ce 58	Pr 59	Nd 60	Pm 61	Sm 62	Eu 63	Gd 64	Tb 65	Dy 66	Ho 67	Er 68	Tm 69	Yb 70	Lu 71
†	Ac 89	Th 90	Pa 91	U 92	Np 93	Pu 94	Am 95	Cm 96	Bk 97	Cf 98	Es 99	Fm 100	Md 101	No 102	Lw 103

2.2 ENERGY LEVELS AND THE PERIODIC TABLE

One of the reasons for the immediate acceptance of Bohr's atomic model was the success in accounting for the periodic recurrence of chemical properties. As discussed in Section 1.6, Bohr postulated that the angular momentum of an electron in an atom could have only certain permitted values. These values are described by the whole number *n*, which is called the *principal quantum number*. In the Bohr theory the limitation on angular momentum gives rise to a parallel limitation on the radius of the electron's path and hence on its energy.

Bohr's assumption established the foundation for *quantum mechanics*, the study of the laws of motion that govern the behavior of small particles.* Particles of small mass, such as electrons, do not follow Newton's laws of motion and the classical laws of electrodynamics which describe the interactions of moving charges. New principles are required. The basic principle is that only specified energy levels are possible for electrons in atoms. These energy levels are numbered, starting with the lowest as 1, the next higher as 2, the next higher as 3, etc. The number of the energy level is *n*, the principal quantum number. A sec-

* Although the laws of quantum mechanics are necessary for describing how small bodies move, they also apply to large bodies. In the latter case the results from quantum mechanics are identical with those obtained more simply from Newton's laws of motion.

ond principle of quantum mechanics is that the electron population of any energy level in an atom is limited to $2n^2$. This means that for the lowest energy level ($n = 1$) the maximum population is $2(1)^2$, or 2. For the second level ($n = 2$), the maximum population is $2(2)^2$, or 8.

We can now draw what is known as an energy-level diagram. Figure 2.3 is such a diagram. The bottom line represents the lowest energy level—the level for which the addition of the greatest energy is required to expel the electron from the atom. Other lines represent levels of higher energy. In principle, there are an infinite number of energy levels, but usually only the lowest seven or eight need be considered. As shown in Figure 2.3, the energy difference between low energy levels is observed to be greater than that between high levels. The spacing can be calculated by using Equation (6) of Section 1.6.

The first principle of quantum mechanics states that electrons are in energy levels and that no electrons have energies that lie between levels. The second principle requires that the maximum population in the first energy level be 2; in the second level, 8; in the third level, 18; in the fourth level, 32; in the fifth level, 50; etc. Electrons in the lowest energy level ($n = 1$) are the ones most tightly bound. They are referred to as being in the K shell, in the K orbit, or in the innermost orbit. The terms "shell" and "orbit" come from the early model of the atom. Originally, Bohr suggested that the electrons move in curved orbits about the nucleus. This motion was not limited to a single plane but occurred in three dimensions, so that the path traced out by an electron described a spherical shell.

All the electrons in a given shell were identified with one energy level. The shell closest to the nucleus corresponded to the lowest energy level; shells farther from the nucleus corresponded to higher energy levels. This picture of the atom is no longer acceptable, but the terms "shell" and "orbit" are still sometimes used to refer to energy levels. The electrons in the second energy level ($n = 2$) are referred to as being in the L shell or L orbit. The higher energy levels are numbered ($n = 3, 4, 5, \ldots$) or lettered ($M, N, O, \ldots$) consecutively from there on. Higher energy levels are referred to as outer energy levels. The letter designation $K, L, M, \ldots$ was originally introduced by workers in X-ray spectroscopy. Transitions of electrons from outer shells to the K shell give rise to the K series of X rays, which were the ones used by Moseley in working out his correlation of frequency with atomic number (Section 1.3).

The limitation of the number of electrons in a given energy level to $2n^2$ can be used to account for the periodic recurrence of properties in the elements if it is assumed that the properties of atoms depend significantly on the number of electrons in the outermost energy level. Imagine the building up of an atom by addition of electrons to a nucleus of the proper atomic number. Each electron enters the lowest energy level available. In the case of hydrogen ($Z = 1$) the lone electron goes into the K shell. In helium ($Z = 2$) both electrons enter the K shell. In lithium ($Z = 3$) the third electron has to go into the L shell, since the maximum population in the K shell is two.

$n=7$
$n=6$
$n=5$
$n=4$
$n=3$
$n=2$
ENERGY →
$n=1$

2.3
Energy levels of electrons in an atom

Periodic law

23

Atomic no.	1	2	3	4	5	6	7	8	9	10	11	12	13	14	15	16	17	18
Element	H	He	Li	Be	B	C	N	O	F	Ne	Na	Mg	Al	Si	P	S	Cl	Ar
Electron population																		
K level	1	2	2	2	2	2	2	2	2	2	2	2	2	2	2	2	2	2
L level			1	2	3	4	5	6	7	8	8	8	8	8	8	8	8	8
M level											1	2	3	4	5	6	7	8
		"inert"								"inert"								"inert"

2.4
Electronic configurations

Figure 2.4 lists the first 18 elements in order of increasing atomic number and shows the number of electrons in the various energy levels. Since the K shell can accommodate only two electrons, it becomes completely populated in the "inert gas" helium. Proceeding from helium, the L-shell population increases from one in lithium to eight in neon. In neon the situation is like that in helium. With two electrons in the K shell and eight electrons in the L shell, the shells which are occupied are completely filled and the shells which are empty are completely empty. Neon is "inert." In other words, after a period, or a cycle of eight atoms, a repetition of the property of "inertness" appears.

In the next eight elements, electrons add to the third, or M, shell, building it up gradually from one to eight electrons. The element argon, number 18, might not be expected to be "inert," because, according to the energy-level diagram, 10 more, or a total of 18, electrons can be put into the M shell. However, argon is observed to be an "inert gas." It must be that eight electrons in the third shell behave like a full shell. This point will be considered in greater detail later in this section.

That the properties of atoms are closely tied to the number of electrons in the outermost energy level can be seen further from the following examples. In the case of lithium there is one electron in the outermost energy level (the L shell). Sodium also has one electron in its outermost level (the M shell). The properties of lithium and sodium are close to being identical, as already noted in Section 2.1. Likewise, beryllium ($Z = 4$) and magnesium ($Z = 12$) are similar. Each has two electrons in its outermost shell. In the periodic table, elements with similar properties are placed under each other. This corresponds to grouping together atoms which have the same number of electrons in the outermost level.

In the periodic table (see Figure 2.2 or the back cover), the first period contains but two elements (H and He), a fact that is consistent with limiting the population of the K level to two electrons. The second period contains eight elements (lithium, beryllium, boron, carbon, nitrogen, oxygen, fluorine, and neon), which is consistent with the gradual filling of the L level to a maximum population of eight electrons.

2.2 Energy levels and
the periodic table

24

The third period, covering sodium through argon, contains only 8 elements, whereas the simple energy-level picture suggests 18. (The reason for this apparent discrepancy is associated with the fact that, after eight electrons have been added to the third shell, the next two electrons go into the fourth shell, even though the third shell is not yet

Element	Z	K level	L level	M level	N level
Potassium	19	$2e^-$	$8e^-$	$8e^-$	$1e^-$
Copper	29	$2e^-$	$8e^-$	$18e^-$	$1e^-$

2.5
Electronic configurations

filled.) In the periodic table the element sodium, which has one electron in its outermost shell, is placed under lithium in group I; magnesium is placed under beryllium in group II; aluminum under boron in
group III; silicon under carbon in group IV; phosphorus under nitrogen
in group V; sulfur under oxygen in group VI; chlorine under fluorine in
group VII; and argon under neon in group 0. Because they have the
same number of electrons in the outermost shell, the elements of each
pair just mentioned have chemical similarity.

The fourth period, potassium through krypton, is even more complicated than the third period. As can be seen from the periodic table,
there are 18 elements in the fourth period, ranging from atomic number 19 to atomic number 36. Of these 18 elements, the first two—K
and Ca—and the last six—Ga, Ge, As, Se, Br, and Kr—correspond to
addition of electrons to the outermost (fourth) shell. The 10 intervening elements—Sc, Ti, V, Cr, Mn, Fe, Co, Ni, Cu, and Zn—have no more
than two electrons in the outermost shell. The buildup of the outermost
shell is interrupted to allow for the belated filling of the next-to-outermost shell. Similar delayed filling of a next-to-outermost shell also occurs in the fifth and sixth periods.

The filling of shells in the fourth period so occurs that there are two
fourth-period elements, potassium ($Z = 19$) and copper ($Z = 29$), both
of which have one electron in the outermost, or fourth, energy level.
Similarly, calcium ($Z = 20$) and zinc ($Z = 30$) have two electrons in the
fourth level. Potassium and copper are similar in some properties, presumably because each has the same number of electrons in its outermost shell. However, K and Cu show differences in other properties,
apparently because there are different numbers of electrons in the second-outermost shell (Figure 2.5). The second shell from the outside
also seems to have an influence, sometimes quite large, on the chemical properties of an atom.

In succeeding periods the electronic-configuration expansion proceeds in a similar but somewhat more complicated fashion. Before
going on, we need to clear up one question raised previously. In the
third period we found 8 elements; from the simple energy-level diagram,
we expected 18. Such an expectation rests on the assumption that all
the electrons in a given shell (i.e., with the same value of n) are of the
same energy. This is true of the hydrogen atom, in its excited states,
provided there are no external electric or magnetic fields acting on the
atom. The presence of such fields can split the excited levels into sublevels, or subshells.

The existence of sublevels can be demonstrated experimentally by
applying an electric field to a specimen whose flame spectrum is being
observed. What is initially a single spectral line may split into two or

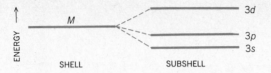

more lines, indicating the existence of energy sublevels arising from the same main level. This effect, called the *Stark effect*, is duplicated in certain atoms where the electrons present produce their own field and cause splitting into sublevels. Schematically, the separation of sublevels can be illustrated as in Figure 2.6.

The number of subshells in any main shell is equal to the principal quantum number n. Thus, the K shell ($n = 1$) consists of only one energy level. The L shell ($n = 2$) consists of two subshells. This means that all the electrons in the L shell need not be of precisely the same energy. One group of electrons may have an energy that is slightly higher than that of the other group. In the M shell ($n = 3$) there are three possible energy levels; in the N shell, four energy levels, etc. The subshells are designated by various devices. We shall find it most convenient to designate the lowest subshell of a given shell as an s subshell. The next higher subshell is labeled a p subshell; the next higher, a d subshell; the one above that, an f subshell.*

The energy-level diagram may now be redrawn. To the left of the dashed line in Figure 2.7 are shown the main shells. To the right of the dashed line are shown component subshells. The relative spacing of the subshells is not the same for all elements, but varies with Z. A distinctive feature of the diagram is the overlapping of the higher-energy subshells, an overlapping which gets more complicated as the fifth and sixth main shells are added to the picture.

Just as the number of electrons that can be put in any main shell is limited, so the population of a subshell is similarly limited. An s subshell can hold 2 electrons, a p subshell 6, a d subshell 10, and an f subshell 14. In Figure 2.7 the numbers in parentheses indicate the maximum population of the shells and subshells.

How does the existence of subshells affect the building of atoms from electrons and nuclei? So far as the first 18 elements are concerned, the number of electrons per main shell is as predicted before. As shown in Figure 2.8, element 18, argon, has two electrons in the $1s$ subshell, two in the $2s$, six in the $2p$, two in the $3s$, and six in the $3p$. Because the next subshell is so much higher in energy than the $3p$ (see Figure 2.7), argon behaves as an "inert" atom. There seems to be special stability associated with eight electrons in any main shell everywhere in the periodic table.

In the next element, potassium, number 19, the nineteenth electron goes into the $4s$ subshell, since the $4s$ is lower in energy than the $3d$ (Figure 2.7), even though the third shell is not yet completely populated.

* The letters s, p, d, and f were originally chosen on the basis of observations of the line spectra. Certain lines were observed to belong to a "sharp" series, and these were associated with energy transitions involving the s subshell; other spectrum lines were classified as belonging to a "principal," "diffuse," or "fundamental" series; hence the designations p, d, and f.

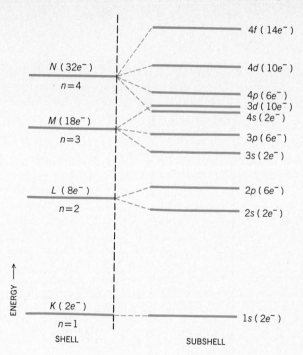

In calcium, element 20, another electron is added to the 4s energy
level. In element 21, scandium, the twenty-first electron goes into the
next available state, the 3d level. With minor irregularities the buildup
of the third subshell proceeds in this fashion in the next eight elements.
The addition of electrons to the 3d subshell, while the 4s subshell is
occupied, has the interesting effect on the chemistry of the elements
from calcium through zinc that the chemical properties of these elements do not change drastically with increasing atomic number. In the
sixth period there is an even better example of this. The elements 57
to 71, called the *lanthanides,* or *rare-earth elements,* are built up by
the addition of electrons primarily to the third-outermost shell. Such
changes deep within the atom do not affect chemical properties very
much. All the lanthanides have nearly identical properties. Elements 89
to 103, called the *actinides,* also exhibit electron buildup in the third-
outermost shell.

The electronic configurations of all the elements are shown in Figure
2.9. These configurations apply to the atoms in their lowest energy states

2.8
Electronic configurations

Element	Atomic no.	Electron population									
		1s	2s	2p	3s	3p	3d	4s	4p	4d	4f
Argon	18	2	2	6	2	6					
Potassium	19	2	2	6	2	6		1			
Calcium	20	2	2	6	2	6		2			
Scandium	21	2	2	6	2	6	1	2			
Titanium	22	2	2	6	2	6	2	2			

Z	Element	1	2		3			4				5				6				7
		s	s	p	s	p	d	s	p	d	f	s	p	d	f	s	p	d	f	s
1	H	1																		
2	He	2																		
3	Li	2	1																	
4	Be	2	2																	
5	B	2	2	1																
6	C	2	2	2																
7	N	2	2	3																
8	O	2	2	4																
9	F	2	2	5																
10	Ne	2	2	6																
11	Na	2	2	6	1															
12	Mg	2	2	6	2															
13	Al	2	2	6	2	1														
14	Si	2	2	6	2	2														
15	P	2	2	6	2	3														
16	S	2	2	6	2	4														
17	Cl	2	2	6	2	5														
18	Ar	2	2	6	2	6														
19	K	2	2	6	2	6		1												
20	Ca	2	2	6	2	6		2												
21	Sc	2	2	6	2	6	1	2												
22	Ti	2	2	6	2	6	2	2												
23	V	2	2	6	2	6	3	2												
24	Cr	2	2	6	2	6	5	1												
25	Mn	2	2	6	2	6	5	2												
26	Fe	2	2	6	2	6	6	2												
27	Co	2	2	6	2	6	7	2												
28	Ni	2	2	6	2	6	8	2												
29	Cu	2	2	6	2	6	10	1												
30	Zn	2	2	6	2	6	10	2												
31	Ga	2	2	6	2	6	10	2	1											
32	Ge	2	2	6	2	6	10	2	2											
33	As	2	2	6	2	6	10	2	3											
34	Se	2	2	6	2	6	10	2	4											
35	Br	2	2	6	2	6	10	2	5											
36	Kr	2	2	6	2	6	10	2	6											
37	Rb	2	2	6	2	6	10	2	6			1								
38	Sr	2	2	6	2	6	10	2	6			2								
39	Y	2	2	6	2	6	10	2	6	1		2								
40	Zr	2	2	6	2	6	10	2	6	2		2								
41	Nb	2	2	6	2	6	10	2	6	4		1								
42	Mo	2	2	6	2	6	10	2	6	5		1								
43	Tc	2	2	6	2	6	10	2	6	6		1?								
44	Ru	2	2	6	2	6	10	2	6	7		1								
45	Rh	2	2	6	2	6	10	2	6	8		1								
46	Pd	2	2	6	2	6	10	2	6	10										
47	Ag	2	2	6	2	6	10	2	6	10		1								
48	Cd	2	2	6	2	6	10	2	6	10		2								
49	In	2	2	6	2	6	10	2	6	10		2	1							
50	Sn	2	2	6	2	6	10	2	6	10		2	2							
51	Sb	2	2	6	2	6	10	2	6	10		2	3							
52	Te	2	2	6	2	6	10	2	6	10		2	4							
53	I	2	2	6	2	6	10	2	6	10		2	5							
54	Xe	2	2	6	2	6	10	2	6	10		2	6							

Z	Element	1	2		3			4				5				6				7
		s	s	p	s	p	d	s	p	d	f	s	p	d	f	s	p	d	f	s
55	Cs	2	2	6	2	6	10	2	6	10		2	6			1				
56	Ba	2	2	6	2	6	10	2	6	10		2	6			2				
57	La	2	2	6	2	6	10	2	6	10		2	6	1		2				
58	Ce	2	2	6	2	6	10	2	6	10	2	2	6			2?				
59	Pr	2	2	6	2	6	10	2	6	10	3	2	6			2?				
60	Nd	2	2	6	2	6	10	2	6	10	4	2	6			2				
61	Pm	2	2	6	2	6	10	2	6	10	5	2	6			2?				
62	Sm	2	2	6	2	6	10	2	6	10	6	2	6			2				
63	Eu	2	2	6	2	6	10	2	6	10	7	2	6			2				
64	Gd	2	2	6	2	6	10	2	6	10	7	2	6	1		2				
65	Tb	2	2	6	2	6	10	2	6	10	9	2	6			2?				
66	Dy	2	2	6	2	6	10	2	6	10	10	2	6			2?				
67	Ho	2	2	6	2	6	10	2	6	10	11	2	6			2?				
68	Er	2	2	6	2	6	10	2	6	10	12	2	6			2?				
69	Tm	2	2	6	2	6	10	2	6	10	13	2	6			2				
70	Yb	2	2	6	2	6	10	2	6	10	14	2	6			2				
71	Lu	2	2	6	2	6	10	2	6	10	14	2	6	1		2				
72	Hf	2	2	6	2	6	10	2	6	10	14	2	6	2		2				
73	Ta	2	2	6	2	6	10	2	6	10	14	2	6	3		2				
74	W	2	2	6	2	6	10	2	6	10	14	2	6	4		2				
75	Re	2	2	6	2	6	10	2	6	10	14	2	6	5		2				
76	Os	2	2	6	2	6	10	2	6	10	14	2	6	6		2				
77	Ir	2	2	6	2	6	10	2	6	10	14	2	6	7		2				
78	Pt	2	2	6	2	6	10	2	6	10	14	2	6	9		1				
79	Au	2	2	6	2	6	10	2	6	10	14	2	6	10		1				
80	Hg	2	2	6	2	6	10	2	6	10	14	2	6	10		2				
81	Tl	2	2	6	2	6	10	2	6	10	14	2	6	10		2	1			
82	Pb	2	2	6	2	6	10	2	6	10	14	2	6	10		2	2			
83	Bi	2	2	6	2	6	10	2	6	10	14	2	6	10		2	3			
84	Po	2	2	6	2	6	10	2	6	10	14	2	6	10		2	4?			
85	At	2	2	6	2	6	10	2	6	10	14	2	6	10		2	5?			
86	Rn	2	2	6	2	6	10	2	6	10	14	2	6	10		2	6			
87	Fr	2	2	6	2	6	10	2	6	10	14	2	6	10		2	6			1?
88	Ra	2	2	6	2	6	10	2	6	10	14	2	6	10		2	6			2
89	Ac	2	2	6	2	6	10	2	6	10	14	2	6	10		2	6	1		2?
90	Th	2	2	6	2	6	10	2	6	10	14	2	6	10		2	6	2		2
91	Pa	2	2	6	2	6	10	2	6	10	14	2	6	10	2	2	6	1		2?
92	U	2	2	6	2	6	10	2	6	10	14	2	6	10	3	2	6	1		2
93	Np	2	2	6	2	6	10	2	6	10	14	2	6	10	4	2	6	1		2?
94	Pu	2	2	6	2	6	10	2	6	10	14	2	6	10	6	2	6			2?
95	Am	2	2	6	2	6	10	2	6	10	14	2	6	10	7	2	6			2?
96	Cm	2	2	6	2	6	10	2	6	10	14	2	6	10	7	2	6	1		2?
97	Bk	2	2	6	2	6	10	2	6	10	14	2	6	10	8	2	6	1		2?
98	Cf	2	2	6	2	6	10	2	6	10	14	2	6	10	10	2	6			2?
99	Es	2	2	6	2	6	10	2	6	10	14	2	6	10	11	2	6			2?
100	Fm	2	2	6	2	6	10	2	6	10	14	2	6	10	12	2	6			2?
101	Md	2	2	6	2	6	10	2	6	10	14	2	6	10	13	2	6			2?
102	No	2	2	6	2	6	10	2	6	10	14	2	6	10	14	2	6			2?
103	Lw	2	2	6	2	6	10	2	6	10	14	2	6	10	14	2	6	1		2?

(in their ground states). The detailed assignment of electrons is based on observations of the spectra and of the magnetic properties (Section 2.4) of the individual elements. The question marks denote cases where the assignment is in doubt. Unfortunately, electronic configurations by themselves do not account for all chemical properties of the elements. Predictions made from these configurations alone are sometimes not borne out.

Finally, it might be noted that electronic configurations are generally designated by the use of superscripts to give the electron population for each subshell. As an example, the ground-state configuration for sodium would be $1s^2 2s^2 2p^6 3s^1$, corresponding to two electrons in the $1s$ subshell, two in the $2s$, six in the $2p$, and one in the $3s$.

2.3 WAVE NATURE OF ELECTRONS

In 1924, de Broglie suggested a possible explanation for the quantized nature of electrons in atoms. He proposed that every moving particle has associated with it a wave nature like that of light. The wavelength of the de Broglie wave is given by

$$\lambda = \frac{h}{mv}$$

where h is Planck's constant and mv is the momentum (i.e., mass times velocity) of the particle. For describing the motion of massive particles the wave character is of little practical consequence, since the associated wavelength is very small relative to pertinent dimensions. However, for describing the motion of low-mass particles, such as electrons, the wavelength is of a magnitude comparable to that of the atomic dimensions in question.

The existence of de Broglie waves leads to the quantum condition in the following way: Imagine an electron moving in a Bohr orbit. It has associated with it a wave of wavelength λ given by the de Broglie condition. If this wavelength did not divide into the path length a whole number of times, then the wave would destructively interfere with itself. A stable orbit would correspond to one in which there was an integral multiple of wavelengths along the circumference of the orbit. Mathematically this corresponds to

$$n\lambda = 2\pi r$$

where n is a whole number and r is the radius of the orbit. Substituting $\lambda = h/mv$, we get

$$n\left(\frac{h}{mv}\right) = 2\pi r$$

and, rearranging, we obtain

$$mvr = n\frac{h}{2\pi}$$

which is the same as Equation (2) in Section 1.6 for the quantum condition assumed by Bohr.

The concept of a de Broglie wave for a particle such as an electron means that the particle cannot be precisely localized. Instead, the electron must be thought of in the somewhat tenuous manner we use for imagining waves. The problem, a general one for particles of low mass, has been treated mathematically by Heisenberg. In his famous *uncertainty principle* (1927) Heisenberg showed that there is an inherent indeterminacy in knowing the combination of a particle's position and momentum. This indeterminacy can be expressed by saying that the uncertainty in the position times the uncertainty in the momentum is of the order of Planck's constant h. What this means is that the more precisely we try to specify one of these variables, the more uncertain we are of the other. For large masses the uncertainty is a trivial fraction of the total, but for small masses of atomic dimension the uncertainty principle places a real restriction upon the extent of permitted knowledge.

To illustrate, suppose we allow an electron in an atom to have an uncertainty in momentum of the same order of magnitude as its momentum. It turns out that the uncertainty of its position is about equal to 10^{-8} cm, or about the size of an atom. To locate the electron more precisely than this is meaningless; to locate it within the order of nuclear dimensions, 10^{-13} cm, is completely out of the question. Stated differently, any experiment, no matter how perfectly designed, to measure the location or the momentum of the electron must by the measuring process change either the momentum or the location by an amount comparable to the value sought.

Since tracks cannot be drawn for electrons in atoms, the best we can do is to speak of the probability or relative chance of finding an electron at a given location within the atom. The calculation of such a probability uses equations which describe the motion of waves and applies them to the de Broglie wave associated with an electron. This procedure, which mathematically is quite involved, is a basic concern of the field called *wave mechanics*.

The probability of finding an electron as calculated from wave mechanics can be specified by a *probability distribution* such as that given in Figure 2.10a. Here the probability of finding a 1s electron at a given location in space is plotted as a function of the distance of that location from the nucleus. The position of greatest probability is at the nucleus. Nowhere is the probability equal to zero. Even at points at very great distances from the nucleus there is some chance, although it is small, of finding the electron. Figure 2.10b is another way of representing the same electronic distribution. Here the intensity of the shading shows the relative probability of finding the 1s electron. Consistent with this picture, one can visualize an electron as forming a rather fuzzy charge cloud about a central nucleus. Sometimes it is convenient simply to indicate the shape of the charge cloud, as is done in Figure 2.10c. Remembering that atoms are three-dimensional, Figure 2.10c should be thought of as a sphere within which the chance of finding the 1s electron is great.

Thus we have in Figure 2.10 three different ways of representing the

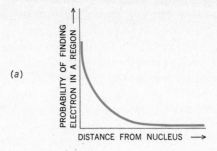

(a)

PROBABILITY OF FINDING ELECTRON IN A REGION →

DISTANCE FROM NUCLEUS →

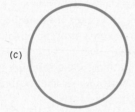

(b)

(c)

2.10
Representations of spatial distributions of 1*s* electron

spatial distribution of an electron in a 1*s* energy level. Since these representations replace the Bohr idea of a simple orbit, they can properly be said to represent 1*s* orbits. To reduce any possible confusion between the old and new ideas, it has become customary to use the term *orbital* when referring to an energy level associated with a given electronic probability distribution.

There is still another way of describing an electron in a 1*s* orbital, a way that serves to relate the idea of electronic "shells" to probability concepts. First, we raise this question: If we imagine starting out from the nucleus and working our way along a straight line from the nucleus to the outside of the atom, how does the chance of finding the 1*s* electron change? Evidently, the chance decreases, which is consistent with Figure 2.10*a*. But suppose, as we move out of the atom, at each radial distance *r* from the nucleus we investigate all the possible locations in three-dimensional space at that distance *r* from the nucleus and determine the chance of finding the 1*s* electron. Then we move farther from the nucleus and investigate all the locations at a slightly bigger *r*. How does the chance of finding the 1*s* electron change? The answer is not immediately obvious, since we have to consider both of the following factors. The chance of finding the electron at a given location decreases as we move away from the nucleus, but the number of locations to be investigated increases as we move away from the nucleus. Mathemat-

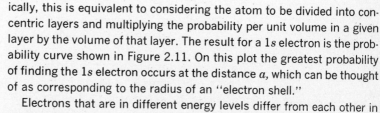

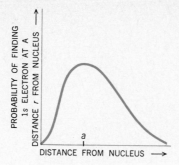

2.11
Probability plot for $1s$ electron

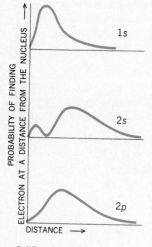

2.12
Probability plots for various electron orbitals

ically, this is equivalent to considering the atom to be divided into concentric layers and multiplying the probability per unit volume in a given layer by the volume of that layer. The result for a $1s$ electron is the probability curve shown in Figure 2.11. On this plot the greatest probability of finding the $1s$ electron occurs at the distance a, which can be thought of as corresponding to the radius of an "electron shell."

Electrons that are in different energy levels differ from each other in having different probability distributions. For example, Figure 2.12 shows the probability that a $1s$, a $2s$, and a $2p$ electron are at various distances from a given nucleus. It should be noted that the distances of maximum probability for the $2s$ and $2p$ electrons are approximately the same and larger than the distance of maximum probability for the $1s$ electron. This is consistent with the fact that the $2s$ and $2p$ electrons are of about the same energy and that this energy is greater than that of the $1s$ electron. The peculiar little bump in the $2s$ distribution indicates that the $2s$ electron spends more of its time close to the nucleus than does the $2p$ electron. This can account for the fact that the $2s$ electron is bound more tightly to the nucleus (is of lower energy) than the $2p$ electron. Furthermore, it should be noted that all three of the distributions shown in Figure 2.12 overlap, implying that outer electrons penetrate the region occupied by inner electrons.

Actually, there is an essential difference between s and p electrons which is not evident from Figure 2.12. The spatial distribution of an s electron is spherically symmetrical; i.e., its probability of being found is identical in all directions from the nucleus. On the other hand, p electrons are more probably found in some directions from the nucleus than in others. In fact, the probability distribution of a p electron can be thought of as forming two diffuse blobs, one on each side of the nucleus, as shown in Figure 2.13. This is called a p orbital, and the electron in a p orbital has equal probability of being found in either half of it. A p subshell can be constructed of three such orbitals all perpendicular to each other, as shown in Figure 2.14. That symmetric about the x axis is called the p_x orbital; that about the y axis, the p_y orbital; that about the z axis, the p_z orbital. Although it is not obvious from Figure 2.14, the combined distribution of one electron in each of a p_x, p_y, and p_z orbital is a sphere.

The d subshell, which can accommodate 10 electrons, can be resolved into five orbitals corresponding to different distributions in space.

Periodic law

33

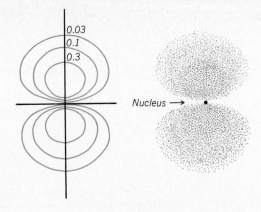

2.13
Representations of spatial distribution of a 2p electron (Contours on left show lines of constant probability given as fractions of the maximum probability per unit volume.)

These orbitals are somewhat more complicated than p or s orbitals. The $3d$ set can be represented as in Figure 2.15. One of the $3d$ orbitals, the one labeled d_{z^2}, is symmetric about the z axis and can be visualized as a squashed doughnut around the pinched waist of an hourglass. The other four of the $3d$ orbitals look like inflated four-leaf clovers. The one designated $d_{x^2-y^2}$ has its maximum electron probability density along

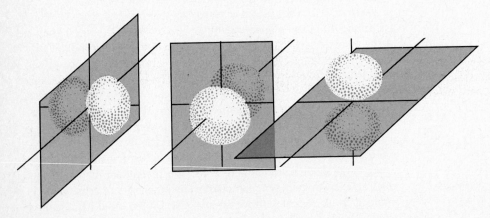

2.14
Shapes of 2p orbitals

the x and y axes. The other three, d_{xy}, d_{yz}, and d_{zx}, have their probability maxima 45° to the axes. As with the set of p orbitals, it turns out that having an electron in each of the five d orbitals gives a spherical electronic distribution.

The f subshell consists of seven orbitals corresponding to different spatial distributions. These distributions are even more complex than the d orbitals. As noted on page 27, electron population changes for the lanthanides ($4f$ subshell) do not affect chemical properties very much. Consequently, we need note only that the geometry of the $4f$ orbitals is such that equal population of all seven orbitals adds up to a sphere.

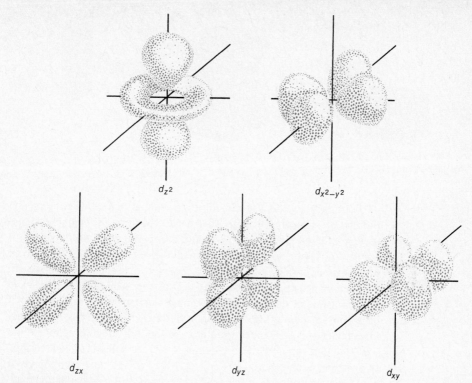

d_{z^2}

$d_{x^2-y^2}$

d_{zx}

d_{yz}

d_{xy}

2.15
Shapes of $3d$ orbitals

2.4 ELECTRON SPIN

In the preceding section it was noted that there is one orbital in an s subshell, three orbitals in a p subshell, five in a d, and seven in an f. Since these subshells can accommodate 2, 6, 10, and 14 electrons, respectively, it follows that any orbital can hold 2 electrons. Actually the two electrons in the same orbital differ in one important respect: they have opposite "spin." The reason for talking about electron spin comes from observations on the magnetic behavior of substances.

It is a familiar observation that certain solids such as iron are strongly attracted to magnets. Such materials are called *ferromagnetic*. Other substances such as oxygen gas and copper sulfate are weakly attracted to magnets. These are called *paramagnetic*. Still other substances such as sodium chloride are very feebly repelled by magnets and are called *diamagnetic*. Ferromagnetism is exclusively a property of the solid state (as will be discussed in Section 21.1), but all three types of magnetic behavior just described are believed to arise from electrons in atoms.

Information about the magnetic behavior of individual atoms can be obtained from an experiment like the one first performed by Stern and Gerlach in 1921. In this experiment, shown in Figure 2.16, a beam of neutral silver atoms (from the vaporization of silver) was passed between the poles of a specially designed magnet. The beam was found to be split into two separate beams; i.e., half of the atoms were deflected in one direction and the rest in the opposite direction.

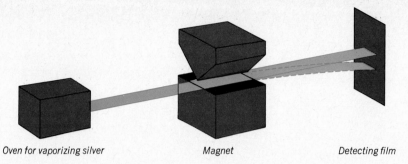

Oven for vaporizing silver   Magnet   Detecting film

2.16
Stern-Gerlach experiment
showing splitting of beam
of silver atoms

In interpreting this experiment it is assumed that an electron can be thought of as a spinning negative charge; and since any spinning charge is magnetic, an electron behaves like a tiny magnet. Two directions of spin are possible; an electron might spin about its axis in either a clockwise or a counterclockwise manner. These two directions of spin would correspond to two magnets oriented in opposite directions. If we have two electrons of opposite spin, we might expect them to attract each other, as two magnets would; but the electrical repulsion due to like negative charges is very much greater than the magnetic attraction. When electrons are required to be together, as in a completely filled subshell of an atom, each electron will pair up with another electron of opposite spin. The electron pair in an orbital is nonmagnetic, because the magnetism of one spin is canceled by the magnetism of the opposite spin.

In silver atoms, as shown by the electronic configuration given in Figure 2.9, all the electrons are found in completed subshells except the one $5s$ electron. This electron obviously cannot be paired with another. Hence, its uncanceled spin gives magnetism to the silver atom. The two deflections observed in the Stern-Gerlach experiment presumably result from a separation of silver atoms of two types which differ in the direction of spin of the unpaired electron, one having clockwise spin and the other counterclockwise.

Any atom which, like the silver atom, contains an odd number of electrons must be paramagnetic. Furthermore, atoms which have an even number of electrons can also be paramagnetic provided that there is an unfilled subshell of electrons. These more complex cases will be considered in Section 19.5. When all the electrons in an atom are paired, there is no paramagnetism. There is only diamagnetism, which occurs in all matter, even though in paramagnetic substances it may be obscured. Diamagnetism arises not from the spin of electrons but from their electric charge. A detailed discussion of diamagnetism is beyond the scope of this book.

2.5 QUANTUM NUMBERS

From the complete mathematical treatment of the wave nature of electrons in atoms there emerges a description of each electron in terms of four index numbers, the so-called quantum numbers. One of these has been mentioned above, the *principal quantum number n.* It gives, other things being equal, the order of increasing distance of the average electron distribution from the nucleus, and hence it is related to the order of the electronic energies. In most cases, however, the electronic energy depends on the second quantum number also.

The second quantum number, usually designated by l, is called the *orbital quantum number.* It denotes the subshell which the electron occupies and indicates the angular shape of the electron distribution. Values permissible for l are 0, 1, 2, ..., $n-1$. $l = 0$ corresponds to an s subshell; $l = 1$, to a p subshell; $l = 2$, to a d subshell; $l = 3$, to an f subshell.

The third quantum number, usually designated by m_l, is called the *magnetic quantum number.* It can be thought of as telling which orbital within a subshell the electron occupies. It is called the magnetic quantum number because a magnetic field will separate the orbitals within the same subshell into discrete energy levels.* For a given value of l, permitted values of m_l are the integers, including zero, from $+l$ to $-l$. Thus, for example, in the d subshell, where l is 2, allowed m_l values are $+2$, $+1$, 0, -1, and -2. Incidentally, it should be noted that there is not a single unique set of orbitals within a subshell; i.e., there are many ways in which a spherical distribution can be broken down into the requisite number of component parts. Specifically, the set of $3d$ orbitals shown in Figure 2.15 is but one such set and is not the same set that would be simply designated by m_l values $+2$, $+1$, 0, -1, -2. However, for our purposes what is important is the fact that there can be but five orbitals in any d subshell.

The fourth quantum number, usually designated m_s, is called the *spin quantum number.* It can have values of either $+\frac{1}{2}$ or $-\frac{1}{2}$, corresponding to the two possible orientations of electron spin. Instead of $+\frac{1}{2}$ and $-\frac{1}{2}$, the orientations are often designated by arrows pointing in opposite directions: ↑ and ↓.

An electron in an atom is completely described once its four quantum numbers have been specified. Furthermore, a fundamental principle, called the *Pauli exclusion principle,* states that no two electrons in the same atom can be completely identical, i.e., have the same values of all four quantum numbers. Because of this limitation and the limitation on permitted values of quantum numbers, the number of electrons in a shell is limited to $2n^2$, as mentioned on page 23. How this comes about is shown in Figure 2.17. The number of entries in the last column indicates the number of electrons that can be accommodated in any shell. For the K shell, this is seen to be 2; for the L, 8; for the M, 18; and for the N, 32. In terms of the principal quantum number n, the maximum population is $2(1)^2$, $2(2)^2$, $2(3)^2$, $2(4)^2$, ..., $2n^2$.

The assignment of electrons to orbitals for building up the periodic table is governed by several factors. These include the Pauli exclusion principle, the relative energies of subshells, and the repulsions between

* This splitting, called the *Zeeman effect,* can be observed experimentally by measuring spectral lines in a magnetic field and noting how one line in the absence of a field may split into several on application of the field.

n	l	m	m_s
1 (K shell)	0 (s subshell)	0	$+\frac{1}{2}, -\frac{1}{2}$
2 (L shell)	0 (s subshell)	0	$+\frac{1}{2}, -\frac{1}{2}$
	1 (p subshell)	$+1$	$+\frac{1}{2}, -\frac{1}{2}$
		0	$+\frac{1}{2}, -\frac{1}{2}$
		-1	$+\frac{1}{2}, -\frac{1}{2}$
3 (M shell)	0 (s subshell)	0	$+\frac{1}{2}, -\frac{1}{2}$
	1 (p subshell)	$+1$	$+\frac{1}{2}, -\frac{1}{2}$
		0	$+\frac{1}{2}, -\frac{1}{2}$
		-1	$+\frac{1}{2}, -\frac{1}{2}$
	2 (d subshell)	$+2$	$+\frac{1}{2}, -\frac{1}{2}$
		$+1$	$+\frac{1}{2}, -\frac{1}{2}$
		0	$+\frac{1}{2}, -\frac{1}{2}$
		-1	$+\frac{1}{2}, -\frac{1}{2}$
		-2	$+\frac{1}{2}, -\frac{1}{2}$
4 (N shell)	0 (s subshell)	0	$+\frac{1}{2}, -\frac{1}{2}$
	1 (p subshell)	$+1$	$+\frac{1}{2}, -\frac{1}{2}$
		0	$+\frac{1}{2}, -\frac{1}{2}$
		-1	$+\frac{1}{2}, -\frac{1}{2}$
	2 (d subshell)	$+2$	$+\frac{1}{2}, -\frac{1}{2}$
		$+1$	$+\frac{1}{2}, -\frac{1}{2}$
		0	$+\frac{1}{2}, -\frac{1}{2}$
		-1	$+\frac{1}{2}, -\frac{1}{2}$
		-2	$+\frac{1}{2}, -\frac{1}{2}$
	3 (f subshell)	$+3$	$+\frac{1}{2}, -\frac{1}{2}$
		$+2$	$+\frac{1}{2}, -\frac{1}{2}$
		$+1$	$+\frac{1}{2}, -\frac{1}{2}$
		0	$+\frac{1}{2}, -\frac{1}{2}$
		-1	$+\frac{1}{2}, -\frac{1}{2}$
		-2	$+\frac{1}{2}, -\frac{1}{2}$
		-3	$+\frac{1}{2}, -\frac{1}{2}$

2.17
Quantum numbers

electrons in orbitals belonging to the same subshell. Figure 2.18 shows an orbital-filling diagram in which each circle represents an orbital belonging to the subshell for which the designation is given in the left margin. The orbitals are filled from the bottom of the diagram working upward. Within any subshell, electrons are spread out one to an orbital before any pairing (two electrons ↑↓ in the same orbital) occurs. The reason for this is that electrons, being of the same negative electric charge, repel each other and hence try to spread over as much space as possible. This they can do by occupying separate orbitals, each of

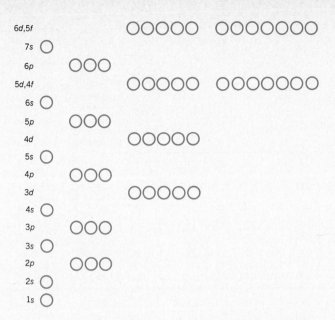

2.18
Orbital-filling diagram

which corresponds to a different distribution in space. After all the orbitals of a given subshell are populated by one electron, pairing begins to occur, because repulsion due to two electrons in the same orbital is usually less than the energy difference to the empty orbital of the next higher subshell.

It should be especially noted that Figure 2.18 is a *filling* diagram and not an energy-level diagram. The reason for this distinction is that there is no single energy-level diagram applicable to all elements, since the relative energies depend on the nuclear charge Z and the number of other electrons present. In building up the periodic table by adding an electron to a previously formed atom, the nuclear charge is also increased by one unit. When this is done, the energy levels shift and in some cases the relative order actually changes.

The order given in Figure 2.18 is that appropriate for the stepwise buildup of the elements and so gives the relative order of adjacent subshells only at the point where filling starts to occur. As an example, the chart shows $4s$ to lie lower than $3d$. $4s$ begins to fill at potassium ($Z = 19$); $3d$ begins to fill at scandium ($Z = 21$). This means that in these elements the $4s$ subshell is lower than the $3d$. However, it says nothing about the relative ordering of subshells in a later element such as Zn ($Z = 30$), in which, in fact, the $3d$ is the lower. A related point to be careful of is to note that Figure 2.18 is not an ionization diagram; i.e., it should not be used to decide which electrons are to be removed when an ion is formed from a particular atom (constant Z). Specifically, in forming Ti^{++} from a neutral titanium atom ($Z = 22$, $1s^2 2s^2 2p^6 3s^2 3p^6 4s^2 3d^2$), it is not the two $3d$ electrons that are lost, but the two $4s$. The point is that in Ti^{++} ion, the $3d$ level is lower in energy than the $4s$, which is contrary to what would be expected from the order-of-filling diagram.

Periodic law

39

1 H 0.37																	2 He —
3 Li 1.23	4 Be 0.89											5 B 0.80	6 C 0.77	7 N 0.74	8 O 0.74	9 F 0.72	10 Ne —
11 Na 1.57	12 Mg 1.36											13 Al 1.25	14 Si 1.17	15 P 1.10	16 S 1.04	17 Cl 0.99	18 Ar —
19 K 2.03	20 Ca 1.74	21 Sc 1.44	22 Ti 1.32	23 V 1.22	24 Cr 1.17	25 Mn 1.17	26 Fe 1.17	27 Co 1.16	28 Ni 1.15	29 Cu 1.17	30 Zn 1.25	31 Ga 1.25	32 Ge 1.22	33 As 1.21	34 Se 1.17	35 Br 1.14	36 Kr —
37 Rb 2.16	38 Sr 1.91	39 Y 1.62	40 Zr 1.45	41 Nb 1.34	42 Mo 1.29	43 Tc —	44 Ru 1.24	45 Rh 1.25	46 Pd 1.28	47 Ag 1.34	48 Cd 1.41	49 In 1.50	50 Sn 1.41	51 Sb 1.41	52 Te 1.37	53 I 1.33	54 Xe —
55 Cs 2.35	56 Ba 1.98	*	72 Hf 1.44	73 Ta 1.34	74 W 1.30	75 Re 1.28	76 Os 1.26	77 Ir 1.26	78 Pt 1.29	79 Au 1.34	80 Hg 1.44	81 Tl 1.55	82 Pb 1.54	83 Bi 1.52	84 Po 1.53	85 At —	86 Rn —
87 Fr —	88 Ra —	†															

*	57 La 1.69	58 Ce 1.65	59 Pr 1.65	60 Nd 1.64	61 Pm —	62 Sm 1.66	63 Eu 1.85	64 Gd 1.61	65 Tb 1.59	66 Dy 1.59	67 Ho 1.58	68 Er 1.57	69 Tm 1.56	70 Yb 1.70	71 Lu 1.56
†	89 Ac —	90 Th 1.65	91 Pa —	92 U 1.42	93 Np —	94 Pu —	95 Am —	96 Cm —	97 Bk —	98 Cf —	99 Es —	100 Fm —	101 Md —	102 No —	103 Lw —

2.19
Atomic radii of the elements (Number above symbol is atomic number, that below is atomic radius in angstrom units, units of 10^{-8} cm.)

2.6 ATOMIC RADII

The size of an atom is a difficult property to determine. For one thing, the electronic probability distribution never becomes exactly zero, even at great distances from the nucleus. Therefore, the distance designated as the boundary of the atom is an arbitrary choice. For another thing, the electronic probability distribution is affected by neighboring atoms; hence, the size of the atom may change in going from one condition to another, as, for example, in going from one compound to another. Therefore, in examining any table of atomic radii we must remember that the values listed may be meaningful only in providing a comparison of sizes. Figure 2.19 gives such a set of atomic radii deduced from interatomic spacings, the distances between centers of adjacent atoms. These interatomic spacings can be determined from X-ray and spectral studies of bound atoms.

In general, the atomic radii decrease in going from left to right across the periodic table and increase in going from top to bottom. How can we explain these trends? Figure 2.20 shows the change of atomic radius within the second period. It also gives the nuclear charge and the electronic configuration. Within the period the nuclear charge increases from +3 to +9. What effect might this have on the K electrons? In

	Li	Be	B	C	N	O	F
Atomic radius, Å	1.23	0.89	0.80	0.77	0.74	0.74	0.72
Nuclear charge	+3	+4	+5	+6	+7	+8	+9
K-level population	$2e^-$	$2e^-$	$2e^-$	$2e^-$	$2e^-$	$2e^-$	$2e^-$
L-level population	$1e^-$	$2e^-$	$3e^-$	$4e^-$	$5e^-$	$6e^-$	$7e^-$

2.20
Change of atomic radius
within a period

each of these elements there are two K electrons. The two electrons are attracted to the nucleus by a force proportional to the nuclear charge. As the nuclear charge increases, the pull on the electrons is increased, and the maximum in the K probability distribution curve (see Figure 2.11) gets closer to the nucleus.

What about the L electrons? Here the problem is complicated by the fact that the L electrons are screened from the nucleus by the K electrons, so that the attractive force of the nuclear positive charge is reduced by the intervening negative charges. In lithium, for example, the outermost electron is attracted not just by a charge of $+3$ but by a charge of $+3$ screened by two intervening negative electrons. The net attractive charge is closer to a $+1$ charge than to a $+3$ charge. In the beryllium atom, the L electrons are attracted by a $+4$ nucleus screened by two negative charges, or effectively a $+2$ charge. Despite screening, in going from left to right across the period, the L electrons have a higher and higher positive charge attracting them to the center of the atom. Just as the K shell becomes smaller because of this effect, the L shell gets smaller also.

How does the size of atoms change within a group? Figure 2.21 gives the data for the alkali elements. There is an increase of size from 1.23 to 2.35 Å in going from top to bottom. Going down the sequence, the number of levels populated is increasing stepwise. The more levels used, the bigger the atom. Because the nuclear charge progressively increases down the sequence, the individual shells get smaller, but adding a shell is apparently such a big effect that it dominates. Similar behavior is found for many of the other groups of the periodic table. There are, however, some places in the periodic table where the size does not change much within the same group. This is particularly true when elements number 57 to 71 intervene between the two atoms compared.

2.21
Change of atomic radius
within a group

Element	Atomic radius, Å	Nuclear charge	Electronic configuration
Li	1.23	+3	$1s^2 2s^1$
Na	1.57	+11	$1s^2 2s^2 2p^6 3s^1$
K	2.03	+19	$1s^2 2s^2 2p^6 3s^2 3p^6 4s^1$
Rb	2.16	+37	$1s^2 2s^2 2p^6 3s^2 3p^6 3d^{10} 4s^2 4p^6 5s^1$
Cs	2.35	+55	$1s^2 2s^2 2p^6 3s^2 3p^6 3d^{10} 4s^2 4p^6 4d^{10} 5s^2 5p^6 6s^1$

2.7 IONIZATION POTENTIAL

When an electron is pulled off a neutral atom, the particle which remains behind is a positively charged particle, or a *positive ion.* The process, called *ionization,* can be described by writing

$$Na \longrightarrow Na^+ + e^-$$

In the process the positive sodium ion, shown on the right with a superscript $+$ to indicate a $+1$ charge, is formed. The electron is shown separately as e^-. The *ionization potential* is the work that is required to separate the negatively charged electron from the positively charged sodium ion that is attracting it. In other words, the ionization potential is the *energy required to pull an electron off an isolated atom.* It can be measured experimentally by observing the spectrum of light emitted by excited atoms. As has been noted in Section 1.5, such a spectrum gives information on excited electronic states of atoms. These higher states converge on the ultimate limit which corresponds to complete removal of the electron from the atom, or ionization. Measurement of the spectral line at the convergence limit gives the energy released when an electron returns to the ground state. This energy must equal that required to remove the electron completely from the atom. Usually, the ionization potential is expressed in units of *electron volts,* one electron volt being the amount of energy corresponding to 3.829×10^{-20} cal. One electron volt per atom is equivalent to 23.06 kcal per Avogadro number of atoms, 6.02×10^{23} atoms.

Figure 2.22 shows the values of the ionization potential for the first 60 elements. Within each period, for example, Li to Ne, there is with some exceptions a fairly steady increase from left to right. Why should it be harder to pull an electron off a neon atom, for example, than off a lithium atom? At least two factors must be considered. First, the nuclear charge increases from left to right across a period. By itself this predicts that the ionization potential should increase from lithium to neon. Second, the atomic radii decrease from left to right. The size effect by itself would also predict that the ionization potential should increase, since the closer an electron is to the nucleus, the harder it is to pull off.

A shell of eight electrons, the so-called *octet,* is a grouping particularly difficult to break up. It is especially hard to pull an electron off an atom having eight electrons in its outermost shell, and atoms such as neon have very high ionization potentials. Many of the apparent irregularities in the ionization potential can be explained by the fact that completed subshells and half-completed subshells have extra stability. Thus, the ionization potentials of Be ($2s$ subshell completed) and N ($2p$ half completed) are higher than might be expected. In general, it is sufficient to remember that the elements of high ionization potential are on the right side of the periodic table and those of low ionization potential are on the left.

How about the trend within a group? Figure 2.22 shows the values of the ionization potential for the alkali elements and the noble gases. In

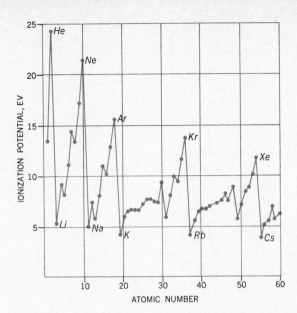

both cases there is a progressive decrease of the ionization potential in going from top to bottom of the group. This is as predicted by the size change alone. The helium atom is quite small; the electron which is being pulled off is close to the nucleus. It is more firmly bound than in neon, in which the electron being pulled off is much farther from the nucleus. The increase in nuclear charge essentially cancels out because of the screening effect of the intervening electrons.

Values of the ionization potentials of the elements are given in Figure 2.23. For each element the value given refers to the first ionization, i.e., the removal of but one electron from the neutral atom. In discussing the chemistry of the elements it is occasionally necessary to refer to second and higher ionizations, corresponding to further removal of electrons. In every case, subsequent ionizations require increasingly large amounts of energy per electron. Furthermore, if the ionization requires breaking into a noble-gas configuration, an extra-large increase is observed. As an illustration, the successive ionization potentials for beryllium ($Z = 4$) are 9.32, 18.21, 153.85, and 217.66 ev, corresponding respectively to removal of the first, second, third, and fourth electrons.

2.8 ELECTRON AFFINITY

Also important for determining chemical properties is the tendency of an atom to pick up additional electrons. This property can be measured by the *electron affinity,* the *energy released when an electron is added to an isolated neutral atom.* When a neutral atom picks up an electron from some source, it forms a negative ion, as indicated by writing

$$X + e^- \longrightarrow X^-$$

The amount of energy released in this process is the electron affinity. Thus, the electron affinity measures the tightness of binding of an addi-

2.23
First ionization potentials of the elements (in electron volts)

1 H 13.6																	2 He 24.6
3 Li 5.4	4 Be 9.3											5 B 8.3	6 C 11.3	7 N 14.5	8 O 13.6	9 F 17.4	10 Ne 21.6
11 Na 5.1	12 Mg 7.6											13 Al 6.0	14 Si 8.2	15 P 11.0	16 S 10.4	17 Cl 13.0	18 Ar 15.8
19 K 4.3	20 Ca 6.1	21 Sc 6.5	22 Ti 6.8	23 V 6.7	24 Cr 6.8	25 Mn 7.4	26 Fe 7.9	27 Co 7.9	28 Ni 7.6	29 Cu 7.6	30 Zn 9.4	31 Ga 6.0	32 Ge 8.1	33 As 9.8	34 Se 9.8	35 Br 11.8	36 Kr 14.0
37 Rb 4.2	38 Sr 5.7	39 Y 6.4	40 Zr 6.8	41 Nb 6.9	42 Mo 7.1	43 Tc 7.3	44 Ru 7.4	45 Rh 7.5	46 Pd 8.3	47 Ag 7.6	48 Cd 9.0	49 In 5.8	50 Sn 7.3	51 Sb 8.6	52 Te 9.0	53 I 10.5	54 Xe 12.1
55 Cs 3.9	56 Ba 5.2	✻	72 Hf 7	73 Ta 7.9	74 W 8.0	75 Re 7.9	76 Os 8.7	77 Ir 9	78 Pt 9.0	79 Au 9.2	80 Hg 10.4	81 Tl 6.1	82 Pb 7.4	83 Bi 7.3	84 Po 8.4	85 At —	86 Rn 10.7
87 Fr —	88 Ra 5.3	†															

✻	57 La 5.6	58 Ce 6.9	59 Pr 5.8	60 Nd 6.3	61 Pm —	62 Sm 5.6	63 Eu 5.7	64 Gd 6.2	65 Tb 6.7	66 Dy 6.8	67 Ho —	68 Er —	69 Tm —	70 Yb 6.2	71 Lu 5.0
†	89 Ac 6.9	90 Th —	91 Pa —	92 U 4	93 Np —	94 Pu —	95 Am —	96 Cm —	97 Bk —	98 Cf —	99 Es —	100 Fm —	101 Md —	102 No —	103 Lw —

tional electron to an atom. The values for the halogen elements are given in Figure 2.24.

Group VII elements are expected to have high electron affinity, because addition of one electron leads to formation of a stable octet. The decrease of electron affinity observed from Cl to I is not unexpected, because the size increases in going down the group. In iodine the electron to be added goes into the fifth shell. Being farther from the nucleus, the added electron is not so tightly bound as one added to the other elements of the group. The unexpectedly low value for fluorine cannot be explained by any simple theory.

A knowledge of electron affinities can be combined with a knowledge

2.24
Electron affinities for group VII

Element	Electron affinity, ev	Electronic configuration
F	3.6	$1s^22s^22p^5$
Cl	3.75	$1s^22s^22p^63s^23p^5$
Br	3.53	$1s^22s^22p^63s^23p^63d^{10}4s^24p^5$
I	3.2	$1s^22s^22p^63s^23p^63d^{10}4s^24p^64d^{10}5s^25p^5$

of ionization potentials to predict which atoms can remove electrons from others. Unfortunately, the measurement of electron affinity is difficult and has been carried out for only a few elements. A method for describing the electron-attracting ability of other atoms will be discussed in the next chapter.

QUESTIONS

2.1 Periodic law (a) By using specific examples, tell what is meant by the periodic law. (b) What information about atomic structure is indicated by the periodic law?

2.2 Quantum numbers Give all four quantum numbers for each electron in a neon atom ($Z = 10$) in its ground state.

2.3 Periodic law How do you *expect* each of the following to change in going from top to bottom of a group in the periodic table: (a) electron configuration, (b) atomic radius, (c) ionization potential, (d) electron affinity?

2.4 Periodic law How do you *expect* each of the following to change in going from left to right in a period of the periodic table: (a) electron configuration, (b) atomic radius, (c) ionization potential, (d) basic nature of hydroxy compounds, (e) metallic character?

2.5 Electron configuration Which of the following elements have no unpaired electrons (i.e., all orbitals empty or populated by a pair of electrons): Mg, S, P, Cl, Mn, Cr?

2.6 Periodic law Give the symbol and locate by group and period number the elements satisfying the following conditions: (a) largest atomic radius, (b) smallest atomic radius of a transition element, (c) largest first ionization potential, (d) smallest first ionization potential, (e) ionization potentials smaller than those of the elements immediately above *and* below in the same group.

2.7 Electron configuration What is the total number of p electrons in the ground state of each of the following atoms: Li, S, La, U, W, Zn?

2.8 Periodic law What is the distinctive feature about the electron configuration of each of the following: (a) group II elements, (b) halogens, (c) noble gases, (d) transition elements, (e) actinides?

2.9 Periodic law Where in the periodic table would you find each of the following: (a) elements that form the most basic hydroxy compounds, (b) elements that form the most acidic hydroxy compounds, (c) nonmetallic elements, (d) least reactive elements, (e) transition elements, (f) the lanthanide elements?

2.10 Electron configuration Which of the following atoms would have a spherically symmetric electron-charge distribution: Na, N, O, B, Mn, Cr?

2.11 Atomic radii By using the data in Figure 2.19, calculate the number of electrons per cubic centimeter in lithium ($Z = 3$) as compared to that in polonium ($Z = 84$).

2.12 Quantum numbers What are the possible values of all four quantum numbers for the highest-energy electron in each of the following atoms: Li, Sc, O, P, V, W?

2.13 De Broglie (a) What is the wavelength associated with an electron of mass 9.1×10^{-28} g moving with a velocity of 2.0×10^8 cm sec^{-1}? (An erg is the same as one g cm^2 sec^{-2}.) (b) What would be the velocity of an electron whose de Broglie wavelength is one angstrom?

2.14 Periodic law (a) Show that the ionization potentials as plotted in Figure 2.22 illustrate the periodic law. (b) Construct a similar plot for the atomic radii of the elements as listed in Figure 2.19. (c) Show that atomic radii also follow periodic-law behavior.

2.15 De Broglie Assuming Monsieur de Broglie weighed 70 kg, what was his wavelength when he was trotting at 3 m sec^{-1}?

2.16 Magnetic properties Which of the following atoms should be deflected in a Stern-Gerlach experiment: Be, Al, Si, W, Zr, Pd?

2.17 Quantum numbers Which of the following sets of quantum numbers represent impossible situations:

(a)	$n = 3$	$l = 3$	(d)	$l = 0$	$m_l = 1$
(b)	$n = 4$	$l = 2$	(e)	$l = 1$	$m_l = 0$
(c)	$n = 5$	$l = 0$			

2.18 Quantum numbers How many electrons can be accommodated in each of the subshells that comprise the sixth quantum shell?

2.19 Atomic radii (a) By using the atomic radii shown in Figure 2.19, calculate the apparent volume of a magnesium atom and of a beryllium atom. (b) These atoms pack to form solid elements in which "interstices between atoms" account for 25.94% of the volume. Calculate the number of atoms per cubic centimeter of beryllium and the number of atoms per cubic centimeter of magnesium. (c) By using the atomic masses (Mg = 24.31 amu and Be = 9.012 amu), calculate the relative densities predicted for these two elements.

2.20 Periodic table Make a right-triangular table in which rows correspond to different principal quantum numbers and columns correspond to different subshells (i.e., one for s, one for p, etc.). Trace a path through the subshell labels in the diagram corresponding to the order of filling in the buildup of the periodic table.

2.21 Quantum numbers (a) Describe as completely as possible, including probability plots, spatial distribution, etc., an electron in an atom with quantum numbers 2, 0, 0, ½. (b) If this is the highest-energy electron in the ground state of the neutral atom and there is no other electron of equal energy in the atom, what is the atom's atomic number?

2.22 Probability distribution (a) Draw a curve showing how the volume changes as a function of r for a spherical shell of uniform thickness. (b) Superimpose on the plot of (a) a curve showing how the electron density probability per unit volume changes with r for a $1s$ electron. (c) Show that multiplication of the values of the curves of (a) and (b) at each distance r produces a new curve showing a maximum.

2.23 *Ionization energy*   Given 6.02×10^{23} atoms consisting of a mixture of boron atoms and sodium atoms. If 169 kcal is required to ionize all these atoms (one electron off each), what fraction of the total are boron atoms?

2.24 *Probability distribution*   Working from Figure 2.13, sketch curves showing what happens to the probability per unit volume for a p_x electron as the distance from the nucleus increases (a) along each of the three axes and (b) along lines that bisect the angles between each pair of axes.

2.25 *Electron orbitals*   (a) Set up a coordinate system with an origin at the center of a cube. Let x, y, and z axes pass through the face centers. With the nucleus located at the origin, tell how orbitals differ in their spatial orientations by noting which (s, p_x, p_y, p_z, d_{xy}, d_{yz}, d_{zx}, d_{z^2}, $d_{x^2-y^2}$) have maximum density directed toward face centers and which toward edge centers. (b) Connect face centers of the above cube to form an octahedron. In terms of the octahedron tell whether each of the above orbitals extends toward a face, edge, or corner of the octahedron.

2.26 *Probability distribution*   For a $3p$ electron the plot of probability density resembles that shown in Figure 2.12 for a $2s$ electron in that the $3p$ also has two maxima separated by a point of zero density. The angular characteristics of all p electrons are alike in being concentrated along one of the axes, as in Figure 2.13. Combine these facts to draw a representation like Figure 2.13 for a $3p$ electron.

2.27 *Ionization*   Given a sample consisting of a mixture of chlorine atoms and bromine atoms. To remove one electron each from all the atoms in the sample requires 582 kcal. On the other hand, if one electron were added to each (neutral) atom in the sample, the total energy liberated would be 170 kcal. How many Cl and how many Br atoms in the original sample?

2.28 *Periodic table*   Construct in either two or three dimensions a periodic table which shows group relations without any gaps between elements of adjacent atomic numbers.

ANSWERS

2.27 4.3×10^{23} Br and 7.8×10^{23} Cl

3 chemical bond

Of fundamental importance to chemistry is the concept of the binding of atoms into aggregates. Any electrically neutral aggregate of atoms held together strongly enough to be considered as a unit is called a *molecule*. The attraction between two atoms within a molecule is called a *chemical bond.*

Hydrogen gas is composed of aggregates of two hydrogen atoms. Water vapor is composed of aggregates of two hydrogen atoms and one oxygen atom. Solid sulfur consists of aggregates of eight sulfur atoms. In each of these cases the aggregate is called a molecule. On the other hand, in solid sodium chloride there are no simple aggregates consisting of a few atoms. All the sodium atoms and all the chlorine atoms in a given crystal are bound into one giant aggregate. The term "molecule" is not useful in cases such as solid sodium chloride.

In this chapter we consider the following questions: Why do atoms bind together to form molecules? Why is there frequently a limit to the number of atoms bound together in a single molecule? Why, for example, is the hydrogen molecule H_2, and not H_3 or H_4? Finally, why do molecules exhibit characteristic shapes? Why, for example, is the H_2O molecule neither linear nor right-angular?

3.1 ELECTRONS IN MOLECULES

In an isolated atom each electron is under the influence of only the nucleus and the other electrons. When two atoms come together, the electrons of one atom come under the influence of the electrons and nucleus of the other. The interaction might produce an attraction between the two atoms. If that is so, an electronic rearrangement must have occurred to give a more stable state. In other words, the formation of a chemical bond suggests that the molecule represents a state of lower energy than the isolated atoms represent.

A detailed description of electrons in molecules is a difficult problem. Two general approaches can be used. One is to consider the entire molecule as a unit with all the electrons moving under the influence of all the nuclei and all the other electrons. This approach recognizes that each electron belongs to the molecule as a whole and may move throughout the entire molecule. The spatial distributions of the electrons in the molecule are called *molecular orbitals* and can be thought of in the same way as the orbitals of electrons in isolated atoms. The other approach to describing molecules is simpler but less correct. It assumes that the atoms in a molecule are very much like isolated atoms, except that one or more electrons from the outer shell of one atom are accommodated in the outer shell of another atom. This method of describing molecules is called the *valence-bond method;* it utilizes directly the orbitals of isolated atoms.

In order to point up the difference in the two ways of viewing molecules, let us consider first the case of the hydrogen molecule. As already indicated, the hydrogen molecule is formed from two hydrogen atoms, each with one proton and one electron. In the molecular-orbital approach the molecule is visualized as consisting of two protons at some distance apart with two electrons placed in an energy level that is characteristic of the whole molecule. In the valence-bond approach the molecule is visualized as consisting of two hydrogen *atoms* close together, with the electron shell of each atom the same as for an isolated hydrogen atom except that part of the time it may contain both electrons. No matter which picture is used, the molecule is held together because the electrons are spread over more space and the attraction of the two positive protons for the two negative electrons exceeds the repulsion between the two protons plus the repulsion between two electrons.

In the more complicated case of hydrogen chloride the molecule is formed from one hydrogen atom and one chlorine atom. The hydrogen atom contributes a +1 nucleus and 1 electron; the chlorine atom, a +17 nucleus and 17 electrons. In the molecular-orbital approach, the molecule is visualized as consisting of the two nuclei at some distance apart, with 18 electrons placed in various energy levels of the molecule as a whole. In the valence-bond approach, the molecule is visualized as consisting of one hydrogen *atom* and one chlorine *atom* close together. The hydrogen atom is assumed to be the same as when it is alone, except that part of the time it now may contain, besides its own electron, one of the electrons from the chlorine atom. As for the chlorine atom, it is assumed that the two inner shells are unchanged. However, part of the time the outer shell may contain, besides the original seven electrons, one additional electron from the hydrogen atom. The one electron from the hydrogen together with one electron from the chlorine are considered as a pair of electrons shared between the atoms. The pair holds the molecule together because it is attracted to both nuclei.

Certainly in a molecule the energy levels of many, if not all, of the electrons are changed from those of isolated atoms. Therefore, it would be desirable to discuss chemical bonding exclusively in terms of molecular orbitals. However, the valence-bond approach is so simple that it remains in great use among chemists. For either approach, it is convenient to consider only outer electrons as the ones involved in the valence, or chemical binding. These electrons are therefore referred to as the *valence electrons*. Sometimes they are shown as dots around the symbol for the element.

3.2 IONIC BONDS

In discussing chemical bonds, we shall assume that bonds can be described as being *ionic bonds,* in which electrons are completely transferred from one atom to another, or as *covalent bonds,* in which electrons are shared between atoms.

The formation of an ionic bond is favored in the reaction of an atom of low ionization potential with an atom of high electron affinity. An example of such a reaction is the one between cesium atoms and chlorine atoms. A cesium atom has a low ionization potential; i.e., not much energy is required to pull off the outer electron. A chlorine atom has a high electron affinity; i.e., considerable energy is released when an electron adds to the neutral atom to produce a noble-gas configuration (so-called "shell of eight," or octet). When a cesium atom and a chlorine atom combine in chemical reaction, an electron is transferred from the cesium to the chlorine. The cesium ion with its resulting positive charge attracts the chloride ion with its resulting negative charge. The attraction is called an *ionic bond* or, sometimes, an *electrovalent bond.**

* In the solid compound cesium chloride each Cs^+ is surrounded by eight Cl^- and each Cl^- by eight Cs^+. The force of attraction is equal to each of the eight near-neighbors. However, it is not generally useful to describe this situation as involving eight distinguishable

The energy changes associated with formation of the ionic bond in cesium chloride can be thought of in three steps:

$$Cs\ (5s^25p^66s) \longrightarrow Cs^+\ (5s^25p^6) + e^- \qquad (1)$$

$$Cl\ (3s^23p^5) + e^- \longrightarrow Cl^-\ (3s^23p^6) \qquad (2)$$

$$Cs^+ + Cl^- \longrightarrow [Cs^+]\,[Cl^-] \qquad (3)$$

The first step requires energy equal to the ionization potential of cesium, 3.89 ev; the second step liberates energy equal to the electron affinity of chlorine, 3.75 ev. It might be noted that the energy liberated in the second step is not enough to compensate for the energy required in the first step; furthermore, this cesium-chlorine case is the one that appears most favorable for electron transfer, since cesium has the lowest ionization potential measured and chlorine has the highest known electron affinity. However, ionic-bond formation can occur because positive and negative ions attract each other to liberate additional energy.

For step (3), the energy liberated when a positive ion of q_1 electronic charge units attracts a negative ion of q_2 electronic charge units to bring the nuclear centers to r Å from each other, the magnitude of the liberated energy in electron volts is $14.4q_1q_2/r$. In the case of Cs^+ and Cl^- the internuclear spacing will be about 3.5 Å, and thus the energy liberated by the ion pairing is 4.1 ev. Clearly, it is step (3) that makes ionic-bond formation possible. Actually, for forming the solid compound, step (3) is even more favorable than indicated by simple ion pairing, since in the solid each positive ion has more than one negative-ion neighbor, and vice versa.

In forming compounds by this process of electron transfer, it is necessary that there be a balance of electrons gained and lost. The reaction between cesium and chlorine requires one atom of cesium for every atom of chlorine. It should be noted that, after reaction, the cesium and chlorine are left with noble-gas octets in their outermost shells. It is a general rule that, when ionic bonds are formed, enough electrons are transferred that the ions produced have octets of electrons, which, as we saw in Chapter 2, tend to be rather stable. As a more complicated example, when barium reacts with chlorine, each barium atom loses its two valence electrons ($6s^2$) to form Ba^{++}. Two chlorine atoms, each picking up one electron, are required to balance this. The compound formed, barium chloride, contains one doubly positive barium ion for every two singly negative chloride ions, as indicated by the formula of the compound $BaCl_2$.

Since, in general, the elements on the left of the periodic table have low ionization potentials and the elements on the right have high electron affinity, ionic bonds are favored in reactions between these elements. Thus, any alkali metal (group I) reacts with any halogen (group VII) to form an ionic compound. Similarly, most of the group II

bonds, since the ionic bond is not confined to a particular orientation in space. Only in the case of gaseous CsCl, in which ion pairs Cs^+Cl^- may exist, does it make sense to speak of a single ionic bond between a particular positive ion and a particular negative ion.

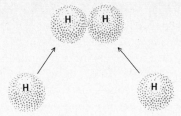

3.1
Valence-bond formation in
H_2

elements react with the halogens or with group VI elements to form ionic bonds. In general, these ionic compounds resemble sodium chloride in that they are white, brittle solids at room temperature which dissolve in water to give conducting solutions. They melt at relatively high temperatures.

3.3 COVALENT BONDS

Most bonds cannot be adequately represented by assuming a complete transfer of electrons from one atom to another. For example, in the hydrogen molecule, H_2, it seems unreasonable that one hydrogen atom should pull an electron from the other, identical hydrogen atom. In such a case it is assumed that electrons are shared between the atoms, and the bond is called *covalent*. The only problem is what is meant by "sharing of the electrons." In the molecular-orbital description the shared electrons are attracted to both nuclei and they are distributed in an orbital that encompasses the whole molecule. On the other hand, in the valence-bond description each of the "shared" electrons is found at any given time associated with one of the nuclei or the other but not with both simultaneously.

In other words, each electron is found in the atomic orbital of one atom or the other, and electron exchange in which the two electrons trade places may occur. In certain cases the valence-bond description also involves having both shared electrons on one atom or the other to give a so-called ionic contribution to the binding. Thus, there is a real difference in the concept of electron sharing as viewed from the two approaches, molecular-orbital and valence-bond. We shall examine each of these further, starting with the simpler valence-bond approach and returning to the molecular-orbital approach in Section 3.9.

Figure 3.1 shows schematically the formation of a covalent bond in the H_2 molecule. Two H atoms come together and are bound into a diatomic unit. Figure 3.2 shows the change in potential energy that accompanies bond formation. When the two atoms are far apart, the potential energy of each is independent of the other and is arbitrarily set at zero (off the far right of the diagram). As the two atoms approach, there is an attraction between them; the energy decreases. This decrease of potential energy is shown by the solid line as it drops from right to left to a minimum value beyond which it shoots up sharply. The energy increase corresponds to a repulsion between like charges at very close distances of approach. The position of the minimum corre-

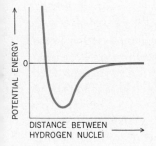

3.2
Change of potential energy as two H atoms come together

Chemical bond

53

sponds to the bond length, i.e., the average distance between the nuclei in the H_2 molecule. Because the potential energy is lowest at this distance, the two H atoms tend to favor this spacing.

Why should there be a minimum in the potential-energy curve? Why are the two atoms attracted? These basic questions are extremely difficult to answer, and no single method gives a completely satisfactory answer in all cases. Valence-bond method assumes that, when the two H atoms come closer, there is increasing chance that an electron from the $1s$ orbital of one atom transfers to the $1s$ orbital of the other atom. However, because of repulsion between electrons, it is not likely that both electrons should stay on the same atom. An exchange occurs; in it either electron may be found on either atom. This is possible according to the Pauli exclusion principle only if the two electrons exchanging have opposite spins. Consequently, the two electrons forming the covalent bond must have their spins opposite, or paired.

However, the question that still remains is why the energy decreases on bond formation. Magnetic attraction between opposite spins is much too feeble to account for the energies involved. There are two major contributions to energy lowering: (1) A general result of wave mechanics is that confining an electron to a smaller volume raises its energy, whereas spreading it out over a larger space lowers its energy. Thus, as the electron distribution changes from confinement on one atom to being spread over two atoms, the energy of the electron diminishes. (2) As the two H atoms come together, each electron feels the attraction of a second positive charge (the other nucleus), which more than compensates for the repulsion between like charges. However, at small internuclear separation the repulsion between like charges becomes dominant and causes the steep rise in potential energy shown on the left side of Figure 3.2.

The sharing of an electron pair as described above constitutes a *single bond*. It is usually represented by a single dash or a pair of dots. Since the sharing results from electron exchange between *two* atoms, the covalent bond so pictured is restricted to joining *two* atoms. In the case of a hydrogen atom, containing but one electron, only one bond can be formed to another atom. For this reason, hydrogen does not form H_3 or H_4, since to do so, at least one H atom would have to form more than one covalent bond.

The fluorine molecule, F_2, is somewhat more complicated. It can be visualized as resulting from the sharing of an electron pair between the p orbitals of two F atoms. A fluorine atom has the electron configuration $1s^2 2s^2 2p^5$ in its ground state. All these subshells are filled except for the $2p$, which can accommodate six electrons. Of the three orbitals making up the $2p$ subshell, two are fully occupied by electron pairs and are not involved in the bonding. The third orbital has a single electron which can exchange with a corresponding electron of opposite spin on a second atom. Thus, the valence-bond description leads to a single covalent bond which, like the bond in H_2, involves a single pair of electrons but, unlike H_2, involves p orbitals rather than s orbitals.

When an H atom and an F atom are brought together, the molecule

HF is formed. This molecule may be visualized as resulting from the sharing of an electron pair between the $1s$ orbital of the hydrogen and a $2p$ orbital of the fluorine. The HF bond is also a single covalent bond, but it differs in a fundamental way from the bonds in H_2 and F_2. The reason for the difference is the unequal attraction of H and F for a shared pair of electrons. In this case the electron pair can be regarded as spending more time on the fluorine than on the hydrogen. We shall return to this question in the following section.

In each of the covalent bonds so far described the atoms involved can be visualized as having attained a stable, i.e., noble-gas, electron configuration. In the bonding of H the additional electron can be thought of as completing the $1s$ subshell, as occurs in the noble gas helium. In the bonding of F the additional electron can be thought of as completing the $2p$ subshell, as occurs in the noble gas neon. In the majority of chemical compounds, covalent bonding occurs so as to produce noble-gas configurations. Except for bonds to H, this means completing the s and p subshells of the outermost shell so they contain eight electrons. This is the basis of the so-called octet rule, which states that *when atoms combine, the bonds formed are such that each atom is surrounded by an octet of electrons.** In F_2, for example, each F has completed its octet and does not bind on additional F atoms.

Besides the single bonds already mentioned, *double* and *triple* bonds may be formed in order that an atom can complete its octet. These correspond respectively to sharing of two pairs and three pairs of electrons between the bonded atoms. A triple bond, for example, would be typified by N_2. In this case each N atom (ground-state configuration $1s^2 2s^2 2p^3$) completes its octet by sharing three pairs of electrons between its p orbitals and the p orbitals of the other N. This is sometimes represented by the "dot formula" :N:::N:, where each N atom is regarded as being surrounded by three pairs of shared electrons and one pair of unshared $2s$ electrons. (In dot formulas, inner-shell electrons are not shown.)

In general, for the same pair of bonded atoms, triple bonds are shorter than double bonds and double bonds are shorter than single bonds. Experiment shows, for example, that the carbon-carbon distance (center to center) is 1.20×10^{-8} cm in acetylene (HC:::CH), 1.33×10^{-8} cm in ethylene ($H_2C::CH_2$), and 1.54×10^{-8} cm in ethane ($H_3C:CH_3$).

In all the cases discussed above each shared pair of electrons

---

* An interesting modification of the octet rule has been suggested recently by J. W. Linnett, who proposes that an octet be considered as two quartets differing in electron spin. The four electrons of each quartet are disposed tetrahedrally about the atom, and the two quartets may be independent of each other. In forming bonds, electron sharing occurs to complete each quartet. In the case of F_2 there are seven electrons of each spin type—three on each F atom and one shared between the atoms. Each F atom thus completes both quartets and there is no net electron spin, since the two sets just cancel. The spin quartets are completed by having two tetrahedra joined through a common corner. The two separate spin systems can be pictured as follows:

$$\begin{array}{cc} \uparrow \quad \uparrow & \downarrow \quad \downarrow \\ \uparrow\, F \uparrow F \uparrow & \downarrow\, F \downarrow F \downarrow \\ \uparrow \quad \uparrow & \downarrow \quad \downarrow \end{array}$$

involves one electron from each of the bonded atoms. There are also cases in which one atom in the bond contributes both of the electrons that are to be shared. Some examples are

$$
\begin{array}{ccc}
\text{H} & & \text{H} \\
\text{H:N:} + \text{H}^+ & \longrightarrow & \left[\text{H:N:H}\right]^+ \\
\text{H} & & \text{H}
\end{array}
$$

$$
\begin{array}{cccc}
\text{H} & :\!\ddot{\text{F}}\!: & & \text{H} \quad :\!\ddot{\text{F}}\!: \\
\text{H:N:} + & \text{B:F:} & \longrightarrow & \text{H:N:B:F:} \\
\text{H} & :\!\ddot{\text{F}}\!: & & \text{H} \quad :\!\ddot{\text{F}}\!:
\end{array}
$$

$$
[:\!\ddot{\text{S}}\!:]^{--} + \cdot\ddot{\text{S}}\!: \longrightarrow [:\!\ddot{\text{S}}\!:\!\ddot{\text{S}}\!:]^{--}
$$

Such bonds are sometimes called *coordinate covalent,* or *donor-acceptor, bonds.* The use of such names is generally unnecessary, since the final bond is independent of what it was formed from. For example, in the first equation above, the four bonds in the ammonium ion, NH_4^+, are identical, although only one of them seems to be a so-called coordinate bond.

3.4 POLARITY OF BONDS

Because electrons may be shared unequally between atoms, it is necessary to have some way to describe the electric-charge distribution in a bond. The usual way is to classify bonds as *polar* or *nonpolar.* For example, the bonds in H_2 and F_2 are called nonpolar; the bond in HF, polar.

Why are the covalent bonds in H_2 and F_2 called nonpolar? In both of these cases the "center of gravity" of the negative-charge distribution is at the center of the molecule, since the electron pair is just as probably found with one nucleus as with the other. The molecule is electrically neutral in two senses of the word. Not only does it contain an equal number of positive and negative charges (protons and electrons) but also the center of the positive charge coincides with the center of the negative charge. The molecule is a *nonpolar molecule;* it contains a *nonpolar bond* because an electron pair is *shared equally* between two atomic kernels.

In the case of HF the bond is called polar because the center of positive charge does not coincide with the center of negative charge. The molecule as a whole is electrically neutral, because it contains an equal number of positive and negative particles. However, owing to the unequal sharing of the electron pair, the fluorine end of the molecule appears negative and the hydrogen end positive. Polarity arises because the shared pair of electrons spends more time on the F than on the H, and not because F has more electrons than H. (The charge of the unshared electrons is balanced by the greater positive charge of the F nucleus.)

As another example of a polar covalent bond we consider the bond between fluorine and chlorine in the molecule ClF. Chlorine, like fluorine, has one vacancy in its p subshell. Exchange involving the p orbitals of the Cl and F can occur to produce a single covalent bond. However, in the covalent bond between Cl and F the pair of electrons is not shared equally, but instead spends more of its time with the fluorine. The fluorine end of the molecule therefore appears negative with respect to the chlorine end. In Figure 3.3 this polarity is indicated by a + and a − to show separation between the centers of positive and negative charge and also by a positive-tailed arrow pointing in the direction of electron shift. The molecule as a whole is electrically neutral—there are just as many positive charges as there are negative charges in the whole molecule—but there is a dissymmetry in the electrical distribution. Molecules in which positive and negative centers do not coincide are called *polar molecules,* and any bond in which sharing between two atoms is *unequal* is a *polar bond.*

In the molecule ClF there are two centers of charge. Such a molecule (or such a bond) is called a *dipole.* A dipole consists of a *positive and an equal negative charge separated* by some distance. Quantitatively, a dipole is described by giving its *dipole moment,* which is equal to the *charge times the distance between the positive and negative centers.*

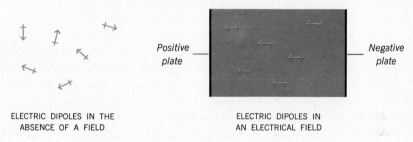

ELECTRIC DIPOLES IN THE
ABSENCE OF A FIELD

ELECTRIC DIPOLES IN
AN ELECTRICAL FIELD

The unit for measuring dipole moments is the Debye unit. One Debye unit corresponds to the dipole moment which would be produced by a negative charge equal to 0.208 that of an electron separated by a distance of one angstrom from an equal but opposite charge. The magnitude of the dipole moment measures the tendency of the dipole to turn when placed in an electric field. As shown in Figure 3.4, each dipole turns because its positive end is attracted to the negative plate and its negative end to the positive plate. Since the positive and negative centers are part of the same molecule, the molecules can only turn; there is no migration toward the plates.

The behavior of dipoles in an electric field gives an experimental method for distinguishing between polar and nonpolar molecules. The experiments involve the determination of a property called the dielectric constant (see Appendix 3.6), which can be measured as follows: It is observed that an electric condenser (two parallel metallic plates, like those shown in Figure 3.4) has the ability to store electric charge. The *capacity* of a condenser, i.e., the amount of charge that can be put on the plates for a given voltage, depends upon the substance between the plates. The *dielectric constant* of the substance is defined as the ratio of the condenser's capacity with the substance between the plates to its capacity with a vacuum between them.

In general, a substance which consists of polar molecules has a high dielectric constant; i.e., a condenser can store much more charge when such a substance is between its plates. This high dielectric constant can be thought of as arising in the following way: As shown in Figure 3.4, dipoles tend to turn in a charged condenser, so that negative ends are near the positive plate and positive ends are near the negative plate. This partially neutralizes the charge on the plates and permits more charge to be added. Thus, measurement of the dielectric constant gives information about the polarity of molecules. The fact that hydrogen gas has essentially no effect on the capacity of a condenser (dielectric constant 1.00026) confirms the idea that H_2 molecules are nonpolar. The quantitative calculation of dipole moments of individual *bonds* from measured dielectric constants is complicated, because in some cases unshared electrons can contribute to the electrical dissymmetry of the molecule. Also, the presence of the charged plates can *polarize,* or can temporarily distort, the charge distribution in molecules. Polarizability such as this can be described in terms of induced dipoles. The induced dipole can be distinguished from the permanent dipole by alternating the charges on the condenser plates at such a high frequency that the molecules cannot orient their permanent dipole moments rapidly enough to keep up with the high-frequency field. In such a case only the polarizability contributes to the dielectric constant. The permanent moment can then be found by difference. It can also be found by measuring the static dielectric constant (at very low frequency) as a function of temperature. The contribution of the permanent dipole moment decreases as the temperature is raised because of increasing disorder at high temperatures. This hinders the lining up of dipoles with the field.

It is possible to predict whether a diatomic molecule is polar or nonpolar. If the two atoms are alike, the *bond* between them must be nonpolar, and therefore the *molecule* is nonpolar. If the two atoms are different, the *bond* is polar, and the *molecule* is also polar. The degree of polarity of diatomic molecules increases as the atoms become more unlike in electron-pulling ability. It is not so easy to predict the polar nature of a molecule containing more than two atoms. Such a *molecule* can be nonpolar even though all the *bonds* in the molecule are individually polar. Carbon dioxide, CO_2, is an example. As shown in Figure 3.5, the two oxygen atoms are bonded to the carbon atom. Since oxygen attracts the shared electrons more than carbon does, each carbon-oxygen bond is polar, with the shared electrons spending more time near the oxygen than near the carbon. The polarity of each bond is as shown in the figure. Because the molecule is linear, the effect of one dipole cancels the effect of the other. As a result, when CO_2 molecules are placed in an electric field, they do not line up, because any turning action of one bond is counteracted by the opposite turning action of the other bond. Carbon dioxide has a low dielectric constant.

Water, H_2O, is a triatomic molecule in which two hydrogen atoms are

3.5
Nonpolar molecule
containing polar bonds

3.4 Polarity of bonds

58

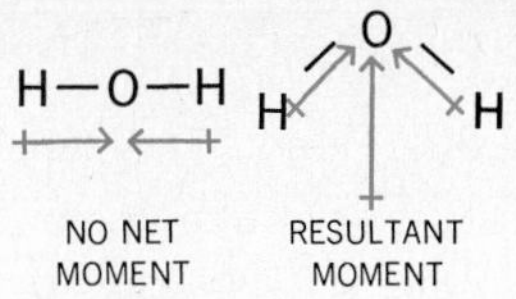

H—O—H

NO NET
MOMENT

RESULTANT
MOMENT

3.6
Possible structures of an
H₂O molecule

bonded to the same oxygen atom. There are two different possibilities for its structure. The structure may be linear, with the three atoms arranged in a straight line, or the atoms may be arranged in the form of a bent chain. The two possibilities are shown in Figure 3.6. The fact that water has a very high dielectric constant supports the structure on the right. The structure on the left would represent a nonpolar molecule in which the two polar bonds would be placed in line, so that there would be no net dipole moment. In the actual molecule of H_2O the two bond dipoles do not cancel out, but instead, owing to the bent structure, give a resultant moment as shown on the right of the figure.

In the light of the foregoing discussion of polar bonds, it is important to note that *there is no sharp distinction between ionic and covalent bonds.* In the chemical bond between atoms A and B, all gradations of polarity are possible, depending on the nature of A and B. If A and B have the same ability to attract electrons, the bond is nonpolar. If the electron-pulling ability of B is greater than that of A, the shared electrons spend more time on B, and the bond becomes more polar. If the electron pulling by B greatly exceeds that by A, the electron pair is not shared but spends all its time on B. The result is a negative ion B^- and a plus ion A^+; the bond is ionic.

3.5 ELECTRONEGATIVITY

In the preceding section we have referred to the electron-pulling ability of atoms in molecules. A quantitative measure of this property could be obtained by taking the average of the ionization potential and the electron affinity of the individual atoms. That both these quantities must be considered can be seen from the following argument: The bond in ClF consists of an electron pair shared unequally between F and Cl. The preference of the electron pair for one atom or the other depends on how much energy is required to pull an electron off one atom (the ionization potential) and how much energy is released when the electron is added to the other atom (the electron affinity). The electron pair will spend more of its time on the F, because the energy required to transfer an electron from Cl to F is less than the net energy required to transfer an electron from F to Cl. In calculating the energy required for these transfers it is necessary to know the ionization potential and electron affinity of each atom. Unfortunately, electron affinities have been measured for only a very few elements, so this method of evaluating the electron-pulling ability of atoms in molecules can be used in but a few cases.

By measuring various properties of molecules, such as dipole moments and energies required to break bonds, it is possible to arrange elements in order of their *electronegativity,* or *tendency to attract shared electrons.* This listing of the elements is called the *scale of electronegativity,* and one method for its determination is outlined in the next section. Numerical values assigned for the electronegativities of the various elements are shown in Figure 3.7. These numbers describe the relative tendency of an atom in forming a bond to go to a negative con-

Chemical bond

59

1 H 2.1																	2 He —
3 Li 1.0	4 Be 1.5											5 B 2.0	6 C 2.5	7 N 3.0	8 O 3.5	9 F 4.0	10 Ne —
11 Na 0.9	12 Mg 1.2											13 Al 1.5	14 Si 1.8	15 P 2.1	16 S 2.5	17 Cl 3.0	18 Ar —
19 K 0.8	20 Ca 1.0	21 Sc 1.3	22 Ti 1.5	23 V 1.6	24 Cr 1.6	25 Mn 1.5	26 Fe 1.8	27 Co 1.8	28 Ni 1.8	29 Cu 1.9	30 Zn 1.6	31 Ga 1.6	32 Ge 1.8	33 As 2.0	34 Se 2.4	35 Br 2.8	36 Kr —
37 Rb 0.8	38 Sr 1.0	39 Y 1.2	40 Zr 1.4	41 Nb 1.6	42 Mo 1.8	43 Tc 1.9	44 Ru 2.2	45 Rh 2.2	46 Pd 2.2	47 Ag 1.9	48 Cd 1.7	49 In 1.7	50 Sn 1.8	51 Sb 1.9	52 Te 2.1	53 I 2.5	54 Xe —
55 Cs 0.7	56 Ba 0.9	57–71 — 1.1–1.2	72 Hf 1.3	73 Ta 1.5	74 W 1.7	75 Re 1.9	76 Os 2.2	77 Ir 2.2	78 Pt 2.2	79 Au 2.4	80 Hg 1.9	81 Tl 1.8	82 Pb 1.8	83 Bi 1.9	84 Po 2.0	85 At 2.2	86 Rn —
87 Fr 0.7	88 Ra 0.9	89 Ac 1.1	90 Th 1.3	91 Pa 1.5	92 U 1.7	93–103 Np–Lw 1.3											

3.7
Electronegativities of the
elements

dition, i.e., to attract a shared electron pair. Fluorine is assigned the highest electronegativity of any element in the periodic table. The noble-gas elements have only recently been found to form chemical bonds, and their values have not yet been agreed upon. Otherwise, as we go from left to right across a period (increasing nuclear charge), the electronegativity increases. The elements at the far left of the periodic table have low electronegativity. The elements at the right have high electronegativity. On the scale of electronegativity, the group VII elements are assigned the values F, 4.0; Cl, 3.0; Br, 2.8; and I, 2.5. The decreasing order is regular, unlike the order of electron affinities. In general, electronegativity decreases going down a group (size increases).

Of what use are these values of electronegativity? For one thing, they can be used in predicting which bonds are ionic and which covalent. Since the electronegativity indicates the relative attraction for electrons, two elements of very different electronegativity, such as Na (0.9) and Cl (3.0), are expected to form ionic bonds. Thus, electronegativities support the expectation that the alkali elements and the group II elements form essentially ionic bonds with the elements of groups VI and VII. Two elements of about equal electronegativity, such as C (2.5) and H (2.1), are expected to form covalent bonds.

Furthermore, electronegativities can be used to predict polarity of covalent bonds. The farther apart in electronegativity two elements are, the more polar the bond should be. Thus, the bond between H and N is more polar than that between H and C. In both cases the hydrogen end should be positive, since H has the lower electronegativity.

3.5 Electronegativity

3.6 BOND ENERGIES AND THE SCALE OF ELECTRONEGATIVITY

One method for setting up the scale of electronegativities involves the use of bond energies. *Bond energy* is defined as the *energy required to break a bond and form neutral atoms*. It can be determined experimentally by measuring the heat involved in chemical reaction. (The determination of heats of reaction is discussed in Section 14.4.) The relation between bond energy and electronegativity can be seen from the following example: It is found that 103 kcal of heat is required to break the Avogadro number of H_2 molecules into individual atoms. Thus, the bond energy of H_2 is 103 kcal per Avogadro number of bonds, or 17.1×10^{-23} kcal per bond. Because the sharing of the electron pair is equal between the two H atoms, it would be reasonable to assume that each bonded atom contributes half of the bond energy, or 8.55×10^{-23} kcal.

Furthermore, it would be reasonable to assume that, in any bond in which hydrogen shares an electron pair *equally* with another atom, the contribution by H to the bond energy should be 8.55×10^{-23} kcal. Similarly, from the bond energy found for Cl_2, 57.2 kcal per Avogadro number of bonds, we deduce that a chlorine atom should contribute 4.75×10^{-23} kcal to any bond in which the sharing of an electron pair is equal.

Suppose we now consider the bond in HCl. This bond is polar, but for the moment let us imagine that the electron pair is shared equally. This amounts to picturing H in HCl to be the same as in H_2 and Cl the same as in Cl_2. If H contributes 8.55×10^{-23} kcal and if Cl contributes 4.75×10^{-23} kcal, the expected bond energy of HCl should be the sum of these contributions, or 13.3×10^{-23} kcal. Actually, the bond energy of HCl found by experiment is 102 kcal per Avogadro number of bonds, or 16.9×10^{-23} kcal per bond. The fact that the observed bond energy, 16.9×10^{-23} kcal, is significantly greater than the *calculated* value, 13.3×10^{-23} kcal, suggests that the electrons are *not* equally shared in HCl. The bond in question is actually more stable (requires more energy to break) than would be predicted by equal sharing.

The enhanced stability of HCl can be attributed to unequal sharing of the electron pair. If the electron pair spent more time on the chlorine, that end of the molecule would become negative and the hydrogen end positive. Since the positive and negative ends would attract each other, there would be additional binding energy. The amount of additional binding energy would depend on the relative electron-pulling ability of the bonded atoms, since the greater the charge difference between the ends of the molecule, the greater the additional binding energy. Thus, it should be possible to estimate relative electronegativities from the difference between experimental bond energies and those calculated by assuming equal sharing.

In Figure 3.8 experimental values of bond energies of the hydrogen halides are compared with values calculated by assuming equal sharing of electrons. It is evident that the discrepancy is greatest in HF and least in HI. This implies that the sharing of electrons between H and F

Bond	Energy, kcal per Avogadro number of bonds			
	X=F	X=Cl	X=Br	X=I
H—H	103.2	103.2	103.2	103.2
X—X	36	57.2	45.4	35.5
H—X (calc.)	70	80.2	74.3	69.4
H—X (obs.)	135	102.1	85.9	70.4
Difference	65	21.9	11.6	1.0

3.8
Bond energies

is more unequal than the sharing between H and I. We could say that HF is more ionic than HI. Numerical values of electronegativity have been selected by a complex procedure so as to account for the discrepancies listed in Figure 3.8. As shown in Figure 3.7, the electronegativity value assigned to H is 2.1. The values assigned to F (4.0), Cl (3.0), Br (2.8), and I (2.5) are consistent with the trend toward equal sharing in the sequence HF, HCl, HBr, HI.

Support for the assignment of electronegativity values comes from measurements of dipole moments. For the hydrogen halides the observed dipole moments are HF, 1.94; HCl, 1.08; HBr, 0.78; and HI, 0.38, expressed in Debye units. The decreasing polarity from HF to HI also indicates a trend toward equal sharing of electrons, which is consistent with decreasing electronegativity from F to I.

3.7 RESONANCE

Occasionally no reasonable electronic picture can be drawn for a molecule to account for its observed properties satisfactorily. Such a problem is encountered in the case of sulfur dioxide, SO_2. This molecule has a high dipole moment; hence, we conclude that it is nonlinear, with the atoms arranged in a bent chain. Sulfur has six outer-shell electrons, and oxygen also has six. There are thus a total of 18. These can be disposed in several ways:

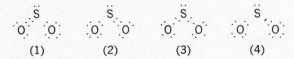

(1)   (2)   (3)   (4)

Neither formula 1 nor formula 2 is consistent with experimental fact, because each formula indicates that the SO_2 molecule has one double (short) sulfur-oxygen bond and one single (long) sulfur-oxygen bond. Experiments show the two bonds to be exactly the same length. Formula 3 is excluded because it contains unpaired electrons. Molecules containing unpaired electrons are paramagnetic (Section 2.4); sulfur dioxide is not. Formula 4 is traditionally excluded because of the convenience of maintaining the sanctity of the octet rule.

A situation in which *no single electronic formula conforms both to observed properties and to the octet rule* is described as *resonance*. The

SO_2 molecule is sometimes described by a combination of formulas 1 and 2. The actual electronic distribution in the molecule is said to be a *resonance hybrid* of these contributing formulas. The choice of the word "resonance" for this situation is unfortunate, because it encourages people to think that the molecule resonates from one structure to the other or that the extra electron pair jumps back and forth from one bond to the other. *Such is not the case.* The molecule has only one real electron structure. The problem is in describing it. The properties of a resonance hybrid do not oscillate from those of one contributing resonance structure to those of the other. The properties are fixed and are those of the actual hybrid structure.

Resonance represents an attempt to patch up the valence-bond description of certain molecules. The difficulty lies in the description and not in the molecule itself. In the molecular-orbital description of molecules the problem does not arise. All the electrons belong to the molecule as a whole, and in SO_2 the troublesome electron pair need not be pictured as being in two places at once.

3.8 SHAPES OF MOLECULES AND HYBRID ORBITALS

Molecules which contain two atoms are necessarily linear, but those containing three or more atoms present complications. For example, why is the water molecule nonlinear? To answer this question, we must consider the nature of the orbitals involved in bonding the hydrogen to the oxygen and specifically the spatial distribution of the electronic charge clouds about each of the nuclei. Imagine assembling the molecule H_2O from two H atoms and one O atom. Each H atom has originally a single electron in a $1s$ orbital, which is spherically symmetrical about the nucleus. The oxygen atom has originally in its outer shell two $2s$ electrons (spherically symmetric) and four $2p$ electrons. Recalling the three p-type orbitals shown in Figure 2.14, we find two of these $2p$ electrons in one of the p orbitals and one electron in each of the other two p orbitals.

In the valence-bond description of bonds the O-to-H bond arises from the sharing of the $1s$ electron of hydrogen with one of the unpaired $2p$ electrons of the oxygen. Such sharing will favor bonding along the direction of the $2p$ orbital used. To tie on two H atoms will require use of two $2p$ orbitals, which are at right angles to each other (see Figure 2.14). Thus, on this simple picture we would expect the two O—H bonds in H_2O to be perpendicular to each other. Actually, they form the somewhat greater angle of $104°31'$. We shall return to this discrepancy later.

Methane, CH_4, has a tetrahedral shape, as shown in Figure 3.9, with the carbon at the center of a tetrahedron and the four hydrogens at the corners. (A tetrahedron is a pyramid whose four faces are equilateral triangles.) The angles between the C—H bonds are $109°28'$. There are obvious problems with this molecule in that the bond angles are not right angles and, furthermore, there are four equivalent C—H bonds to be formed and we have but three p orbitals. Evidently we need to use

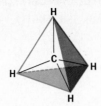

3.9
Tetrahedral CH$_4$ molecule

the 2s orbital of carbon also. In fact, the formation of the CH$_4$ molecule can be pictured as involving the replacement of the one 2s and the three 2p orbitals on the carbon by a new set of four, equivalent *hybrid orbitals* directed toward the corners of a tetrahedron.

These orbitals are frequently represented by the designation *sp*³, where the superscripts do not give electron population, but tell only that one *s* and three *p* orbitals have been merged into four orbitals that are equivalent to each other. Hybrid-orbital formation is made necessary because the separate identification of *s* and *p* orbitals is possible only in an isolated atom. As soon as other atoms are brought up to the original atom, the energy levels of the latter get mixed up and are replaced by a new set of hybrid orbitals. Electron sharing between the *sp*³ orbitals and the 1s orbitals of the hydrogens leads to the observed tetrahedral shape.

The use of hybrid, tetrahedral orbitals can account for the observed shapes of molecules other than methane even when there are not four attached atoms. For example, the NH$_3$ molecule can be imagined as having been built from a nitrogen atom with its five outer-shell electrons distributed among four equivalent tetrahedral orbitals in such a way that two of the electrons are paired and occupy one orbital. The other three electrons are shared with the H atoms using the other three tetrahedral orbitals. The result, as shown in Figure 3.10, is a pyramidal molecule in which the three hydrogens form the base and the lone pair of electrons the apex. The observed angles between N—H bonds in NH$_3$ are 108°, which is very nearly what is expected for a tetrahedron.

Tetrahedral orbitals can also help explain the observed bond angle in H$_2$O. Following the reasoning of the preceding paragraph, we expect to find that H$_2$O is similar to NH$_3$ except that there are two lone pairs of electrons in the case of H$_2$O. Figure 3.11 attempts to show that the two lone pairs of electrons and the two bound hydrogens are directed approximately toward the corners of a tetrahedron.

The *sp*³ hybrid orbitals are useful not only for describing simple molecules such as CH$_4$ but also for describing more complicated molecules such as C$_2$H$_6$, C$_3$H$_8$, and C$_4$H$_{10}$. In these chainlike hydrocarbons each carbon atom can be regarded as having four *sp*³ hybrids directed toward the corners of a tetrahedron. Consequently, the preferred bonding directions are toward the corners of a tetrahedron. Electron sharing with a 1s orbital of an H atom forms a C—H bond in that direction, whereas electron sharing with an *sp*³ hybrid of another C atom forms a

3.10
Ammonia molecule

3.11
Water molecule

3.8 Shapes of molecules
and hybrid orbitals

64

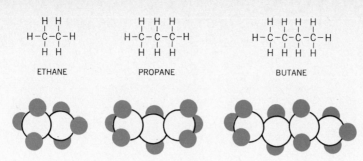

ETHANE PROPANE BUTANE

3.12
Shapes of chain
hydrocarbons

C—C bond at 109° to the C—H bond. Structures that may result are shown in Figure 3.12.

The tetrahedral sp^3 hybrids are not the only hybrid orbitals possible. Other common examples are sp, sp^2, dsp^2, and d^2sp^3. In each case there will be the same number of equivalent orbitals as atomic orbitals that were mixed in. Mixing of an s orbital and a p orbital produces two orbitals, each called an sp hybrid, which are directed at 180° from each other. An example is afforded by the mercury atom in $HgBr_2$. In the ground state, Hg ($Z = 80$) has $6s^26p^0$ in its outer shell. In binding the two bromine atoms (Br, $Z = 35$, $4s^24p^5$ in outermost shell) the Hg uses two sp hybrids, each of which is used in electron sharing with a p orbital of a bromine. Consistent with this picture is the fact that molecule Br—Hg—Br is linear. A more complicated example of sp hybridization is found in acetylene, C_2H_2. We shall return to this case after discussing the related molecule, ethylene, C_2H_4.

The ethylene molecule, often represented as $H_2C{=}CH_2$, is planar in the sense that all six atoms lie in the same plane. The bond angles are all close to 120°; the C—C—H angles are actually 122° and the H—C—H angles 116°. This shape can be accounted for reasonably well by assuming use of sp^2 hybrid orbitals. Mixing of one s orbital and two p orbitals produces three equivalent orbitals, all in a plane, at angles of 120° to each other. The bonding directions of these sp^2 hybrid orbitals relative to the unhybridized p orbital are shown in Figure 3.13. Electron exchange between an sp^2 orbital of a carbon and an s orbital of a hydrogen gives a C—H bond. The four C—H bonds use four of the six available sp^2 hybrid orbitals. The other two sp^2 hybrid orbitals, one from each atom, allow electron exchange between the carbon atoms to give a C—C bond.

Electron exchange can also occur between the unhybridized p orbital of one carbon and the unhybridized p orbital of the other carbon. This produces another bond, which has a peculiar shape since it results from side-to-side pairing of p orbitals rather than end-to-end. Thus, the two carbon atoms are seen to be held together by two bonds of different shape, one of which is concentrated directly between the two nuclei and the other of which is split into two regions lying to the sides of the internuclear line. A bond of the first type is generally called a σ (*sigma*) bond; a bond of the second type, a π (*pi*) bond. It must be noted that a π bond, like a σ bond, is only one bond in that it involves but a single

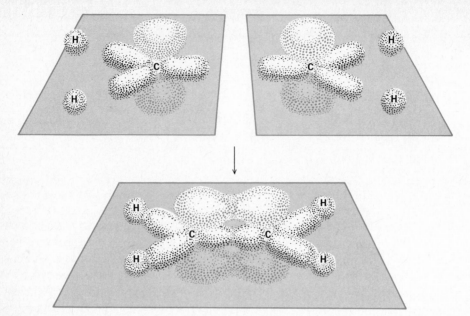

3.13
A valence-bond
formulation of ethylene
(unhybridized *p* orbital
shown in color)

pair of electrons shared between two atoms. The combination of one σ
bond and one π bond constitutes what is called a *double bond*. In summary, for the molecule C_2H_4 the four hydrogen atoms are held to the
carbons by four σ bonds and the two carbons are held together by the
combination of a σ plus a π bond.

Returning to acetylene, we can account for its linear structure,
H—C≡C—H, as follows: For each carbon we imagine formation of two
sp hybrid orbitals from the carbon's 2*s* and one of its 2*p* orbitals (let us

3.14
A valence-bond
formulation of acetylene
(unhybridized *p* orbitals
shown in color)

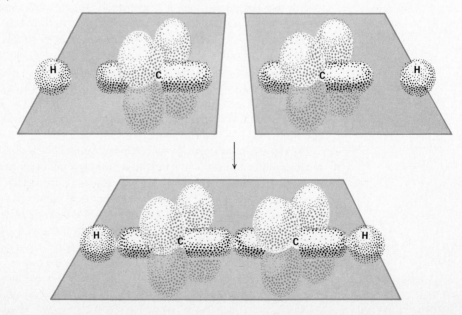

Designation	Typical combination	Bond angle, deg	Geometry
sp	$s + p_x$	180	Linear
sp^2	$s + p_x + p_y$	120	Trigonal
sp^3	$s + p_x + p_y + p_z$	109.47	Tetrahedral
dsp^2	$d_{x^2-y^2} + s + p_x + p_y$	90	Square planar
d^2sp^3	$d_{x^2-y^2} + d_{z^2} + s + p_x + p_y + p_z$	90	Octahedral

3.15
Hybrid orbitals

call it p_x). One of the sp hybrid orbitals is used to bind on a hydrogen atom by means of a σ bond; the other sp orbital forms a σ bond to the other carbon. As shown in Figure 3.14, the unhybridized p orbitals (p_y and p_z) of the carbon are in a plane perpendicular to the direction along which bonding occurs, i.e., the line through the four atoms. Electron exchange between the p_y orbital of one carbon and the p_y orbital of the other carbon gives a π bond; electron exchange between the p_z of one and the p_z of the other gives another π bond. Thus, the carbon atoms in acetylene are held together by a triple bond consisting of one σ bond and two π bonds.

In the examples discussed above, hybrid orbitals that consisted of various combinations of s and p orbitals were utilized. The geometry of these hybrids is summarized in Figure 3.15. Included also are two commonly used sets of hybrids having an admixture of d orbitals. The dsp^2 hybrids are four orbitals directed toward the corners of a square, or, in other words, at 90° angles. These are best visualized as being concentrated along the x and y axes. An example of square planar geometry is afforded by $PtCl_4^{--}$ in K_2PtCl_4, where the anion consists of four chlorine atoms arranged in a square around the platinum. The d^2sp^3 hybrid set consists of six equivalent orbitals directed along the x, y, and z axes, as toward the corners of an octahedron. The set is constructed from those two d orbitals (Figure 2.15) that are directed along the axes, viz., d_{z^2} and $d_{x^2-y^2}$, and a full set of s and p orbitals. The molecule SF_6, which has an octahedral structure, can be rationalized as resulting from formation of six σ bonds about the sulfur, each of these arising from a d^2sp^3 hybrid orbital on the sulfur and a p orbital of the fluorine.

3.9 MOLECULAR ORBITALS

One of the surprising aspects of valence-bond descriptions of molecules is that such a simple picture so adequately deals with a large variety of cases. However, it is glaringly obvious from the nature of the assumptions that it is incorrect. To assume that an electron-orbital characteristic of an isolated atom is not changed by the presence of a second attracting center is at best only a crude approximation. In molecular-orbital theory the problem is met by placing the nuclei at the sites they occupy in the final molecule and then allowing the electrons to distribute themselves in the electric field arising from the nuclei and the other electrons in the molecule.

Chemical bond

67

Such molecular orbitals are difficult, if not impossible, to calculate exactly. However, they can be approximated by realizing that the part of a molecular orbital that lies close to one atomic nucleus will greatly resemble an atomic orbital centered on that nucleus. Likewise, the part of the molecular orbital that lies near a second nucleus will resemble an atomic orbital centered on the second nucleus. For the region where the electron is about equally far from both nuclei, the molecular orbital must take account of a mutual attraction. The most common way to approximate these conditions is to assume that the molecular orbital is a sum of atomic orbitals of the bonded atoms. The addition of orbitals is not simple, however, since *two* atomic orbitals when combined must produce *two* molecular orbitals. In other words, as with orbital hybridization (page 64), the number of resulting orbitals must equal the number of orbitals fed into the combination. This will be illustrated by the following examples.

Let us construct the molecular orbitals for the H_2 molecule. We start by fixing the two protonic nuclei at the observed internuclear distance. Molecular orbitals for electrons can be set up by combining the $1s$ orbital of one H atom with the $1s$ orbital of the other H atom. Figure 3.16 shows the two ways in which this can be done. The $+$ signs refer to the positions of the positively charged nuclei; the shaded area represents the electronic distribution. The lower molecular orbital results from simple addition of the two $1s$ distributions. In it the region between the two nuclei, where the two individual $1s$ orbitals would overlap, is correspondingly intensified. This indicates that the lower molecular orbital has appreciable probability density between the nuclei, producing a net bonding effect. For this reason it is called a *bonding orbital*. The upper molecular orbital represents the other possible way to combine two $1s$ orbitals. Recalling the wave nature of electrons, this upper orbital can be imagined as resulting from the addition of two waves of opposite phase, so that destructive interference occurs where they overlap.

In any case, the second way to combine orbitals produces a molecular orbital which differs from the first in that electron probability density in the region of overlap cancels rather than reinforces. The small probability for finding electron density in the region between the nuclei means that the two positive nuclei are not well shielded from each other. Consequently, there is a large repulsion between the nuclei which tends to push them apart. For this reason, this type of molecular orbital is called an *antibonding orbital*.

Antibonding orbitals are generally marked with asterisks. The designation σ for molecular orbitals is a general one used for any molecular orbital in which electron density is symmetric all the way around the line drawn through the two nuclei. The subscript $1s$ in σ_{1s} and σ_{1s}^* denotes the atomic orbitals from which the molecular orbitals were formed. Finally, it should be noted that the molecular orbital, σ_{1s}, with electron density between the nuclei is lower in energy than either the other molecular orbital, σ_{1s}^*, or the two isolated orbitals. This lowering of the energy resulting from transferring two electrons from two $1s$

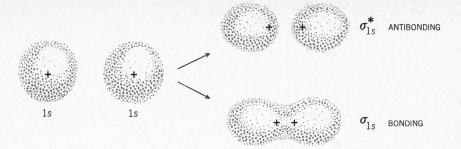

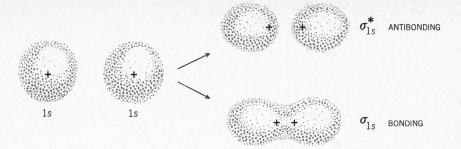 1s   1s σ^*_{1s} ANTIBONDING σ_{1s} BONDING

3.16
Molecular-orbital
formation by combination
of 1s atomic orbitals

orbitals to the σ_{1s} molecular orbital corresponds to the bond energy of the H_2 molecule.

The molecular-orbital diagram of Figure 3.16 can be used to describe what happens when two helium atoms come together. Each helium has two electrons, so there are four electrons to be accommodated. Molecular orbitals, just like atomic orbitals, can hold only a single pair of electrons, i.e., two electrons of opposite spin. In He_2 one pair of electrons would have to be in the σ^*_{1s} orbital, since only one pair can be in the σ_{1s} orbital. The bonding due to the pair in the σ_{1s} is canceled by the antibonding (repulsion due to insufficiently shielded nuclei) due to the pair in the σ^*_{1s}. It seems to be generally true that antibonding orbitals are a bit more antibonding than bonding orbitals are bonding. In other words, for Figure 3.16 the energy of σ^*_{1s} is farther above the energy of the isolated orbitals than that of σ_{1s} is below it. Consequently, He_2 is energetically unstable with respect to two helium atoms.

In the elements beyond helium the second quantum shell ($n = 2$) is involved, which means that both s and p orbitals are available. Just like $1s$ orbitals, the $2s$ orbitals can give rise to molecular orbitals, σ_{2s} and σ^*_{2s}. With two lithium atoms (ground state $1s^22s^1$), we assume that the inner-shell electrons ($1s^2$) are not appreciably affected when the two Li atoms come together, but instead remain in atomic orbitals. However, the outer electron of each atom must be accommodated in a molecular orbital. Both electrons go into the σ_{2s}, which, being a bonding orbital, lowers the energy and allows formation of the molecule Li_2. This molecule has been detected in the vapor state, where it is estimated to comprise some 10% of the molecules at the boiling point of lithium.

For the next element, beryllium ($Z = 4$, $1s^22s^2$), formation of Be_2 would require one pair of electrons in the σ^*_{2s} molecular orbital as well as one pair in σ_{2s}. Just as in He_2, the antibonding effect is somewhat greater than the bonding effect, so no stable molecule is formed.

For the element boron ($Z = 5$, $1s^22s^22p^1$) and the subsequent elements p orbitals must be considered. From the three kinds of p orbitals (p_x, p_y, p_z) two kinds of molecular orbitals will result: σ orbitals that are symmetric about the bond axis and π orbitals that are not so symmetric. Furthermore, some of these will be bonding while others will be antibonding. Figure 3.17 shows how σ and π orbitals can arise from combining the different p orbitals. Let us designate as the x axis the line joining the two nuclei; the y and z axes are then perpendicular

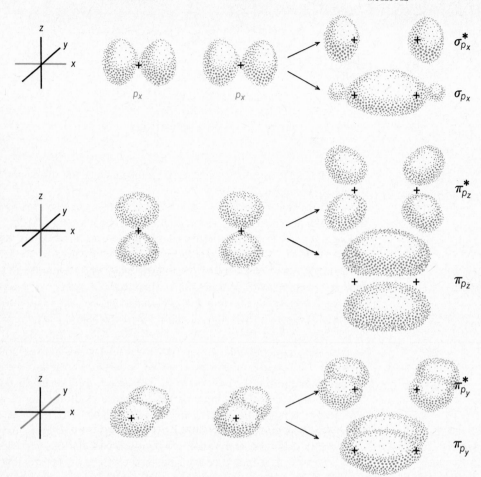

3.17
Formation of molecular orbitals by combination of 2p atomic orbitals

to the internuclear line. As shown on the top line of Figure 3.17, allowing the p_x orbital of atom 1 to combine with the p_x orbital of atom 2 produces two molecular orbitals, σ_{p_x} and $\sigma_{p_x}^*$, corresponding to the bonding and the antibonding possibilities. As Figure 3.17 shows, both of these are symmetric around the line connecting the two nuclei. For this reason they are both "sigma" and differ only in that σ_{p_x} has appreciable electron density between the nuclei whereas $\sigma_{p_x}^*$ has not.

On the bottom two lines of Figure 3.17 are represented the cases in which p orbitals overlap, not end to end, but side to side. In this way the p_z orbital of atom 1 combines with the p_z orbital of atom 2 to produce two molecular orbitals, π_{p_z} and $\pi_{p_z}^*$. These are not symmetric around the bond line; instead, one of them, the bonding orbital π_{p_z}, looks like two "sausage" clouds lying on either side of the bond line; the other one, the antibonding orbital $\pi_{p_z}^*$, has four top-like lobes extending outward from the two nuclei. The combination of the p_y orbitals to form π_{p_y} and $\pi_{p_y}^*$ is the same except that the atomic and molecular orbitals are rotated by 90° so as to be perpendicular to the

3.9 Molecular orbitals

70

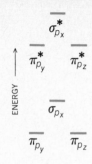

ENERGY →

$\sigma_{p_x}^*$

$\pi_{p_y}^*$ $\pi_{p_z}^*$

σ_{p_x}

π_{p_y} π_{p_z}

3.18
Relative energy of some
molecular orbitals

plane of the paper. Except for this rotation, the π_{p_y} and π_{p_z} are identical, as are the $\pi_{p_y}^*$ and $\pi_{p_z}^*$.

Figure 3.18 shows the relative disposition of these molecular orbitals on an energy diagram. (The order of energy levels has been in dispute. The one shown is consistent with the most recent experiments.) In building up diatomic molecules by adding electrons to molecular orbitals the principles followed are the same as those for building up atoms by adding electrons to atomic orbitals: (1) No more than one pair of electrons may occupy a particular molecular orbital. (2) The lowest-energy molecular orbital that is available will fill first. (3) If there is more than one molecular orbital at the same level of energy, electrons spread out to avoid each other by occupying separate orbitals, thus leading to unpaired electron spins.

Returning to the element boron ($Z = 5$, $1s^2 2s^2 2p^1$), two boron atoms will have two p electrons that need to be accommodated in the molecular orbitals of Figure 3.18. There are two lowest-lying orbitals, and the electrons will distribute themselves one to each. Consequently, the B_2 molecule is expected to be both stable (since the orbitals are bonding ones) and paramagnetic (since there are two unpaired electrons). On the other hand, in the case of two carbon atoms ($Z = 6$, $1s^2 2s^2 2p^2$), where there are four p electrons to be accommodated, the two lowest-energy orbitals are filled. Consequently, C_2 is diamagnetic. Because C_2 has twice as many electrons in bonding orbitals as B_2 has, the molecule C_2 is expected to be considerably more stable than B_2 with respect to separated atoms. In fact, the bond energy for C_2 is about twice as great as for B_2 (150 kcal compared to about 70 kcal per Avogadro number of molecules).

The next three elements give the diatomic molecules N_2, O_2, and F_2. Their respective bond energies are 225, 118, and 36 kcal per Avogadro number of molecules. How can these be accounted for? The atoms N ($Z = 7$, $1s^2 2s^2 2p^3$), O ($Z = 8$, $1s^2 2s^2 2p^4$), and F ($Z = 9$, $1s^2 2s^2 2p^5$) have three, four, and five p electrons, respectively. The assignment of these electrons in the diatomic molecules is as shown in Figure 3.19. In N_2 each N contributes three electrons, so there are six electrons, which fill the three lowest orbitals shown in the figure. This configuration is consistent both with the greater stability of N_2 over C_2 (three pairs of bonding electrons in N_2 compared to two pairs in C_2) and with the diamagnetic nature of N_2 (no unpaired electrons).

In O_2 there are two additional electrons, one from each atom, to be accommodated. Since all the bonding orbitals are filled, these electrons must be placed in antibonding orbitals. Of the antibonding orbitals the lowest lying are two of equal energy, the $\pi_{p_y}^*$ and the $\pi_{p_z}^*$. To minimize electrical repulsion between like charges, the electrons distribute themselves one in each orbital. The spins are unpaired, and the O_2 molecule, consequently, is paramagnetic. The presence of two antibonding electrons weakens the bonding between the two O atoms, and hence O_2 is more weakly bound than N_2 is. Whereas N_2 can be considered to have a triple bond (three bonding pairs or six bonding electrons), O_2 can be thought of as having a double bond (six bonding electrons minus two

Chemical bond

71

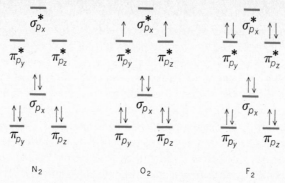

N_2 O_2 F_2

3.19
Molecular-orbital
occupancy in N_2, O_2, and
F_2

antibonding electrons, which is about equivalent to a net of two bonding pairs). In general, the term *bond order* is defined as equal to half the number of bonding electrons minus half the number of antibonding ones.

Finally, F_2 has an additional two electrons, which will complete the $\pi_{p_y}^*$ and $\pi_{p_z}^*$ orbitals. The bond is thus further weakened and is equivalent to at most a single bond. In fact, the bond in F_2 is among the weakest of single covalent bonds, presumably because the effect of the two antibonding pairs is greater than that of two of the three bonding pairs. The dominance of antibonding orbitals over equal numbers of bonding orbitals also shows itself in the nonexistence of Ne_2. Neon ($Z = 10$, $1s^2 2s^2 2p^6$) has six p electrons; in Ne_2 there would have to be three pairs of bonding electrons and three pairs of antibonding electrons, which would lead to no net attraction.

For diatomic molecules the molecular-orbital approach is a real improvement over the valence-bond approach. For example, molecular-orbital theory accounts for both the paramagnetism and the bond strength of O_2, whereas valence-bond theory does not.* For more complex molecules, molecular-orbital descriptions are usually at least as satisfactory as valence-bond ones. Furthermore, they have the advantage of not requiring resonance (Section 3.7) and giving more reasonable pictures of electron sharing.

The final representation of the electric-charge distribution in a molecule is difficult, because electron density from one molecular orbital may overlap that from another. As an illustration, we might consider

---

* The double-quartet theory (footnote, page 55) does, however, account for both properties. Each O atom contributes 6 electrons to give a total of 12 for O_2. These 12 can be disposed in double quartets so that 7 (3 on each atom and 1 shared) belong to one spin system and 5 (1 on each atom and 3 shared) belong to the opposite spin system. The "up-spin" and "down-spin" systems can be pictured respectively as resulting from the joining of two tetrahedra

$$\begin{array}{ccc} & \uparrow \quad \uparrow & \downarrow \\ \uparrow O \uparrow O \uparrow & \downarrow O \downarrow O \downarrow \\ \uparrow \quad \uparrow & \downarrow \end{array}$$

via a common corner and from the joining of two tetrahedra via a common face. With these two systems superimposed on each other, the final molecule has two uncompensated "up" spins and four shared electrons. Thus, the magnetism and the bond order of O_2 are accounted for.

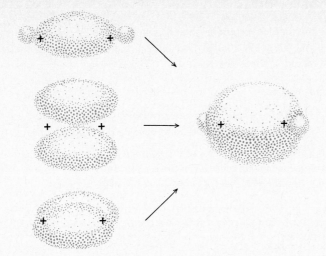

3.20
Electron distribution of
some molecular orbitals
in N₂

the N_2 molecule. Disregarding the s orbitals, the picture that emerges is something like that shown in Figure 3.20. It should be noted that there are no discontinuities that separate one atom from the other or one orbital from another. Consequently, the final picture consists merely of two positive centers embedded in a diffuse, ellipsoidal charge cloud somewhat like a football. The cross section perpendicular to the bond axis is circular in symmetry. In other words, the two π orbitals overlap with each other to produce uniform electron density all around the molecule axis. Similarly, there is a blending of the two π orbitals and the σ orbital.

For a more complex case, such as ethane, the molecular-orbital picture leads to a charge distribution like that shown in Figure 3.21 (which is to be contrasted with the valence-bond picture of Figure 3.12). In contrast to the valence-bond description in which atomic orbitals sit side by side, the molecular-orbital picture consists of electron orbitals which may be between atoms and extend over several atoms. The molecular orbitals are constructed by overlapping atomic orbitals, which may be hybrid atomic orbitals. In the ethane case, sp^3 hybrids of the two carbons are combined to give the central orbital, which is mainly between the two carbons; combination of an sp^3 hybrid of one carbon with the $1s$ orbital of a hydrogen gives an orbital connecting the carbon and hydrogen. The whole distribution is even more fuzzy

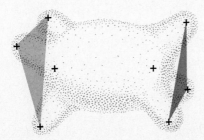

and more symmetric than that shown in the figure, which has been simplified in order to show perspective. A fair representation of the C_2H_6 molecule charge distribution is a sausage-shaped cloud slightly bulging at the two ends.

QUESTIONS

3.1 Covalent bond   Tell the difference in the concept of electron sharing in the molecular-orbital and valence-bond approaches.

3.2 Valence bond   Using the valence-bond approach, tell which of the following species illustrate (*a*) polar, (*b*) multiple, (*c*) coordinate covalent bonding: F_2, HCl, CO, N_2H_4, S_3^{--}, PH_4^+, CO_2, OF_2.

3.3 Multiple bonds   Assuming that the octet rule applies, show that each of the following contains a double or triple bond: H_2CO, CS_2, HN_3, CN_2^{--}.

3.4 Electronegativity   By using the values of Figure 3.7, give a good example of each of the following: (*a*) a pair of atoms that forms a bond more ionic than LiI, (*b*) two unlike atoms that form a nonpolar covalent bond, (*c*) a vertical sequence in which the electronegativity increases from top to bottom.

3.5 Molecular orbitals   (*a*) Give the relative order of bond strengths in the following series of species: O_2, O_2^+, O_2^-, O_2^{++}, O_2^{--}. (*b*) Do the same thing for N_2, N_2^+, N_2^-, N_2^{++}, N_2^{--}.

3.6 Molecular orbitals   Draw as best you can the charge clouds for O_2, CO, and NO.

3.7 Ionic bond   Show quantitatively for which pairs of elements an electron should transfer completely from the element of low ionization potential to the element of high electron affinity (even if the + and − ions remain separated at great distance).

3.8 Dipole moment   Given that the molecule XY_3 has a dipole moment. What can you say about each of the following: (*a*) the nature of XY bonds, (*b*) the shape of XY_3, (*c*) the relative strengths of the X—Y, X—X, and Y—Y bonds?

3.9 Resonance   The formate ion, $HCOO^-$, consists of a central carbon to which is bonded one hydrogen and each of the two oxygens. (*a*) Show that resonance can be used to account for the fact that the two oxygens are equivalent. (*b*) For the CO bonds give the bond order and the charge on each oxygen.

3.10 Electronegativity   (*a*) How is it possible that fluorine has a higher electronegativity than chlorine but a lower electron affinity? (*b*) What does this imply about the relative ionization potentials of the two atoms?

3.11 Electronegativity   Given the following as observed bond energies, in kilocalories per Avogadro number of bonds:

A—A	80 kcal	A—B	150 kcal
B—B	100 kcal	A—C	130 kcal
C—C	120 kcal	B—C	120 kcal

What can you say about the relative electronegativity of A, B, and C?

3.12 Shapes of molecules   Predict the shapes of the following: FOF, H_2NNH_2, HCN, CH_3OH.

3.13 Hybrid orbitals   Which sets of hybrid orbitals would account for the following facts? (*a*) ClBeCl is a linear molecule. (*b*) The Cl—B—Cl angle in BCl_3 is 120°. (*c*) $SiCl_4$ is not a planar molecule and does not have a dipole moment.

3.14 Resonance   Discuss critically the following statement: The molecular-orbital approach is inferior to the valence-bond approach because it cannot take account of resonance.

3.15 Molecular orbitals   Draw pictures showing the spatial distribution of the bonding molecular orbitals in each of the following: H_2CCH_2, HOOH, HCCH, OCO. (*Note:* Make molecular orbitals by using hybrid orbitals.)

3.16 Ionic bonds   On the basis of the ionic attraction term $14.4q_1q_2/r$ of Section 3.2 and by using values from Figures 2.23 and 2.24 and Appendix 8, show quantitatively for which of the following there is a net decrease of energy for ionic-bond formation: (*a*) Na + Cl, (*b*) Li + I, (*c*) Ag + Br, (*d*) Au + I.

3.17 σ and π bonds   Show by drawing cross sections of electron density that (*a*) a σ bond is symmetrical about the bond axis, (*b*) a π bond is not, but (*c*) the combination of two π bonds is.

3.18 Dipole moment   (*a*) Tell how it might come about that the measured dielectric constant may be greater for a substance of lower dipole moment. (*b*) How could you test experimentally your hypothesis in a particular case?

3.19 Molecular orbitals   (*a*) Draw all the molecular-orbital energy levels (sigma, pi, bonding, and antibonding) which can be made from all six atomic *p* orbitals on two adjacent atoms. (*b*) Show the population of the molecular orbitals of (*a*) for each of the following: NN, NO, OO, FF, CC, CO. (*c*) Give the bond order of each of the molecules in (*b*) and tell which of them is paramagnetic.

3.20 Hybrid orbitals   (*a*) Show with a sketch that combination of one $d_{x^2-y^2}$, one *s*, one p_x, and one p_y orbital leads to a set of four orbitals directed toward the corners of a square. (*b*) Show that combination of one $d_{x^2-y^2}$, one d_{z^2}, one *s*, and three *p* orbitals leads to a set of six orbitals directed toward the corners of an octahedron.

3.21 Dipole moment   The measured dipole moment for a gaseous KCl molecule is 10.6 Debye units. The measured internuclear distance is 2.67 Å. (*a*) What would be the dipole moment expected for a +1 and −1 pair of ions at this internuclear distance? (*b*) From the observed moment for KCl, what would be the apparent charges of K and Cl?

3.22 Ionic bonds   On separating an adjacent Na^+ and Cl^- pair, at what distance of separation would you expect an electron to jump from Cl^- to Na^+?

3.23 Dipole moment Given that the net dipole moment for the H_2O molecule is 1.84 Debye units. (*a*) By using the fact that the H—O—H bond angle is 104.45°, calculate the dipole moment attributable to each O—H bond. (*b*) Assuming that each bond dipole can be treated as a pair of equal but opposite charges located at the atomic centers, calculate the magnitude of these charges from the observed O—H bond length of 0.958 Å.

ANSWERS

3.23 (*b*) 0.326 of an electron charge

4 stoichiometry

The word "stoichiometry" comes from the Greek *stocheion,* meaning element, and *metron,* meaning measure. It is the aspect of chemistry that concerns itself with weight relations in chemical reactions. Stoichiometry rests on the concept of a chemical equation, which in turn is dependent on the idea of a chemical formula. The quantitative interpretation of chemical formulas is tied to the concept of atomic mass. Thus, stoichiometry is the manipulation of atomic masses to account for the amounts of material observed to be used up and produced in chemical changes.

4.1 GRAM-ATOMS

Since atoms are extremely small, any laboratory experiment dealing with weighable amounts of elements must necessarily involve tremendous numbers of atoms. For example, in making hydrogen fluoride, it is not possible to weigh out one hydrogen and one fluorine atom. It is, however, possible to get equal numbers of hydrogen and of fluorine atoms by using the relative masses of these atoms. From the atomic masses (1.00797 amu for H and 18.9984 amu for F) we know that an average fluorine atom is 18.9984/1.00797 times as heavy as an average hydrogen atom. Suppose we take any definite number of fluorine atoms and an equal number of hydrogen atoms. The weight of the entire collection of fluorine atoms is 18.9984/1.00797 times as great as the weight of the entire collection of hydrogen atoms.

Conversely, any weight of fluorine that is 18.9984/1.00797 times as great as a weight of hydrogen must contain just as many fluorine atoms as there are hydrogen atoms. For example, 18.9984 g of fluorine contains the same number of atoms as does 1.00797 g of hydrogen. In general, when we take weights equal to the relative atomic masses of different elements, we always have the same number of atoms. We can take these weights in grams, pounds, or any other convenient units. In other words, 18.9984 lb of fluorine contains the same number of atoms as 1.00797 lb of hydrogen.

The *gram-atom* is defined as a collection of atoms whose total mass is the number of grams numerically equal to the atomic mass. Since sulfur has an atomic mass of 32.064 amu, a collection of sulfur atoms weighing 32.064 g is one gram-atom of sulfur. Since the atomic mass of iron is 55.847 amu, a collection of iron atoms weighing 55.847 g is one gram-atom of iron. The collections have different weights, but each has the same number of atoms.

The concept of the gram-atom enables us to choose the proper number of atoms for reaction. Suppose we wish to make a compound in which there is one atom of iron for each atom of sulfur. If we take one gram-atom of iron and one gram-atom of sulfur, there are just exactly enough iron atoms to match the sulfur atoms. Furthermore, the weights taken are of a size that can be handled with usual laboratory apparatus. Because equal numbers of gram-atoms of different elements contain equal numbers of atoms, it is convenient to refer to amounts of elements in terms of numbers of gram-atoms. For instance 3.2 g of sulfur is 3.2/32.064, or 0.10 gram-atom.

EXAMPLE 1

In a chemical reaction requiring three atoms of magnesium for two atoms of nitrogen, how many grams of nitrogen are required by 4.86 g of magnesium? (The atomic mass of Mg is 24.3 amu and that of N is 14.0 amu.)

$$\frac{4.86 \text{ g Mg}}{24.3 \text{ g gram-atom}^{-1} \text{ Mg}} = 0.200 \text{ gram-atom Mg}$$

Need two-thirds as many N gram-atoms as Mg gram-atoms.

0.200 gram-atom Mg needs (⅔)(0.200) = 0.133 gram-atom N

$$(0.133 \text{ gram-atom N}) \left(14.0 \frac{g}{\text{gram-atom N}}\right) = 1.86 \text{ g}$$

With modern techniques, it is possible to determine the *number of atoms in one gram-atom*. This number, referred to as the *Avogadro number*, is 6.02252×10^{23}. It should be remembered to at least three significant figures: 6.02×10^{23}. Probably the most accurate determination of the Avogadro number is based on the study of solids. From the measured mass per unit volume (density) of the solid, the volume of one gram-atom can be calculated. The spacing of atoms in a solid can be found by using X rays. This enables a precise determination of the number of atoms in the volume which contains one gram-atom. The method is illustrated in the following example, which was chosen for simplicity and does not give as precise a value as can be obtained from substances with more complicated structures.

EXAMPLE 2

The density of solid AgCl is 5.56 g cc^{-1}. The solid is made up of a cubic array of alternate Ag$^+$ and Cl$^-$ ions at a spacing of 2.773 Å between centers. From these data calculate the Avogadro number.

The mass of AgCl that contains a gram-atom of each element is 107.870 g plus 35.453 g, or 143.323 g. From the density, 5.56 g cc^{-1}, we find that the volume occupied is

$$\frac{143.323 \text{ g}}{5.56 \text{ g cc}^{-1}} = 25.78 \text{ cc}$$

This corresponds to a cube of edge length

$$\sqrt[3]{25.78 \text{ cc}} = 2.954 \text{ cm}$$

Along one edge there are

$$\frac{2.954 \text{ cm}}{2.773 \times 10^{-8} \text{ cm ion}^{-1}} = 1.065 \times 10^{8} \text{ ions}$$

The total number of ions in the cube, which has 1.065×10^8 ions along each edge, is

$$(1.065 \times 10^8)^3 = 1.209 \times 10^{24}$$

Since the cube contains one Avogadro number of Ag$^+$ and one Avogadro number of Cl$^-$, the Avogadro number from these data seems to be 6.04×10^{23}.

A knowledge of the number of atoms in a gram-atom, 6.02×10^{23}, can be used to calculate the mass of individual atoms as well as the number of atoms in any given mass of the element.

EXAMPLE 3

The heaviest atom so far prepared has a mass of 257 amu. What is its mass in grams?

One gram-atom has a mass of 257 g and contains 6.02×10^{23} atoms.

One atom has a mass of

$$\frac{257 \text{ g gram-atom}^{-1}}{6.02 \times 10^{23} \text{ atoms gram-atom}^{-1}} = 4.27 \times 10^{-22} \text{ g}$$

EXAMPLE 4

The dot at the end of this sentence has a mass of about one microgram (1×10^{-6} g). Assuming that the black stuff is carbon, calculate the approximate number of atoms of carbon needed to make such a dot.

The atomic mass of carbon is 12.0 amu.

One gram-atom of carbon is 12.0 g and contains 6.02×10^{23} atoms.

$$\left(\frac{1 \times 10^{-6} \text{ g of carbon}}{12.0 \text{ g gram-atom}^{-1}}\right)\left(6.02 \times 10^{23} \frac{\text{atoms}}{\text{gram-atom}}\right) = 5 \times 10^{16} \text{ atoms}$$

Before leaving the subject of gram-atoms, we should perhaps mention that it is fairly common among chemists to substitute the term "mole of atoms" for gram-atom. So long as it is clear that atoms and not molecules are being counted, there is no problem. However, in some cases confusion might arise. For example, one mole of sulfur might mean either the Avogadro number of S atoms or the Avogadro number of S_8 molecules.

4.2 SIMPLEST FORMULAS

Of the various types of chemical formulas, the simplest formula, also called the empirical formula, gives the bare minimum of information about a compound. It states only the *relative* number of gram-atoms in the compound. The convention used in writing the simplest formula is to write the symbols of the elements and affix subscripts to designate the relative numbers of gram-atoms of these elements. The formula A_xB_y represents a compound in which there are x gram-atoms of A for every y gram-atoms of B. Because of the relationship between gram-atoms and atoms, the simplest formula also gives information about the relative number of atoms in the compound. In A_xB_y there are x atoms of element A for every y atoms of type B. Nothing is to be inferred about the nature of this association—in particular, nothing about the size or makeup of the molecular aggregate—except the *relative* number of atoms in it.

The simplest formula is always the direct result of an experiment. This procedure is illustrated in the following examples:

EXAMPLE 5

When a weighed piece of metal M is heated with excess sulfur, a chemical reaction occurs between the metal and sulfur. The excess sulfur is then driven off, leaving only the compound, consisting of combined metal and sulfur. From the weight of M and weight of compound, the weight of sulfur in the compound can be deduced. Here are some sample figures from an experiment of this type:

Weight of metal	2.435 g
Weight of compound	3.397 g
Weight of sulfur	0.962 g

What is the simplest formula of the compound?

Since the simplest formula gives the relative numbers of gram-atoms in the compound, we must calculate how many gram-atoms of M and S have combined. If the atomic weight of M is 121.75 and that of S is 32.064, then

$$\text{Number of gram-atoms of M} = \frac{\text{weight of M}}{\text{weight of 1 gram-atom of M}}$$

$$= \frac{2.435 \text{ g}}{121.75 \text{ g gram-atom}^{-1}}$$

$$= 0.0200 \text{ gram-atom of M}$$

$$\text{Number of gram-atoms of S} = \frac{\text{weight of S}}{\text{weight of 1 gram-atom of S}}$$

$$= \frac{0.962 \text{ g}}{32.064 \text{ g gram-atom}^{-1}}$$

$$= 0.0300 \text{ gram-atom of S}$$

In this compound there is 0.0200 gram-atom of M combined with 0.0300 gram-atom of S. Since the relative number of gram-atoms of M to S is 0.0200 to 0.0300, or 2 to 3, the simplest formula is M_2S_3.

EXAMPLE 6

The analysis of a compound is often given in terms of percentage composition. What is the simplest formula of a compound which on analysis shows 50.05% S and 49.95% O by weight?

For the simplest formula we need the relative numbers of gram-atoms of sulfur and oxygen in the compound. Since only relative numbers are involved, we may consider any amount of compound, 1 g, 32.064 g, or any other weight. We shall work this problem in two ways for illustration.

(a) In 32.064 g of compound there are 16.05 g of sulfur (50.05% of 32.064 g) and 16.02 g of oxygen (49.95% of 32.064 g).

$$\text{Number of gram-atoms of S} = \frac{\text{weight of S}}{\text{weight of 1 gram-atom of S}}$$

$$= \frac{16.05 \text{ g}}{32.064 \text{ g gram-atom}^{-1}}$$

$$= 0.5006 \text{ gram-atom of S}$$

$$\text{Number of gram-atoms of O} = \frac{\text{weight of O}}{\text{weight of 1 gram-atom of O}}$$

$$= \frac{16.02 \text{ g}}{15.999 \text{ g gram-atom}^{-1}}$$

$$= 1.001 \text{ gram-atoms of O}$$

The simplest formula is $S_{0.5006}O_{1.001}$, or SO_2.

(*b*) In 100.0 g of compound there are 50.05 g of sulfur and 49.95 g of oxygen.

$$\text{Number of gram-atoms of S} = \frac{\text{weight of S}}{\text{weight of 1 gram-atom of S}}$$

$$= \frac{50.05 \text{ g}}{32.064 \text{ g gram-atom}^{-1}}$$

$$= 1.561 \text{ gram-atoms of S}$$

$$\text{Number of gram-atoms of O} = \frac{\text{weight of O}}{\text{weight of 1 gram-atom of O}}$$

$$= \frac{49.95 \text{ g}}{15.999 \text{ g gram-atom}^{-1}}$$

$$= 3.122 \text{ gram-atoms of O}$$

The simplest formula is $S_{1.561}O_{3.122}$, or SO_2.

4.3 MOLECULAR FORMULAS

A second type of formula is the molecular formula. In the molecular formula the subscripts give the *actual* number of atoms of an element in one molecule of the compound. The molecule was defined previously as an aggregate of atoms bonded together tightly enough to be conveniently treated as a recognizable unit. In order to write the molecular formula, it is necessary to know how many atoms constitute the molecule. To find the actual number of atoms in a molecule, various experimental techniques can be used. For instance, X-ray determination of the positions of atoms in solids can give this information. Furthermore, as discussed in Chapters 5 and 8, some of the properties of gases and solutions depend on the number of atoms in each molecular aggregate. A few molecular formulas thus determined are shown in Figure 4.1, where they are compared with the corresponding simplest formulas. In some cases, e.g., water and sucrose, the molecular and simplest formulas are identical. In other cases they are not. We cannot tell from a formula whether it is molecular or simplest. However, if the subscripts

Substance	Molecular formula	Simplest formula
Benzene	C_6H_6	CH
Acetylene	C_2H_2	CH
Phosphorus	P_4	P
Water	H_2O	H_2O
Sucrose (a sugar)	$C_{12}H_{22}O_{11}$	$C_{12}H_{22}O_{11}$
Glucose (a sugar)	$C_6H_{12}O_6$	CH_2O
Nicotine	$C_{10}H_{14}N_2$	C_5H_7N

4.1
Molecular and simplest formulas

given have a common divisor, the chance is good that it is a molecular formula. The molecular formula gives all the information the simplest formula gives, and more besides.

4.4 MOLES

The formula mass (or formula weight) is the sum of all the atomic masses in the formula under consideration, be it simplest or molecular. For NaCl, the formula mass is the atomic mass of sodium, 22.9898 amu, plus the atomic mass of chlorine, 35.453 amu, a total of 58.443 amu. For $C_{12}H_{22}O_{11}$, the formula mass is equal to 12 times the atomic mass of carbon plus 22 times the atomic mass of hydrogen plus 11 times the atomic mass of oxygen, or 342.302 amu. In all cases, the formula mass depends on which formula is written. If the molecular formula is used, the formula mass is called the *molecular mass*. For example, 342.302 amu is the molecular mass of sucrose.

As noted above, the formula mass is given in atomic mass units. An amount of a substance whose mass in grams numerically equals the formula mass is called a *gram-formula*. A gram-formula is usually referred to as a *gram-mole*, or simply a *mole*. In the case of $C_{12}H_{22}O_{11}$, where the formula mass is 342.302 amu, one gram-formula or one gram-mole weighs 342.302 g. A pile of this sugar weighing 342.302 g is one gram-mole. The formula mass can also be used in terms of tons, ounces, pounds, or other units of mass to give ton-moles, ounce-moles, etc. In other words, 342.302 tons of sugar is one ton-formula, or one ton-mole, of sugar. Since we are primarily concerned with gram-moles, it is convenient to omit the prefix "gram-" and to understand that "mole" means gram-mole.

There is an important relationship between number of moles and number of particles. Let us consider sulfur chloride, the molecular formula of which is S_2Cl_2. One mole of S_2Cl_2 weighs 135 g and contains 64 g of sulfur and 71 g of chlorine. In 64 g of S (atomic mass 32), there are 64/32, or 2, gram-atoms of S; in 71 g of Cl (atomic mass 35.5), there are 71/35.5, or 2, gram-atoms of Cl. Since one gram-atom contains the Avogadro number of atoms, two gram-atoms of S contain $2 \times 6.02 \times 10^{23}$ atoms of S, and two gram-atoms of Cl contain $2 \times 6.02 \times 10^{23}$ atoms of Cl. The molecular formula, S_2Cl_2, indicates that two atoms of S and two atoms of Cl comprise one molecule of S_2Cl_2. Therefore, $2 \times 6.02 \times 10^{23}$ atoms of S and $2 \times 6.02 \times 10^{23}$ atoms of chlorine comprise 6.02×10^{23} molecules. For any substance whose molecular formula is known, *one mole contains the Avogadro number of molecules.*

Let us consider the relationship between number of moles and number of particles for a compound whose molecular formula is not known. Such a compound is phosphorus dichloride, whose simplest formula is PCl_2. One mole of PCl_2 weighs 102 g and contains 31 g of phosphorus and 71 g of chlorine. In 31 g of P (atomic mass 31) there is 31/31, or 1, gram-atom of P; in 71 g of Cl (atomic mass 35.5), there is 71/35.5, or 2, gram-atoms of Cl. One gram-atom of P contains 6.02×10^{23} atoms of P; two gram-atoms of Cl contain $2 \times 6.02 \times 10^{23}$ atoms of Cl. Since the molecular formula of PCl_2 is not known, the number of atoms in the molecule is not known. Therefore, we can make no statement about the number of molecules in one mole of PCl_2. If we define a *formula-unit* as consisting of one P atom and two Cl atoms, there are then 6.02×10^{23} such formula-units in one mole of PCl_2. For any substance, *one mole contains the Avogadro number of formula-units.* Only if the formula is a molecular formula is the formula-unit the same as the molecule. Even though formulas are based on experimentally determined percentage composition, it is sometimes necessary to calculate percentage composition from a formula.

EXAMPLE 7

What is the percent composition of $Al_2(SO_4)_3$? Atomic masses are Al 26.98, S 32.06, O 16.00.

One mole of $Al_2(SO_4)_3$ contains
2 gram-atoms Al, or 2×26.98 g Al, or   53.96 g Al
3 gram-atoms S, or 3×32.06 g S, or   99.18 g S
12 gram-atoms O, or 12×16.00 g O, or   192.00 g O
                                                                    _____
                                                                    345.14 g total mass

$$\text{Percent aluminum} = \frac{53.96 \text{ g}}{345.14 \text{ g}} \times 100 = 15.63\%$$

$$\text{Percent sulfur} = \frac{99.18 \text{ g}}{345.14 \text{ g}} \times 100 = 28.74\%$$

$$\text{Percent oxygen} = \frac{192.00 \text{ g}}{345.14 \text{ g}} \times 100 = 55.63\%$$

4.5 CHEMICAL REACTIONS

The other principal division of stoichiometry is concerned with mass or weight changes in chemical reactions. Before considering these quantitative aspects, we need to examine ways of describing chemical change. It is possible to group chemical reactions into two broad classes: (1) reactions in which there is no electron transfer and (2) reactions in which there is electron transfer from one atom to another atom.

Reactions in which no electrons are transferred usually involve the joining or separating of ions or molecules. An example of a "no-electron-transfer" reaction occurs when a solution of sodium chloride is mixed with a solution of silver nitrate. The solution of sodium chloride contains sodium ions and chloride ions (Section 8.4). The solution of silver nitrate contains silver ions and nitrate ions. When the two solutions are mixed, a chemical reaction occurs, as shown by the formation of a white precipitate. This white solid consists of silver ions and the chloride ions clumped together in large aggregates. In the final solution, sodium ions and nitrate ions remain as they were initially. In the chemical reaction, the silver ions have combined with chloride ions to form solid silver chloride, which is insoluble in the water. In shorthand form, the reaction is indicated as

$$Ag^+(soln) + \cancel{NO_3^-(soln)} + \cancel{Na^+(soln)} + Cl^-(soln) \longrightarrow$$
$$AgCl(s) + \cancel{Na^+(soln)} + \cancel{NO_3^-(soln)}$$

where the abbreviation (*soln*) indicates that the ion is in solution and the notation (*s*) emphasizes the fact that AgCl is formed as a solid. The strikeovers indicate cancellation of ions which do not change in the course of the reaction. The final net reaction is

$$Ag^+(soln) + Cl^-(soln) \longrightarrow AgCl(s)$$

Reactions in which electrons are transferred from one atom to another are known as *oxidation-reduction reactions*. Many of the most important chemical reactions fall into this class. For example, the combining of a sodium atom with a chlorine atom can be regarded as resulting from the transfer of an electron from the sodium to the chlorine, as shown schematically in Figure 4.2. A less obvious example of an oxidation-reduction reaction is that in which hydrogen and oxygen form water. In this case there is a change of the sharing of electrons during the course of the reaction:

$$H:H + :\overset{..}{O}: \longrightarrow H:\overset{..}{O}:$$
$$\overset{}{\underset{H}{}}$$

What happens to the hydrogen in the course of this reaction? In the initial state two hydrogen nuclei share a pair of electrons. Since the two hydrogen nuclei are identical, they share the pair equally, and each hydrogen atom has a half-time share of an electron pair. In the final state the hydrogen shares a pair of electrons with oxygen. Since oxygen is the more electronegative, the electron pair is not shared equally but belongs more to the oxygen than to the hydrogen. In the course of the reaction there is thus a change in the electron sharing; i.e., a partial transfer of electrons.

Na $\odot$ + $\cdot\overset{..}{\underset{..}{Cl}}$: $\longrightarrow$ Na$^+$ $[:\overset{..}{\underset{..}{Cl}}:]^-$

4.2
Chemical reaction with electron transfer

4.6 OXIDATION NUMBERS

In order to keep track of electron shifts in oxidation-reduction reactions, it is convenient to introduce the *oxidation number,* sometimes called the *oxidation state.* The oxidation number is defined as the charge which an atom appears to have (with emphasis on the word "appears") when electrons are counted according to some rather arbitrary rules: (*a*) Electrons shared between two unlike atoms are counted with the more electronegative atom. (*b*) Electrons shared between two like atoms are divided equally between the sharing atoms.

What is the oxidation number of hydrogen in the H_2 molecule? The electron pair is shared by two identical atoms, and so, according to the second rule, half of the electrons are counted with each atom. Since the hydrogen nucleus has a $+1$ charge and since one negative charge is counted with the nucleus, the apparent charge of each hydrogen atom is zero. The oxidation number of hydrogen in H_2 is 0.

What are the oxidation numbers of hydrogen and oxygen in H_2O? Oxygen is the more electronegative, and so, according to the first rule, the shared electrons are counted with the oxygen, as shown by the line in Figure 4.3. The hydrogen appears to have a charge of $+1$ and is assigned an oxidation number of $+1$. Since eight electrons are counted with the $+6$ oxygen kernel (nucleus plus inner-shell electrons), the apparent charge of oxygen is -2. Oxygen has an oxidation number of -2 in H_2O.

In principle, electronic pictures can be drawn for all molecules and electrons counted in this way to deduce the oxidation numbers of the various atoms. This is laborious. It is more convenient to use the following operational rules, which are derived from rules (*a*) and (*b*).

1. In free elements, each atom has an oxidation number of 0, no matter how complicated the molecule is. Hydrogen in H_2, sodium in Na, sulfur in S_8, and phosphorus in P_4 all have oxidation numbers of 0.

2. In simple ions (which contain one atom) the oxidation number is equal to the charge on the ion. In these cases, the apparent charge of the atom is the real charge of the ion. In the tripositive aluminum ion, the oxidation number of the aluminum ion is $+3$. Iron, which can form a dipositive or a tripositive ion, sometimes has an oxidation number of $+2$ and sometimes $+3$. In the dinegative oxide ion, the oxidation number of oxygen is -2. It is useful to remember that *elements of group I of the periodic table, lithium, sodium, potassium, rubidium, cesium, and francium, form only $+1$ ions. Their oxidation number is $+1$ in all compounds. The group II elements, beryllium, magnesium, calcium, strontium, barium, and radium, form only $+2$ ions and hence always have oxidation numbers of $+2$ in all compounds.*

3. In compounds containing oxygen, the oxidation number of each oxygen atom is generally -2. There are two kinds of exceptions. One arises in the case of the peroxides, compounds of oxygen in which there is an oxygen-oxygen bond. In peroxides, e.g., hydrogen peroxide (H_2O_2), only seven electrons are counted with the $+6$ kernel of oxygen. Figure 4.4 shows how the electrons are assigned. In the hydrogen-oxygen bond the electrons are counted with oxygen, the more electronegative atom. In the oxygen-oxygen bond the electron pair is shared between two like atoms and is split equally between the sharing partners. The apparent charge of the oxygen is thus -1. Oxygen has an oxidation number of -1 in all peroxides. The second exception is even less common. It occurs when oxygen is bonded to fluorine, the only

H $\ddot{:}\overset{..}{O}\ddot{:}$ O *kernel* $+6$
H   H *kernel* $+1$

4.3
Assignment of oxidation numbers in H_2O

$\ddot{:}\overset{..}{O}\ddot{:}\overset{..}{O}\ddot{:}$ O *kernel* $+6$
H   H   H *kernel* $+1$

4.4
Assignment of oxidation numbers in H_2O_2

4.6 Oxidation numbers

4.5
Assignment of oxidation
numbers in OF$_2$

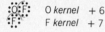

O *kernel* + 6
F *kernel* + 7

atom which is more electronegative than oxygen. When oxygen is bonded to fluorine, shared electrons are counted with the fluorine. The assignment of oxidation numbers in the compound oxygen difluoride is shown in Figure 4.5. The oxidation number of fluorine is −1, and the oxidation number of oxygen is +2.

4. *In compounds containing hydrogen, the oxidation number of hydrogen is generally +1.* This rule covers practically all the hydrogen compounds. It fails in the case of the hydrides, in which hydrogen is bonded to an atom less electronegative than hydrogen. For example, when hydrogen is bonded to sodium in the compound sodium hydride, NaH, the hydrogen is the more electronegative atom, and two electrons are counted with it. In hydrides, the oxidation number of hydrogen is −1.

5. *All oxidation numbers must be consistent with the conservation of charge.* Charge must be conserved in the sense that the sum of all the apparent charges in a particle must equal the net charge of that particle. This leads to the following conditions: *(a) for neutral molecules, the oxidation numbers of all the atoms must add up to zero; (b) for complex ions (charged particles which contain more than one atom), the oxidation numbers of all the atoms must add up to the charge on the ion.* As an example of a neutral molecule, we consider the case of H$_2$O. The oxidation number of hydrogen is +1. There are two hydrogen atoms. The total apparent charge contribution by hydrogen is +2. The oxidation number of oxygen is −2. The whole molecule looks to be neutral.

The neutrality rule enables us to assign oxidation numbers to any atom. For example, what is the oxidation number of sulfur in H$_2$SO$_4$? The oxidation number of hydrogen is +1; the oxidation number of oxygen is −2. The two hydrogens give an apparent charge of +2; the four oxygens give an apparent charge of −8. For neutrality the sulfur must contribute +6. Since there is but one sulfur atom, the oxidation number of sulfur is +6. In H$_2$S$_2$O$_3$ hydrogen contributes an apparent charge of +2; oxygen contributes a total apparent charge of −6. For neutrality the sulfur contribution must be +4. Since there are two sulfur atoms, the oxidation number of each is +2.

Since oxidation numbers are quite arbitrary, they may have values which at first sight appear strange. For example, in cane sugar, C$_{12}$H$_{22}$O$_{11}$, the oxidation number of carbon is 0. The total apparent charge of 22 hydrogen atoms is canceled by that of 11 oxygen atoms. According to the oxidation number, each carbon atom appears to contribute no charge to the molecule. Fractional oxidation numbers are also possible, as in Na$_2$S$_4$O$_6$, where the oxidation number of sulfur is +1¾.

In complex ions the apparent charges of all the atoms must add up to equal the charge on the ion. This is true in hydroxide ion, OH$^-$, for example, where the superscript minus indicates that the ion has a net charge of −1. Since oxygen has an oxidation number of −2 and since hydrogen has an oxidation number of +1, the total apparent charge is −2 + 1 = −1, which is the same as the actual charge of the ion. In Cr$_2$O$_7^{--}$, a dinegative ion, the seven oxygen atoms contribute −14.

Chromium must contribute $+12$ in order to make the ion have a net charge of -2. Since there are two chromium atoms in the complex, each chromium has an oxidation number of $+6$.

In order to avoid confusion with the actual charge on an ion, which is written as a superscript, the oxidation number of an atom, when needed, is written beneath the atom to which it applies. For example, in

$$\underset{+5\ -2}{P_2O_7^{-4}}$$

the charge on the ion is -4; the oxidation numbers are $+5$ and -2. It should be emphasized strongly that oxidation numbers are not actual charges of atoms. In the specific case of $P_2O_7^{-4}$ it can be shown experimentally that the aggregate carries a -4 charge; however, it cannot be shown experimentally that the charge of P is $+5$ and that of the O is -2. The $+5$ and -2 are arbitrarily assigned numbers, and we must not conclude that $P_2O_7^{-4}$ contains P^{+5} ions and O^{-2} ions.

Oxidation number is not the same thing as valence. Valence, or combining capacity, can be interpreted in several ways. For example, it represents the number of hydrogen atoms which can be combined with a given atom. It also represents the number of single bonds which an atom can form. In any case valence is a pure number and has no plus or minus associated with it. On the other hand, oxidation number is positive or negative. For example, in water the valence of oxygen is two, but its oxidation number is *minus* two. Furthermore, there may actually be a difference in the magnitude of the valence and the oxidation number. In hydrogen peroxide (Figure 4.4) each oxygen atom has two single bonds, one that goes to oxygen and one to hydrogen. The valence of oxygen is therefore two. As indicated before, the oxidation number of oxygen in H_2O_2 is -1.

4.7 OXIDATION-REDUCTION

The term *oxidation* refers to any chemical change in which there is an *increase in oxidation number*. For example, when hydrogen, H_2, reacts to form water, H_2O, the hydrogen atoms change oxidation number from 0 to $+1$. The H_2 is said to undergo oxidation. When sugar, $C_{12}H_{22}O_{11}$, is burned to give carbon dioxide, CO_2, carbon atoms increase in oxidation number from 0 to $+4$. The sugar is oxidized. The term *reduction* applies to any *decrease in oxidation number*. For example, when oxygen, O_2, reacts to form H_2O, oxygen atoms change oxidation number from 0 to -2. This is a decrease in oxidation number; hence O_2 is said to undergo reduction. In oxidation and reduction the increase and decrease of oxidation numbers result from a shift of electrons. The only way by which electrons can be shifted away from an atom is for them to be pulled toward another atom. In this process the oxidation number of the first atom increases and the oxidation number of the second atom decreases. Oxidation and reduction must always occur together and must just compensate each other.

The *oxidizing agent* is, by definition, the *substance that does the*

Term	Oxidation-number change	Electron change
Oxidation	Increase	Loss of electrons
Reduction	Decrease	Gain of electrons
Oxidizing agent	Decrease	Picks up electrons
Reducing agent	Increase	Supplies electrons
Substance oxidized	Increase	Loses electrons
Substance reduced	Decrease	Gains electrons

4.6
Oxidation-reduction terms

oxidizing; it is the substance containing the atom which shows a decrease in oxidation number. For example, if in a reaction $KClO_3$ is converted to KCl, each chlorine atom decreases in oxidation number from $+5$ to -1. This amounts to getting six electrons (six negative charges) from other atoms. Thus, $KClO_3$ must cause oxidation and is acting as an oxidizing agent. Similarly, a *reducing agent* is the *substance that does the reducing; it is the substance containing the atom which shows an increase in oxidation number.* In the reaction of $C_{12}H_{22}O_{11}$ to give CO_2, $C_{12}H_{22}O_{11}$ is a reducing agent, because it contains carbon atoms which increase in oxidation number. It should be evident that when a substance acts as a reducing agent, it itself must be oxidized in the process. Figure 4.6 summarizes the terms used to describe oxidation-reduction.

Listed in Figure 4.7 are some examples of oxidation-reduction processes. The numbers below the formulas indicate the oxidation numbers of interest. It must be emphasized that the term "oxidizing agent" or "reducing agent" refers to the entire substance and not to just one atom. For example, in the next-to-last reaction of the table, the oxidizing agent is $KClO_3$ and not $+5$ Cl. It can be shown that $KClO_3$ picks up electrons and therefore is an oxidizing agent, but it *cannot* be shown that it is the chlorine atom in $KClO_3$ that picks up electrons, because of the arbitrary rules for assigning oxidation numbers.

4.7
Oxidation-reduction
reactions

Oxidizing agents	+	Reducing agents	$\longrightarrow$	Products
O_2		H_2		H_2O
0		0		$+1-2$
Cl_2		Na		NaCl
0		0		$+1-1$
H^+		Mg		$Mg^{++} + H_2$
$+1$		0		$+2$ 0
$KClO_3$		$C_{12}H_{22}O_{11}$		$KCl + CO_2 + H_2O$
$+5$		0		-1 $+4$
H_2O_2		H_2O_2		$H_2O + O_2$
-1		-1		-2 0

In the last reaction listed in Figure 4.7, H_2O_2 acts both as a reducing agent and an oxidizing agent. In oxidizing and reducing itself, it is said to undergo *auto-oxidation*, or *disproportionation*.

4.8 BALANCING CHEMICAL EQUATIONS

Chemical equations are shorthand designations which give information about a chemical reaction. We shall generally use *net equations,* which *specify only the substances used up and the substances formed* in the chemical reaction. Net equations omit anything which remains unchanged. The convention used in writing equations is to place what disappears (the *reactants*) on the left-hand side and what appears (the *products*) on the right-hand side. The reactants and products are separated by a single arrow $\longrightarrow$, an equal sign $=$, or a double arrow $\rightleftharpoons$, depending on what aspect of the chemical reaction is being emphasized. An example of a net equation is

$$Cl_2(g) + H_2O + Ag^+ \longrightarrow AgCl(s) + HOCl + H^+$$

The reactants and products are designated by symbols or formulas. The symbol can be thought of as representing either one atom or one gram-atom. The formula represents either one formula-unit or one mole. The notation (g) indicates the gas phase, and (s) the solid phase. *When no such phase notation appears, the aqueous phase is understood.*

To be valid, a chemical equation must satisfy three conditions. First, it must be consistent with the experimental facts; i.e., it must state what chemical species disappear and appear. Second, it must be consistent with the conservation of mass. (Since we cannot destroy mass, we must account for it. If an atom disappears from one substance, it must appear in another.) Third, the chemical equation must be consistent with the conservation of electric charge. (Since we cannot destroy electric charge, we must account for it.) The second and third conditions are expressed by saying that the equation must be *balanced.* A balanced equation contains the same number of atoms of the different kinds on the left- and right-hand sides; furthermore, the net charge is the same on both sides.

How do we go about writing balanced equations? One method, usually reserved for simple reactions, is to balance the equation by inspection. For example, in the reaction between a solution of silver nitrate and a solution of sodium chloride, silver ions and chloride ions disappear and solid silver chloride appears. The equation for the reaction is

$$Ag^+ + Cl^- \longrightarrow AgCl(s)$$

Since there is one silver atom on the left and one on the right and since there is one chlorine atom on the left and one on the right, mass balance is satisfied. The net electric charge on the left is zero ($+1$ for the silver ion plus -1 for the chloride ion totals zero), and the net charge on the right is zero. Therefore, the equation is also electrically balanced.

In the reaction between solid sodium and gaseous diatomic chlorine, solid sodium chloride is formed, so we write first

$$Na(s) + Cl_2(g) \longrightarrow NaCl(s)$$

To balance this equation, we note that we have two chlorine atoms on the left, so we ought to have two chlorine atoms on the right. We cannot change the subscript of Cl in the formula NaCl, because that would give the formula of a different compound. We can change only the coefficients; hence we put 2 in front of the NaCl. With two sodium atoms on the right we now need two sodium atoms on the left; therefore, we also place a 2 in front of the Na.

The equation now reads

$$2Na(s) + Cl_2(g) \longrightarrow 2NaCl(s)$$

and has been balanced by inspection.

There are more complicated reactions involving electron transfer where balancing by inspection gets to be quite a chore. For example, suppose that in the reaction which occurs between potassium dichromate, sulfur, and water, the products are taken to be sulfur dioxide, potassium hydroxide, and chromic oxide.

$$K_2Cr_2O_7(s) + H_2O + S(s) \longrightarrow SO_2(g) + KOH(s) + Cr_2O_3(s)$$

Although the equation can be balanced by inspection, it is easier to balance it by matching up the electron transfer, i.e., the oxidation and the reduction. So far as electron transfer is concerned, we have to worry only about those atoms which change oxidation number. On applying the rules for assigning oxidation numbers, we see that sulfur changes oxidation number from 0 to +4 and chromium from +6 to +3. As indicated below, each sulfur atom appears to lose four electrons and each chromium atom appears to gain three electrons.

Since each formula-unit of $K_2Cr_2O_7$ contains two chromium atoms, a formula-unit will pick up six electrons. These electrons must be furnished by the S. In order that the electron loss and the electron gain be equal, for every two $K_2Cr_2O_7$ formula-units that disappear (12 electrons picked up) three S atoms must be used up (12 electrons furnished). This is indicated by writing 2 in front of the $K_2Cr_2O_7$ and the Cr_2O_3 and 3 in front of the S and the SO_2 to give

$$2K_2Cr_2O_7(s) + H_2O + 3S(s) \longrightarrow 3SO_2(g) + KOH(s) + 2Cr_2O_3(s)$$

Although the tough part is over, the equation is not balanced. To complete the job, the other coefficients must be made consistent. We can make them so by inspection. From the above equation we can see that we get four potassium atoms on the right, so we place a 4 in front of the KOH. The result

$$2K_2Cr_2O_7(s) + H_2O + 3S(s) \longrightarrow 3SO_2(g) + 4KOH(s) + 2Cr_2O_3(s)$$

is still not balanced. Balance can be achieved by counting up either the H atoms or the O atoms on the right. This shows that two molecules of H_2O are required. The balanced equation is

$$2K_2Cr_2O_7(s) + 2H_2O + 3S(s) \longrightarrow 3SO_2(g) + 4KOH(s) + 2Cr_2O_3(s)$$

Here in summary for future reference are the steps followed:

1   Assign oxidation numbers for those atoms which change.
2   Decide on number of electrons to be shifted per atom.
3   Decide on number of electrons to be shifted per formula-unit.
4   Compensate electron gain and loss by writing appropriate coefficients for the oxidizing agent and the reducing agent.
5   Insert other coefficients consistent with the conservation of matter.

In aqueous solution, balancing oxidation-reduction equations is different because we usually know in advance only the formulas of the oxidizing and the reducing agents as well as their products. The final balanced equation will involve these species, but it may also include H_2O and H^+ or OH^-, depending on whether the solution is acid or basic. The insertion of these additional species is part of the process of balancing equations in aqueous solutions. As an illustration, we consider the problem of balancing the equation for the oxidation of H_2SO_3 by $Cr_2O_7^{--}$ *in acid solution* to form HSO_4^- and Cr^{+3}. The stepwise procedure is as follows:

1   Assign oxidation numbers:

$$\underset{+6\ -2}{Cr_2O_7^{--}} + \underset{+1+4\ -2}{H_2 S\ O_3} \longrightarrow \underset{+3}{Cr^{+3}} + \underset{+1+6\ -2}{H\ S\ O_4^-}$$

2   Balance the electron transfer for those atoms that change oxidation number:

$$\underset{+6}{Cr_2O_7^{--}} + \underset{+4}{3H_2S O_3} \longrightarrow \underset{+3}{2Cr^{+3}} + \underset{+6}{3HSO_4^-}$$

$$\uparrow 3e^- \times 2 = 3 \times \downarrow 2e^-$$

After the coefficient 3 has been placed in front of H_2SO_3 on the left side, the right side is made consistent as regards chromium and sulfur atoms.

3   Balance the net charge by adding (for acid solutions) H^+ as required to give the same charge on both sides. In the last step the net charge on the left is -2 (-2 from one $Cr_2O_7^{--}$ and 0 from three H_2SO_3), and the net charge on the right is $+3$ ($+6$ from two Cr^{+3} and -3 from three HSO_4^-). By adding five H^+ to the left, the net charge will come out to be $+3$ on both sides.

$$Cr_2O_7^{--} + 3H_2SO_3 + 5H^+ \longrightarrow 2Cr^{+3} + 3HSO_4^-$$

4   Count up oxygen atoms and add H_2O to side that is deficient in O.

$$Cr_2O_7^{--} + 3H_2SO_3 + 5H^+ \longrightarrow 2Cr^{+3} + 3HSO_4^- + 4H_2O$$

5 As a check, count up hydrogen atoms on both sides to make sure they are equal. In this case, there are 11 on each side.

This method of balancing equations works for basic solutions as well, except that, *in basic solution,* hydrogen ions do not exist in any appreciable concentration. The balancing of the net charge is done by placing hydroxide ions where needed. As an example, consider the preceding oxidation-reduction as carried out in basic solution. In basic solution, the oxidizing agent exists in the form of CrO_4^{--} and the reducing agent in the form of SO_3^{--}. The products can be written CrO_2^- and SO_4^{--}. The sequence of steps follows:

1 $\underset{+6\ -2}{Cr\,O_4^{--}} + \underset{+4\ -2}{S\,O_3^{--}} \longrightarrow \underset{+3\ -2}{Cr\,O_2^-} + \underset{+6\ -2}{S\,O_4^{--}}$

2 $\underset{+6}{2CrO_4^{--}} + \underset{+4}{3SO_3^{--}} \longrightarrow \underset{+3}{2CrO_2^-} + \underset{+6}{3SO_4^{--}}$

$2 \times \uparrow 3e^- = 3 \times \downarrow 2e^-$

3 $2CrO_4^{--} + 3SO_3^{--} \qquad\qquad \longrightarrow 2CrO_2^- + 3SO_4^{--}$

Net charge: Net charge:

$(2)(-2) + (3)(-2) = -10 \qquad (2)(-1) + (3)(-2) = -8$

To maintain net charge, we need two plus charges on the left or two minus charges on the right. To place $2H^+$ on the left is forbidden, since the original solution is basic and does not contain any appreciable concentration of hydrogen ions. The alternative is to place two hydroxide ions on the right.

4 $2CrO_4^{--} + 3SO_3^{--} \longrightarrow 2CrO_2^- + 3SO_4^{--} + 2OH^-$

Place one H_2O on the left to balance oxygen atoms.

$2CrO_4^{--} + 3SO_3^{--} + H_2O \longrightarrow 2CrO_2^- + 3SO_4^{--} + 2OH^-$

An alternative method of balancing equations avoids the problem of assigning oxidation numbers. This is the method of half-reactions (sometimes called the "ion-electron" method). The method is based on splitting the reaction into two parts—an oxidation half and a reduction half. The two half-reactions are balanced separately, showing electrons, and then combined in order to eliminate the electrons from the final balanced equation. To illustrate, we consider the same reaction as before, i.e., the oxidation of H_2SO_3 by $Cr_2O_7^{--}$ in acid solution to form HSO_4^- and Cr^{+3}. The detailed steps, *for acid solution,* are as follows:

1 Separate the change into half-reactions.
2 Balance each half-reaction separately:
   a. Change coefficients to account for all atoms except H and O.
   b. Add H_2O to side deficient in O.
   c. Add H^+ to side deficient in H.
   d. Add e^- to side deficient in negative charge.

3   Multiply half-reactions by appropriate numbers needed to balance electrons, and add.

4   Subtract any duplications on left and right.

Step 1:

$$H_2SO_3 \longrightarrow HSO_4^-$$

$$Cr_2O_7^{--} \longrightarrow Cr^{+3}$$

Step 2a:

$$H_2SO_3 \longrightarrow HSO_4^-$$

$$Cr_2O_7^{--} \longrightarrow 2Cr^{+3}$$

Step 2b:

$$H_2SO_3 + H_2O \longrightarrow HSO_4^-$$

$$Cr_2O_7^{--} \longrightarrow 2Cr^{+3} + 7H_2O$$

Step 2c:

$$H_2SO_3 + H_2O \longrightarrow HSO_4^- + 3H^+$$

$$Cr_2O_7^{--} + 14H^+ \longrightarrow 2Cr^{+3} + 7H_2O$$

Step 2d:

$$H_2SO_3 + H_2O \longrightarrow HSO_4^- + 3H^+ + 2e^-$$

$$Cr_2O_7^{--} + 14H^+ + 6e^- \longrightarrow 2Cr^{+3} + 7H_2O$$

[Two electrons have been added to the right side since, in step (*2c*), the left side has a net charge of 0 and the right side has a net charge of $+2$. The right side of (*2c*) is deficient in negative charge by two units.]

[Six electrons have been added to the left since, in step (*2c*), the left side has a net charge of $+12$ and the right side has $+6$.]

Step 3:

$$3(H_2SO_3 + H_2O \longrightarrow HSO_4^- + 3H^+ + 2e^-)$$

$$Cr_2O_7^{--} + 14H^+ + 6e^- \longrightarrow 2Cr^{+3} + 7H_2O$$

$$\overline{3H_2SO_3 + 3H_2O + Cr_2O_7^{--} + 14H^+ + 6e^- \longrightarrow}$$
$$3HSO_4^- + 9H^+ + 6e^- + 2Cr^{+3} + 7H_2O$$

[The top half-reaction has been multiplied by 3 to get six electrons in each half of the reaction.]

Step 4:

Since $3H_2O$, $9H^+$, and $6e^-$ are duplicated on left and right sides, these can be subtracted to give:

$$3H_2SO_3 + Cr_2O_7^{--} + 5H^+ \longrightarrow 3HSO_4^- + 2Cr^{+3} + 4H_2O$$

If the reaction occurs in basic solution, the equation must not contain H^+. In order to add H atoms in step (*2c*), add H_2O molecules equal in number to the deficiency of H atoms and an equal number of OH^- ions to the opposite side. The rest of the method is the same. An example of reaction in basic solution is the change

$$Cr(OH)_3(s) + IO_3^- \longrightarrow I^- + CrO_4^{--}$$

The half-reactions are

$$Cr(OH)_3(s) + 5OH^- \longrightarrow CrO_4^{--} + 4H_2O + 3e^-$$

$$IO_3^- + 3H_2O + 6e^- \longrightarrow I^- + 6OH^-$$

and the final net equation is

$$2Cr(OH)_3(s) + IO_3^- + 4OH^- \longrightarrow 2CrO_4^{--} + I^- + 5H_2O$$

4.9 CALCULATIONS USING CHEMICAL EQUATIONS

A chemical equation is valuable from two standpoints. It gives information on an atomic scale and also on a laboratory scale. For example,

$$8KClO_3(s) + C_{12}H_{22}O_{11}(s) \longrightarrow 8KCl(s) + 12CO_2(g) + 11H_2O(g)$$

Atomic scale:

8 formula-units + 1 formula-unit $\longrightarrow$
                              molecule

   8 formula-units + 12 formula-units + 11 formula-units
                          molecule   molecule

Lab scale:

8 moles + 1 mole $\longrightarrow$ 8 moles + 12 moles + 11 moles

980.424 g + 342.302 g $\longrightarrow$ 596.44 g + 528.12 g + 198.17 g

On an atomic scale, the equation states that 8 formula-units of $KClO_3$ (each formula-unit containing a potassium atom, a chlorine atom, and three oxygen atoms) react with 1 formula-unit of $C_{12}H_{22}O_{11}$ to produce 8 formula-units of KCl, 12 formula-units of CO_2, and 11 formula-units of H_2O. Since the numbers are important only in a *relative* sense, the equation also indicates, for example, that 8 *dozen* formula-units of $KClO_3$ react with 1 *dozen* formula-units of $C_{12}H_{22}O_{11}$ to produce 8 *dozen* formula-units of KCl, 12 *dozen* formula-units of CO_2, and 11 *dozen* formula-units of H_2O. Multiplying the equation through by the Avogadro number converts it from the atomic scale to something which is useful in the laboratory. The Avogadro number of formula-units is one mole, so that the equation signifies that 8 moles of $KClO_3$ react with 1 mole of $C_{12}H_{22}O_{11}$ to give 8 moles of KCl plus 12 moles of CO_2 plus 11 moles of H_2O. From the formula masses of the various compounds we can get further quantitative information from the equation. Eight moles of $KClO_3$ weigh eight times the formula mass, or 8×122.553 g, or 980.424 g; 1 mole of sucrose weighs 342.302 g; 8 moles of KCl weigh 8×74.555, or 596.44 g; 12 moles of CO_2 weigh 12×44.010, or 528.12 g; and 11 moles of H_2O weigh 11×18.015, or 198.17 g. The total mass on the left-hand side of the equation is 1322.73 g, and that on the right-hand side, 1322.73 g. Mass is conserved, as it must be.

Once a balanced chemical equation is obtained, it can be used for solution of problems involving weight relationships in chemical reactions. This is illustrated by the following examples:

EXAMPLE 8

How many grams of $KClO_3$ must be decomposed to give 0.96 g of oxygen?

It is known that, on heating, the white solid $KClO_3$ decomposes to form the white solid KCl and the gas oxygen, O_2. To answer the question, we need the equation for the decomposition. In this equation $KClO_3$ is placed on the left and KCl and O_2 on the right.

$$K Cl \ O_3(s) \longrightarrow KCl(s) + O_2(g)$$

$$\underset{+5 \ -2}{} \qquad\qquad \underset{-1 \qquad 0}{}$$

$$6e^- \uparrow \quad \downarrow 2e^- \times 3$$

The chlorine atom changes oxidation number from +5 to −1. It appears to gain six electrons. Oxygen changes oxidation number from −2 to 0; each atom appears to lose two electrons. The formula-unit is such that there are three oxygen atoms for every chlorine atom, so that the compound itself has taken care of the electron gain and the electron loss. One K and one Cl on the left require one K and one Cl on the right. Three oxygen atoms on the left require three oxygen atoms on the right. We can get these three oxygen atoms on the right by placing the coefficient ³⁄₂ before the formula O_2, giving

$$KClO_3(s) \longrightarrow KCl(s) + \tfrac{3}{2}O_2(g)$$

Multiplying through by 2 to get rid of the fraction gives

$$2KClO_3(s) \longrightarrow 2KCl(s) + 3O_2(g)$$

We now have the balanced equation and can proceed to solve the problem. Since a chemical equation may always be read directly in terms of moles, it is convenient to solve problems in terms of moles.

$$0.96 \text{ g } O_2 = \frac{0.96 \text{ g}}{32 \text{ g mole}^{-1}} = 0.030 \text{ mole}$$

$$(0.030 \text{ mole } O_2)\left(\frac{2 \text{ moles } KClO_3}{3 \text{ moles } O_2}\right) = 0.020 \text{ mole } KClO_3$$

$$(0.020 \text{ mole } KClO_3)\left(122.55 \frac{\text{g}}{\text{mole}}\right) = 2.5 \text{ g}$$

EXAMPLE 9

On heating, 4.90 g of $KClO_3$ shows a weight loss of 0.384 g. What percent of the original $KClO_3$ has decomposed?

The weight loss is due to the fact that a gas is driven off. The only gas formed in this reaction is oxygen, as seen from the equation obtained in Example 8.

$$2KClO_3(s) \longrightarrow 2KCl(s) + 3O_2(g)$$

$$0.384 \text{ g } O_2 = \frac{0.384 \text{ g}}{32.0 \text{ g mole}^{-1}} = 0.0120 \text{ mole } O_2$$

To get 0.0120 mole O_2, we need to decompose

$$(0.0120 \text{ mole } O_2)\left(\frac{2 \text{ moles } KClO_3}{3 \text{ moles } O_2}\right) = 0.00800 \text{ mole } KClO_3$$

We originally had $\dfrac{4.90 \text{ g } KClO_3}{122.6 \text{ g mole}^{-1}} = 0.0400 \text{ mole } KClO_3$.

$$\text{Percent decomposed} = \frac{\text{moles decomposed}}{\text{moles available}} \times 100$$

$$= \frac{0.00800}{0.0400} \times 100, \text{ or } 20.0\%$$

EXAMPLE 10

In the reaction of vanadium oxide, VO, with iron oxide, Fe_2O_3, the products are V_2O_5 and FeO. How many grams of V_2O_5 can be formed from 2.00 g of VO and 5.75 g of Fe_2O_3?

In solving this problem, we first write the balanced equation

$$2VO(s) + 3Fe_2O_3(s) \longrightarrow 6FeO(s) + V_2O_5(s)$$

Next we decide which reactant limits the amount of products and which reactant is present in excess. To do this, we convert the data into moles. The formula mass of VO is 66.94; the formula mass of Fe_2O_3 is 159.69.

$$2.00 \text{ g VO} = \frac{2.00 \text{ g}}{66.94 \text{ g mole}^{-1}} = 0.0299 \text{ mole VO}$$

$$5.75 \text{ g } Fe_2O_3 = \frac{5.75 \text{ g}}{159.69 \text{ g mole}^{-1}} = 0.0360 \text{ mole } Fe_2O_3$$

From the equation, 0.0299 mole VO requires

$$(0.0299 \text{ mole VO})\left(\frac{3 \text{ moles } Fe_2O_3}{2 \text{ moles VO}}\right) = 0.0449 \text{ mole } Fe_2O_3$$

Therefore, 0.0360 mole Fe_2O_3 is limiting and the 0.0299 mole VO provides an excess. Calculation from the equation is based on Fe_2O_3.

$$(0.0360 \text{ mole } Fe_2O_3)\left(\frac{1 \text{ mole } V_2O_5}{3 \text{ moles } Fe_2O_3}\right) = 0.0120 \text{ mole } V_2O_5$$

$$(0.0120 \text{ mole } V_2O_5)\left(181.9 \frac{\text{g}}{\text{mole}}\right) = 2.18 \text{ g}$$

EXAMPLE 11

The reaction $Cl_2(g) + S_2O_3^{--} \longrightarrow SO_4^{--} + Cl^-$ is to be carried out in basic solution. Starting with 0.15 mole Cl_2, 0.010 mole $S_2O_3^{--}$, and 0.30 mole OH^-, how many moles of OH^- will be left in solution after the reaction is complete? Assume no other reactions take place.

First balance the equation and find the following:

$$4Cl_2(g) + S_2O_3^{--} + 10 \text{ OH}^- \longrightarrow 2SO_4^{--} + 8Cl^- + 5H_2O$$

Decide whether Cl_2 or $S_2O_3^{--}$ is in excess. The equation requires that there be 4 moles Cl_2 per mole $S_2O_3^{--}$. The given 0.15 mole Cl_2 per 0.010 mole $S_2O_3^{--}$ is considerably in excess over the needed ratio, so Cl_2 is in excess and, of the two reagents, $S_2O_3^{--}$ is limiting.

Next decide whether $S_2O_3^{--}$ or OH^- is in excess. The equation requires that there be 10 moles OH^- per mole $S_2O_3^{--}$.

0.010 mole $S_2O_3^{--}$ requires

$$(0.010 \text{ mole } S_2O_3^{--})\left(\frac{10 \text{ mole } OH^-}{1 \text{ mole } S_2O_3^{--}}\right) = 0.10 \text{ mole } OH^-$$

Have left $0.30 - 0.10 = 0.20$ mole OH^-.

4.10 GRAM-EQUIVALENTS

In solving the above problems it was necessary to use balanced chemical equations. In many cases balancing the equation can be bypassed by introducing a new quantity, the *gram-equivalent. One gram-equivalent of an oxidizing agent* is defined as that *mass of the substance that picks up the Avogadro number of electrons* in a particular reaction. *One gram-equivalent of a reducing agent* is defined as that *mass of the substance that releases the Avogadro number of electrons* in a particular reaction. The gram-equivalents are defined in this way so that one gram-equivalent of any oxidizing agent reacts exactly with one gram-equivalent of any reducing agent.

In the reaction of aluminum, Al, and oxygen, O_2, to produce Al_2O_3, aluminum changes oxidation number from 0 to $+3$ and oxygen changes oxidation number from 0 to -2. Each atom of Al releases three electrons, so one gram-atom of Al (which is the Avogadro number of Al atoms) releases three times the Avogadro number of electrons. That mass of Al which releases the Avogadro number of electrons is one-third a gram-atom. So, for Al, one gram-equivalent is one-third a gram-atom, or ($\frac{1}{3}$)(26.98), or 8.993, g. Each atom of O picks up two electrons. Each O_2 molecule picks up four electrons. One mole of O_2 picks up four times the Avogadro number of electrons. That mass of O_2 which picks up the Avogadro number of electrons is one-fourth a mole. So, for O_2, one gram-equivalent is one-fourth a mole, or ($\frac{1}{4}$)(32.00), or 8.000, g. In the reaction of Al with O_2, 8.993 g of aluminum reacts exactly with 8.000 g of oxygen.

EXAMPLE 12

When magnesium burns in oxygen, it forms magnesium oxide. In a given experiment 1.2096 g of oxide is formed from 0.7296 g of magnesium. What is the mass of one gram-equivalent of magnesium in this reaction?

Mass of oxygen combined $= 1.2096 - 0.7296 = 0.4800$ g

Since oxygen changes oxidation number from 0 to -2 (rule 3 in Section 4.6), each oxygen atom appears to gain two electrons. To gain the Avogadro number of electrons requires ½ gram-atom, or 8.000 g oxygen.

$$0.4800 \text{ g oxygen} = \frac{0.4800 \text{ g}}{8.000 \text{ g g-equiv}^{-1}} = 0.06000 \text{ g-equiv of oxygen}$$

0.06000 g-equiv oxygen requires 0.06000 g-equiv Mg.

0.7296 g Mg used is 0.06000 g-equiv Mg.

$$\frac{0.7296 \text{ g Mg}}{0.06000 \text{ g-equiv}} = 12.16 \text{ g per gram-equivalent Mg}$$

For compounds, the weight of one gram-equivalent can be calculated by dividing the weight of one mole by the electron gain or loss per formula-unit. This calculation requires knowledge of products. As an illustration, when HNO_3 (formula mass 63.013) is reduced to NO, the change in oxidation number of nitrogen is from $+5$ to $+2$; therefore, the mass of one gram-equivalent of HNO_3 is 63.013/3, or 21.004, g. However, when HNO_3 is reduced to NH_3, the nitrogen changes oxidation number from $+5$ to -3, and the mass of one gram-equivalent of HNO_3 is 63.013/8, or 7.8766, g. Thus, the mass of one gram-equivalent depends on what product is formed.

EXAMPLE 13

How many grams of hydrogen sulfide, H_2S, react with 6.32 g of potassium permanganate, $KMnO_4$, to produce K_2SO_4 and MnO_2?

Mn changes oxidation number from $+7$ to $+4$ in this reaction.

One gram-equivalent of $KMnO_4$ weighs 158.04/3, or 52.680, g.

$$6.32 \text{ g of } KMnO_4 = \frac{6.32 \text{ g}}{52.680 \text{ g g-equiv}^{-1}} = 0.120 \text{ g-equiv}$$

0.120 g-equiv $KMnO_4$ requires 0.120 g-equiv H_2S.

S changes oxidation number from -2 to $+6$ in this reaction.

One gram-equivalent H_2S weighs 34.080/8, or 4.260, g.

$$0.120 \text{ g-equiv } H_2S = (0.120 \text{ g-equiv})\left(4.260 \frac{\text{g}}{\text{g-equiv}}\right) = 0.511 \text{ g}$$

In the above examples, two things might be noticed. In the first place, it was not necessary to write balanced equations to solve the type of problem given. Secondly, although oxidation-number changes were used to find the mass of a gram-equivalent, we could equally well have written the half-reaction and noted directly the number of electrons gained or lost per formula-unit. For example, when $H_2C_2O_4$ is oxidized to CO_2, its mass per gram-equivalent is 45.018 g. This corresponds to the half-reaction $H_2C_2O_4 \longrightarrow 2CO_2 + 2H^+ + 2e^-$, which shows that molar mass of $H_2C_2O_4$, 90.036 g, needs to be divided by 2 to give the mass per gram-equivalent.

Gram-equivalents are also useful for acid-base reactions. For example, in the complete neutralization of $Ca(OH)_2$ by H_3PO_4, the non-net equation is

$$3Ca(OH)_2 + 2H_3PO_4 \longrightarrow Ca_3(PO_4)_2 + 6H_2O$$

Since each mole of $Ca(OH)_2$ furnishes two moles of OH^- and each mole of H_3PO_4 furnishes three moles of H^+, complete neutralization occurs if three moles of $Ca(OH)_2$ per two moles of H_3PO_4 are used. From such an equation the usual stoichiometric calculations can be made. It is more convenient, however, to consider neutralization reactions by fixing attention only on the hydrogen ion and hydroxide ion. For this purpose, gram-equivalents are convenient. One *gram-equivalent of an acid* is the *mass of acid required to furnish one mole of* H^+; one *gram-equivalent of a base* is the *mass of base required to furnish one mole of* OH^- *or accept one mole of* H^+. One gram-equivalent of any acid just reacts with one gram-equivalent of any base.

One of the simplest acids is HCl, hydrochloric acid, one mole of which weighs 36.5 g. Since one mole of HCl can furnish one mole of H^+, 36.5 g of HCl is one gram-equivalent. For HCl, and for all other monoprotic acids, one mole is the same as one gram-equivalent. For a diprotic acid such as H_2SO_4, one mole of acid can furnish on demand two moles of H^+. By definition, two moles of H^+ is the amount furnished by two gram-equivalents of acid. Therefore, for complete neutralization one mole of H_2SO_4 is identical with two gram-equivalents. Since one mole = 98 g = two gram-equivalents, one gram-equivalent of H_2SO_4 weighs 49 g. For complete reaction of a triprotic acid such as H_3PO_4, one mole is equal to three gram-equivalents. The situation is similar for bases. If the base is NaOH, one mole gives one mole of OH^-. Therefore, one mole of NaOH is one gram-equivalent. If the base is $Ca(OH)_2$, one mole is two gram-equivalents.

EXAMPLE 14

1.00 g of the acid $C_6H_{10}O_4$ requires 0.768 g of KOH for complete neutralization. How many neutralizable hydrogen atoms are in this molecule?

$$0.768 \text{ g KOH} = \frac{0.768 \text{ g}}{56.1 \text{ g g-equiv}^{-1} \text{ KOH}} = 0.0137 \text{ g-equiv KOH}$$

0.0137 g-equiv base neutralizes 0.0137 g-equiv acid.

$$\frac{1.00 \text{ g } C_6H_{10}O_4}{0.0137 \text{ g-equiv acid}} = 73.0 \text{ g g-equiv}^{-1}$$

One mole $C_6H_{10}O_4$ weighs 146.1 g.

$$\frac{73.0 \text{ g g-equiv}^{-1}}{146.1 \text{ g mole}^{-1}} = 0.500 \text{ mole g-equiv}^{-1}$$

Therefore, each mole furnishes two moles H^+, or each molecule of $C_6H_{10}O_4$ contains two replaceable H atoms.

4.1 Gram-atoms   Which has greatest mass: one atom, one gram, or one gram-atom?

4.2 Gram-atoms   How many gram-atoms of carbon in each of the following: (*a*) 1.00 g carbon, (*b*) 4.22×10^{21} atoms of carbon, (*c*) 12.0 amu of carbon, (*d*) 1.00 g carbon dioxide (CO_2)?

4.3 Gram-atoms   (*a*) In a chemical reaction requiring two atoms of Al for three atoms of S, how many gram-atoms of Al are required per gram-atom of S? (*b*) In this reaction, how many grams of Al are required per gram of S?

4.4 Gram-atoms   Spinel has percent composition by weight: 17.1% Mg, 37.9% Al, and 45.0% O. What is the relative number of gram-atoms of each element in this compound?

4.5 Simplest formula   A compound is formed between 5.49 g Mn and 2.13 g O. What is its simplest formula?

4.6 Percent composition   Calculate the percent iron (by weight) in each of the following: (*a*) Fe_2O_3, (*b*) Fe_3O_4, (*c*) FeS_2, (*d*) $FeCO_3$, (*e*) $KFe(SO_4)_2$.

4.7 Equations   Balance each of the following:

(*a*) $C_2H_4O + O_2 \longrightarrow CO_2 + H_2O$
(*b*) $C_{10}H_{14}N_2 + O_2 \longrightarrow CO_2 + H_2O + N_2$
(*c*) $KMnO_4 + H_2C_2O_4 \longrightarrow K_2CO_3 + CO_2 + MnO_2 + H_2O$
(*d*) $Re_2O_8 + H_2S \longrightarrow Re_2S_7 + H_2O + S$
(*e*) $H_2S + ClO_3^- \longrightarrow HSO_4^- + Cl^- + H^+$

4.8 Gram-atoms   Elements A, B, and C have atomic masses of 106.4, 30.97, and 195.1 amu, respectively. Calculate the relative number of atoms in equal-mass samples of the three elements.

4.9 Gram-atoms   Calculate the mass, in grams, of each of the following: (*a*) 1.65 gram-atoms of oxygen, (*b*) one atom of oxygen, (*c*) the oxygen in 1.00 g of carbon dioxide (CO_2), (*d*) one amu.

4.10 Simplest formula   Write the simplest formula for each of the following: (*a*) contains 0.55 gram-atom Ca, 1.1 gram-atom Al, and 2.2 gram-atom O, (*b*) contains 1.56 g Fe, 0.755 g Al, and 1.34 g O, (*c*) contains 1.89 g Na, 0.0820 gram-atom Al, and 2.62 g O.

4.11 Moles   Given 1.00 g of butyric acid. Its simplest formula is C_2H_4O. Calculate each of the following for the sample: (*a*) the number of moles of C_2H_4O formula-units, (*b*) the number of gram-atoms of each element, (*c*) the number of moles of $C_4H_8O_2$ molecules.

4.12 Oxidation numbers   Assign oxidation numbers to each atom in the following: (*a*) $KHSO_4$, (*b*) $C_2H_4O_2$, (*c*) H_3PO_2, (*d*) KI_3, (*e*) CoF_6^{-3}, (*f*) $Ca_5F(PO_4)_3$.

4.13 Equations   Write a complete balanced equation for each of the following changes. In each case label the oxidizing agent, the reducing agent, the substance oxidized, and the substance reduced.

$$(a) \quad Sn^{++} + IO_3^- \longrightarrow Sn^{+4} + I^- \qquad \text{(acid)}$$
$$(b) \quad ClO^- + S_2O_3^{--} \longrightarrow Cl^- + SO_4^{--} \qquad \text{(base)}$$

4.14 Formulas A given sample contains 0.15 mole of X. Analysis shows 1.5 gram-atoms of carbon, 2.1 g of hydrogen, and 1.8×10^{23} atoms of nitrogen. (a) What is the simplest formula of X? (b) What is its molecular formula?

4.15 Half-reactions Write a balanced half-reaction for each of the following changes:

$$(a) \quad BrO_3^- \longrightarrow Br^- \qquad \text{(acid)}$$
$$(b) \quad H_2S \longrightarrow HSO_4^- \qquad \text{(acid)}$$
$$(c) \quad NO_3^- \longrightarrow N_2O \qquad \text{(acid)}$$
$$(d) \quad I_3^- \longrightarrow IO_3^- \qquad \text{(acid)}$$
$$(e) \quad ClO^- \longrightarrow Cl^- \qquad \text{(base)}$$
$$(f) \quad HO_2^- \text{ (peroxide)} \longrightarrow O_2 \qquad \text{(base)}$$
$$(g) \quad Mo(s) \longrightarrow MoO_4^{--} \qquad \text{(base)}$$
$$(h) \quad Sb_2O_5(s) \longrightarrow SbH_3 \qquad \text{(base)}$$

4.16 Equations (a) Complete and balance the following in acid solution: $Cl_2O + NO_2 \longrightarrow Cl^- + NO_3^-$. (b) How many grams of NO_2 are needed to react with 0.263 mole Cl_2O? (c) How many moles of H^+ would be produced in (b)?

4.17 Stoichiometry Given 3.69 g of C_2H_5OH. In this sample, there are how many of each of the following: (a) grams of oxygen, (b) moles of C_2H_5OH, (c) gram-atoms of hydrogen, (d) atoms of carbon, (e) gram-equivalents for a reaction in which C_2H_5OH is oxidized to CO_2 and H_2O?

4.18 Gram-equivalents Calculate the mass, in grams, of each of the following: (a) one gram-equivalent of the diprotic acid H_2SO_4, (b) one gram-equivalent of the base $La(OH)_3$, (c) amount of $Ca(OH)_2$ required to neutralize 0.030 g-equiv of H_3PO_4, (d) amount of H_3PO_4 required to neutralize 0.030 mole of $Ca(OH)_2$.

4.19 Gram-atoms A compound which contains one atom of X and two atoms of Y for each three atoms of Z is made by mixing 5.00 g of X, 1.15×10^{23} atoms of Y, and 0.0300 gram-atom of Z. Given that only 4.40 g of compound results, calculate the atomic mass of Y if the atomic masses of X and Z are 60.0 and 80.0 amu, respectively.

4.20 Gram-atoms In air, element X is oxidized to the compound XO_2. If 1.00 g of X reacts with 0.696 g of oxygen, what is the atomic mass of X?

4.21 Avogadro number The density of a particular crystal of LiF is 2.65 g cc^{-1}. X-ray analysis shows that the Li^+ and F^- ions are arranged in a cubic array at a spacing of 2.01 Å. From these data calculate the apparent Avogadro number.

4.22 Formulas and equations (a) Na will react with $NaNO_3$ in the presence of water to form the compound sodium hyponitrite (and NaOH). Sodium hyponitrite is 43.4% Na, 26.4% N, and 30.2% O by weight. What is its simplest formula? (b) The molecular formula used for sodium hyponitrite contains two N atoms. By using this formula, write a balanced equation for the formation of sodium hyponitrite by the reaction of part (*a*), and assign oxidation numbers to all atoms in the equation. (*c*) What weight of sodium hyponitrite can be made from 1.00 g Na and 1.00 g $NaNO_3$?

4.23 Moles and gram-equivalents In the reaction $Zn + 2MnO_2 \longrightarrow Zn(MnO_2)_2$ how many moles of MnO_2 are there in each of the following: (*a*) 4.34 g of MnO_2, (*b*) 4.34 g-equiv of MnO_2, (*c*) amount of MnO_2 required to react with 4.34 g of Zn, (*d*) amount of MnO_2 required to react with 4.34 g-equiv of Zn, (*e*) amount of MnO_2 required to pick up 4.34×10^{22} electrons from Zn?

4.24 Gram-equivalents What is the mass of one gram-equivalent of the oxidizing agent and of the reducing agent in the following reaction?

$$5Zn + V_2O_5 \longrightarrow 5ZnO + 2V$$

4.25 Stoichiometry How many grams of Bi_2Te_3 can be made from 3.00 g of Bi and 2.00 g of Te?

4.26 Stoichiometry How many moles of $Zn(FeS_2)_2$ can be made from 2.00 g of Zn, 3.00 g of Fe, and 4.00 g of S?

4.27 Stoichiometry How many grams of NO_2 can be prepared from 40.0 g of O_2 and 10.0 g of NH_3 in a reaction which forms NO_2 and H_2O?

4.28 Equations How many moles of H^+ are formed or used up in each of the following reactions if there initially are 0.15 mole of oxidizing agent and 0.15 mole of reducing agent?

(*a*) $H_2SO_3 + IO_3^- \longrightarrow HSO_4^- + I^-$
(*b*) $H_3AsO_4 + I^- \longrightarrow HAsO_2 + I_2$
(*c*) $H_3PO_2 + VO_4^{-3} \longrightarrow V^{+2} + H_3PO_3$
(*d*) $Fe^{++} + O_2 \longrightarrow Fe^{+3} + H_2O$
(*e*) $H_2O_2 + CrO_3 \longrightarrow Cr^{+3} + O_2$

4.29 Gram-equivalents Order the following oxidizing agents by increasing mass per gram-equivalent: (*a*) $KMnO_4$ (going to MnO_2), (*b*) $KMnO_4$ (going to Mn^{++}), (*c*) $K_2Cr_2O_7$ (going to Cr^{+3}), (*d*) KIO_3 (going to I^-), (*e*) KClO (going to Cl^-).

4.30 Gram-equivalents (*a*) Titration of 1.60 g of citric acid requires 1.00 g of NaOH. What is the mass of one gram-equivalent of citric acid? (*b*) If the molecular formula of citric acid is $C_6H_8O_7$, how many protons per molecule are replaced in (*a*)?

4.31 Equations Complete and balance each of the following reactions in aqueous solutions:

(*a*) $MnO_4^- + Fe^{++} \longrightarrow Mn^{++} + Fe^{+3}$ (acid)
(*b*) $Fe_3O_4(s) + MnO_4^- \longrightarrow Fe_2O_3(s) + MnO_2(s)$ (base)
(*c*) $H_4IO_6^- + I^- \longrightarrow I_3^-$ (acid)
(*d*) $MnO_2(s) + HO_2^-$ (peroxide) $\longrightarrow MnO_4^{--}$ (base)
(*e*) $WO_3(s) + CN^- \longrightarrow W(CN)_8^{-4} + O_2$ (base)
(*f*) $H_2S_2O_3 \longrightarrow S + HSO_4^-$ (acid)

4.32 Stoichiometry $MgCO_3(s)$ and $CaCO_3(s)$, when heated, decompose to form $CO_2(g)$, $MgO(s)$, and $CaO(s)$. What is the percent of $MgCO_3$ in an $MgCO_3$-$CaCO_3$ mixture which decreases in mass by 50.0% when heated long enough to expel all the CO_2?

4.33 Stoichiometry When solid ammonium dichromate, $(NH_4)_2Cr_2O_7$, is heated, it decomposes to give solid Cr_2O_3 and gaseous N_2 and gaseous H_2O. In a given experiment the following data are obtained:

Crucible + $(NH_4)_2Cr_2O_7$ = 33.622 g
Crucible + Cr_2O_3 = 29.608 g

What is the weight of the crucible?

4.34 Oxidation-reduction (a) The ion X^{+n} is oxidized to XO_3^- by MnO_4^- going to Mn^{++} in acid solution. Given that 2.68×10^{-3} mole of X^{+n} requires 1.61×10^{-3} mole of MnO_4^-, what is the value of n? (b) What is the weight of one gram-equivalent of XCl_n for the above reaction if the atomic weight of X is 97.0?

4.35 Stoichiometry You are given a 2.180-g sample containing a mixture of XO and X_2O_3. It takes 0.0150 mole of $K_2Cr_2O_7$ to oxidize the sample completely to form XO_4^- and Cr^{+3}. If 0.0187 mole of XO_4^- is formed, what is the atomic mass of X?

ANSWERS

4.2 (a) 0.0833   (b) 0.00701   (c) 1.66×10^{-24} (d) 0.0227
4.3 (a) 0.667 gram-atom   (b) 0.561 g   *4.4* 1:2:4   *4.5* Mn_3O_4
4.8 A:B:C = 1.83:6.30:1.00   *4.9* (a) 26.4   (b) 2.66×10^{-23} g
(c) 0.727 g   (d) 1.66×10^{-24} g   *4.10* (a) $CaAl_2O_4$ (b) $FeAlO_3$
(c) $NaAlO_2$ *4.11* (a) 0.0227   (b) 0.0454 C, 0.0908 H, 0.0227 O
(c) 0.0114   *4.17* (a) 1.28   (b) 0.0800   (c) 0.480   (d) 9.64×10^{22}
(e) 0.960   *4.19* 70.0 amu   *4.20* 46.0 amu   *4.21* 6.03×10^{23}
4.25 4.18 g   *4.26* 0.0269 mole   *4.27* 27.0 g   *4.30* (a) 64.0 g   (b) 3
4.32 73%   *4.33* 23.512 g   *4.35* 99 amu

5 gases

The properties of any chemical substance are dependent not only on its chemical identity but also on its state. For example, oxygen gas has oxidizing properties dependent on its chemical identity, but it also has the properties characteristic of any substance in the gaseous state, e.g., compressibility, rapid diffusion, and high thermal expansion. In this chapter we shall consider the general properties of all gases and try to account for them in terms of kinetic theory. Because of relatively small intermolecular attractions, the gaseous state has proved more amenable to theoretical attack than the other states of matter.

5.1 VOLUME

The volume of any substance is the space occupied by that substance. If the substance is a gas, the volume of a sample is the same as the volume of the container in which the sample is held. Ordinarily, this volume is specified in units of liters (l), milliliters (ml), or cubic centimeters (cc). As the name implies, one cubic centimeter is the volume of a cube one centimeter on an edge. A liter is now defined as the volume of a cube that is one decimeter on edge. Thus, a liter is exactly 1000 times as great as a cubic centimeter. It follows that one milliliter, which is a thousandth of a liter, is exactly equal to one cubic centimeter. This equality was not always true, since the liter was originally defined as the volume occupied by one kilogram of water at the temperature of its maximum density. However, the difference was only 27 parts per million.*

The volume of liquids and solids does not change much with a change of pressure or temperature. Consequently, to describe the amount of a solid or liquid being handled, e.g., the number of moles, it is usually sufficient to specify only the volume of the sample. For gases, this cannot be done. As an example, 1 ml of hydrogen at a certain pressure and temperature will contain a different number of moles and have a weight different from that of 1 ml at some other pressure and temperature. In order to determine the number of moles in a given volume of gas, it is necessary to know the pressure and temperature.

When solids or liquids are mixed together, the total volume is roughly equal to the sum of the original volumes. However, this is not necessarily true of gases when the final volume after mixing depends on the final pressure. If the final pressure is allowed to rise sufficiently, two or more gases can occupy the same volume. Since all gases *can mix in any proportion,* they are said to be *miscible.*

5.2 TEMPERATURE

It is a familiar observation that a hot substance and a cold substance placed in contact with each other change so that the hot substance gets colder and the cold substance hotter. This is interpreted as resulting from a flow of heat energy from the hot body to the cold body. The hot body is said to have a higher temperature; the cold body, a lower temperature. Therefore, *temperature determines the direction of heat flow* in the sense that heat always flows from a region of higher temperature to one of lower temperature.

The international scale for measuring temperature is an absolute scale in the sense that it starts with the absolute zero. Absolute zero is the lower limit of temperature, and temperatures lower than it are unattainable. The scale is called the Kelvin scale after the English thermodynamicist Lord Kelvin, who proposed it in the year 1848. It is

*In 1964 the Twelfth General Conference on Weights and Measurements met over liters in Paris. The conference reluctantly diminished the size of the liter by 27 parts per million, thus warming the hearts of the wine merchants and simplifying life for scientists who have been plagued by the trivial conversion factor. *Nunc est bibendum.*

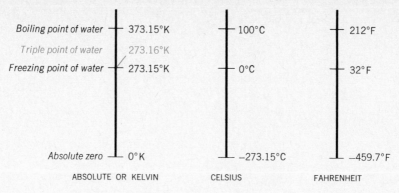

Boiling point of water	373.15°K	100°C	212°F
Triple point of water	273.16°K		
Freezing point of water	273.15°K	0°C	32°F
Absolute zero	0°K	−273.15°C	−459.7°F
	ABSOLUTE OR KELVIN	CELSIUS	FAHRENHEIT

now defined by assigning the value 273.16°K (degrees Kelvin) to the temperature at which H_2O coexists in the liquid, gaseous, and solid states. This point, called the triple point (Section 7.7), corresponds to an equilibrium between liquid water, water vapor, and ice. Thus, the size of the degree Kelvin is defined as 1/273.16 of the temperature difference between absolute zero and the triple point of H_2O. The triple point of H_2O is 0.01° higher than the normal* freezing point of H_2O, so that on the Kelvin scale the normal freezing point of H_2O is 273.15°K.

The normal freezing point of H_2O (273.15°K) is set as the zero point of the Celsius scale. On the Celsius scale the size of the degree, designated by °C, is taken to be the same as the degree Kelvin. The normal boiling point of H_2O—i.e., the boiling point at an atmosphere of pressure—on the Celsius scale turns out to be 100°C. Because there are 100 degrees between the normal freezing and boiling points of H_2O, this temperature scale is sometimes called the centigrade scale. A comparison of the Kelvin scale with the Celsius and Fahrenheit scales is shown in Figure 5.1. Although the size of one degree is the same on the Celsius and Kelvin scales, the Fahrenheit degree is only five-ninths as large. Temperature on the Celsius scale is converted to temperature on the Kelvin scale by adding 273.15°:

$$°C + 273.15 = °K$$

To convert Fahrenheit temperature to Kelvin temperature, it is also necessary to correct for the difference in the size of the degree

$$(°F - 32) \times \tfrac{5}{9} + 273.15 = °K$$

5.3 PRESSURE

Just as temperature determines the direction of heat flow, so pressure is a property which determines the direction of mass flow. Unless otherwise constrained, matter tends to move from a place of higher pressure to a place of lower pressure. Quantitatively, *pressure* is defined as *force per unit area.* Force is defined as that which tends to change the state

* The normal freezing point is the temperature at which H_2O freezes under an atmosphere of pressure; the triple point is the temperature at which H_2O freezes under its own vapor pressure.

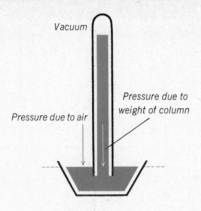

Vacuum

Pressure due to air

Pressure due to weight of column

of rest or motion of an object. The fundamental unit of force is the dyne, which is the force required to accelerate one gram of matter by one centimeter per second in one second. Force can also be expressed in terms of pounds weight. The units for expressing pressure can thus be dynes per square centimeter or pounds per square inch.

In *fluids,* a general term which includes *liquids and gases,* the pressure at a given point is the same in all directions. This can be visualized by considering a swimmer under water. At a given depth, no matter how he turns, the pressure exerted on all sides of him by the water is always the same. However, as he increases his depth, the pressure increases. This comes about because of the pull of gravity on the water above him. We can picture his body as being compressed by the weight of the column of water above him. In general, for all fluids, the greater the depth of immersion, the greater the pressure.

The earth is surrounded by a blanket of air approximately 500 miles thick. In effect, we live at the bottom of a fluid, the atmosphere, which exerts a pressure. The existence of this pressure can be shown by filling a long tube with mercury and inverting it in a dish of mercury. (Any other liquid would do, but mercury has the advantage of not requiring too long a tube.) Some of the mercury runs out of the tube, but not all of it. The setup, called a *barometer,* is represented in Figure 5.2. No matter how large the diameter of the tube and no matter how long the tube, the difference in height between the mercury level inside and outside the tube is the same. The fact that all the mercury does not run out shows that there must be a pressure exerted on the surface of the mercury in the dish sufficient to support the column of mercury.

To a good approximation, the space above the mercury level is a vacuum (contains only mercury vapor) and exerts no pressure on the upper mercury level. The pressure at the bottom of the mercury column is due only to the weight of the mercury column. As noted, it is a general property of liquids that at any given level in the liquid the pressure is constant. In Figure 5.2 the dashed line represents the level which is of interest. At this level, outside the tube, the force per unit area is due to the atmosphere and can be labeled as P_{atm}. The pressure inside the tube is due to the pressure of the column of mercury and can be labeled P_{Hg}. The equality $P_{atm} = P_{Hg}$ provides us with a method for measuring the pressure exerted by the atmosphere.

Atmospheric pressure changes from day to day and from one altitude to another. A *standard atmosphere,* referred to as 1 atm, is defined as the pressure which supports a column of mercury that is 760 mm high at 0°C at sea level.* Pressure can be expressed either in terms of number of atmospheres or number of millimeters of mercury (mm Hg). The pressure unit mm Hg is increasingly referred to as a *torr,* in honor of Evangelista Torricelli, the inventor of the barometer. We can also express pressure by the height of a water column. Since water has a density of 1 g ml⁻¹, whereas mercury has a density of 13.6 g ml⁻¹, a given pressure supports a column of water that is 13.6 times as high as one of mercury. One atmosphere of pressure supports 76 cm of mercury or (76)(13.6) cm of water, the latter being roughly 34 ft. In terms of pounds per square inch, a standard atmosphere is 14.7 psi.

The device shown in Figure 5.3 is a *manometer,* used to measure the pressure of a sample of gas. This manometer is constructed by placing a liquid in the bottom of a U tube with the gas sample in one arm of the U. If the right-hand tube is open to the atmosphere, the pressure which is exerted on the right-hand surface is atmospheric pressure P_{atm}. At the same liquid level in both arms of the tube, the pressures must be equal; otherwise, there would be a flow of liquid from one arm to the other. At the level indicated by the dashed line in Figure 5.3, the pressure in the left arm is equal to the pressure of the trapped gas P_{gas} plus the pressure of the column of liquid above the dashed line P_{liq}. We can therefore write

$$P_{atm} = P_{gas} + P_{liq}$$

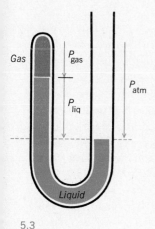

5.3
Manometer

or

$$P_{gas} = P_{atm} - P_{liq}$$

The atmospheric pressure can be measured by a barometer, and P_{liq} can be obtained from the difference in height between the liquid level in the right and left arms and the known density of the liquid. P_{atm} and P_{liq} must be expressed in the same units. For example, if P_{atm} is in millimeters of mercury (torr) and the manometer liquid is not mercury, the difference in height must be converted to its mercury equivalent. If the bottom of the U tube consists of flexible rubber tubing, the right arm can be raised with respect to the left arm until the two liquid levels are at the same height, in which case $P_{liq} = 0$, so $P_{gas} = P_{atm}$.

---

* If we think of pressure as weight per unit area, we can see why it is necessary that both 0°C and sea level be specified in defining the standard atmosphere. The density of liquid mercury changes with temperature, and therefore the weight of a 760-mm-high Hg column of fixed cross section changes with temperature. Hence the temperature must be specified. Similarly, the force of gravity changes slightly with altitude, and hence the weight of the Hg column changes when moved away from sea level.

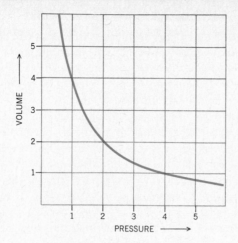

5.4 *P-V* RELATION

A characteristic property of gases is their great compressibility. This behavior is summarized quantitatively in Boyle's law (1662). *Boyle's law* states that *at constant temperature a fixed mass of gas occupies a volume inversely proportional to the pressure exerted on it.* Boyle's law can be summarized by a pressure-volume, or *P-V*, plot like that shown in Figure 5.4. In this graph the horizontal axis represents the pressure of a given sample of gas and the vertical axis the volume occupied by it. The curve is a hyperbola, the equation for which is PV = constant, or V = constant$/P$. (The size of the constant is fixed once the mass of the sample and its temperature are specified.) If at 4 atm the volume is 1 liter, then at 1 atm the volume is 4 liters. This can be seen from either the graph or the equation.

The behavior specified by Boyle's law is not always observed. For any gas the law is most nearly followed at lower pressures and at higher temperatures; but as the pressure is increased or as the temperature is lowered, deviations may occur. This can be seen by considering the experimental data listed in Figure 5.5. In each of these experiments, the quantity of gas is fixed at 39.94 g and the temperature is fixed at either 100 or −50°C. The pressure is measured when the given mass of gas is contained in different volumes. The PV products in the last column, obtained by multiplying the values in the second and third columns, should, according to Boyle's law, be constant at a constant temperature. The data indicate that, at the high temperature, Boyle's law is closely obeyed. However, at the low temperature, the PV product is not constant but drops off significantly as the pressure increases; Boyle's law is not obeyed. In other words, as the temperature of argon is decreased, its behavior deviates from that specified in Boyle's law.

The fact that deviations from Boyle's law increase at higher pressures can be seen from the experimental data for acetylene given in Figure 5.6. When the pressure is doubled from 0.5 to 1.0 atm, the PV prod-

Temperature, °C	V, liters	P, atm	P × V
100	2.000	15.28	30.560
	1.000	30.52	30.520
	0.500	60.99	30.500
	0.333	91.59	30.500
− 50	2.000	8.99	17.980
	1.000	17.65	17.650
	0.500	34.10	17.050
	0.333	49.50	16.500

5.5
Pressure-volume data for
39.94 g of argon gas

uct is essentially unchanged, so that in this pressure range acetylene follows Boyle's law reasonably well. However, when the pressure is doubled from 4.0 to 8.0 atm, the PV product decreases by more than 3%; in this pressure range, Boyle's law is not followed so well. For any gas, the lower the pressure the closer the approach to Boyle's law behavior. When the law is obeyed, the gas is said to show *ideal* behavior.

P, atm	0.5	1.0	2.0	4.0	8.0
PV	1.0057	1.0000	0.9891	0.9708	0.9360

5.6
PV products for a sample
of acetylene at 0°C

A careful study of the deviations from ideal behavior led the Dutch scientist J. D. van der Waals to propose a modified version of the P-V relation. His modification is based on the observation that observed pressures generally are smaller than predicted by Boyle's law and observed volumes are generally greater than so predicted. The pressure defect is complex and changes with the gas volume. This is seen from the van der Waals relation

$$\left(P + \frac{n^2a}{V^2}\right)(V - nb) = \text{a constant}$$

which is related to the Boyle's law expression

$$(P_{ideal})(V_{ideal}) = \text{a constant}$$

by the correction term n^2a/V^2 added to the observed pressure and the correction term nb subtracted from the observed volume. n is the number of moles in the sample; a and b are constants that are characteristic of the gas in question. As we shall see in Section 5.12, a has been interpreted as being connected with molecular attractions and b has been connected with molecular volumes. Representative values of the van der Waals constants are given in Figure 5.7. Finally, it should be noted that at very high pressures and low temperatures even the van der Waals relation fails to represent the observed data. Other special relations have been proposed to handle such cases.

Gas	a, liter^2 atm mole^{-2}	b, liter mole^{-1}
Helium	0.0341	0.0237
Argon	1.35	0.0322
Nitrogen	1.39	0.0391
Carbon dioxide	3.59	0.0427
Acetylene	4.39	0.0514
Carbon tetrachloride	20.39	0.1383

5.7
Van der Waals constants

5.5 V-T RELATION

Another characteristic property of gases is their thermal expansion. Like most other substances, all gases increase in volume when their temperature is raised. Experimentally, the increase of volume with increasing temperature can be measured by confining a fixed mass of gas in a glass tube with a blob of liquid mercury, as shown in Figure 5.8. The mercury blob is free to move, so that the gas sample remains at constant pressure. It is observed that, as the gas is heated, the mercury moves out and the volume of the gas sample increases.

Constant pressure
of atmosphere

Gas sample   Mercury drop

5.8
Gas thermometer

Typical numerical data are plotted in Figure 5.9. The points fall on a straight line, indicating that the volume varies linearly with temperature. If the temperature is lowered sufficiently, the gas liquefies, and no more experimental points can be obtained. However, if the straight line is extended, or extrapolated, to lower temperatures, as shown by the dotted line, it reaches a point of zero volume. The temperature at which the dotted line reaches zero volume is $-273.15°C$. It is significant that the value, $-273.15°C$, does not depend on the kind of gas used or on the pressure at which the experiment is performed. Designating $-273.15°C$ as absolute zero is reasonable, since temperatures below this would correspond to negative volume.

If volume-temperature data like those plotted in Figure 5.9 are given in terms of absolute temperature, it is found that, *at constant pressure, the volume occupied by a fixed mass of gas is directly proportional to the absolute temperature.* This summarization of gas behavior, called *Charles' law* (1787), can be expressed mathematically as $V = $ (constant) $\times\ T$, where T is in degrees Kelvin. The value of the constant depends on pressure and on the mass of gas.

Actually, Charles' law, like Boyle's law, represents the behavior of an *ideal,* or *perfect,* gas. For any *real* gas at high pressures and at temperatures near the liquefaction point, deviations from Charles' law are observed. Near the liquefaction point the observed volume is less than that predicted by Charles' law.

Because of the Charles' law relation of volume to absolute tempera-

5.5 *V-T* relation

112

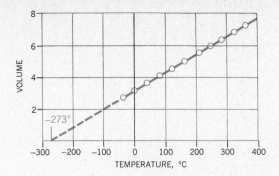

ture, calculations involving gases require conversion of temperatures to the Kelvin scale. It is also convenient in working with gases to have a reference point. The customary reference point for gases is at 273°K (0°C) and one standard atmosphere (760 torr) pressure. These conditions are called *standard temperature and pressure* (STP).

5.6 PARTIAL PRESSURES

The behavior observed when two or more gases are placed in the same container is summarized in Dalton's law of partial pressures (1801). *Dalton's law* states that the *total pressure exerted by a mixture of gases is equal to the sum of the partial pressures* of the various gases. The *partial pressure* of a gas in a mixture is defined as the *pressure the gas would exert if it were alone in the container*. Suppose a sample of hydrogen is pumped into a box and its pressure is found to be 6 torr and a sample of oxygen is pumped into a second box, of equal volume, and its pressure found to be 10 torr. If both samples are now transferred to a third box of equal volume, the pressure is observed to be 16 torr. For the general case, Dalton's law can be written

$$P_{total} = P_1 + P_2 + P_3 + \cdots$$

where the subscripts denote the various gases occupying the same volume. Actually, Dalton's law is an idealization, but it is closely obeyed by most mixtures of gases.

In many laboratory experiments dealing with gases, the gases are collected above water, and water vapor contributes to the total pressure measured. Figure 5.10 illustrates an experiment in which oxygen gas is collected by water displacement. If the water level is the same inside and outside the bottle, then we may write

$$P_{atm} = P_{oxygen} + P_{water\ vapor}$$

$$P_{oxygen} = P_{atm} - P_{water\ vapor}$$

P_{atm} is obtained from a barometer. As we shall see later (Section 7.2), $P_{water\ vapor}$ depends only on the temperature of the water. This so-called vapor pressure of water has been measured at various water temperatures and is recorded in tables such as the one given in Appendix 5. Thus, the partial pressure of oxygen can be determined from an observed pressure and temperature and by reference to a table of vapor-

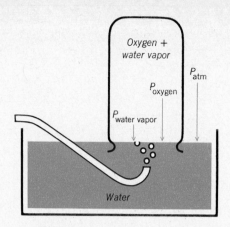

Oxygen +
water vapor

P_{atm}

P_{oxygen}

$P_{water\ vapor}$

Water

pressure data. The following example shows how Dalton's law of partial pressures enters into calculations involving gases.

EXAMPLE 1

If 40.0 liters of nitrogen are collected over water at 22°C when the atmospheric pressure is 727 torr, what is the volume of the dry nitrogen at standard temperature and pressure, assuming ideal behavior?

The initial volume of the nitrogen is 40.0 liters. The final volume is unknown. The initial pressure of the nitrogen gas is the atmospheric pressure, 727 torr minus the vapor pressure of water. From Appendix 5 it is noted that, at 22°C, water has a vapor pressure of 20 torr. The initial temperature of the nitrogen is 22°C or 273 + 22 = 295°K. Final conditions are standard; i.e., the final pressure is 760 torr and the final temperature is 273°K. The problem is solved by considering separately how the volume is affected by a change in pressure and a change in temperature.

Pressure changes to 760/707 of its original value.

Volume changes inversely, or to 707/760 of its original value.

Temperature changes to 273/295 of its original value.

Volume changes proportionally, or to 273/295 of its original value.

$$V_{final} = V_{initial} \times \frac{\text{correction for}}{\text{pressure change}} \times \frac{\text{correction for}}{\text{temperature change}}$$

$$= 40.0 \text{ liters} \times (707/760) \times (273/295)$$

$$= 34.4 \text{ liters}$$

5.7 AVOGADRO PRINCIPLE

In the preceding section we assumed that, when gases are mixed, they do not react with each other. However, sometimes they do react. For example, when a spark is passed through a mixture of hydrogen and oxygen gas, reaction occurs to form gaseous water. Similarly, when a mixture of hydrogen and chlorine gas is exposed to ultraviolet light, reaction occurs to form the gas hydrogen chloride. In any such reaction involving gases it is observed that at constant temperature and pressure the volumes of the individual gases which actually react are simple multiples of each other.

As a specific example, in the reaction of hydrogen with oxygen to form water, two liters of hydrogen are required for every liter of oxygen. In the reaction of hydrogen with chlorine, each liter of hydrogen requires one liter of chlorine, and two liters of hydrogen chloride gas are formed. These observations are summarized in *Gay-Lussac's law of combining volumes* (1809), which states that, *at a given pressure and temperature, gases combine in simple proportions by volume and the volume of any gaseous product bears a whole-number ratio to that of any gaseous reactant.*

In the law of multiple proportions the observation of simple ratios between combining weights of elements implies that matter is atomic. Similarly, the occurrence of simple ratios between combining volumes of gases suggests that there is a simple relation between gas volume and number of molecules. Avogadro, in 1811, was the first to propose that equal volumes of gases at the same temperature and pressure contain equal numbers of molecules. That this principle accounts for Gay-Lussac's law can be seen from the following example:

When hydrogen combines with chlorine, the product, hydrogen chloride, can be shown by chemical analysis to contain equal numbers of hydrogen and chlorine atoms. These equal numbers of H and Cl atoms come from the original molecules of hydrogen gas and chlorine gas. If we assume that both hydrogen and chlorine molecules are diatomic, then equal numbers of hydrogen and chlorine molecules are required for reaction. According to the Avogadro principle, these occupy equal volumes, which is consistent with the observation that the combining volumes of hydrogen and chlorine gas are equal.

The assumption that hydrogen and chlorine molecules are diatomic rather than monatomic can be justified as follows: If hydrogen were monatomic, i.e., consisted of individual H atoms, and if chlorine were also monatomic, then one liter of hydrogen (x atoms) would combine with one liter of chlorine (x atoms) to give one liter of HCl gas (x molecules). This is contrary to the observation that the volume of HCl formed is *twice* as great as the volume of hydrogen or of chlorine reacted. It must be that the hydrogen and chlorine molecules are more complex than monatomic. If hydrogen and chlorine are diatomic, then one liter of hydrogen (x molecules, or $2x$ atoms) will combine with one liter of chlorine (x molecules, or $2x$ atoms) to form two liters of hydrogen chloride ($2x$ molecules). This agrees with experiment.*

---

* This reasoning can also be used to show that water is H_2O and not HO. It is observed that two volumes of hydrogen react with one volume of oxygen to form two volumes of gaseous water. Since one volume of oxygen gives two volumes of water, the oxygen molecule must contain an even number of oxygen atoms. If oxygen, like hydrogen, is diatomic, the fact that two volumes of hydrogen are needed per volume of oxygen implies that the water molecule contains twice as many H atoms as O atoms.

Gas	Molar volume, liters
Hydrogen	22.432
Nitrogen	22.403
Oxygen	22.392
Carbon dioxide	22.263
Ideal gas	22.414

5.11
Molar volumes at STP

As first shown by Cannizzaro (1858), the Avogadro principle can be used as a basis for the determination of molecular masses. If two gases at the same temperature and pressure contain the same number of molecules in equal volumes, the masses of equal volumes give directly the relative masses of the two kinds of molecules. For example, at STP 1 liter of acetylene is observed to weigh 1.17 g and 1 liter of oxygen, 1.43 g. Since the number of molecules is the same in both samples, according to the Avogadro principle, each acetylene molecule must be 1.17/1.43 or 0.818 times as heavy as each oxygen molecule. Since the diatomic oxygen molecule has a molecular mass of 32.0 amu, the molecular mass of acetylene is 26.2 amu.

The volume occupied at STP by 32.00 g of oxygen (one mole) has been determined by experiment to be 22.4 liters. This is called the *molar volume* of oxygen at STP, and, within the limits of ideal behavior, it should be the volume occupied by one mole of any gas at STP. Figure 5.11 shows the observed molar volumes of some gases. The value for the ideal gas is obtained from measurements made on gases at high temperatures and low pressures (where gas behavior is more nearly ideal) and extrapolated to STP by using Boyle's and Charles' laws. For the first three gases, agreement with ideality is quite satisfactory. Even for the fourth, carbon dioxide, the agreement is better than 1%. Consequently, we can usually assume that at STP the molar volume of any gas is 22.4 liters. The following example shows how the molar volume can be used to determine molecular mass and molecular formulas.

EXAMPLE 2

Chemical analysis shows that ethylene has a simplest formula corresponding to one atom of carbon for two atoms of hydrogen. It has a density of 1.25 g per liter at standard temperature and pressure. What are the molecular mass and the molecular formula of ethylene?

At STP one mole of gas (if ideal) has a volume of 22.4 liters. Each liter of ethylene weighs 1.25 g, so one mole of ethylene weighs 22.4 times 1.25 g or 28.0 g. One mole is equal to the gram-formula mass. Since the simplest formula is CH_2, the molecular formula must be some multiple of that, or $(CH_2)_x$. The formula mass of CH_2 is the atomic mass of carbon plus twice the atomic mass of hydrogen, or 14.0. For $(CH_2)_x$, the formula mass is equal to x times 14.0. By experiment, this is equal to 28.0, so x must be equal to 2. The molecular formula of ethylene is $(CH_2)_2$, or C_2H_4.

5.8 EQUATION OF STATE

Boyle's law, Charles' law, and the Avogadro principle can be combined to give a general relation between the volume, pressure, temperature, and number of moles of a gas sample. Such a general relation is called an *equation of state,* because it tells how, in going from one gaseous state to another, the four variables V, P, T, and n change. Using $\propto$ to denote proportionality, Boyle's law, Charles' law, and the Avogadro principle can be written respectively:

$$V \propto \frac{1}{P} \text{ at constant } T \text{ and } n$$

$$V \propto T \text{ at constant } P \text{ and } n$$

$$V \propto n \text{ at constant } T \text{ and } P$$

Combining these, we write

$$V \propto \left(\frac{1}{P}\right)(T)(n).$$

(That this last relation embodies each of the other three can be seen by imagining any two of the variables, such as T and n, to be constant and noting the relation of the other two.) Written as a mathematical equation, the general relation becomes

$$V = R \left(\frac{1}{P}\right)(T)(n) \qquad \text{or} \qquad PV = nRT$$

R is inserted as the constant of proportionality; it is called the universal gas constant. The equation $PV = nRT$ is called the *equation of state for an ideal gas,* or the *perfect-gas law.*

The numerical value of R can be found by substituting experimental quantities in the equation. At STP, $T = 273.15°K$, $P = 1$ atm, and, for 1 mole of gas ($n = 1$), $V = 22.414$ liters. Consequently

$$R = \frac{PV}{nT} = \frac{(1)(22.414)}{(1)(273.15)} = 0.082057$$

The units of R in this case are liter-atmospheres per degree per mole. In order to use this value of R in the equation of state, P must be expressed in atmospheres, V in liters, n in moles, and T in degrees Kelvin.

EXAMPLE 3

The density of an unknown gas at 98°C and 740 torr pressure is 2.50 g per liter. What is the molecular mass of this gas, assuming ideal behavior?

$$\text{Temperature} = 98 + 273 = 371°\text{K}$$

$$\text{Pressure} = \frac{740}{760} = 0.974 \text{ atm}$$

From the equation of state, $PV = nRT$, we can calculate the number of moles in 1 liter:

$$\frac{n}{V} = \frac{P}{RT} = \frac{(0.974)}{(0.0821)(371)} = 0.0320$$

Since 0.0320 mole weighs 2.50 g, 1 mole weighs 2.50/0.0320, or 78.1, g.

From the equation of state just described, $PV = nRT$, it is seen that the constant for Boyle's law ($PV =$ a constant) is just equal to nRT. As noted in Section 5.4, the work of van der Waals showed that it is not the simple product PV that remains constant at constant temperature but the more complex expression $(P + n^2a/V^2)(V-nb)$. Setting this product equal to nRT, we obtain the so-called van der Waals equation of state:

$$\left(P + \frac{n^2a}{V^2}\right)(V-nb) = nRT$$

EXAMPLE 4

By using the data in Figure 5.7, calculate the pressure exerted by 0.250 mole of carbon dioxide in 0.275 liter at 100°C and compare with the value expected for an ideal gas. The actual observed value is 26.1 atm.

$P = ?$; $n = 0.250$ mole; $a = 3.59$ liter^2 atm mole^{-2}; $V = 0.275$ liter; $b = 0.0427$ liter mole^{-1}; $R = 0.08206$ liter-atm; $T = 373°\text{K}$.

$$\left[P + \frac{(0.250)^2(3.59)}{(0.275)^2}\right][0.275 - (0.250)(0.0427)]$$

$$= (0.250)(0.08206)(373)$$

$$P = 26.0 \text{ atm}$$

From $PV = nRT$, $P_{\text{ideal}} = 27.8$ atm.

5.9 GRAHAM'S LAW OF DIFFUSION

A gas spreads to occupy any volume accessible to it. This spontaneous spreading of a substance throughout a phase is called *diffusion*. Diffusion can readily be observed by liberating some ammonia gas in a room. Its odor soon fills the room, indicating that the ammonia has become distributed throughout the entire volume of the room. Furthermore, it is found for a series of gases that the lightest gas (i.e., the one of lowest molecular mass) diffuses most rapidly. Quantitatively, under the same conditions the *rate of diffusion of a gas is observed to be inversely proportional to the square root of its molecular mass*. This is Graham's *law of diffusion* (1829), and in mathematical form it is written

$$R = \frac{\text{constant}}{\sqrt{m}} \qquad \text{or} \qquad \frac{R_1}{R_2} = \frac{\sqrt{m_2}}{\sqrt{m_1}}$$

R_1 and R_2 are the rates of diffusion of gases 1 and 2 and m_1 and m_2 are the respective molecular masses. In the case of oxygen gas and hydrogen gas

$$\frac{R_{H_2}}{R_{O_2}} = \frac{\sqrt{m_{O_2}}}{\sqrt{m_{H_2}}} = \sqrt{\frac{32}{2}} = \sqrt{16} = 4$$

The fact that heavier gases diffuse more slowly than light gases has been applied on a mammoth scale to effect the separation of uranium isotope U^{235} from U^{238}. Natural uranium consisting of 99.3% U^{238} and 0.7% U^{235} is converted to the gas UF_6, and the mixture of the gases is passed at low pressure through a porous solid. The heavier $U^{238}F_6$ diffuses less rapidly than $U^{235}F_6$; hence, the gas mixture which first emerges from the solid is richer in the light isotope than the starting mixture is. Since the square root of the ratio of molecular masses is only 1.0043, the step must be repeated thousands of times, but eventually, substantial enrichment of the desired 235 isotope is obtained.

5.10 KINETIC THEORY

One aspect of observed gas behavior which gives the strongest clue to the nature of gases is the phenomenon known as *Brownian motion.* This motion, first observed by the botanist Robert Brown, in 1827, is the *irregular zigzag movement of extremely minute particles when suspended in a liquid or a gas.* Brownian motion can be observed by focusing a microscope on a particle of smoke illuminated from the side. The particle does not settle to the bottom of its container but moves continually to and fro and shows no sign of coming to rest. The smaller the suspended particle observed, the more violent is this permanent condition of irregular motion. The higher the temperature of the fluid, the more vigorous is the movement of the suspended particle.

The existence of Brownian motion contradicts the idea of matter as a quiescent state and suggests that the molecules of matter are constantly moving. A particle of smoke appears to be jostled by its neighboring molecules, and thus indirectly the motion of the smoke particle reflects the motion of the submicroscopic, invisible molecules of matter. Here then is powerful support for the suggestion that matter consists of extremely small particles which are ever in motion. This "moving-molecule" theory is known as the *kinetic theory of matter.* Its two basic postulates are that molecules of matter are in motion and that heat is a manifestation of this motion.

Like any theory, the kinetic theory represents a model which is proposed to account for an observed set of facts. In order that the model be practical, certain simplifying assumptions must be made about its properties. The validity of each assumption and the reliability of the whole model can be checked by how well the facts are explained. For a perfect gas the following assumptions are made:

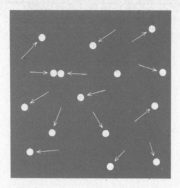

5.12
Kinetic model of a gas

1. Gases consist of tiny molecules, which are so small and so far apart on the average that the actual volume of the molecules is negligible compared to the empty space between them.

2. In the perfect gas there are no attractive forces between molecules. The molecules are completely independent of each other.

3. The molecules of a gas are in rapid, random, straight-line motion, colliding with each other and with the walls of their container. In each collision it is assumed that there is no net loss of kinetic energy, although there may be a transfer of energy between the partners in the collision.

4. At a particular instant in any collection of gas molecules, different molecules have different speeds and, therefore, different kinetic energies. However, the average kinetic energy of all the molecules is assumed to be directly proportional to the absolute temperature.

Before discussing each of these assumptions, we might ask how the model is related to the observable quantities V, P, and T. The accepted model of a gas is that of empty space in which tiny points representing molecules are in violent motion, colliding with each other and with the walls of the container. Figure 5.12 shows an exaggerated version of this model. The *volume* of a gas is mostly empty space, but it is *occupied* in the sense that moving particles occupy the entire region in which they move. *Pressure,* defined as force per unit area, is exerted by gases because molecules collide with the walls of the container. Each collision produces a tiny impulse, and the sum of all the impulses on one square centimeter of wall in one second is the pressure. *Temperature* gives a quantitative measure of the average motion of the molecules.

That assumption 1 is reasonable can be seen from the fact that the compressibility of gases is so great. Calculations show that, in oxygen gas, for example, at STP, 99.96% of the total volume is empty space at any instant. Since there are 2.7×10^{19} molecules per cubic centimeter of oxygen gas at STP, the average spacing between molecules is about 37×10^{-8} cm, which is about 13 times the molecular diameter. When oxygen or any other gas is compressed, the average spacing between molecules is reduced, i.e., the fraction of free space is diminished.

The validity of assumption 2 is supported by the observation that gases spontaneously expand to occupy all the volume accessible to them. This behavior occurs even in a highly compressed gas, where the molecules are fairly close together and any intermolecular forces should be greatest. It must be that there is no appreciable binding of one molecule of a gas to its neighbors.

As already indicated, the observation of Brownian motion implies that molecules of a gas move, in agreement with assumption 3. Like any moving body, a molecule has an amount of kinetic energy equal to $\frac{1}{2}ms^2$, where m is the mass of the molecule and s is its speed. That molecules move in straight lines follows from the assumption of no attractive forces. Only if there were attractions between them could molecules be swerved from straight-line paths. Because there are so many molecules in a gas sample and because they are moving so rapidly (at 0°C the average speed of oxygen molecules is about 1000 miles per hour), there are frequent collisions between molecules.

It is necessary to assume that the molecular collisions are elastic (like collisions between billiard balls). Otherwise, kinetic energy would be lost by conversion to potential energy (as by distorting molecules); motion of the molecules would eventually stop; and the molecules would settle to the bottom of the container. It might be noted that the distance a gas molecule has to travel before colliding elastically with another gas molecule is much greater than the average spacing between molecules, because the molecules have many near misses. In oxygen at STP the average distance between successive collisions, called the *mean free path,* is approximately 1000 times the molecular diameter.

Assumption 4 has two parts: (*a*) there is a distribution of kinetic energies and (*b*) the average kinetic energy is proportional to the absolute temperature. The distribution, or range, of energies comes about as the result of molecular collisions, which continually change the speed of a particular molecule. A given molecule may move along with a certain speed until it hits another molecule, to which it loses some of its kinetic energy, and perhaps, later, it gets hit by a third molecule and gains kinetic energy. This exchange of kinetic energy between neighbors is constantly going on, so that it is only the total kinetic energy of a gas sample that stays the same (provided, of course, that no energy is added to the gas sample from the outside, as by heating). The total kinetic energy of a gas is made up of the contributions of all the molecules, each of which may be moving at a different speed. The situation is summarized in Figure 5.13, which indicates the usual distribution of kinetic energies in a gas sample. Each point on the curve tells what fraction of the molecules has the specified value of the kinetic energy.

The temperature of a gas can be raised by the addition of heat. What happens to the molecules as the temperature is raised? The heat which is added is a form of energy, and so it can be used to increase the speed of the molecules and, therefore, the average kinetic energy. This is shown in Figure 5.14, where the dashed curve describes the situation at higher temperature. Temperature serves to measure the average kinetic energy.

The assumption that average kinetic energy is directly proportional

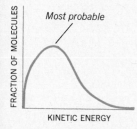

5.13
Energy distribution in a gas

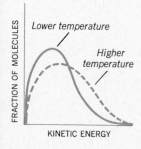

5.14
Energy distributions in gas samples at two temperatures

to the absolute temperature is supported by the fact that predictions based on the assumption agree with experiment. For example, it follows that two different gases at the same temperature must have equal average kinetic energies. If the two gases A and B have different molecular masses m_A and m_B, then the speeds s_A and s_B must be related as follows:

Average kinetic energy of A = average kinetic energy of B

$$\tfrac{1}{2}m_A s_A{}^2 = \tfrac{1}{2}m_B s_B{}^2$$

$$\frac{s_A}{s_B} = \sqrt{\frac{m_B}{m_A}}$$

It is reasonable to assume that the rate of diffusion of a gas is directly proportional to the average speed of its molecules. Thus, we can write

$$\frac{\text{Rate of diffusion of A}}{\text{Rate of diffusion of B}} = \sqrt{\frac{m_B}{m_A}}$$

This inverse proportionality between diffusion rate and the square root of the molecular mass is found experimentally (as Graham's law).

5.11 KINETIC THEORY AND EQUATION OF STATE

The equation of state of an ideal gas, $PV = nRT$, can be derived from kinetic theory by considering in detail how the pressure of a gas arises from molecular impacts. Suppose we imagine a gas confined in a cubic box, as in Figure 5.12. The pressure of the gas is proportional to the *number of molecular impacts* on a square centimeter of wall area per second and is also proportional to the *impulse* (see Appendix 3.3), or change of momentum, of *each impact*. The number of impacts multiplied by the impulse of each is the total pressure.

Let N = number of molecules in box

m = mass of each molecule

s = average speed of each molecule

l = length of edge of cubic box

The motion of any molecule in the box can be resolved into three components along the three edge-directions of the box. We can therefore assume that the net effect on the walls is the same as if one-third of the molecules in the box were constrained to move normal to a pair of opposite faces. Thus, $\tfrac{1}{3}N$ molecules will be colliding with any chosen face of the cubic box. How frequently will each of these molecules make a molecular impact on the wall of interest? Between successive impacts on the same wall the molecule has to travel the length of the box and back, i.e., the distance $2l$. Since it is traveling at speed s cm sec^{-1}, in 1 sec its total distance traveled is s cm. During this second, it will collide with the wall $s/2l$ times.

Impacts per face per sec $= (\tfrac{1}{3}N)\left(\dfrac{s}{2l}\right)$

Area of face $= l^2$

Impacts per cm^2 per sec $= \tfrac{1}{3}N\dfrac{s/2l}{l^2}$

Since the volume V of the box is l^3, the expression becomes

Impacts per cm^2 per sec $= \dfrac{Ns}{6V}$

To get the impulse per impact, it is necessary to note that the impulse is equal to the change of momentum. In a collision in which a molecule of mass m and speed s bounces off the wall with equal speed but in the opposite direction (denoted by $-s$), the momentum changes from an initial value ms to a final value $-ms$ and therefore by an amount equal to $2ms$.

$$\text{Pressure} = \frac{\text{force}}{\text{area}} = \left(\frac{\text{impacts}}{\text{area sec}}\right)\left(\frac{\text{impulse}}{\text{impact}}\right)$$

$$P = \left(\frac{Ns}{6V}\right)(2ms) = \frac{N}{3V}ms^2$$

The proportionality between average kinetic energy $\tfrac{1}{2}ms^2$ and absolute temperature T can be written as

$$\tfrac{1}{2}ms^2 = \tfrac{3}{2}kT$$

where the constant k, called the Boltzmann constant, has the value 1.3805×10^{-16} erg deg^{-1}, or 1.362×10^{-25} liter-atm deg^{-1}. By substituting in the previous equation we find

$$P = \frac{2N}{3V}\left(\frac{1}{2}ms^2\right) = \frac{2N}{3V}\left(\frac{3}{2}kT\right) = \frac{N}{V}kT$$

The number of molecules N is just equal to $6.0225 \times 10^{23}\, n$, where n is the number of moles. The Boltzmann constant k times the Avogadro number is the gas constant R.

$$P = \frac{nRT}{V}$$

5.12 DEVIATIONS FROM IDEAL BEHAVIOR

The model of a gas as consisting of point masses moving independently of each other leads to the ideal equation of state $PV = nRT$. Yet, as we have seen, gases are better described by other equations of state such as the van der Waals equation

$$\left(P + \frac{n^2a}{V^2}\right)(V - nb) = nRT$$

What does this indicate about the kinetic molecular model? In the first place, molecules are not point masses, but have finite dimensions. This shows up in the van der Waals equation in the term nb. The quantity $V - nb$ can be thought of as representing the *free volume* accessible to the molecules. That is, each molecule is not free to move in volume V but only in that part of V that is not actually "filled" by other molecules. If the quantity nb is thought of as the *excluded volume,* then b is an effective volume per mole that is characteristic of the size of the molecules of a particular substance. It has been shown that the actual volumes of molecules should be about a quarter of the values indicated by b.

A second reason for nonideal behavior is that, contrary to the assumption noted previously, there are attractive forces between molecules. The effect of such forces is to reduce the pressure exerted by a collection of gas molecules. The quantity $P + n^2a/V^2$ can be thought of as being equivalent to an ideal pressure as specified by the ideal equation of state. The actual pressure to be observed, P, is less than the ideal pressure by the amount n^2a/V^2. This correction term contains the quantity n/V squared, where n/V represents the number of moles, and hence the number of gas molecules, per unit volume. n/V, the *concentration* of gas molecules, when squared gives the probability of collisions between molecules (Section 10.5). a is a proportionality constant that indicates the magnitude of the cohesive force between molecules in collision. Thus, a, whose magnitude gives a measure of the deviation from ideality, multiples the probability of collision to give the decrement from ideal pressure.

The attractive forces described by the van der Waals constant a are special in that they must operate only at very short distances, i.e., during collision. In some cases it is easy to see the reason for attractive forces between molecules. For example, in polar molecules, the positive end of one molecule may attract the negative end of another molecule. It is not surprising, therefore, that polar substances deviate markedly from ideal behavior. Water vapor, as an illustration, is so nonideal that, even at room temperature, it liquefies under slight pressure.

It is not so easy to see the reason for attractive forces between nonpolar molecules. Suppose we consider two neon atoms extremely close together, as shown in Figure 5.15. We can imagine that *instantaneously* the electron distribution in atom 1 is unsymmetrical, with a slight preponderance on one side. For a fraction of a microsecond, the atom is in a state in which one end appears slightly negative with respect to the other end; i.e., the atom is momentarily a dipole. The neighboring atom, as a result, is distorted, because the positive end of atom 1 displaces the electrons in atom 2. As shown in the figure, there is an instantaneous dipole in each of the neighboring atoms, with a consequent attraction. This picture persists only for an extremely short time, because the electrons are in motion. As electrons in atom 1 move to the other side, electrons in atom 2 follow. In fact, we can think of van der Waals forces as arising because electrons in adjacent molecules are beating in time, so as to produce fluctuating dipoles which give rise to an instantaneous attraction. The attraction is strong when particles are close together but rapidly weakens as they move apart. The more

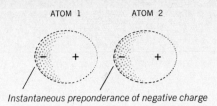

ATOM 1   ATOM 2

Instantaneous preponderance of negative charge

electrons there are in a molecule and the less tightly bound these electrons are, the greater are the van der Waals forces.

The attractive forces become less important as the temperature increases, because a rise in temperature produces an effect that opposes
the attractive forces. This effect is a disordering one due to the molecular motion, which increases in speed as the temperature rises. Disordering arises because the molecules of a gas move in random fashion. The attractive forces try to draw the molecules together, but the
latter, because of their motion, stay apart. As the temperature is lowered, the molecules have less ability to overcome the attractive forces.
The attractive forces are unchanged, but the motion of the molecules
decreases; hence, the attraction becomes relatively more important.

At sufficiently low temperature the attractive forces, no matter how
weak they are, take over and draw the molecules together to form
a liquid. The *temperature at which gas molecules coalesce to form a
liquid* is called the *liquefaction temperature*. Liquefaction is easier at
high pressures, where distances between molecules are smaller and
hence intermolecular forces are greater. The higher the pressure of a
gas, the easier the gas is to liquefy and the less it needs to be cooled
to accomplish liquefaction. Thus, the liquefaction temperature increases with increasing pressure.

5.13 CRITICAL TEMPERATURE

There is for each gas a temperature above which the attractive forces
are not strong enough to produce liquefaction no matter how high the
pressure. This temperature, called the *critical temperature* of the substance, is designated by T_c. It is defined as the *temperature above
which the substance can exist only as a gas*. Above the critical temperature the motion of the molecules is so violent that, no matter
how high the pressure, the molecules occupy the entire available volume as a gas. The critical temperature depends on the magnitude of
the attractive forces between the molecules.

Figure 5.16 contains values of the critical temperature for some
common substances. Listed also is the *critical pressure, the pressure
which must be exerted to produce liquefaction at the critical temperature*. Above the critical temperature, no amount of pressure can produce
liquefaction. For example, above 647°K (374°C), H_2O exists only in the
gaseous state. The high critical temperature indicates that the attractive forces between the polar water molecules are so great that, even at
647°K, they can produce coalescence. The attractive forces between

Substance	Critical temperature, °K	Critical pressure, atm
Water, H_2O	647	217.7
Sulfur dioxide, SO_2	430	77.7
Hydrogen chloride, HCl	324	81.6
Carbon dioxide, CO_2	304	73.0
Oxygen, O_2	154	49.7
Nitrogen, N_2	126	33.5
Hydrogen, H_2	33	12.8
Helium, He	5.2	2.3

5.16
Critical constants

SO_2 molecules are less than those between water molecules; hence, the critical temperature of SO_2 is lower than that of water, and liquefaction cannot be achieved above 430°K (157°C).

In the extreme case of helium the attractive forces are so weak that liquid helium can exist only below 5.3°K (−267.9°C). At this very low temperature the molecular motion is so slow that the weak van der Waals forces can hold the atoms together in a liquid. In Figure 5.16 the order of decreasing critical temperature is also the order of decreasing attractive forces, and we can think of the critical temperature as giving a measure of the attractive forces between molecules.

5.14 COOLING BY EXPANSION

Substances with high critical temperatures are easy to liquefy; substances with low critical temperatures must be cooled before they can be liquefied. For example, oxygen cannot be liquefied at room temperature (298°K or so). It must be cooled below 154°K (−119°C) before liquefaction can occur. This cooling would be quite difficult were it not that gases sometimes cool themselves on expansion.* For example, if a gas expands against a piston, the gas does work in pushing the piston. The energy for this work can come from the kinetic energy of the gas molecules. A decrease in the kinetic energy of the molecules is observed as a lowering of the temperature. However, a temperature drop is sometimes observed for an expanding gas which does no external work.

The cause of cooling by unrestrained expansion can be seen by considering the experiment shown in Figure 5.17. The box shown is perfectly insulated from its surroundings, so that no heat can get in from

* The word "sometimes" takes into consideration the fact that cooling does not occur at *any* temperature but only below the *inversion temperature,* which for most gases is roughly six times the critical temperature. Above the inversion temperature, a gas warms when suddenly expanded; below the inversion temperature, it cools. Since most inversion temperatures are above room temperature, most gases near room temperature cool on expansion and heat on compression. However, the inversion temperatures of hydrogen and helium are below room temperature (195°K and 45°K, respectively), and consequently these gases at room temperature heat up when allowed to expand into a vacuum.

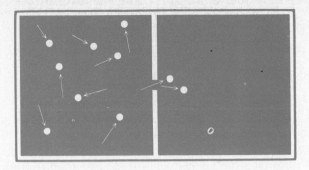

the outside. It is divided into two compartments by a diaphragm. The left-hand compartment contains compressed gas; the right-hand compartment is originally empty. If a hole is now punched in the diaphragm, the gas streams into the vacuum. A thermometer in the path of the streaming gas would show a drop in temperature. As the gas streams into the empty space, molecules work against the attractive forces of their neighbors. This requires energy; and since no outside energy is available, the molecules must use up some of their kinetic energy. The average kinetic energy, as measured by the temperature, drops. If there were no attractive forces between molecules, there would be no cooling effect. Indeed, the fact that cooling is observed indicates that there *are* attractive forces between gas molecules.*

The commercial liquefaction of gases makes use of cooling by expansion. In order to liquefy air, for example, it is first compressed to high pressure, cooled with a refrigerant to remove the heat that accompanies compression, and then allowed to expand. Some of the air liquefies as a result of cooling on expansion; the rest is passed over the incoming pipes containing the compressed air to cool it further.

QUESTIONS

5.1 Gas laws   A pure gas has a density of 1.50 g cc^{-1} at 30.0°C and 720.0 torr. Assuming ideal behavior, calculate its molecular mass.

5.2 Gas laws   Inject simultaneously 0.64 g of O_2 and 0.63 g of N_2 into a 4.68-liter box at 100°C. What is the final pressure?

5.3 Pressure   Give the pressure, in atmospheres, corresponding to each of the following: (*a*) 32 cm Hg, (*b*) 740 torr, (*c*) 32 meters H_2O, (*d*) 4.41 psi.

5.4 Pressure   A sample of oxygen is collected by water displacement as shown in Figure 5.10 except that the water level inside the container

* The opposite effect, warming on unrestrained expansion above the inversion temperature, indicates that there are also repulsive forces between gas molecules. Below the inversion temperature, these repulsions are masked by the larger attractions; however, as the temperature is raised above the inversion temperature, the attractive forces become less important and the repulsive forces, small as they are, dominate. The repulsions can be viewed as arising from the noninterpenetrability of molecules, and hence they are related to the *b* of the van der Waals equation.

is 5 cm higher than outside. The barometer reads 727 torr; the water temperature is 23°C. What is the pressure of the oxygen?

5.5 Gas laws How many moles are there in each of the following: (a) 2.0 liters of ideal gas at STP, (b) 22.4 cc of ideal gas at 755 torr and 26°C, (c) 38.6 cc of ideal gas collected over water at 25°C and a barometric pressure of 728 torr?

5.6 Van der Waals equation What pressures would be exerted by 0.100 mole of each of the following gases confined to 0.400 liter at 127°C: (a) ideal gas, (b) helium, (c) carbon dioxide, (d) acetylene?

5.7 Charles' law Given an open bottle of air at 19°C. To what temperature must the bottle be subjected so that the number of molecules in the bottle (a) increases by 25%, (b) decreases by 25%?

5.8 Boyle's law An ideal-gas bubble of 1.0-cm radius is released at the bottom of a mercury column that is 5.0 meters high and is open to the atmosphere. Calculate the radius of the bubble after each meter rise in the column.

5.9 Graham's law Using H_2 as your standard, estimate the relative rates of diffusion of the following gases: CO, N_2, NH_3, $CHCl_3$.

5.10 Avogadro principle How many molecules are there in each of the following: (a) 1.00 cc of ideal gas at STP, (b) 1.00 cc of liquid H_2O at STP (density $= 0.999$ g cc^{-1}), (c) 1.00 cc of solid H_2O at STP (density $= 0.917$ g cc^{-1})?

5.11 Kinetic theory If the average speed of O_2 molecules at STP is 1000 miles per hour, what is the average speed of CO_2 molecules at 27°C?

5.12 Air density On a particularly uncomfortable day the atmospheric pressure is 740 torr, the temperature is 35°C, and the relative humidity is 90% (i.e., partial pressure of H_2O is 90% of that given by the equilibrium vapor pressure of water). Assuming ideal behavior and an average molecular mass for dry air of 28.95, calculate the density of the humid air.

5.13 Molecular formula Cyanogen has 46.2% carbon and 53.8% nitrogen by weight. At a pressure of 0.932 atm and a temperature of 20°C, 1.00 g of cyanogen occupies 0.496 liter. What is the molecular formula of cyanogen?

5.14 Van der Waals Assuming that the van der Waals b is approximately 4 times the volume of the molecules, calculate the apparent van der Waals radii for the substances listed in Figure 5.7.

5.15 Kinetic theory By using the fact that the average kinetic energy is given by $\frac{3}{2}kT$, calculate the average speed of a CCl_4 molecule at 27°C.

5.14 Cooling by expansion

128

5.16 Graham's law The reaction between gaseous NH_3 and gaseous HBr produces the white solid NH_4Br. Suppose that NH_3 and HBr are introduced simultaneously into the opposite ends of an open tube that is 1 meter long. Where would you expect the white solid to form?

5.17 *Gas laws* When heated strongly enough, solid calcium oxalate, CaC_2O_4, decomposes to give $CaO(s)$, $CO(g)$, and $CO_2(g)$. Suppose that a 1.00-g sample is completely decomposed and the product gases are collected at 18°C and 743 torr total pressure. What volume would be collected? Assume ideal behavior.

5.18 *Gas laws* When solid NH_4NO_2 is heated, it decomposes to give $N_2(g)$ and $H_2O(g)$. How many grams of NH_4NO_2 would be required to prepare 0.690 liter of N_2 collected over water at 27°C and 737 torr barometric pressure?

5.19 *Avogadro number* When radium undergoes radioactive disintegration, alpha particles (helium nuclei) are formed. These alpha particles pick up electrons to form neutral He. The number of alpha particles can be counted with a Geiger counter. In a typical experiment, 1.84×10^{17} alpha particles were counted, and the resultant gas occupied a volume of 0.713 cc at 24°C and a pressure of 7.93 torr. Assuming ideal-gas behavior, calculate the apparent Avogadro number.

5.20 *Buoyancy* Years ago, balloons were filled with hot air. The average molecular mass for air is 29.0. For a day when the barometric pressure is 760 torr and the temperature is 17°C, suppose the air inside the balloon is 182°C. What volume balloon would be needed to lift a man if his mass, plus that of the empty balloon, were 80.0 kg? Assume ideal behavior and that buoyancy equals mass of air displaced.

5.21 *Kinetic theory* Given at STP 1.0 g of H_2 gas in one container and 1.0 g of CH_4 gas in another container. Compare these two samples quantitatively with respect to (*a*) number of molecules in the sample, (*b*) average speed of the molecules, (*c*) number of molecular impacts per unit wall area per second, (*d*) impulse of each impact, (*e*) average kinetic energy of the molecules.

5.22 *Gas reaction* A mixture is made from 0.100 mole $H_2S(g)$ and 0.200 mole $O_2(g)$ in 6.00 liter at 27°C. A reaction occurs; in it H_2S is oxidized by O_2 to $H_2O(g)$ and $SO_2(g)$ at 127°C. What change in pressure has occurred?

5.23 *Gas reaction* A mixture consisting of $CO(g)$ and $CO_2(g)$ exerts a pressure of 1.00 atm at 25°C. Enough oxygen is added to double the pressure. Subsequent passage of a spark results in a pressure increase to 2.56 atm and a temperature increase to 175°C as CO converts to CO_2. Assuming ideal behavior, what percent of the original molecules were CO?

5.24 *Kinetic theory* Given two boxes of the same volume. Box *A* contains H_2 gas at 0°C and 1.00 atm pressure; box *B* contains H_2 gas at 273°C and 2.00 atm pressure. Indicate quantitatively how each of the following quantities compares in the two boxes: (*a*) average kinetic energy per molecule, (*b*) number of molecules in the box, (*c*) average speed of the molecules, (*d*) number of molecular impacts per unit wall area per second, (*e*) impulse of each impact.

5.25 Kinetic theory Given a box containing a sample of CO_2 gas at STP. Approximately how many collisions per second do the CO_2 molecules make per square centimeter of wall area?

5.26 Gas laws Given a mixture of $N_2(g)$ and $H_2(g)$ having a density of 0.505 mg cc^{-1} at 19°C and 748 torr. What percent of the mass is hydrogen?

5.27 Kinetic theory 40.0 liters of oxygen gas are collected by water displacement at 20°C. The partial pressure of the oxygen is 720 torr; the vapor pressure of water at 20°C is 18 torr. Compare quantitatively each of the following properties for the H_2O molecules and the O_2 molecules in this sample: (a) number of molecules in the vapor phase, (b) average speed of the molecules, (c) average kinetic energy of the molecules, (d) number of collisions per unit wall area per second, (e) impulse of each collision with the wall.

5.28 Gas laws When $Al_4C_3(s)$ is treated with water, part of it is converted to CH_4 and the rest of it is converted to C_2H_4, forming $Al(OH)_3(s)$ in the process. Suppose that 1.00 g of $Al_4C_3(s)$ produces 0.480 liter of gas mixture collected over water at 25°C and 752 torr barometric pressure. Calculate the percent of Al_4C_3 that converts to CH_4.

5.29 Kinetic theory By using $PV = nRT$ and assuming the molecules to be arranged in a simple cubic pattern, calculate the apparent distance between H_2O molecules at the critical temperature and critical pressure of H_2O as given in Figure 5.16.

ANSWERS

5.2 0.28 atm   5.4 702 torr   5.6 (a) 8.21   (b) 8.25   (c) 8.07 (d) 8.04   5.7 (a) −54°C   (b) 116°C   5.11 894 miles per hour 5.14 He, 1.33 Å; Ar, 1.47 Å; N_2, 1.57 Å; CO_2, 1.62 Å; C_2H_2, 1.72 Å; CCl_4, 2.40 Å   5.15 427 miles per hour   5.18 1.68 g 5.22 From 1.23 to 1.37 atm   5.23 60%   5.25 1.8×10^{23} 5.26 9.93%   5.28 80.5%   5.29 7.40 Å

6 solids

Whereas the gaseous state is characterized by disorder, in that molecules of a gas are not constrained to occupy fixed positions in space, the solid state is characterized by order. The atoms of a solid are arranged in regular patterns, the existence of which simplifies the understanding of the solid state. The deciphering of solid-state structures is a challenging problem, since the observed properties ultimately are determined by the structure. The concept of ordered arrangement of atoms in the solid state is very old, being originally based on the observation that crystals show planar faces with characteristic angles between them. However, the working out of detailed atomic arrangements was made possible only after the discovery of X rays and their application to the study of crystals.

SODIUM CHLORIDE   QUARTZ   ALUM

6.1 PROPERTIES OF SOLIDS

Unlike a gas, which expands to occupy any accessible volume, a solid sample has a characteristic volume that does not change with the volume of the container or with any but quite large changes of pressure or temperature. In other words, compared with gases solids are nearly incompressible and have low thermal coefficients of expansion. According to molecular theory, this results from the existence of strong attractive forces between closely spaced molecules. In addition, there are strong repulsive forces arising from the Pauli exclusion principle (Section 2.5) which keep electron clouds of molecules from penetrating each other significantly.

Another marked difference between the solid and gaseous states is in the diffusion rates. Whereas any gas can diffuse through another in a time short enough to allow easy observation, many solids diffuse so slowly as to make changes essentially imperceptible. For example, rock layers have been in contact with each other for millions of years and still retain sharp boundaries. However, in nonsilicate solids considerably more rapid diffusion has been demonstrated: metals interpenetrate to a depth of 0.1 mm in a matter of hours at elevated temperatures that are still below the melting point. Based on the picture that solids consist of molecules in virtual contact, it is reasonable that diffusion should be a slow process in solids. In fact, from this view one might ask why diffusion occurs at all. One principal reason is that solids are generally imperfect, having, for example, vacancies where atoms or molecules should reside. Motion into these vacancies permits diffusion to occur at a rate proportional to the number of vacancies per unit volume. For many purposes, the existence of these defects can be ignored, but for certain properties such as diffusion, conductivity, and mechanical strength, their presence can be decisive.

Solids form *crystals,* definite geometric forms which are distinctive for the substance in question. The crystals of a given substance are bounded by plane surfaces, which are called *faces.* The faces always intersect at an angle characteristic of the substance. For example, sodium chloride crystallizes in the form of cubes with faces which intersect at an angle of 90°. When a crystal is broken, it splits, or shows *cleavage,* along certain preferred directions, so that the characteristic faces and angles result even when the material is ground to a fine powder. In

Figure 6.1 are shown the usual crystal shapes of various common chemicals. It should be pointed out that the same chemical substance can under different conditions form different kinds of crystals. For instance, although NaCl almost always crystallizes as cubes, it can also be made to crystallize as octahedral crystals like the crystal shown for alum. The occurrence of different crystal forms of the same chemical is called *polymorphism.* The existence of characteristic crystals is prime support for the idea that the molecules or atoms which make up a crystal are arranged in orderly patterns characteristic of the substance.*

6.2 DETERMINATION OF STRUCTURE

Information about the arrangement of fundamental particles in solids can be gained from the external symmetry of crystals. However, much more information is obtained from X-ray diffraction. X rays are radiant energy much like light, but they are more energetic and have greater penetrating power (Section 1.3). They can be produced by bombarding a metal with energetic electrons. The energy of the electrons is transferred to the atoms of the metal and excites electrons of the atoms of the metal to a higher energy level. When the electrons fall from a high energy level to a low energy level, they emit energy in the form of X rays. The target metal is usually copper or molybdenum.

Figure 6.2 shows the setup for the study of crystalline materials. X rays are collimated into a beam by a lead shield with a hole in it. If sufficiently thick, the shield stops all X rays except the beam which comes through the hole. A well-formed crystal is mounted in the path

---

* Not all solids are crystalline in form. Some substances, such as glass, have the solid-state properties of extremely slow diffusion and virtually complete maintenance of shape and volume but do not have the ordered crystalline state. These substances are sometimes called *amorphous solids.*

6.2
X-ray determination of structure

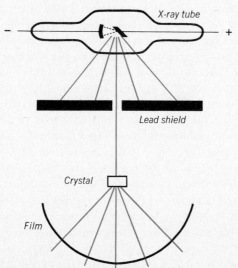

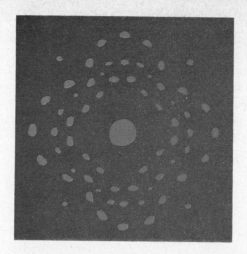

of the X-ray beam. As the X rays penetrate the crystal, the atoms which make up the crystal scatter, or deflect, some of the X rays from their original path. The X rays are detected by a piece of photographic film at some distance from the crystal. The X-ray beam exposes the film, and when the film is developed, a spot appears at points where the beam struck it. The developed film shows not just one spot, but a pattern which is uniquely characteristic of the crystal investigated.

In Figure 6.3 is shown the pattern for a crystal of sodium chloride. The big spot in the center corresponds to the main unscattered beam. The other spots represent a scattering of part of the original beam through various characteristic angles. The creation of many beams from one is like the effect observed when a light beam falls on a diffraction grating—a piece of glass on which are scratched thousands of parallel lines that are opaque and leave, in effect, many narrow slits of unscratched surface for light to pass through. The spreading of the light wave from each slit results in interference between waves from different slits, giving rise to alternate regions of light and dark. The diffraction of X rays by crystals is similar to diffraction of light by a grating, and it suggests that crystalline materials consist of regular arrangements of atoms in space in which the lines of atoms act like tiny slits for the X rays.

The diffraction of X rays by a crystal is a complex phenomenon involving the interaction between incoming X rays and the electrons that make up atoms. We can consider the X rays to consist of waves of electrical pulsations and their interactions with atoms as producing corresponding pulsations of the electrons in each atom. Thus, each atom in the path of an X-ray beam receives pulsations and regenerates them as waves in all directions. Consider (as shown in Figure 6.4) two atoms, side by side in an X-ray beam, set into electrical pulsation at the same frequency. Viewed from head-on (position A), the signals from the two are received in phase so that the signal from one reinforces that from the other. This need not be true when viewed at some angle to the incident beam. In general, the signals will be out of phase with

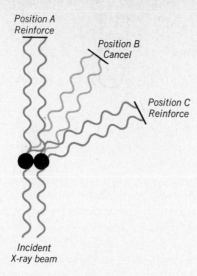

Position A
Reinforce

Position B
Cancel

Position C
Reinforce

Incident
X-ray beam

6.4
Two-atom model for X-ray
scattering

each other (position B), because one signal has to travel farther than the other. If, however, the path difference is just exactly equivalent to a whole wavelength (position C), there will again be reinforcement of the signals.

For a real crystal consisting of many atoms regularly arranged, there will be certain angles (relative to the incident X-ray beam) at which there will be reinforcement in the emergent beam so as to produce spots on a photographic film. From the angles at which spots appear it is possible to determine the distance between diffracting planes of atoms. The relation between the X-ray angles and the interplanar distances is given by the Bragg equation

$$n\lambda = 2d \sin \theta$$

where n is a whole number (usually equal to 1), λ is the wavelength of the X-ray beam, and d is the distance between the planes of atoms that produce constructive interference along a direction that makes an angle 2θ with the direction of the incident beam. The Bragg equation can be derived by using a reflection analogy as shown in Figure 6.5; however, it must be emphasized that X-ray diffraction is a much more complex process than a simple reflection from planes of atoms. Since θ, the

6.5
Reflection analogy for
Bragg's law

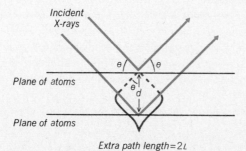

Incident
X-rays

θ θ

Plane of atoms

θ
d

Plane of atoms

Extra path length $= 2L$

angle of incidence, is also the angle which subtends l, half the extra path length ($\sin \theta = l/d$), and since the extra path length, $2l$, must equal an integral number of wavelengths ($n\lambda$), it follows that $n\lambda = 2l = 2(d \sin \theta)$.

6.3 SPACE LATTICE

A careful mathematical analysis of a spot pattern resulting from X-ray diffraction enables X-ray crystallographers to calculate the positions particles might occupy in order to produce such a pattern. The process of calculation is an indirect one which involves guessing probable structures, calculating the X-ray patterns they would produce, and comparing these with experiment. The pattern of points which describes the arrangement of molecules or atoms in a crystal is known as a *space lattice*. In Figure 6.6 is shown the space lattice of sodium chloride, NaCl.* Each of the points corresponds to the position of the center of an ion. ×'s locate positive sodium ions, and circles negative chloride

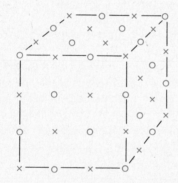

6.6
Space lattice of NaCl

ions. The points do not represent sodium ions and chloride ions; they represent only the positions occupied by the centers. In fact, in sodium chloride the ions are of different size and are practically touching each other, as shown in Figure 6.7.

The space lattice has to be thought of as extending in all directions throughout the entire crystal. In discussing the space lattice it is sufficient to consider only enough of it to represent the order of arrangement. This small fraction of a space lattice, which sets the pattern for the whole lattice, is called the *unit cell*. It is defined as the *smallest portion of the space lattice which, moved a distance equal to its own dimensions in various directions, generates the whole space lattice.* A unit cell of sodium chloride is the cube shown in Figure 6.8. If this cube is moved through its edge length in the x direction, the y direction, and the z direction many times, the whole space lattice can be reproduced.

*In the strictest sense, a space lattice is concerned only with points, and hence all points in a space lattice must be identical. In this sense, NaCl can be represented by two identical interpenetrating space lattices, one for the positions of the sodium ions and one for those of the chloride ions.

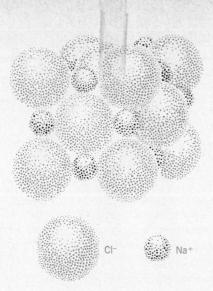

Cl⁻   Na⁺

Several different kinds of unit-cell symmetry occur in crystalline substances. The simplest, known as *simple cubic,* is shown in Figure 6.9a. Each point at the corner of the cube represents a position occupied by an atom or a molecule. The dotted lines represent the three characteristic directions of space, or *axes,* along which the structure must be extended to reproduce the entire space lattice. Closely related to simple-

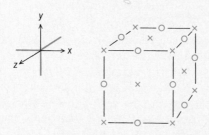

cubic symmetry is *body-centered cubic,* the unit cell for which is shown in Figure 6.9b. It is made up of points at the corners of a cube, with an additional point in the center. In *face-centered-cubic* symmetry there are points at the corners of the cube with additional points in the middle of each face, as shown in Figure 6.9c.

Other kinds of symmetry are considerably more complicated. To produce *tetragonal* symmetry, the cube is elongated in one direction. The

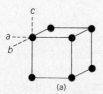

(a)

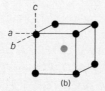

(b)

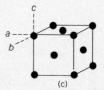

(c)

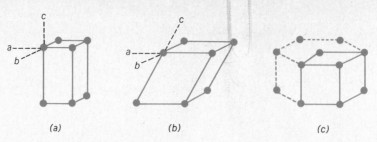

(a)   (b)   (c)

lines of atoms still form right angles with each other, but the distance between points along one axis differs from that along the other two. Figure 6.10a shows a tetragonal unit cell. The separation of points along the a axis is the same as that along the b axis, but that along the c axis is different. In *rhombic,* also called *orthorhombic,* symmetry, the unit cell retains mutually perpendicular edges, but the point separation is unequal in the a, b, and c directions. In *monoclinic* crystals the three axes a, b, and c are no longer perpendicular to each other. Monoclinic symmetry differs from rhombic symmetry in that the c axis does not make a right angle with the ab plane. An example is shown in Figure 6.10b. In *triclinic* symmetry none of the three axes a, b, and c is perpendicular to any of the others. In the *hexagonal* type of symmetry, as shown in Figure 6.10c, the atoms or molecules are arranged in the form of hexagons, with the hexagons stacked on top of each other.

6.4 PACKING OF ATOMS

The unit cells just discussed actually concern only points that locate atomic or molecular centers. Atoms are space-filling entities, and structures can be described as resulting from the packing together of representative spheres. The most efficient packing together of equal spheres, called closest packing, can be achieved in two ways, each of which utilizes the same fraction (0.7406) of total space. One of these close-packing arrangements is called *hexagonal close-packed*. It can be envisioned as being built up as follows: Place a sphere on a flat surface. Surround it with six equal spheres as close as possible in the same plane. Looking down on the plane, the projection is as shown in Figure 6.11a. Now form a second layer of equally bunched spheres, staggered as shown in Figure 6.11b so that the second-layer spheres nestle into the depressions formed by the first-layer spheres. A third layer can now be added with each sphere directly above a sphere of the first layer. The fourth layer lies directly above the second layer, and so forth in alternating fashion until the hexagonal close-packed structure has been generated.

The other close-packed structure, called *cubic close-packed*, results if the buildup of layers a and b is the same as that described above but then a third layer c is added, as shown in Figure 6.11c. The spheres of the layer c are not directly above those of either layer a or layer b. In generating this cubic close-packed structure the sequence of layers is

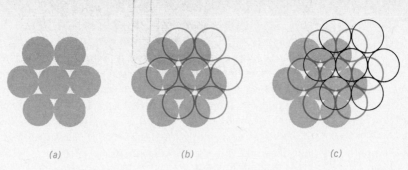

6.11
Close-packing of spheres

$abcabc \cdots$ as contrasted to the sequence $ababab \cdots$ for hexagonal close-packing.

These two structures can also be represented in terms of unit cells. For hexagonal close-packing, a unit cell is like that of Figure 6.10c except that the b layer is inserted between the top and bottom faces so as to add three lattice points at mid-height in the hexagonal prism shown. For cubic close-packing the unit cell turns out to be the same as a face-centered cube, the body diagonal of which is perpendicular to the stacking layers. This can be seen from Figure 6.12, which also shows hexagonal close-packing.

Among the common materials that crystallize with hexagonal close-packing are many of the metals, such as magnesium, zinc, cadmium, titanium, and hafnium. Also showing hexagonal close-packing is solid H_2, where tumbling H_2 molecules are equivalent to the close-packing spheres. Cubic close-packing is shown by other metals, such as stron-

6.12
Hexagonal and cubic
close-packing

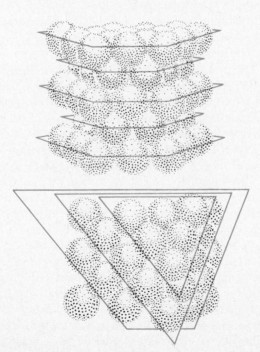

tium, aluminum, copper, silver, and gold, as well as by simple rotating molecules such as CH_4 and HCl.

Close-packing of spheres can also be used to describe many ionic solids. For example, NaCl can be viewed as a cubic close-packed array of chloride ions with the sodium ions fitting into interstices between the chloride layers (Figure 6.7). Interstices between layers of close-packed spheres are of two kinds, one of which (called a tetrahedral hole) has four spheres adjacent to it and the other of which (called an octahedral hole) has six spheres adjacent to it. The difference between the two kinds is illustrated in Figure 6.13. The a layer of close-packed spheres is represented by filled balls, and the b layer above it by open balls. On the left, marked by color, is a grouping of four adjacent balls (three from layer a and one from layer b) surrounding a tetrahedral hole. This is called a tetrahedral hole because a small atom inserted in the hole would have four neighboring atoms arranged at the corners of a regular tetrahedron. Such a grouping of four spheres and its relation to a tetrahedron is shown at the bottom of the figure. It should be recalled that a regular tetrahedron is a triangular-based pyramid in which each of the four faces is an equilateral triangle.

On the right in Figure 6.13, also marked in color, is a grouping of six adjacent balls (three from layer a and three from layer b) surrounding an octahedral hole. The octahedron, as indicated at the bottom of the figure, is an eight-faced figure all of whose faces are equilateral triangles. In the NaCl structure the Na^+ ions are regarded as being in the octahedral holes created between layers of Cl^- ions. It turns out that the number of octahedral holes is just equal to the number of packed spheres, so that the number of Na^+ ions accommodated just equals the number of Cl^- ions. Similarly, MgO, which has the same structure as NaCl (called the *rock-salt structure*), can be regarded as an array of close-packed oxide ions with a magnesium ion in each of the octahedral holes. The rock-salt structure is also found in other halides of Li, Na, K, and Rb and in oxides and sulfides of group II metals and of some transition metals (for example, TiO, MnO, MnS).

The structure of Li_2O can be built up by taking a cubic close-packed array of oxide ions and inserting Li^+ into each of the tetrahedral holes. It turns out that in a close-packed arrangement of spheres there are twice as many tetrahedral holes as there are spheres. This can be seen with the aid of Figure 6.13. The tetrahedral hole indicated is formed by one sphere of the top layer b and three spheres of the bottom layer a. There is such a hole directly under each sphere of the top layer. In addition, there are tetrahedral holes formed from three spheres of the top layer and one from the bottom. Thus, there is also one tetrahedral hole above each sphere of the bottom layer. In the crystal as a whole there is one tetrahedral hole above and one below every close-packed atom, and, therefore, there are twice as many tetrahedral holes as close-packed atoms.

In the Li_2O structure, which is an example of a class of structures called *antifluorite*, every tetrahedral hole contains a positive ion. Other examples of this structure are afforded by oxides, sulfides, selenides, and tellurides of Li, Na, and K. A closely related structure is the so-called

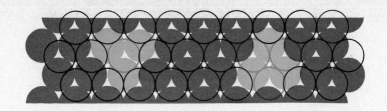

6.13
Tetrahedral and octahedral
holes between layers of
close-packed spheres

fluorite structure, typified by the mineral fluorite, CaF_2. It differs only in that the positive and negative ions have been interchanged; i.e., the F^- ions are tetrahedrally surrounded by Ca^{++} ions. The fluorite structure is also found in other fluorides of group II elements and some oxides such as UO_2.

Another important structure is the *zincblende structure,* named after the mineral ZnS. It can be visualized as consisting of a cubic close-packed array of sulfur atoms with zinc atoms disposed in one-half of the tetrahedral holes. If a hole above a particular sulfur atom is occupied, then the one below it is not. Examples of the zincblende structure include CuCl, CuBr, CuI, AgI, and BeS, as well as the technically important group III-V compounds. The latter are formed from an element of group III (for example, Al, Ga, In) plus an element of group V (for example, P, As, Sb), and they are important in solid-state electrical devices such as transistors and rectifiers.

In the compounds thus far discussed in this section, only the holes of one kind (i.e., tetrahedral *or* octahedral) have been utilized. More complicated structures can be built up by using both kinds of holes simultaneously. A most important example is the spinel structure, named after the mineral spinel, $MgAl_2O_4$. This consists of a cubic close-packed array of oxide ions with Mg^{++} in tetrahedral holes and Al^{+3} in octahedral holes. Only one-eighth of the tetrahedral holes are occupied and one-half of the octahedral. There are many compounds with the spinel structure (for example, $NiAl_2O_4$, $MgCr_2O_4$, $ZnFe_2O_4$) in which the dipositive ions reside in tetrahedral holes and the tripositive ions in octahedral holes. Such compounds are referred to as *normal spinels.*

There are other compounds in which the dipositive ions go to octahedral holes and the tripositive ions are distributed half and half between tetrahedral and octahedral holes. Such compounds are called *inverse spinels.* Examples include $MgFe_2O_4$ and $MgIn_2O_4$, where the Mg^{++} ions are in octahedral holes and the Fe^{+3} or In^{+3} are split. Fe_3O_4, the mineral magnetite (also called lodestone), is an interesting example of an inverse spinel. It can be written $Fe^{II}Fe_2^{III}O_4$ to indicate the presence of Fe^{++} and Fe^{+3}. The Fe^{++} ions occupy octahedral holes, and the Fe^{+3} ions are divided between tetrahedral and octahedral interstices. An electron can jump from an Fe^{++} to an Fe^{+3} that is also in an octahedral hole, thereby giving rise to electrical conductivity, intense light absorption responsible for the black color, and ferromagnetism arising from magnetic interaction between structurally equivalent ions.

6.5 TYPES OF SOLIDS

Often, instead of classifying by the symmetry of their arrangements, it is more useful to classify solids by the units that occupy the lattice points. There are four types of crystals: *molecular, ionic, covalent,* and *metallic.* Figure 6.14 lists for each type the nature of the units that occupy lattice points, the forces that bind these units together, characteristic properties, and some typical examples.

Molecular solids are those in which the lattice points are occupied by molecules. In a molecular solid the bonding *within* the molecule is covalent and, in general, is much stronger than the bonding *between* the molecules. The bonding between molecules can be of two types, dipole-dipole or van der Waals. Dipole-dipole attraction is encountered in solids consisting of polar molecules. In the case of water, for example, the negative end of one molecule attracts the positive end of a neighboring molecule. Van der Waals attractions (Section 5.12) are present in all molecular solids. Because the total intermolecular attraction is small, molecular crystals usually have low melting temperatures. Furthermore, molecular substances are usually quite soft, because the molecules can be easily displaced from one site to another. Finally, they are nonconductors of electricity, because there is no easy way for an electron associated with one molecule to jump to another molecule. Most substances which exist as gases at room temperature form molecular solids at low temperature.

In an *ionic solid* the units that occupy the lattice points are positive and negative ions. For example, in Na_2SO_4 some of the lattice points are occupied by sodium ions, Na^+, and the others by sulfate ions, SO_4^{--}. The forces of attraction are those between a positive and a negative charge and are high. Hence ionic solids usually have fairly high melting points, well above room temperature. Sodium sulfate, for example, melts at 884°C. Also, ionic solids tend to be brittle and fairly hard, with great tendency to fracture by cleavage. In the solid state, the ions are generally not free to move; therefore, these ionic substances are poor conductors of electricity. However, when melted, they become good conductors.

In a *covalent solid* the positions are occupied by atoms, which share electrons with their neighbors. The covalent bonds extend in fixed directions, so that the result is a giant interlocking structure. The classic example of a covalent solid is diamond, in which each carbon atom is joined by pairs of shared electrons to four other carbon atoms, as shown in Figure 6.15. Each of these carbon atoms in turn is bound to four carbon atoms, etc., giving a giant three-dimensional molecule. In any solid of this type the bonds between the individual atoms are

	Molecular	Ionic	Covalent	Metallic
Units that occupy lattice points	Molecules	Positive ions Negative ions	Atoms	Positive ions in electron gas
Binding force	Van der Waals Dipole-dipole	Electrostatic attraction	Shared electrons	Electrical attraction between + ions and − electrons
Properties	Very soft Low melting point Volatile Good insulators	Quite hard and brittle Fairly high melting point Good insulators	Very hard Very high melting point Nonconductors	Hard or soft Moderate to very high melting point Good conductors
Examples	H_2 H_2O CO_2	NaCl KNO_3 Na_2SO_4 $MgAl_2O_4$	Diamond, C Carborundum, SiC Quartz, SiO_2	Na Cu Fe

6.14
Types of solids

6.15
Diamond structure

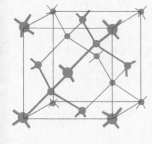

covalent and, usually, are quite strong. Substances with covalent structures generally have high melting points, are quite hard, and frequently are poor conductors of electricity.

In a *metallic solid* the points of the space lattice are occupied by positive ions. This array of positive ions is immersed in a cloud of highly mobile electrons derived from the outer atomic shells. In solid sodium, for example, sodium ions, arranged in a body-centered cubic pattern, are permeated by a cloud of electrons, or *electron gas,* as it is often called, arising from the contribution by each neutral sodium atom of its lone outermost electron. The electron gas belongs to the whole crystal. A metal like sodium is held together by the attraction between the positive ions and the cloud of negative electrons. In other cases, e.g., tungsten, there is covalent binding between the positive ions superimposed on the ion-to-electron gas attraction. Because electrons can wander at will throughout the metal, a metallic solid is characterized by high electrical and thermal conductivity. The other properties of metallic solids vary widely. Sodium, for example, has a low melting point; tungsten has a very high melting point. Sodium is soft and can be cut with a knife; tungsten is very hard.

What does the term "molecule" mean in regard to these various solids? In a molecular crystal, for example, solid CO_2, it is possible to distinguish discrete molecules. Each C atom has two relatively close O atoms as neighbors, and all other atoms are at considerably greater distances. In an ionic substance like sodium chloride this is not true. Each sodium ion is equally bound to its neighboring six chloride ions, as shown in Figure 6.7. These six chloride ions must be considered as belonging to the same aggregate as the original sodium ion. But each chloride ion in turn is bonded to six sodium ions, which must also be counted as part of the aggregate. Actually, all the ions in the whole crystal belong to the same aggregate, or giant molecule. A similar situation occurs in metallic and covalent crystals, in which all the ions or atoms are bound together as one giant aggregate. The term "molecule" is not useful for ionic, metallic, or covalent solids.

6.6 CRYSTAL ENERGIES

The magnitude of the attractive forces operative in crystals can be gauged by the crystal energy (also called lattice energy). The crystal energy is the amount of energy required to convert one mole of material from the solid state to a gaseous state in which the gaseous species are the same as the units that occupy the lattice points. In the case of a molecular solid the crystal energy corresponds to the energy of sublimation, i.e., the energy needed to produce one mole of molecular gas. In the case of an ionic solid the crystal energy is the energy needed to separate the positive and negative ions in one mole of solid to form a gas of ions. The crystal energy of a covalent solid is usually considered to be that needed to form an atomic gas. In the case of a metal the problem is somewhat different in that positive ions occupy

Ne	0.6	NaCl	184	C	170
CO_2	5.6	MgO	938	SiO_2	411
Cl_2	7.4	CaF_2	624	Na	25
H_2O	10.4	$MgAl_2O_4$	4745	W	200

6.16
Crystal energies,
kcal mole^{-1}

the original lattice points but the final gaseous state consists of neutral atoms.

Some typical values of crystal energies are listed in Figure 6.16. As can be seen, the values for the molecular substances are very low, indicating small intermolecular attractions in the solid. The largest values are generally found for ionic solids. These are especially interesting because they can be calculated in a rather simple way. Consider the case of NaCl. Each Na^+ is attracted by neighboring Cl^- but repelled by successive layers of Na^+. The farther-removed layers, although containing progressively more ions, contribute progressively less attraction or repulsion because of the rapid falloff of electrical interactions with increasing distance. The net effect of all the other ions on a particular ion in the NaCl structure can be represented by multiplying the energy of attraction between an Na^+ and Cl^- pair by 1.748.

As mentioned in Section 3.2, the energy of attraction between two hard-sphere ions of charges q_1 and q_2 at separation distance r is $14.4 q_1 q_2 / r$ electron volts. In solid NaCl the ionic charges equal unity and the internuclear spacing is 2.81Å, from which it follows the attraction energy is 14.4/2.81, or 5.12, ev. To convert electron volts per ion pair to kilocalories per mole requires multiplication by 23.06. This gives 118 kcal per mole of ion pairs. Putting these into the solid state increases the attraction energy to (118)(1.748), or 206, kcal mole^{-1}. This calculation is valid only for incompressible spheres with the electric charge at the center. Realizing that we are dealing with atoms that can be compressed and electrically distorted to produce van der Waals attractions, we need to correct for these effects. There are several ways of estimating the correction terms resulting from these effects, but they all agree that the simple calculation above is about 10% too high. When the 206 kcal is reduced by this 10% factor, the agreement with the experimental value of 184 kcal is not bad.

6.7 SOLID-STATE DEFECTS

The preceding discussion concerned only ideal crystals. An ideal crystal is one which can be completely described by the unit cell; i.e., it contains no *lattice defects*. There are several important kinds of lattice defects. One, called *lattice vacancies,* arises if some of the lattice points are unoccupied. Another, called *lattice interstitials,* arises

(a)   (b)

6.17
Lattice defects:
(a) vacancies in NaCl,
(b) misplaced Ag$^+$ in AgBr

if atoms occupy positions between lattice points. All crystals are imperfect to a slight extent and contain defects. For example, in NaCl some of the sodium ions and chloride ions are missing from the regular pattern (Figure 6.17a). In silver bromide, AgBr, some of the silver ions are missing from their regular positions and are found squeezed in between other ions (Figure 6.17b). Lattice vacancies occur to some extent in all crystals; their presence helps to explain how diffusion and ionic conductivity can occur in the solid state. Lattice interstitials are considerably less probable; they occur when small positive ions can move into positions between the normal planes of large negative ions. The presence of interstitial Ag$^+$ in AgBr is believed to be important for the formation of a photographic image when AgBr crystals are exposed to light.

Another kind of defect commonly found in solids, whose importance is only just now being recognized, is the *dislocation*. Dislocations are of two general types: *edge dislocations* and *screw dislocations*. These are shown in Figure 6.18. A simple way to visualize an edge dislocation is as resulting from having a plane of atoms inserted only part way into a crystal. In a screw dislocation there is a line of atoms which represents

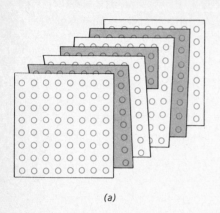

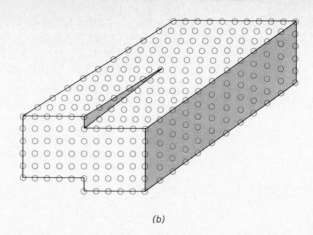

(a)   (b)

6.18
Dislocations: (a) edge
dislocation, (b) screw
dislocation

an axis about which the crystal planes are warped to give an effect similar to the threads of a screw. In the latter case, what would be a round trip about the screw axis results in a displacement to the crystal plane below. The points where edge or screw dislocation lines emerge to the surface of a crystal represent points of strain and enhanced chemical reactivity. Etching of metal crystals by acids occurs preferentially at such points. Current research aimed at producing materials more resistant to corrosive attack and of greater mechanical strength involves elimination of dislocations and other solid-state defects.

In addition to the defects arising from structural imperfections are defects of a more chemical nature in that they are associated with the presence of chemical impurities. Such impurities can drastically change the properties of materials, and hence their controlled introduction is being exploited in producing new materials with desirable combinations of properties. As an example of how properties can be modified by impurities, it might be noted that the addition of less than 0.1% $CaCl_2$ to NaCl can raise the conductivity by 10000 times. This comes about as follows. In the mixed crystal the Cl^- ion lattice is unchanged, but the Ca^{++} ions occupy positions on the Na^+ lattice. Because of the requirement for electrical neutrality, each insertion of Ca^{++} for Na^+ leads to creation of a lattice vacancy. The vacancy allows for ion mobility and hence increased conductivity.

A more practical utilization of impurity defects is made for germanium and silicon crystals. The electrical conductivity of these group IV elements, in the pure state, is extremely low. However, on addition of trace amounts of elements from either group III or group V, the conductivity is greatly enhanced. Both germanium and silicon have the diamond structure, shown in Figure 6.15. Each atom is bonded to four neighbors by four σ bonds. These require all four outer electrons of each group IV atom. In the pure elements Ge and Si there are no conduction electrons (except at very high temperatures). When, for example, a group V element—P, As, Sb, or Bi—is substituted for a Ge atom, an extra electron above that required for forming four covalent bonds is introduced. This extra electron can act something like a conduction electron in metals, and hence an arsenic-doped germanium crystal exhibits marked conductivity. If, on the other hand, a group III element—B, Al, Ga, or In—is substituted for a Ge atom, an electron deficiency in the covalent-bonding network is introduced. Such an electron vacancy is not confined to the impurity atom site, but can move through the structure as other electrons move in to fill it. Thus, the introduction of electron vacancies, or "holes" as they are sometimes called, by doping Ge with group III atoms allows the electron motion necessary for increased conductivity.

As will be discussed in Section 23.2, the conductivity of semiconductors generally increases as the temperature is raised, which is opposite to the behavior of metals. Impurity-doped germanium and silicon act as semiconductors, because there is weak binding of the excess electron or the hole to the impurity center responsible for it. Additional energy, as supplied by a temperature rise, is needed to free the electron or hole sufficiently for conductivity. Semiconductors in which electric transport is mainly by "excess" electrons are called n type (n for negative), and those in which electric transport is mainly by "holes" are called p type (p for positive). It must be emphasized that both n- and p-type semiconductors are electrically neutral. The electron "excess" or "deficiency" is with respect to that required for covalent bonding, not with respect to electrical neutrality. To illustrate, substitution of As for Ge introduces not only an additional electron but also an additional unit of positive nuclear charge.

An interesting application of impurity semiconductors results from combination of n- and p-type materials to form a junction, the so-called n-p junction. This device can pass electric current more easily in one direction than in the reverse, and hence it can act as a rectifier for converting alternating current to direct current. Figure 6.19 shows schematically why there should be a difference in the ease of passing current in the two directions. The left side of the junction is n type, and the minuses represent the extra electrons arising from the group V impurity centers; the right side of the junction is p type, and the pluses represent the electron holes arising from the group III impurity centers. When an external voltage is applied (as shown in Figure 6.19a) so as to favor motion of electrons from left to right and motion of holes from right to left, conductivity readily occurs. At the interface between the n- and p-type zones, electrons coming from the left annihilate holes coming from the right. Conductivity does not stop, because the external voltage acts to supply more n carriers on the left and p carriers on the right. On the other hand, when the external voltage is reversed (as shown in Figure 6.19b), so as to separate the n and p carriers, conductivity stops. There is no way in which new carriers can be regenerated at the n-p interface.

Finally, we might note as a special kind of solid-state defect the deviations from stoichiometry, or the formation of nonstoichiometric compounds. Classic examples include $Cu_{1.97}S$, $MnO_{1.95}$, TiO_x (where x can range from 0.85 to 1.18), and Na_xWO_3 (where x can range from 0.3 to 0.98 without change of structure). In these nonstoichiometric

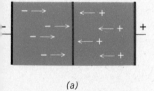

(a)

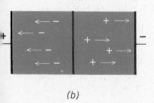

(b)

6.19
The n-p junction with two directions, (a) and (b), of external voltage

materials there are generally vacancies that can be populated by an excess or deficiency of one element over what is required by simple rules of stoichiometry. For example, TiO is cubic with a rock-salt structure of Ti^{++} and O^{--} except that 15% of each kind of site is vacant. Addition of either element will change the Ti/O ratio by 15% in either direction. One striking result of deviations from stoichiometry is the change in color that occurs, for example, in sodium halide crystals heated in Na vapor. Crystals of various colors result as the Na-to-halide ratio increases to values such as 1.001. It is believed that the Na enters the structure of NaX to form an Na^+ ion that occupies a normal positive-ion site plus an electron that is trapped at a negative-ion site. Such trapped electrons are sometimes referred to as F centers (from the German *Farben*, or color).

QUESTIONS

6.1 Unit cells How many atoms or the equivalent are there per unit cell of the following: (*a*) simple cubic, (*b*) body-centered cubic, (*c*) face-centered cubic, (*d*) hexagonal close-packed?

6.2 Diffusion Discuss the role of defects in solid-state diffusion.

6.3 Unit cell CsCl has a structure in which eight ions of one type form a cube centered on one ion of the other type. (*a*) Describe a unit cell for the structure. (*b*) Tell what the positive-ion lattice and negative-ion lattice separately look like.

6.4 X rays At what principal angle should diffraction occur when copper radiation ($\lambda = 1.54$ Å) interacts with lattice planes that are 1.54 Å apart?

6.5 Crystal energies KF has the rock-salt structure. By using 2.67 Å for the internuclear separation, calculate the crystal energy for this material. Include a 10% correction for the repulsion. (The experimental value is 192 kcal mole^{-1}.)

6.6 X rays A given crystal, when irradiated with copper radiation ($\lambda = 1.54$ Å), gives diffraction at angles of 10, 15, and 25°. To what interplanar spacings d can these be attributed, assuming $n = 1$ in each case?

6.7 Defects Predict whether each of the following impurities leads to an *n*- or *p*-type semiconductor: (*a*) Ga in Ge, (*b*) B in Si, (*c*) Si in Ge, (*d*) B in GaP.

6.8 Forces Discuss the role of repulsive forces in the formation of crystalline solids.

6.9 Close-packing Show that cubic close-packing of hard spheres fills up 74.06% of the available space.

6.10 Unit cells Suppose you have a cubic unit cell with A atoms at the corners, B atoms at the face centers, and a C atom in the body-centered position. What is its simplest formula? How many nearest neighbors does each kind of atom have?

6.11 Density   A particular solid has a structure in which W atoms are located at cube corners, O atoms at the centers of cube edges, and Na atoms at cube centers. The cube edge is 3.86 Å. (*a*) What is the formula of this material? (*b*) What is its theoretical density? (*c*) What happens to (*a*) and (*b*) if Na is extracted from half of its normal sites and the cube edge shrinks to 3.82 Å?

6.12 Spinels   Unlike Fe_3O_4, which is a good conductor, Co_3O_4 is a poor conductor. In terms of the spinel structure, suggest a possible explanation.

6.13 Defects   The observed density of crystals is generally less than calculated from X-ray spacings of atoms because of lattice vacancies. How would this influence the determination of the Avogadro number by the X-ray method (page 79)?

6.14 Defects   Platinum has a face-centered cubic structure in which the unit-cell edge length is 3.914 Å. Its observed density is 21.45 g cc^{-1}. Calculate the apparent fraction of vacant sites.

6.15 Crystal energies   NaCl and MgO have the same, rock-salt structure. The internuclear spacings are 2.81 and 2.10 Å, respectively. (*a*) What ratio of crystal energies would you expect for these two substances? (*b*) Compare your value with that obtained from Figure 6.16. Show that van der Waals attraction could account for the direction of the discrepancy.

6.16 Surface   Atoms on the surface of a crystal are likely to have properties somewhat different from those of interior atoms. What size cubic crystals, consisting of one kind of spheres (radius 2.0 Å) in cubic close-packed array, would be needed to assure that less than 0.1% of the atoms are on the surface?

6.17 Close-packing   Compare tetrahedral and octahedral holes by calculating the sizes of hard spheres that will just fit into each kind of hole as formed by spheres of unit radius.

6.18 Close-packing   For close-packed spheres of unit radius, what is the distance between the layers as defined by sphere centers?

6.19 Rock-salt structure   (*a*) Assume that, in the rock-salt structure, the positive and negative ions are hard spheres in contact with each other. What ratio of radii is needed so that the larger negative ions will also be in contact with each other? (*b*) Under the conditions specified in (*a*), calculate the fraction of the unit-cell volume that is empty.

ANSWERS

6.5 196 kcal mole^{-1} 6.6 4.43 Å, 2.98 Å, 1.82 Å   6.14 0.0074
6.16 8.5 × 10^{-5} cm on edge   6.17 0.225 and 0.414 Å   6.18 1.633
6.19 (*a*) 0.414:1 (*b*) 0.207

7 liquids and changes of state

The gaseous state (because of independence of molecules) and the solid state (because of characteristic order) are considerably better understood than the liquid state. In the liquid state the close spacing of molecules leads to large intermolecular forces that are strongly dependent on the detailed nature of the molecules involved. Because the molecules are not fixed in arrangements of repetitive order, determination of the structures of liquids is very difficult. There is, nevertheless, vestigial order in liquids which is intermediate between that of the solid and gaseous states. In this chapter we shall consider not only the properties of liquids but also the changes of state that relate liquids to solids and gases.

7.1 PROPERTIES OF LIQUIDS

Liquids are practically incompressible. Unlike gases, there is little or no change in volume when the pressure on a liquid is changed. Theory accounts for this by the assumption that the amount of free space between the molecules of a liquid is almost a minimum. Any attempt to compress the liquid meets with resistance as the electron cloud of one molecule repels the electron cloud of an adjacent molecule.

Liquids maintain their volume no matter what the shape or size of the container. A 10-ml sample of liquid occupies a 10-ml volume, whether it is placed in a small beaker or in a large flask, whereas a gas spreads out to fill the whole volume accessible to it. Gases do not maintain their volume, because the molecules are essentially independent of each other and can move into any space available. In liquids the molecules are close together, so that mutual attractions are strong. Consequently, the molecules are clustered together.

Liquids have no characteristic shape. A liquid sample assumes the shape of the bottom of its container. The assumption is that there are no fixed positions for the molecules. The molecules are free to slide over each other in order to occupy positions of the lowest possible potential energy with respect to gravitational attraction by the earth.

Liquids diffuse, but slowly. When a drop of ink is released in water, there is at first a rather sharp boundary between the ink cloud and the water. Eventually the color diffuses throughout the rest of the liquid. In gases diffusion is much more rapid. Diffusion is able to occur because molecules have kinetic energy and move from one place to another. In a liquid molecules do not move far before colliding with neighboring molecules. The mean free path, i.e., the average distance between collisions, is short. Eventually each molecule of a liquid does migrate from one side of its container to the other, but it has to suffer many billions of collisions in doing so. In gases there is less obstruction to the migrating molecule. Because a gas is mostly empty space, the mean free path is much longer. Hence the molecules of one gas can mix rather quickly with those of another.

Liquids evaporate from open containers. Although there are attractive forces which hold the molecules together, the molecules with kinetic energy great enough to overcome attractive forces can escape into the gas phase. In any collection any given molecule does not have the same energy all the time. There is perpetually an exchange of energy between colliding molecules. The collection might start out with all molecules of the same energy, but this situation would not persist long. Two or more molecules may simultaneously collide with a third molecule. Molecule 3 now has not only its initial energy but possibly some extra energy received from its neighbors. Molecule 3 is now a molecule which is higher than average in kinetic energy. If it happens to be near the surface of the liquid, it may be able to overcome the attractive forces of neighbors and go off into the gas phase.

Figure 7.1 shows a typical energy distribution for the molecules of a sample of liquid at a given temperature. The curve is quite similar to

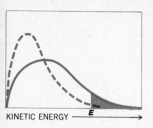

KINETIC ENERGY ⟶ E

7.1
Energy distribution in a
liquid

the one given previously for a gas. The value marked E corresponds to the minimum kinetic energy required by a molecule to overcome attractive forces and escape from this liquid. All the molecules in the shaded area of the curve have enough energy to overcome attractive forces. These are the molecules that have the possibility of escaping, provided that they are close enough to the surface. If these highly energetic molecules leave the liquid, the average kinetic energy of those left behind is lower. That is because each molecule that escapes carries with it more than an average amount of energy, part of which it uses in working against the attractive forces. Since the remaining molecules have lower average kinetic energy, the temperature drops. Evaporation is therefore accompanied by cooling.

When a liquid evaporates from a noninsulated container such as a beaker, the temperature of the liquid cannot fall very far before there is an appreciable heat flow from the surroundings into the liquid. If the rate of evaporation is not too great, this flow of heat is sufficient to supply the energy required for evaporation. As a consequence, the temperature of a liquid remains that of the room, even though the liquid is evaporating. Eventually, the liquid disappears. When evaporation proceeds from a container insulated to reduce heat flow, the heat flow from the surroundings is less and the temperature of the liquid drops. An example of such an insulated container is the Dewar flask (or vacuum bottle). The essential feature of the Dewar flask is double-walled construction with vacuum between the walls. The vacuum jacket acts as an insulator to retard heat flow into or out of the container.

When a liquid evaporates from a Dewar flask, the flow of heat from the surroundings may not be fast enough to compensate for the evaporation. The temperature of the liquid drops; the average kinetic energy of the molecules decreases; and the rate of evaporation diminishes until the heat flow into the liquid just equals the heat required for evaporation. At the lower temperature the distribution of the kinetic energies is shifted to the left, as shown by the dotted line in Figure 7.1. As the temperature decreases, the fraction of energetic molecules decreases and the rate of evaporation decreases. The liquid level stays nearly constant. The temperature now stays constant but at a value which may be considerably lower than the original temperature. Liquid air, an extremely volatile liquid, remains in an open Dewar flask at approximately $-190°C$ for many hours.

7.2 EQUILIBRIUM VAPOR PRESSURE

When a bell jar is placed over a beaker of evaporating liquid, as shown in Figure 7.2, the liquid level drops for a while and then becomes constant. This can be explained as follows: Molecules escape from the liquid into the gas, or vapor, phase. After escaping, they are confined to a limited space. As the molecules accumulate in the space above the liquid, there is an increasing chance that in their random motion some of them will return to the liquid. Eventually, a situation is established in which molecules are returning to the liquid just as fast as other mole-

Liquids and changes
of state
153

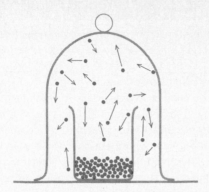

cules are leaving it. At this point the liquid level no longer drops, because the number of molecules evaporating per second is equal
to the number of molecules condensing per second. A condition
in which two changes exactly oppose each other is referred to as
dynamic equilibrium. Although the system is not at a state of rest,
there is no net change in the system. The amount of liquid in the
beaker stays constant; the concentration of molecules in the vapor
above the liquid is constant. A particular molecule spends part of its
time in the liquid and part in the vapor phase. As molecules pass from
liquid to gas, other molecules move from gas to liquid, keeping the
number of molecules in each phase constant.

The molecules which are in the vapor exert a pressure. At equilibrium, this pressure is characteristic of the liquid. It is known as
the *equilibrium vapor pressure.* As the term implies, it is the *pressure
exerted by a vapor when in equilibrium with its liquid.* The magnitude
of the equilibrium vapor pressure depends (1) on the nature of the
liquid and (2) on its temperature.

1. The nature of the liquid is involved, since each liquid has characteristic attractive forces between its molecules. Molecules which have
large mutual attraction have a small tendency to escape into the vapor
phase. Such a liquid has a low equilibrium vapor pressure. Liquids composed of molecules with small mutual attraction have a high escaping
tendency and therefore a high equilibrium vapor pressure.

2. As the temperature of a liquid is raised, the average kinetic
energy of the molecules of the liquid increases. The number of high-
energy molecules capable of escaping also becomes larger, so that the
equilibrium vapor pressure increases.

There are various devices for measuring equilibrium vapor pressure,
one of which is shown in Figure 7.3. It consists of a barometer set up
in the usual manner. The difference between the upper mercury level
and the lower mercury level represents the atmospheric pressure.
Above the mercury there is a vacuum. By squeezing on the rubber
bulb, a drop of liquid can be ejected into the mercury. Since practically
any liquid is less dense than mercury, it will float to the top of
the mercury, where enough of it will evaporate to establish its equilibrium vapor pressure. This vapor pressure pushes down the mercury

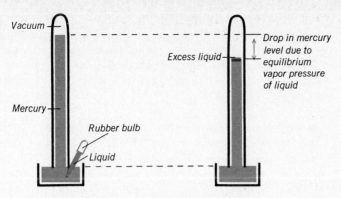

column. (The excess liquid also acts to push down the mercury column, but this is a negligible effect, especially when there is little excess.)

The extent to which the mercury level is depressed gives a quantitative measure of the vapor pressure of the liquid. At 20°C, water, H_2O, has an equilibrium vapor pressure of 17.5 torr; carbon tetrachloride, CCl_4, 91.0 torr; and chloroform, $CHCl_3$, 160 torr. These values of the vapor pressure give an idea of the escaping tendencies of molecules from the various liquids. In chloroform, for example, the attractive forces between molecules are smaller than in water, and chloroform evaporates to give a higher vapor pressure than water.

By repeating the above experiment at different temperatures, it is possible to determine vapor pressure of liquids as a function of temperature. Appendix 5 is a table showing the results for water in great de-

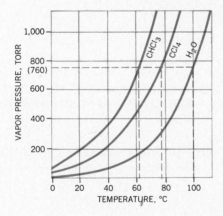

tail. The general behavior of water, carbon tetrachloride, and chloroform is shown by the graph in Figure 7.4. The vertical scale represents the vapor pressure and the horizontal scale the temperature. As the temperature increases, the vapor pressure rises, first slowly and then more steeply, until at high temperatures it is rising almost vertically. (The curve continues to the critical temperature. It does not go beyond the critical temperature, because above the critical temperature the liquid cannot exist.) A curve of this shape is frequently better presented by a different plot in which the logarithm of the pressure (Appendix 2.2) is plotted against the reciprocal temperature, as shown in Figure 7.5. It should be noted that, because of the reciprocal relation, high temperature is at the left of the figure and low temperature at the right. The analytic expression describing these curves is

$$\log p = \frac{-\Delta H'}{4.58T} + C$$

where p is the vapor pressure, T is the temperature, $\Delta H'$ is the heat required to transform one mole of liquid to the ideal-gas state,* and C is a constant dependent on the liquid and units used for expressing pressure. The number 4.58 comes from (2.303)(1.987), where the number 2.303 arises from using base 10 logarithms instead of natural logarithms and the number 1.987 is the value of the universal gas constant R in units of calories per mole-degree. Consistent with this, $\Delta H'$ is given in calories per mole. In a graph such as Figure 7.5 the slope of the line is $-\Delta H'/4.58$. The slope will be constant—i.e., the line will be straight—so long as $\Delta H'$ has a constant value independent of change in temperature. This is generally true so long as the temperature range is not too large.

The constant C can be eliminated by subtracting the above equation for a liquid at a given temperature from that for the same liquid at another temperature. By denoting these conditions as T_1, T_2 and the corresponding vapor pressures as p_1, p_2, respectively, we get

$$\log p_1 - \log p_2 = \frac{-\Delta H'}{4.58T_1} + \frac{\Delta H'}{4.58T_2}$$

$$\log \frac{p_1}{p_2} = \frac{\Delta H'}{4.58} \left(\frac{1}{T_2} - \frac{1}{T_1} \right)$$

By use of this last equation, sometimes called the Clausius-Clapeyron equation, it is possible to evaluate $\Delta H'$ by substituting in the measured values of p_1 and p_2 at T_1 and T_2. Conversely, if $\Delta H'$ were known, the vapor pressure p_1 at one temperature T_1 could be calculated from a measured vapor pressure p_2 at some other temperature T_2.

EXAMPLE 1

The vapor pressure of carbon tetrachloride is 100 torr at 23°C and 400 torr at 58°C. Calculate the $\Delta H'$ in this temperature range.

$$p_1 = 100 \text{ torr} \qquad \text{at} \qquad T_1 = 296°\text{K}$$

$$p_2 = 400 \text{ torr} \qquad \text{at} \qquad T_2 = 331°\text{K}$$

$$\log \frac{100}{400} = \frac{\Delta H'}{4.58} \left(\frac{1}{331} - \frac{1}{296} \right)$$

$$\Delta H' = 7700 \text{ cal mole}^{-1}$$

* The prime on ΔH emphasizes two assumptions: (1) the vapor is ideal; (2) ΔH does not change with temperature. If both these assumptions are valid, straight-line plots are obtained as in Figure 7.5. If either assumption is a poor one, then the ΔH will not generally agree with the directly measured heat of vaporization.

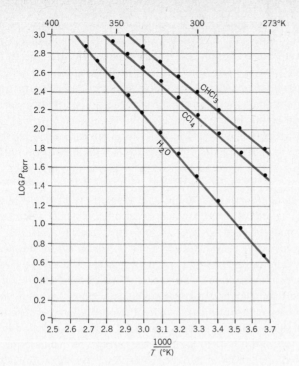

7.5
Plot of log vapor pressure
vs. reciprocal temperature

EXAMPLE 2

Given that $\Delta H' = 7700$ cal mole^{-1} for carbon tetrachloride and that
the vapor pressure is 100 torr at 23°C, calculate the vapor pressure
expected at 38°C.

$$p_1 = 100 \text{ torr} \qquad \text{at} \qquad T_1 = 296°\text{K}$$

$$p_2 = \quad ? \quad \text{torr} \qquad \text{at} \qquad T_2 = 311°\text{K}$$

$$\log \frac{100}{p_2} = \frac{7700}{4.58}\left(\frac{1}{311} - \frac{1}{296}\right)$$

$$p_2 = 190 \text{ torr}$$

7.3 BOILING POINTS

Boiling is a special case of vaporization; it is the passage of a liquid from
an open vessel into the vapor state through the formation of bubbles.*
A liquid is said to boil at its *boiling point* (abbreviated bp), which is the
*temperature at which the vapor pressure of the liquid is equal to the
prevailing atmospheric pressure.* At the boiling point, the vapor pressure of the liquid is high enough that the atmosphere can be pushed

Liquids and changes
of state

157

* When water is heated in an open container, it is usually observed that, as the liquid is
warmed, tiny bubbles gradually form at first and then, at a higher temperature, violent bubbling
commences. The first bubbling should not be confused with boiling. The tiny bubbles are
due to the expulsion of the air usually dissolved in water.

aside. Therefore, bubbles of vapor can form in the interior of the liquid, allowing vaporization to occur at any point in the liquid. In general, a molecule can evaporate only if two requirements are met: It must have enough kinetic energy, and it must be close enough to a liquid-vapor boundary. At the boiling point, bubbling enormously increases the liquid-vapor boundary, and therefore it is necessary only that molecules have enough kinetic energy to escape from the liquid. Any heat added to a liquid at its boiling point is used to give more molecules sufficient energy to escape; hence, the average kinetic energy of molecules remaining in the liquid cannot increase. The temperature of a pure boiling liquid is therefore constant.

The boiling point of a liquid depends on the pressure to which the liquid is subjected. For instance, when the atmospheric pressure is 700 torr, water boils at 97.7°C; at 760 torr, it boils at 100°C. To avoid ambiguity, it is necessary to define a *standard,* or *normal, boiling point.* The normal boiling point is the temperature at which the vapor pressure of a liquid is equal to one standard atmosphere, or 760 torr. The normal boiling point is the one usually listed. It can be determined from the vapor-pressure curve by finding the temperature which corresponds to 1 atm pressure. Figure 7.4 shows that the normal boiling point of water is 100°C, that of carbon tetrachloride is 76.8°C, and that of chloroform is 61°C. In general, the higher the normal boiling point, the greater must be the attractive forces between the molecules of a liquid.*

The change of boiling point with pressure can be computed from the Clausius-Clapeyron equation if we know either $\Delta H'$ and the normal boiling point or the vapor pressures at two temperatures near the boiling point. The following example illustrates how the boiling point of water can be calculated for an altitude of 8500 ft, where the atmospheric pressure is about three-fourths of a standard atmosphere.

EXAMPLE 3

Given that $\Delta H'$ of water at 100°C is 9700 cal mole^{-1}. Calculate the boiling point of water at a pressure of 0.750 atm.

$$p_1 = 1.00 \text{ atm} \quad \text{at} \quad T_1 = 373°K$$

$$p_2 = 0.750 \text{ atm} \quad \text{at} \quad T_2 = \quad ?$$

$$\log \frac{1.00}{0.750} = \frac{9700}{4.58}\left(\frac{1}{T_2} - \frac{1}{373}\right)$$

$$T_2 = 365°K, \text{ or } 92°C$$

---

*It is usually observed that, in a series of similar compounds, such as CH_4, C_2H_6, and C_3H_8, the normal boiling point is highest for the compound of greatest molecular mass. Although it is tempting to explain a high boiling point in terms of large gravitational attraction between heavy molecules, gravitational attraction in reality is small. A more reasonable explanation is that heavy molecules usually contain more electrons than light molecules and hence have greater van der Waals attractions.

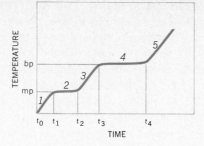

7.4 HEATING CURVES

As noted above, the addition of heat to a liquid at its boiling point does not raise the temperature of the liquid, but is used to convert liquid to gas. A similar phenomenon occurs at the melting point of a solid, where the added heat is used to convert solid to liquid. At temperatures other than these, there will be increases of temperature accompanying the addition of heat. Why should there be a difference? To answer this, we look at the general problem of adding heat to a sample of substance that starts at absolute zero as an ordered solid, melts to give the less-ordered liquid, and finally boils to produce the completely disordered gaseous state. The temperature variations which accompany changes of states are represented in Figure 7.6. The curve shown is a *heating curve* corresponding to the uniform addition of heat to an initially solid substance. Since heat is added at a constant rate, distance on the time axis is also a measure of the amount of added heat.

At time t_0 the temperature is absolute zero. As heat is added, each particle vibrates back and forth about a lattice point, which thus represents the center of this motion. As more heat is added, the vibration becomes greater. Though no change is visible, because the amplitude of the vibration is so small, the crystal progressively becomes slightly less ordered. The heat added increases the kinetic motion of the particles. Since temperature measures average kinetic energy, temperature rises along portion 1 of Figure 7.6. This continues until the melting point of the substance is reached.

At the melting point (abbreviated mp) the vibration of particles is so vigorous that any added heat serves to loosen binding forces between neighboring particles. Consequently, from time t_1 to t_2, added heat goes not to increase the average kinetic energy, but to increase the potential energy of the particles. Potential energy is increased because work is done against attractive forces. During this period, there is no change in average kinetic energy, and so the substance stays at the same temperature. From t_1 to t_2 the amount of solid gradually decreases, and the amount of liquid increases. The *temperature at which the solid and liquid coexist* is defined as the *melting point* of the substance.

The amount of heat necessary to melt one mole of solid is called the *molar heat of fusion*. It gives a measure of the difference in heat content between the solid and liquid states and is equal to the amount of heat energy that must be added to overcome the extra attraction that exists in the solid between the particles at the lattice sites. The heat of fusion of NaCl is 7.25 kcal mole^{-1}, and that of H_2O is 1.44 kcal mole^{-1}, values that reflect the greater attractive forces in NaCl.

Eventually (at time t_2), sufficient heat is added to tear all the particles from the crystal structure. Along portion 3 of the curve, added heat increases the average kinetic energy of the particles, and the temperature of the liquid rises. This continues until the boiling point (bp) is reached. At the boiling point added heat is used to overcome the attraction of one particle for its neighbors in the liquid. Along portion 4 of the curve there is an increase in the potential energy of the particles but no change in their average kinetic energy. From time t_3 to t_4, liquid converts to gas. Finally, after all the liquid has been converted to gas, added heat raises the kinetic energy of the particles, as shown by the rising temperature along portion 5.

The amount of heat necessary to vaporize one mole of liquid is called the *molar heat of vaporization*. This quantity gives a measure of the attractive forces characteristic of the liquid. The heat of vaporization of water is 9.72 kcal mole^{-1}, and that of chloroform is 7.04 kcal mole^{-1}. These values support the notion that attractive forces between water molecules are greater than those between chloroform molecules.

7.5 COOLING CURVES

The *cooling curve* results when heat is removed at a uniform rate from a substance. For a pure substance that is initially a gas, the temperature as a function of time is shown in Figure 7.7. As heat is removed from the gas, the temperature of the gas drops along the line marked g. During this time, the average kinetic energy of the gas particles must decrease in order to compensate for the removal of energy to the outside. This slowing down proceeds until the particles are so sluggish that the attractive forces become dominant.

At t_1 the particles coalesce to form a liquid. In the liquefaction process, particles leave the gas and enter the liquid state. Since energy is required to take a particle from the liquid to the gas state, the reverse process, in which a particle is taken from the gas to the liquid, releases energy. This decrease of potential energy on condensation supplies heat, which compensates for that being removed from the system. Thus, as liquefaction proceeds, the temperature does not fall, and the particles do not slow down in their motion. As a result, the gas and liquid are both at the same temperature, and the average kinetic energy of the particles in both phases is the same. From time t_1 to t_2 the temperature remains constant at T_1, the *condensation,* or *liquefaction, temperature*.

At time t_2 all the gas particles have condensed into the liquid state. Further removal of energy from the system causes the particles to slow down. As the average kinetic energy decreases, the temperature drops, as shown, along the line marked l. This drop continues until t_3, when the liquid begins to convert to solid.

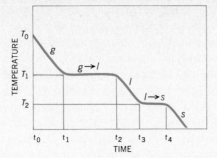

In crystallization the particles line up in a definite geometric pattern, and as they go from the liquid state to the solid state, their freedom of motion is diminished. As each particle moves into position to form the crystal structure, the potential energy of the particle drops. The removal of heat energy to the outside is compensated for by the energy available from this decrease in potential energy. The average kinetic energy of the particle stays constant during the crystallization process. At the crystallization temperature the motion of the particles is not slower when the particles are in the solid than it is when they are in the liquid, but it is a more restricted motion. From time t_3 to t_4 the temperature remains constant as the liquid converts to solid. When all the particles have crystallized, further removal of heat drops the temperature, as shown, along the final part s of the curve.

The cooling curve is just the reverse of the warming curve. The temperature at which gas converts to liquid (liquefaction point) is the same as the temperature at which liquid converts to gas (boiling point). Similarly, the temperature at which liquid converts to solid (freezing point) is the same as the temperature at which solid converts to liquid (melting point).

7.6 SUPERCOOLING

Most cooling curves are not quite so simple as the one in Figure 7.7. The complication usually occurs on the portion of the cooling curve corresponding to the transition from liquid to solid. Instead of following the dashed flat portion, as shown in Figure 7.8, the temperature follows the dip. The liquid does not crystallize at the freezing point, but instead *supercools*. Supercooling arises in the following way: The particles of a liquid have little recognizable pattern and move around in a disordered manner. At the freezing point they should line up in characteristic crystalline arrangement, but only by chance do they start crystallizing correctly. Often they do not snap into the correct pattern immediately, and when heat continues to be removed from the system without crystallization's occurring, the temperature falls below the freezing point. Particles continue moving through various patterns until by accident they hit on the right one. Once this pattern has been built up to sufficient size, other particles rapidly crystallize on it. When a multi-

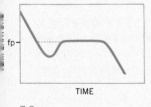

Liquids and changes
of state

tude of particles crystallize simultaneously, enough potential energy is converted to kinetic energy to *heat up* the sample. The temperature actually increases until it coincides with the freezing-point temperature. From there on, the behavior is normal.

Supercooling may be reduced by two methods. The most frequent is to stir the liquid as vigorously as possible. This apparently increases the chance of forming the right crystal pattern. A second method involves the introduction of a seed crystal on which further crystallization can occur, thereby perpetuating the proper structure.

Some substances never crystallize in cooling experiments, but instead remain permanently in the *undercooled,* or *supercooled, state.* Such substances are called *glasses,* after their most famous example. Glasses owe their existence to the fact that supercooled atoms may be trapped in a disordered arrangement typical of liquids because the atoms have relatively so little kinetic energy that they are not able to move into an ordered array.

Supercooled liquids are quite common. They include, besides glass, many plastics, such as polyethylene, vinyl polymers, and Teflon. They have many of the properties of solids and are not what we call fluid. However, the X-ray pictures of glasses are quite different from the X-ray pictures of solids. As discussed previously, an X-ray picture of a solid gives an orderly pattern of spots corresponding to diffraction from different planes of atoms. In the supercooled liquid there are no planes of atoms from which to get diffraction. Instead of a spot pattern, the X-ray pictures of a supercooled liquid show concentric rings, like those for liquids. The existence of these rings indicates that there is a certain amount of order, but it is far from perfect. Another indication that glasses are not true solids is their behavior on being broken. Instead of showing cleavage with formation of flat faces and characteristic angles between faces, glasses break to give conchoidal fractures such as are observed on the chips of a broken bottle.

7.7 SOLID-GAS EQUILIBRIUM

As in a liquid, particles of a solid can escape into the vapor phase to establish vapor pressure. In a solid all the particles do not have the same energy. There is a distribution of energy in which most of the particles have energy near the average but some have less while others have more. Those particles which at any one time are of higher than average energy and are near the surface can overcome the attractive forces of their neighbors and escape into the vapor phase. If the solid is confined in a closed container, eventually there will be enough particles in the vapor phase that the rate of escape is equal to the rate of return. A dynamic equilibrium is set up; in it there is an equilibrium vapor pressure characteristic of the solid. Since the escaping tendency of particles depends on the magnitude of the intermolecular forces, the equilibrium vapor pressure differs from one substance to another. If the attractive forces in the solid are small, as in the case of a molec-

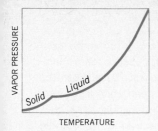

VAPOR PRESSURE

TEMPERATURE

7.9
Temperature variation of
vapor pressure

ular crystal, the escaping tendency is great, and vapor pressure is high. In the ionic crystal the binding forces are usually large, and the vapor pressure is low.

The vapor pressure of solids also depends on temperature. The higher the temperature, the more energetic the particles and the more easily they can escape. The more that escape, the higher the vapor pressure. Quantitative measurements of the vapor pressure of solids can be made in the same way as for liquids. Figure 7.9 shows how the vapor pressure of a given substance changes with temperature. At absolute zero the particles of a solid have no escaping tendency, so the vapor pressure is zero. As the temperature is raised, the vapor pressure rises. It rarely gets to be very high before the solid melts. Above the melting point the vapor-pressure curve is just that of the liquid.

In Figure 7.9 any point along the portion of the curve marked Solid corresponds to an equilibrium between vapor and solid. The number of particles leaving the solid is equal to the number returning. When the temperature is raised, more particles shake loose from the crystal per unit time than return. This causes a net increase in the concentration of particles in the vapor phase, which in turn causes an increased rate of condensation to the solid. Eventually, equilibrium is reestablished at the new temperature.

The behavior of an equilibrium system when it is upset by an external action is the subject of the famous *principle of Le Chatelier,* first published in 1884. Le Chatelier stated that, *if a stress is applied to a system at equilibrium, then the system readjusts, if possible, to reduce the stress.* Raising the temperature of a solid-vapor equilibrium system amounts to applying to the system a stress in the form of added heat. Since the conversion from solid to gas is endothermic (uses up heat)

$$\text{Solid} + \text{heat} \rightleftharpoons \text{gas}$$

the stress of added heat can be absorbed by converting some of the solid to gas.

At the point where the vapor-pressure curve of a liquid intersects that of the solid (i.e., where vapor pressure of the solid equals vapor pressure of the liquid), there is simultaneously an equilibrium between solid and gas, between liquid and gas, and between solid and liquid. This point of intersection at which *solid, liquid, and gas coexist in equilibrium* is called the *triple point.* Every substance has a characteristic triple point fixed by the nature of the attractive forces between its particles. The triple-point temperature of water is 273.16°K (or 0.01°C), and the triple-point pressure is 4.58 torr. It should be noted that the triple-point temperature of water is not quite the same as the normal melting point, which is 273.15°K. This difference comes about because the normal melting point is defined as the melting point at one atmosphere pressure and because the melting point changes as pressure is changed. At the triple point the only pressure exerted is the vapor pressure of the substance.

Liquids and changes
of state

163

The relation between the solid, liquid, and gaseous states of a given substance as a function of the temperature and pressure can be summarized on a single graph known as a *phase diagram*. Each substance has its own particular phase diagram which has been worked out from experimental observation. Figure 7.10 gives the phase diagram of H_2O. On this diagram various points represent the substance H_2O in the solid, liquid, or gaseous state, depending on its temperature and pressure. Each of the three regions corresponds to a one-phase system. For all values of pressure and temperature falling inside such a single-phase region, the substance is in the state specified. For example, at 380 torr pressure H_2O at $-10°C$ is in the solid state, at $+10°C$ in the liquid state, and at $+100°C$ in the gas state. The lines which separate one region from another are equilibrium lines, representing an equilibrium between two phases. In the diagram the S-L line represents equilibrium between the solid and liquid; the L-G line, equilibrium between liquid and gas; and the S-G line, equilibrium between solid and gas. The intersection of the three lines corresponds to the triple point, where all three phases are in equilibrium with each other.

The usefulness of a phase diagram can be illustrated by considering the behavior of H_2O when heat is added at a constant pressure. This corresponds to moving across the phase diagram from left to right. We distinguish three representative cases:

1. Pressure of the H_2O *is kept at 760 torr.* The experiment is this: A chunk of ice is placed in a cylinder so as to fill the cylinder completely, with no empty space. A piston resting on the ice carries a weight which corresponds to 1 atm of pressure. The H_2O starts as a solid. As heat is added, the temperature of the H_2O is raised. This corresponds to moving along the dashed line a in Figure 7.10. When the S-L line is reached, the added heat melts the ice. Solid-liquid equilibrium persists at the normal melting point of 0°C until all the solid is converted to liquid. There is no gaseous H_2O thus far, because the vapor pressure of solid ice is much lower than the pressure required to push the piston out to make room for the vapor. As heating continues, liquid H_2O warms up from 0°C until the L-G line is reached, at a temperature which corresponds to 100°C. At this temperature liquid-gas equilibrium is established. The system stays at 100°C as the liquid converts to gas. At 100°C the vapor pressure is great enough to move the piston and make room for the voluminous vapor phase. Since the external pressure is fixed at 1 atm, liquid converts completely to gas at the normal boiling temperature. From then on, the gas simply warms up.

2. Pressure of the H_2O *is kept at 380 torr.* Again the H_2O starts as the solid. The temperature is raised, moving to the right along dashed line b. The H_2O stays as a solid until it reaches the temperature that corresponds to melting. Because of the tilt of the S-L line toward the left (the tilt has been somewhat exaggerated in Figure 7.10), the temperature at which melting occurs is slightly higher at 380 torr than at 760 torr. At 380 torr ice melts not at 0°C but slightly above zero. The

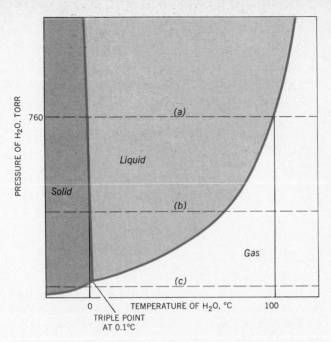

PRESSURE OF H₂O, TORR

760 ——————————— (a) ———————————

Liquid

Solid

(b)

Gas

(c)

0 TEMPERATURE OF H₂O, °C 100

TRIPLE POINT
AT 0.1°C

7.10
Phase diagram of H₂O
(scale of axes somewhat
distorted)

difference in melting-point temperature is only about 0.005°. After all the ice has been converted to liquid at +0.005°C, further addition of heat warms the liquid up until boiling occurs at the L-G line. Boiling occurs when the vapor pressure of the water reaches 380 torr. The temperature at which this happens is 82°C, considerably lower than the normal boiling point of 100°C. Above 82°C only gaseous water exists at 380 torr.

3. *Pressure of the* H_2O *is kept at 1 torr*. If the pressure exerted by the H_2O is kept at 1 torr by suitable means such as regulated pumping, the H_2O can exist only along the dashed line marked *c*. As the temperature is raised, solid H_2O warms up until it reaches the S-G line. Solid-gas equilibrium is established; solid converts to gas. When all the solid has been converted, the temperature of the gas rises. There is no melting in this experiment, and no passage through the liquid state.

An interesting aspect of the H_2O phase diagram is that the S-L line, representing equilibrium between solid and liquid, tilts to the left with increasing pressure. This is unusual; for most substances the S-L line tilts to the right. The direction of the tilt is important, since it tells whether the melting point rises or falls with increased pressure. In the case of H_2O, as pressure is increased (*up* on the phase diagram), the temperature at which solid and liquid coexist decreases (*left* on the phase diagram). The melting-point decrease is 0.01°C atm⁻¹.

The lowering of the ice melting point by increased pressure is predicted by Le Chatelier's principle. The density of ice is 0.9 g cc⁻¹; the density of water is 1.0 g cc⁻¹. In the solid state 1 g of H_2O occupies a volume of 1.1 cc; in the liquid state 1 g of H_2O occupies 1.0 cc. Thus, a given mass of H_2O occupies a larger volume as solid than as liquid.

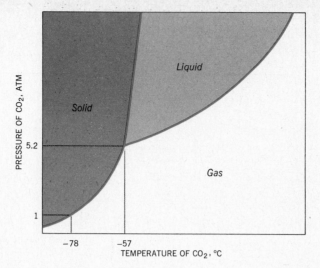

PRESSURE OF CO_2, ATM

Solid

Liquid

5.2

Gas

1

−78 −57

TEMPERATURE OF CO_2, °C

7.11
Phase diagram of CO_2

An equilibrium system consisting of water and ice at 1 atm is at the normal melting point of 0°C. If the pressure on the H_2O is increased, there is a stress which the system can relieve by shrinking in volume. It can shrink in volume by converting from ice to water; hence, melting is favored. But melting is an endothermic process and requires heat. If the system is insulated, the only source of heat is the kinetic energy of the molecules. Consequently, the molecules slow down, and the temperature drops. The result is that solid ice and liquid water under increased pressure coexist at a lower temperature.

Another phase diagram of interest is that of carbon dioxide, CO_2. In general appearance, as shown in Figure 7.11, it is similar to that of H_2O. However, the solid-liquid equilibrium line tilts to the right instead of to the left, since the melting point of CO_2 rises with increased pressure. The triple-point pressure of CO_2 is 5.2 atm; the triple-point temperature is −57°C. Since the triple-point pressure is considerably above normal atmospheric pressure, liquid carbon dioxide is not observed under normal conditions. In order to get liquid carbon dioxide, the pressure must be higher than 5.2 atm. At 1 atm only solid and gas can exist. When solid carbon dioxide in the form of dry ice is used as a refrigerant at 1 atm pressure, the conversion of solid to gas occurs at −78°C. There is no increase in temperature of the carbon dioxide until all the solid disappears.

7.9 ENTROPY, FREE ENERGY, AND SPONTANEOUS CHANGE

It would seem to be obvious that processes occur spontaneously to produce a state of lower energy. However, we know that a chunk of ice above its melting temperature spontaneously melts, forming a state of higher energy. Apparently, more than energy is involved in determining the direction of spontaneous changes.

The additional factor which must be considered is the tendency of a system to assume the most random molecular arrangement possible. In other words, systems tend to become disordered. The reason for this tendency is that random molecular motion more probably produces a disordered than an ordered state. The disorder is described quantitatively in terms of a property called the *entropy,* and we say that a disordered state has a higher entropy than an ordered state. As a specific example, H_2O in the form of liquid water has a higher entropy than H_2O in the form of solid ice.

In the same sense that natural processes which result in a decrease of energy are favored, those which result in an increase of entropy are also favored. In certain cases, as in melting ice, the two factors may oppose each other so that there is a question of which one wins out. Above the melting point the entropy increase is dominant, so spontaneous melting occurs; below the melting point the energy decrease is dominant, so spontaneous freezing occurs. It turns out that the temperature itself is the critical factor and governs how important the entropy increase is relative to the energy change. At the absolute zero of temperature, the entropy term contributes nothing in determining the direction of spontaneous change, so that the most stable state is that of lowest energy. As the temperature rises, molecular motion increases and the tendency to disorder becomes more important in determining the direction of change. At sufficiently high temperatures the entropy factor becomes large enough to overcome even an unfavorable energy change.

Quantitatively, the interplay of the energy and entropy factors can be described by using a concept called the *free energy.* This is generally symbolized by G, in honor of Willard Gibbs, the Yale professor of mathematics who founded chemical thermodynamics. (F is frequently used in place of G.) The definition of free energy is given by the relation

$$G = H - TS$$

where H is the *heat content* (also called *enthalpy*) of a substance, S is its entropy, and T is the absolute temperature.

The heat content H differs from the internal energy E by the factor PV, i.e., the pressure-volume product:

$$H = E + PV$$

Of prime importance are changes in the various quantities. For example, the change in heat content ΔH, which is the heat content of the final state of a substance minus the heat content of the initial state, is $\Delta E + \Delta(PV)$, where ΔE is the change in internal energy and $\Delta(PV)$ is the change in the pressure-volume product in going from the initial to the final state. The term $\Delta(PV)$ is generally small, especially at atmospheric pressure where it becomes equal to $P \, \Delta V$, this being the work accompanying a change of volume ΔV at a constant pressure P. For changes at constant pressure, therefore, we can write

$$\Delta H = \Delta E + P \, \Delta V$$

which states that the increase in heat content equals the increase in internal energy plus the work done by the system in expanding through ΔV against the pressure imposed by the surroundings. In other words, if we wish to increase the energy E of a system by a certain amount ΔE, we must add enough heat ΔH to supply the energy needed to do the work $P \Delta V$ as well as increase the energy by the amount ΔE.

Because $P \Delta V$ is generally small compared to ΔE, chemists frequently get away with substituting "energy changes" for "enthalpy changes," that is, ΔE for ΔH. However, free-energy changes strictly depend on enthalpy changes:

$$\Delta G = \Delta H - \Delta(TS)$$

This states that the free-energy difference between the initial and final states of a substance, ΔG, is equal to the difference in heat content less the difference in the temperature-entropy product $\Delta(TS)$. If G is identified with energy that is freely available, then the above relation states that this available energy is less than the heat content by the amount TS. The temperature-entropy product TS is sometimes referred to as the "unavailable energy." We get a hint at the reason for this terminology by recalling that S measures the randomness in a substance and T gives the thermal disordering influence.

For an isothermal change, i.e., one that occurs at a fixed temperature T, the free-energy change is given by

$$\Delta G = \Delta H - T \Delta S$$

The importance of this equation stems from the fact that at constant temperature and pressure a change can occur spontaneously only if there is a decrease in free energy. In other words, ΔG should be negative, corresponding to a free energy lower in the final state than in the initial one. A negative ΔG can be produced by a decrease in enthalpy or an increase in entropy. The former ($\Delta H < 0$) would correspond in general to an energetically favorable process, i.e., one in which energy decreases; the latter ($\Delta S > 0$) corresponds to one in which disorder increases and so is favored by random thermal motion.

For many processes ΔH and ΔS have the same sign; for example, for melting of a solid both are positive. In such cases T will be all-important in deciding which term prevails. At sufficiently low T, ΔH will predominate. For the melting process, where ΔH is positive, ΔG will also be positive at sufficiently low T and melting will not occur. At very high temperature, the $T \Delta S$ term predominates over ΔH. Since ΔS for melting is positive, $-T \Delta S$ can cause ΔG to be negative. Hence, melting should occur. At one temperature, $T \Delta S$ just matches ΔH. ΔG at this temperature is equal to zero, and solid and liquid coexist in equilibrium. The temperature of this coexistence is, of course, the melting, or freezing, point.

Finally, we should note that the criterion for equilibrium between two states at constant temperature and pressure is that the free energy be equal in the two states, or that $\Delta G = 0$. The quantitative application of this criterion to a typical system is illustrated in the following example.

7.9 Entropy, free energy, and spontaneous change

EXAMPLE 4

For the melting of sodium chloride the heat required is 7.25 kcal mole^{-1}. The entropy increase is 6.73 cal mole^{-1} deg^{-1}. Calculate the melting point from these data.

At the melting point

$$\Delta G = 0 = \Delta H - T_{mp} \Delta S$$

$$\Delta H = T_{mp} \Delta S$$

$$T_{mp} = \frac{\Delta H}{\Delta S} = \frac{7250 \text{ cal mole}^{-1}}{6.73 \text{ cal mole}^{-1} \text{ deg}^{-1}} = 1080°K$$

EXAMPLE 5

At 0°C ice has a density of 0.917 g cc^{-1} and an entropy of 9.070 cal mole^{-1} deg^{-1}. At this temperature liquid water has a density of 0.9998 g cc^{-1} and an entropy of 14.326 cal mole^{-1} deg^{-1}. Calculate (a) the change of entropy ΔS, (b) the change of enthalpy ΔH, and (c) the change of energy ΔE for the conversion of one mole of ice to liquid water at the normal melting point.

(a) $\Delta S = S_{liq} - S_{solid} = 14.326 - 9.070 = 5.256$ cal mole^{-1} deg^{-1}

(b) $\Delta H = T_{mp}\Delta S = (273.15°)(5.256$ cal mole^{-1} deg$^{-1})$

$$= 1436 \text{ cal mole}^{-1}$$

(c) $\Delta E = \Delta H - P\Delta V$

$$\Delta V = V_{liq} - V_{solid} = \frac{18.015 \text{ g mole}^{-1}}{0.9998 \text{ g cc}^{-1}} - \frac{18.015 \text{ g mole}^{-1}}{0.917 \text{ g cc}^{-1}}$$

$\Delta V = -1.63$ cc mole^{-1} $= -0.00163$ liter mole^{-1}

$P\Delta V = (1.00$ atm$)(-0.00163$ liter mole$^{-1})$

$$= -0.00163 \text{ liter-atm mole}^{-1}$$

One liter-atmosphere is 24.22 cal.

$P\Delta V = (-0.00163$ liter-atm mole$^{-1})(24.22$ cal liter^{-1} atm$^{-1})$

$$= -0.00395 \text{ cal}$$

Therefore, $\Delta E = \Delta H - P\Delta V = 1436 + 0.0395 = 1436$ cal mole^{-1}.

QUESTIONS

7.1 *States of matter*   Prepare a table showing how the liquid, solid, and gaseous states compare with respect to each of the following: compressibility, fluidity, rate of diffusion, average potential energy of the molecules at the triple point, average kinetic energy of the molecules at the triple point.

7.2 *Vapor pressure*   Given a closed container of volume 1.00 liter which has in it 0.100 mole of ideal gas and water vapor in equilibrium with 4.00 ml of liquid water at 25°C. (*a*) Calculate the total pressure in the container at this temperature. (*b*) Calculate the total pressure at 80°C. (*c*) How much liquid water remains at 80°C?

7.3 Cooling curves   Suppose that a given pure liquid that tends to form a glass is allowed to cool to room temperature from some elevated temperature. Sketch what the cooling curve probably looks like.

7.4 Supercooled liquid   As a supercooled liquid crystallizes, what happens to the temperature? Explain.

7.5 Triple point   The triple point of H_2O occurs at 4.58 torr and 0.01°C. The density of liquid water at this temperature is 0.9998 g cc^{-1}; of solid ice, 0.917 g cc^{-1}. Calculate the molar volume of H_2O in each of the three phases.

7.6 Dynamic equilibrium   Devise an experiment to show that a solid-liquid equilibrium is a dynamic one.

7.7 Clausius-Clapeyron equation   What is the temperature of boiling water inside a pressure cooker operating at a gauge pressure (i.e., pressure above atmosphere) of 15.0 psi? Assume atmospheric pressure to be 1.00 atm, which is 14.7 psi. For H_2O, $\Delta H'$ is 9700 cal mole^{-1} at 100°C.

7.8 Liquid density   In liquid mercury just above the freezing point the structure as deduced from X-ray scattering suggests that each mercury atom is surrounded on the average by six near-neighbors at 3.0 Å and eleven next-to-near-neighbors at 4.2 Å. By considering a sphere of radius 4.2 Å centered on one atom and containing the near-neighbors but only half of each next-to-near-neighbor, calculate the approximate density of the liquid.

7.9 Clausius-Clapeyron equation   The vapor pressure of NH_3 is 100 torr at -68.4°C and 400 torr at -45.4°C. (*a*) Calculate $\Delta H'$ for the vaporization of NH_3. (*b*) If $\Delta H'$ remains constant up to the boiling point, what should the boiling point be?

7.10 Heat of fusion   Consider the melting of a solid to produce a liquid of lower density. Suggest two reasons why heat needs to be added to accomplish this process and tell which is more important.

7.11 Heat content   (*a*) Showing heat content on the vertical axis and temperature on the horizontal axis, plot the course of the addition of heat to solid ice to convert it first to liquid and finally to gas. (*b*) Describe what happens to the added heat on a molecular scale for each portion of the curve in (*a*).

7.12 Vapor pressure   Suppose that 1.00 g of H_2O is injected into an evacuated 1.00-liter container at 18°C. (*a*) What fraction of the H_2O evaporates? (*b*) If the temperature is raised to 105°C, what fraction of the H_2O evaporates?

7.13 Clausius-Clapeyron equation   Given that $\Delta H'$ of water at 100°C is 9700 cal mole^{-1}, calculate the vapor pressure expected for liquid water at 110°C.

7.14 Phase diagram (a) Draw a P-T phase diagram for a typical substance, showing clearly the triple point. (b) Choose a point in the liquid region. Starting with this point as one corner, draw a square path which encloses the triple point. (c) Describe the pressure, temperature, and phase changes that correspond to each leg of the path.

7.15 Fusion By using the appropriate values from Example 4 in Section 7.9, calculate the free-energy change ΔG corresponding to the fusion of one mole of NaCl solid at $1050°K$ and $1100°K$.

7.16 Entropy of fusion For the salts LiCl, NaCl, KCl, and RbCl, the heats of fusion are 3200, 7250, 6100, and 4400 cal mole^{-1}, respectively. The corresponding melting points are 610, 804, 772, and 717°C. By calculation, show that the trend in entropy of fusion parallels that in ΔH and T_{mp}.

Liquid	Boiling point, °C	Heat of vaporization, cal mole^{-1}
Ethyl ether	34.6	6500
Benzene	80.2	7350
Cyclohexane	80.7	7180
Toluene	110.6	7990

7.17 Entropy of vaporization An empirical rule, called Trouton's rule, states that for nonpolar liquids the entropy increase on boiling is approximately the same for all liquids. (a) Show this is true from the data in the accompanying table. (b) Suggest a reason why polar liquids such as water show greater entropies of vaporization than those calculated above.

7.18 Liquid structure Consider a liquid formed by melting a solid of simple cubic structure. On melting, the internuclear distance increases from 3.52 to 3.59 Å and the density decreases from 3.19 to 2.90 g cc^{-1}. Assuming that the liquid can be pictured as retaining a simple cubic configuration but with an appropriate number of vacancies, calculate the percent of positions that are vacant.

7.19 States of matter Given H_2O at its triple point. Compare the three states with respect to each of the following: (a) potential energy per mole, (b) kinetic energy per mole, (c) free energy per mole, (d) enthalpy per mole, (e) entropy per mole.

7.20 Vapor pressure (a) Given a cylinder with a movable piston trapping a fixed mass of H_2O vapor (no air) at 25°C. Plot the pressure as a function of volume as the piston is gradually pushed in. Assume temperature is kept constant. (b) How would the answer to (a) be changed if some air were also present?

7.21 Change of state (a) Draw a labeled heating curve for a solid starting below its normal melting point and continuing above its normal boiling point to the temperature of its critical point. (b) On the same axes draw the curve for the same substance covering the same temperature range, but this time at its critical pressure. (c) Account for the differences between the two curves. (d) Indicate those portions of both curves where the kinetic energy is constant but the potential energy is increased. Tell why the system goes spontaneously to a state of higher potential energy in these regions. (e) Sketch a phase diagram for the substance, making certain it is consistent with the heating curves.

7.22 *Critical point* (a) Draw a P-T phase diagram for a typical substance, showing clearly the critical point. (b) Choose a point in the liquid region. (c) Trace a path corresponding to the following *consecutive* steps:

(1) At constant temperature, pressure is raised to a point above the critical pressure.
(2) At constant pressure, temperature is raised to above the critical temperature.
(3) At constant temperature, pressure is lowered to the initial pressure of (b).
(4) At constant pressure, temperature is lowered to the initial temperature of (b).

(d) Imagine a liquid sample that completely fills a cylinder with a movable piston. If the sample follows the path described in (c), tell at which of the steps a meniscus could exist.

7.23 *Triple point* Given a tumbler containing an ice cube in equilibrium with liquid water and with water vapor in the space above it. (a) If the barometric pressure is one atmosphere, how does the temperature of the system compare with the triple-point temperature of H_2O? (b) Your answer would be changed if the air of the atmosphere were removed. Explain why. (*Hint:* The pressure exerted by one gas is independent of the presence of other gases.)

ANSWERS

7.2 (a) 2.48 atm   (b) 3.37 atm   (c) 3.71 ml   7.7 121°C   7.9 (a) 5590 cal mole^{-1} (b) −32.9°C   7.12 (a) 0.0154   (b) 0.692 7.16 3.62, 6.73, 5.84, 4.44 cal mole^{-1} deg^{-1} 7.17 21.1, 20.8, 20.3, 20.8 cal mole^{-1} deg^{-1} 7.18 3.6%

8 solutions

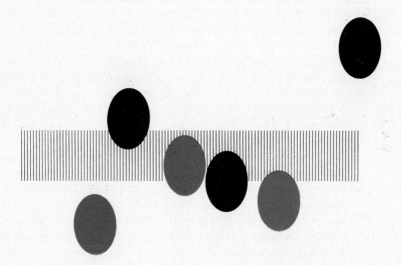

The preceding discussion of the solid, liquid, and gaseous states was limited to pure substances. In practice, we continually deal with mixtures; hence the question that arises is the effect of mixing in a second component. A mixture is classified as heterogeneous or homogeneous. By its nature, a heterogeneous mixture consists of distinct phases, and the observed properties are largely the sum of those of the individual phases. However, a homogeneous mixture consists of a single phase which has properties that may differ drastically from those of the individual components. These homogeneous mixtures, or solutions, are of widespread importance in chemistry and deserve intensive study.

8.1 TYPES OF SOLUTIONS

Solutions, defined as *homogeneous mixtures of two or more components,* can be gaseous, liquid, or solid. Gaseous solutions are made by dissolving one gas in another. Since all gases mix in all proportions, any mixture of gases is homogeneous and is a solution. The kinetic picture of a gaseous solution is like that of a pure gas, except that the molecules are of different kinds. Ideally, the molecules move independently of each other.

Liquid solutions are made by dissolving a gas, liquid, or solid in a liquid. If the liquid is water, the solution is called an *aqueous* solution. In the kinetic picture of a sugar-water solution, sugar molecules are distributed at random throughout the bulk of the solution. It is evident that on this molecular scale the term "homogeneous" has little significance. However, experiments cannot be performed with less than billions of molecules, so for practical purposes the solution is homogeneous.

Solid solutions are solids in which one component is randomly dispersed on an atomic or molecular scale throughout another component. As in any crystal, the packing of atoms is orderly, even though there is no particular order as to which lattice points are occupied by which kind of atom. Solid solutions are of great practical importance, since they make up a large fraction of the class of substances known as alloys. An *alloy* may be defined as a combination of two or more elements which has metallic properties. Sterling silver, for example, is an alloy consisting of a solid solution of copper in silver. In brass, an alloy of copper and zinc, it is possible to have a solid solution in which some copper atoms of the face-centered-cubic structure of pure copper have been replaced by zinc atoms. Some kinds of steel are alloys of iron and carbon and can be considered as solid solutions in which carbon atoms are located in some of the spaces between iron atoms. The iron atoms are arranged in the regular structure of pure iron. It should be pointed out, however, that not all alloys are solid solutions. Some alloys, such as bismuth-cadmium, are heterogeneous mixtures containing tiny crystals of the constituent elements. Others, such as $MgCu_2$, are intermetallic compounds which contain atoms of different metals combined in definite proportions.

Two terms that are convenient in the discussion of solutions are *solute* and *solvent.* Accepted procedure is to refer to the substance present in larger amount as the solvent and to the substance present in smaller amount as the solute. However, the terms can be interchanged whenever it is convenient. For example, in speaking of solutions of sulfuric acid and water, sulfuric acid is sometimes referred to as the solute and water as the solvent even when the water molecules are in the minority.

8.2 CONCENTRATION

The properties of solutions, e.g., the color of a dye solution or the sweetness of a sugar solution, depend on the solution concentration. There are several common methods for describing concentration.

The *mole fraction* is the ratio of the number of moles of one component to the total number of moles in the solution. For example, in a solution containing 1 mole of alcohol and 3 moles of water, the mole fraction of alcohol is ¼ and that of water ¾.

The *molarity* of a solute is the number of moles of solute per liter of solution and is usually designated by a capital M. A 6.0-molar solution of HCl is labeled 6.0 M. The label means that the solution has been made up in a ratio that corresponds to adding 6.0 moles of HCl to enough water to make a liter of solution.

The *molality* of a solute is the number of moles of solute per 1000 g of solvent. It is usually designated by a small m. The label 6.0 m HCl is read "6.0 molal" and represents a solution made by adding, to every 6.0 moles of HCl, 1000 g of water.

The *normality* of a solute is the number of gram-equivalents (Section 4.10) of solute per liter of solution. It is usually designated by a capital N. The label 0.25 N KMnO$_4$ is read "0.25 normal" and represents a solution which contains 0.25 g-equiv of potassium permanganate per liter of solution. (As indicated previously, the size of a gram-equivalent may vary from one reaction to another.)

The *percent of solute* is an ambiguous designation which may refer to percent by weight or percent by volume. If the former is meant, and it usually is, it is the percent of the total solution mass contributed by the solute. Thus, 3% H$_2$O$_2$ by weight would be 3 g of H$_2$O$_2$ per 100 g of solution. Percent by volume is the percent of the final solution volume represented by the volume of the solute taken to make the solution. For example, 12% alcohol by volume would represent a solution made from 12 ml of alcohol and enough solvent to bring the total volume up to 100 ml.

Occasionally one finds use of still another concentration designation, the *formality*. This designation (abbreviated F) refers to the number of gram-formulas of solute per liter of solution and is used especially when one wishes to make a distinction between what is formally placed in a solution and what is actually there.

8.3 PROPERTIES OF SOLUTIONS

How are the properties of a solvent affected by the addition of a solute? Specifically, how are the properties of water affected by the addition of sugar? Suppose we consider the following experiment: Two beakers, one containing pure water (beaker I) and the other containing a sugar-water solution (beaker II), are set under a bell jar, as shown in Figure 8.1. As time goes on, we observe that the level of pure water in beaker I drops, while the level of the solution in beaker II rises. There is transfer of water from pure solvent to solution, presumably through the vapor phase. This transfer occurs because the escaping tendency, or vapor pressure, of pure water is higher than the escaping tendency of H$_2$O from the sugar-water solution.

Another experimental observation which supports the idea that addition of a solute lowers the escaping tendency of solvent molecules is the lowering of the freezing point. For example, when sugar is added to

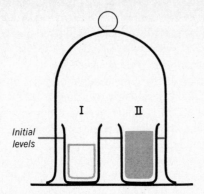

8.1
Experimental comparison
of the escaping tendency
of water from pure water
(I) and an aqueous
solution (II)

water, it is found necessary to cool below 0°C in order to freeze out ice. The implication is that the tendency of H_2O to escape from the liquid phase (into the solid phase) is decreased by the presence of solute.

The lowering of the freezing point and the reduction of the vapor pressure are found, at least in dilute solutions, to be directly proportional to the concentration of added solute particles. Apparently, the most important effect of the solute is to reduce the concentration of H_2O molecules. In the solution only a certain fraction of the molecules are H_2O molecules, and therefore the escape of H_2O molecules from the solution is less probable than their escape from pure water.

Figure 8.2 shows on a phase diagram the effect on the solvent, water, of one particular concentration of solute. The solid lines represent the phase diagram of pure H_2O; the dashed lines, that of the solution. The dashed line on the left corresponds to equilibrium between solid H_2O (ice) and the liquid solution. It represents the temperatures at which pure solid H_2O freezes out when the particular solution is cooled at different pressures. The dashed line on the right corresponds to equilibrium between gaseous H_2O and the liquid solution. It represents the temperatures at which pure gaseous H_2O boils off when the solution is heated at various pressures.

The most striking feature shown on the phase diagram is the extension, at all pressures, of the liquid range, both to higher temperatures and to lower temperatures. The liquid phase of water has been made more probable by the addition of solute. Associated with this is the fact that the vapor pressure of the water has been reduced. For example, as seen from Figure 8.2, at 100°C the vapor pressure of the water is not 1 atm, but less than that. Because the vapor pressure of water is lowered, the solution does not boil at 100°C, but instead boils at some other temperature at which vapor pressure becomes equal to 1 atm. If the solute contributes nothing to the vapor pressure (is nonvolatile, as, for example, sugar is), then the normal boiling point of the solution can be read directly from the phase diagram. Similarly, there is a depression of the normal freezing point.

Quantitatively, the lowering of the vapor pressure of a solvent by addition of a solute is described by Raoult's law: *the fractional lower-*

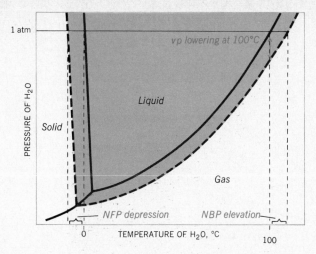

8.2
Comparison of phase
diagram of water and an
aqueous solution (Dashed
lines refer to solution.)

*ing of the vapor pressure of a solvent is equal to the mole fraction of
solute present.* This can be written

$$\frac{p_1{}^0 - p_1}{p_1{}^0} = x_2$$

where $p_1{}^0$ is the vapor pressure of the pure solvent and p_1 is the partial pressure of the solvent above a solution in which the mole fraction
of solute is x_2. Since the mole fractions of solute and solvent, x_1 and
x_2, must add to give unity, we can write alternatively

$$x_2 = 1 - x_1$$

$$1 - x_1 = \frac{p_1{}^0 - p_1}{p_1{}^0} = 1 - \frac{p_1}{p_1{}^0}$$

$$x_1 = \frac{p_1}{p_1{}^0}$$

$$p_1 = x_1 p_1{}^0$$

From the last relation it can be seen that Raoult's law amounts to a
direct proportionality between the solvent vapor pressure and its mole
fraction. In practice, Raoult's law is an idealization best realized in
dilute solutions. As the concentration of solute is increased, the vapor
pressure of the solvent component deviates from ideal behavior, usually
in the positive sense (e.g., chloroform and ethyl alcohol) but for certain
cases in the negative sense (e.g., chloroform and acetone). Typical behavior is shown in Figure 8.3.

From ideal Raoult's law behavior it can be seen why the freezing-
point lowering and the boiling-point elevation are proportional to the
concentration of solute molecules in solution. In either case the concentration of solute is important in determining the mole fraction of
solvent. As the concentration of solute is increased, that of the solvent
is decreased, and its vapor pressure decreases proportionately. As

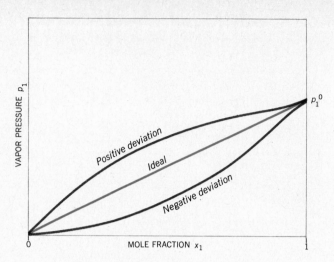

VAPOR PRESSURE p_1

Positive deviation

Ideal

Negative deviation

$p_1^{\,0}$

MOLE FRACTION x_1

0   1

8.3
Raoult's law behavior

shown in Figure 8.2, the extent to which the dashed curve falls below
the solid curve is the amount of the vapor-pressure lowering; it controls
both the boiling-point elevation and the freezing-point lowering. For the
boiling point it is necessary to increase the temperature to compensate
for the vapor-pressure decrease. Over the small range of values in
question, we can assume that the required temperature increase is
directly proportional to the vapor-pressure decrease. Since the vapor-
pressure decrease in turn is proportional to the mole fraction of solute,
it follows that the elevation of the boiling point should be directly proportional to the mole fraction of solute. These relations can be written
as follows:

$$\Delta T_{bp} \propto \Delta p \propto x_2$$

where ΔT_{bp} is the elevation of the boiling point, Δp is the vapor-pressure lowering, and x_2 is the mole fraction of solute. By definition,

$$x_2 = \frac{n_{\text{solute}}}{n_{\text{solute}} + n_{\text{solvent}}}$$

where n is the number of moles. In dilute solution, n_{solute} is very small
compared to n_{solvent} and can be neglected in the denominator.

$$x_2 \cong \frac{n_{\text{solute}}}{n_{\text{solvent}}} = \frac{m}{1000 \, \text{M}}$$

The last relation shows that, for a solution of molality m, the ratio of
moles of solute to moles of solvent is just the molality m divided by the
number of moles of solvent (molecular mass M) in 1000 g. Hence, it
follows that for a dilute solution the boiling-point elevation is proportional to the molality of solute. This can be written

$$\Delta T_{bp} = Bm$$

where B is a proportionality constant called the *molal boiling-point
elevation constant*. The value of B depends on the solvent but not on

the solute. For H_2O, B equals 0.52°C per molal solution. This value compares to 2.6°C m^{-1} for benzene, 1.24°C m^{-1} for ethyl alcohol, and 5.05°C m^{-1} for carbon tetrachloride.

The quantitative description of freezing-point lowering is worked out along lines similar to the above. Over small ranges of concentration we can assume that the lowering of the triple-point temperature (see Figure 8.2) is proportional to the lowering of the triple-point vapor pressure. We assume further that the lowering of the triple-point temperature is directly reflected as the lowering of the normal freezing point. Thus, we can write the approximation

$$\Delta T_{mp} \propto \Delta p_{\text{triple point}} \propto x_2 = \frac{m}{1000/M}$$

or

$$\Delta T_{mp} = Fm$$

where F is a proportionality constant called the *molal freezing-point lowering constant*. As with the boiling-point elevation constant B, the freezing-point depression constant F depends on the solvent but not on the solute. For H_2O, F equals 1.86°C m^{-1}, which compares with 5.1°C m^{-1} for benzene and 6.9°C m^{-1} for naphthalene.

The above derivations of boiling-point and freezing-point formulas are approximate and rest on assumptions that are justified only for dilute solutions. In concentrated solutions B and F may vary somewhat. Two other points need special emphasis. The first is that the solute must be dissolved *only* in the liquid phase; in other words, the solute cannot be volatile, nor can it form a solid solution in the solid phase. The second point is that the number of solute particles in the solution should be the same as the number of molecules placed in the solution; in other words, if the solution process causes dissociation of the molecules, then it will be the total concentration of all kinds of particles that determines the freezing and boiling points of the solution. In the following example, we assume that there are no complications of these kinds.

EXAMPLE 1

When 45 g of glucose is dissolved in 500 g of water, the solution has a freezing point of −0.93°C. (*a*) What is the molecular mass of glucose? (*b*) If the simplest formula is CH_2O, what is the molecular formula of glucose?

(*a*) The freezing point of H_2O is reduced 1.86°C by 1 mole of particles per 1000 g of H_2O. If the freezing point of H_2O is reduced 0.93°C, the solution must have

0.93/1.86 mole of particles per 1000 g of H_2O, or

0.50 mole of particles per 1000 g of H_2O, or

0.25 mole of particles per 500 g of H_2O

Since there is 45 g of glucose per 500 g of H_2O,

$$45 \text{ g} = 0.25 \text{ mole}$$

$$1 \text{ mole} = 180 \text{ g}$$

Therefore, molecular mass of glucose is 180 amu.

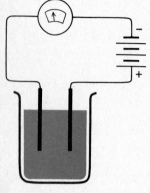

8.4

Experiment to determine
conductivity of a solution

(b) Molecular formula must be some multiple x of CH_2O, or $(CH_2O)_x$.

The simplest-formula mass is $12 + 2 + 16 = 30$ amu.

The molecular mass is 180 amu, or x times 30, so $x = 6$.

The molecular formula is $(CH_2O)_6$, or $C_6H_{12}O_6$.

8.4 ELECTROLYTES

As first shown by Svante Arrhenius in 1887, there are many cases in which the solution process is accompanied by dissociation, or breaking apart, of molecules. The dissociated fragments are usually electrically charged, so that electrical measurements can show whether dissociation has occurred. Charged particles, or ions, moving in solution, constitute an electric current, so that a measurement of electrical conductivity of the solution is all that is required. Figure 8.4 is a schematic diagram of an apparatus for determining whether a solute is dissociated into ions. The pair of electrodes is connected in series with an ammeter to a source of electricity. So long as the two electrodes are kept separated, no electric current can flow through the circuit, and the meter reads zero. When the two electrodes are joined by an electrical conductor, the circuit is complete and the meter swings. When the electrodes are dipped into a beaker of water, the meter stays near zero, indicating that water does not conduct electricity appreciably. When

Electrolytes		Nonelectrolytes	
HCl	Hydrochloric acid	$C_{12}H_{22}O_{11}$	Sucrose
H_2SO_4	Sulfuric acid	C_2H_5OH	Ethyl alcohol
$HC_2H_3O_2$	Acetic acid	N_2	Nitrogen
NaOH	Sodium hydroxide	O_2	Oxygen
$Ca(OH)_2$	Calcium hydroxide	CH_4	Methane
NaCl	Sodium chloride	CO	Carbon monoxide
Na_2SO_4	Sodium sulfate	CH_3COCH_3	Acetone

8.5
Classification of solutes

sugar is dissolved in the water, the solution does not conduct; but when NaCl is dissolved in the water, the solution does conduct. By such experiments it is possible to classify substances as those which produce conducting solutions and those which produce essentially nonconducting solutions. Solutes of the first class are called *electrolytes,* and those of the second *nonelectrolytes.* Figure 8.5 gives the names and formulas of several examples.

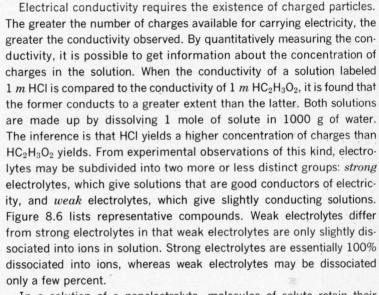

Strong electrolytes		Weak electrolytes	
HCl	Hydrochloric acid	HC$_2$H$_3$O$_2$	Acetic acid
NaOH	Sodium hydroxide	TlOH	Thallous hydroxide
NaCl	Sodium chloride	HgCl$_2$	Mercuric chloride
KCN	Potassium cyanide	HCN	Hydrogen cyanide
BaSO$_4$	Barium sulfate	CdSO$_4$	Cadmium sulfate

8.6
Classification of
electrolytes

Electrical conductivity requires the existence of charged particles. The greater the number of charges available for carrying electricity, the greater the conductivity observed. By quantitatively measuring the conductivity, it is possible to get information about the concentration of charges in the solution. When the conductivity of a solution labeled 1 m HCl is compared to the conductivity of 1 m HC$_2$H$_3$O$_2$, it is found that the former conducts to a greater extent than the latter. Both solutions are made up by dissolving 1 mole of solute in 1000 g of water. The inference is that HCl yields a higher concentration of charges than HC$_2$H$_3$O$_2$ yields. From experimental observations of this kind, electrolytes may be subdivided into two more or less distinct groups: *strong* electrolytes, which give solutions that are good conductors of electricity, and *weak* electrolytes, which give slightly conducting solutions. Figure 8.6 lists representative compounds. Weak electrolytes differ from strong electrolytes in that weak electrolytes are only slightly dissociated into ions in solution. Strong electrolytes are essentially 100% dissociated into ions, whereas weak electrolytes may be dissociated only a few percent.

In a solution of a nonelectrolyte, molecules of solute retain their identity. For example, when sugar dissolves in water, as shown in Figure 8.7, the sugar molecules exist in the solution as solvated, or hydrated, molecules. The hydrated sugar molecule (consisting of a sugar molecule surrounded by a cluster of water molecules) is an uncharged, or neutral, species. When positive and negative electrodes are inserted in a solution containing hydrated sugar molecules, there is no reason for the particles to move one way or the other, since they are neutral. Hence there is no electrical conductivity.

● SUGAR MOLECULE

● WATER MOLECULE

8.7
Schematic representation
of sugar dissolving

Electrolytes (before being dissolved) may be ionic or molecular substances. In the case of *ionic substances* it is not surprising that there are charged particles in solution, because the undissolved solid is already made up of charged particles. The solvent rips the lattice apart into its constituent pieces. Figure 8.8 shows what is thought to happen when the ionic solid NaCl dissolves in water. Since the chloride ion is negative, the positive ends of water molecules cluster about the chloride ion, with the hydrogen atoms facing the chloride ion. The chloride ion surrounded by its cluster of water molecules moves off into the solution. It is now a hydrated chloride ion. The species is negatively charged because the chloride ion itself is negatively charged. At the same time, the sodium ion undergoes similar hydration with the difference that the negative or oxygen end of the water molecule faces the

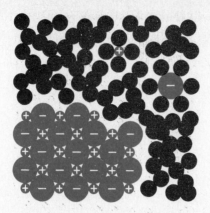

positive ion. Since the solution as a whole must be electrically neutral, equal numbers of hydrated sodium ions and hydrated chloride ions are formed. When positive and negative electrodes are inserted into this solution, the positively charged hydrated sodium ions are attracted to the negative electrode and the negatively charged hydrated chloride ions are attracted to the positive electrode. There is a net transport of electric charge as the positive charge moves in one direction and the negative charge moves in the opposite direction. (Electric conductivity is discussed in greater detail in Section 13.1.)

Ions may also be formed when certain *molecular substances* are dissolved in the proper solvent. For example, molecules of HCl are neutral, distinct species which in the pure solid, liquid, or gaseous state do not conduct electricity because no ions are present. However, when HCl is placed in water, the resulting solution conducts electricity, indicating the formation of charged particles. Electrically neutral HCl molecules have interacted with the solvent to form ions. As shown in the equation,

$$H\!:\!\overset{..}{\underset{H}{O}}\!: \; + \; H\!:\!\overset{..}{\underset{..}{Cl}}\!: \; \longrightarrow \; H\!:\!\overset{..}{\underset{H}{O}}\!:\!H^+ \; + \; :\!\overset{..}{\underset{..}{Cl}}\!:\!{}^-$$

HCl can be considered to transfer a proton to H_2O to form H_3O^+ and Cl^-. Positive and negative ions are formed, even though none is present in pure HCl. The positively charged H_3O^+ is referred to as a *hydronium or oxonium ion*. The negative ion is the chloride ion. Both of these ions are hydrated, since there are water molecules stuck on them just as on an ionic solute. The ionization of a solute by water can be considered a chemical reaction and can be described by a chemical equation such as

$$HCl + H_2O \longrightarrow H_3O^+ + Cl^-$$

Since H_3O^+ can be considered as a hydrated proton and since water of hydration is often omitted from chemical equations, the above equation can be written more simply as

$$HCl \longrightarrow H^+ + Cl^-$$

with the tacit understanding that all species are hydrated. However, the practice of omitting water of hydration from chemical equations is dangerous unless we constantly bear in mind that, in aqueous solution, water is always associated with any dissolved species and may affect its properties. The danger is greatest in the case of the hydrogen ion, because a bare hydrogen ion is nothing but a proton (nucleus of H atom). Whereas H^+ is essentially of zero size, H_3O^+ has a volume which is about 10^{15} times as great and is comparable in size with other ions.*

8.5 PERCENT DISSOCIATION

The extent of dissociation of solutes varies widely. Some substances, such as HCl, are essentially completely dissociated into ions in aqueous solution. Other substances, such as $HC_2H_3O_2$, are only slightly dissociated. The percent dissociation can be determined by measuring any property that depends on the concentration of ions. Conductivity measurements can be used, as well as freezing-point lowering. The latter is somewhat easier in most cases and can be used because the freezing-point depression of a solvent is proportional to the molal concentration of particles dissolved in the solvent. As an example, consider the solution of an electrolyte AB in water. If some of the AB molecules are dissociated into A^+ and B^- ions, then the solution contains three kinds of particles: undissociated AB molecules, A^+ ions, and B^- ions. Each particle contributes to the freezing-point depression. By determining the freezing-point lowering of a specific solution of AB, the total concentration of particles and thus the percent dissociation of AB can be calculated.

EXAMPLE 2

The freezing point of 0.0100 m AB solution is $-0.0193°C$. What percent of the AB molecules have been dissociated by the water?

$$\text{Total concentration of particles} = \frac{0.0193°C}{1.86°C\ m^{-1}} = 0.0104\ m$$

Let x = concentration of AB particles that dissociate. This gives x molal A^+ and x molal B^-, leaving $(0.0100 - x)$ molal undissociated AB. Total concentration of particles is $x + x + (0.0100 - x) = (0.0100 + x)$ molal. Equating, we get

0.0104 molal $= (0.0100 + x)$ molal

$x = 0.0004\ m$

The fraction of AB molecules dissociated is equal to the number of AB molecules dissociated divided by the number of AB molecules initially available.

* The problem is by no means closed at this point. There is substantial evidence that H_3O^+ is bound to three surrounding water molecules to form the species $H_9O_4^+$. Fortunately, this species has never been given a name.

$$\text{Fraction of AB dissociated} = \frac{0.0004}{0.0100} = 0.04, \text{ or } 4\%$$

Measurements on various electrolytes under different conditions indicate that the percent dissociation of an electrolyte depends on the nature of the solute, the nature of the solvent, the concentration of the solute, and the temperature.

1. Nature of the solute. When a molecule AB is dissociated into ions A^+ and B^-, the bond AB must be broken. The extent to which this operation can be performed depends on the nature of A and B. For example, under comparable conditions, HCl in water is 100% dissociated, whereas HF in water is only 1% dissociated.

2. Nature of the solvent. This point is easily overlooked, because we usually think only of water as the solvent. In solvents other than water the behavior of solutes may be different. As an example, under comparable conditions, in water HCl is 100% dissociated, but in benzene it is less than 1% dissociated. Also, it is possible for an electrolyte which in water is less dissociated than HCl to be more dissociated than HCl in another solvent.

3. Temperature. There is no simple rule for the effect of temperature on percent dissociation. The percent dissociation of some substances increases as the temperature is raised; the percent dissociation of other substances decreases or is unchanged. Some substances show a combination of all effects. For example, acetic acid is 1% dissociated in a given solution at room temperature; at higher temperatures and also at lower temperatures it is less than 1% dissociated.

4. Concentration. The percent dissociation of an electrolyte increases as the concentration of the electrolyte decreases. The more dilute a solution, the higher the percent dissociation. Figure 8.9 gives numerical values of the percent dissociation of $HC_2H_3O_2$ into hydrogen

Concentration	Percent dissociation
1 M $HC_2H_3O_2$	0.4
0.1 M $HC_2H_3O_2$	1.3
0.01 M $HC_2H_3O_2$	4.3
0.001 M $HC_2H_3O_2$	15
0.00001 M $HC_2H_3O_2$	75

8.9
Concentration dependence
of percent dissociation

ion and acetate ion, $C_2H_3O_2^-$, in solutions of various concentrations. In the more dilute solutions a higher percentage of the electrolyte is dissociated into positive and negative ions. An extreme case of an almost infinitely dilute solution can be imagined as one made by putting one molecule of AB in a barrel of solvent. When the molecule breaks up to form ions, the chance that the ions will come together is vanishingly small. Since the one molecule is dissociated, the percent dissociation

Concentration	Observed freezing point, °C	Freezing-point lowering, °C per molal NaCl
0.1 m NaCl	−0.347	3.47
0.01 m NaCl	−0.0361	3.61
0.001 m NaCl	−0.00366	3.66
0.0001 m NaCl	−0.000372	3.72

8.10
Concentration dependence
of freezing-point lowering

must be 100%. At infinite dilution, all electrolytes approach 100% dissociation.*

The definition that a strong electrolyte is one that is highly dissociated and a weak electrolyte is one that is slightly dissociated is ambiguous, since in very dilute solutions all electrolytes are almost completely dissociated. The ambiguity is reduced by adopting the convention that a 1 M solution be the criterion. If the substance in 1 M solution is highly dissociated, it is generally called a strong electrolyte; if in 1 M solution it is slightly dissociated, it is generally called a weak electrolyte.

8.6 INTERIONIC ATTRACTIONS

In a solution of NaCl in water the hydrated Na^+ and Cl^- ions are separated, on the average, by many H_2O molecules. It is in this sense that NaCl is 100% dissociated and is expected to depress the freezing point of water by twice the normal amount. However, the solute particles carry electric charges; hence, there are attractions between the separated ions of opposite charge. Owing to these attractions, the positive and negative ions in a water solution of NaCl do not act completely independently of each other. Therefore, 1 mole of NaCl is not quite so effective in lowering the freezing point of water as 2 moles of nonelectrolyte are.

The attraction between ions decreases rapidly with increasing distance. In a dilute solution of NaCl the ions are rather widely separated and the interionic attractions are small. However, as the concentration is increased, the ions are closer together, the interionic attractions are bigger, and the ions act less independently of each other. The freezing-point lowering *per mole* of NaCl is smaller in concentrated solutions than in dilute solutions, as shown in Figure 8.10. Taken at face value, the numbers seem to indicate that, in 0.1 m solution, 1 mole of NaCl produces fewer particles than it does in more dilute solution. The trend is the same as that observed for a weak electrolyte such as $HC_2H_3O_2$. It is not surprising that for many years chemists were unable to decide whether or not NaCl is completely dissociated in water.

* Strictly speaking, 100% dissociation can be reached only if the solvent has no dissociation fragments in common with the solute. For example, in water there is a trace of H^+ and OH^- from self-dissociation of H_2O, the presence of which prevents complete dissociation of solutes such as HX or MOH. For the example of Figure 8.9 the maximum attainable percent dissociation cannot exceed 99.4%, a number which is fixed by the dissociation constant of acetic acid (see page 263).

The Debye-Hückel interionic-attraction theory of electrolytes accounts quantitatively for the attraction between completely dissociated ions and justifies the view that NaCl and other ionic solids are completely dissociated in water solution. Further, this theory can be applied to calculate the interionic attractions in a solution of a weak electrolyte. This calculation must be made for accurate determination of percent dissociation from freezing-point data. Even the Debye-Hückel theory does not account for the observed freezing-point lowering by electrolytes in concentrated solutions. One important effect is that there are insufficient water molecules to hydrate all the ions. Concentrated solutions are not well understood at present.

8.7 SOLUBILITY

The term "solubility" is used in several senses. It describes the qualitative idea of the solution process. It also is used quantitatively to describe the composition of solutions. The solutions considered up to now represent *unsaturated solutions,* to which solute can be added successively to produce a whole series of solutions differing in concentration. With any solute and solvent a large number of unsaturated solutions are possible. However, in most cases, the process of adding solute cannot go on indefinitely. Eventually, a stage is reached beyond which the addition of solute to a specified amount of solvent does not produce another solution of higher concentration. Instead, solute remains undissolved. In these cases there is a limit to the amount of solute which can be dissolved in a given amount of solvent. The solution which represents this limit is called a *saturated solution,* and the concentration of the saturated solution is called the *solubility* of the given solute in the particular solvent used.

The best way to ensure having a saturated solution is to have an excess of solute in contact with the solution. If the solution is unsaturated, solute disappears until saturation is established. If the solution is saturated, the amount of excess solute remains unchanged, as does the concentration of the solution. The system is in a state of equilibrium. Apparently, it is a state of dynamic equilibrium, since, for example, an irregularly shaped crystal of solute dropped into the solution changes its shape although remaining constant in mass. In the equilibrium state, dissolving of solute is still occurring but is compensated for by precipitation of solute out of solution. The number of solute particles going into solution per unit time is equal to the number of solute particles leaving the solution per unit time. The concentration of solute in the solution remains constant; the amount of solute in excess remains constant. The amount of excess solute present in contact with the saturated solution does not affect the concentration of the saturated solution. In fact, it is possible to filter or separate the excess solute completely and still have a saturated solution. For convenience, a *saturated solution is defined as one which is or would be in equilibrium with excess solute.*

The concentration of the saturated solution, i.e., the solubility, depends on (1) the nature of the solvent, (2) the nature of the solute,

(3) the temperature, and (4) the pressure. In considering these we should keep in mind that three important interactions operate in the dissolving process: Solute particles are separated one from the other (this takes energy); solvent particles are pushed apart to make a hole to accommodate the solute (this also takes energy); solvent particles attract the solute particles (this provides energy). This set of interactions—solute-solute, solvent-solvent, and solute-solvent—is useful in discussing the magnitude of the solubility. However, as mentioned in Section 7.9, the tendency for spontaneous change is decided not only by energy balance but also by entropy changes. In the case of the solution process this means that due consideration must be given to the fact that the solution represents a more disordered and hence more probable state than that of the unmixed components. Thus, dissolving will frequently occur—because of this entropy increase—even when the solute-solvent interactions are not energetically favorable enough to compensate for the sum of solute-solute and solvent-solvent interactions.

1. Nature of the solvent. A useful generalization much quoted in chemistry is that "like dissolves like." More specifically, high solubility occurs when the molecules of the solute are similar in structure and electrical properties to the molecules of the solvent. When there is a similarity of electrical properties, e.g., high dipole moment, between solute and solvent, then solute-solvent attractions are particularly strong. When there is dissimilarity, solute-solvent attractions are weak. For this reason a polar substance such as H_2O usually is a good solvent for a polar substance such as alcohol but a poor solvent for a nonpolar substance such as gasoline.

In general, an ionic solid has a higher solubility in a polar solvent than in a nonpolar solvent. For example, at room temperature the solubility of NaCl in H_2O is 311 g per liter of solution, whereas the solubility of NaCl in gasoline is essentially zero. Also, the more polar the solvent, the greater the solubility of ionic solids. For example, at room temperature, the solubility of NaCl in ethyl alcohol is 0.51 g per liter of solution, compared to 311 g per liter of solution in water. The difference is ascribed to the lower polarity (lower dipole moment) of the ethyl alcohol molecule, with resulting lower attractions for the ions.

2. Nature of the solute. Changing the solute means changing the solute-solute and solute-solvent interactions. At room temperature the amount of sucrose that can be dissolved in water is 1311 g per liter of solution. This is more than 4 times as great as the solubility of NaCl. However, these numbers are rather misleading. The number of particles involved can better be seen by comparing the molar solubilities. A saturated solution of NaCl is 5.3 M, whereas a saturated solution of sugar is 3.8 M. On a molar basis NaCl has a higher solubility in H_2O than sugar has. Since the attractions in solid NaCl are greater than those in sugar, the reason for the higher solubility of NaCl apparently lies in the fact that the interactions between Na^+ and Cl^- and water molecules are greater than the interactions between the sugar molecules and water molecules.

What effect has the presence of one solute in a solution on the solubility of another solute in that same solution? As a crude approxima-

Substance	0°	10°	20°	30°	40°	50°
$AgC_2H_3O_2$	0.72	0.88	1.04	1.21	1.41	1.64
$AgNO_3$	122	170	222	300	376	455
KCl	27.6	31.0	34.0	37.0	40.0	42.6
$NaCl$	35.7	35.8	36.0	36.3	36.6	37.0
Li_2CO_3	1.54	1.43	1.33	1.25	1.17	1.08
$CO_2(g)$ at 1 atm	0.33	0.23	0.17	0.13	0.097	0.076
$SO_2(g)$ at 1 atm	22.8	16.2	11.3	7.8	5.4	4.5
$O_2(g)$ at 1 atm	0.0070	0.0054	0.0044	0.0037	0.0033	0.0030

8.11
Change of solubility with temperature (solubility in grams of solute per 100 g of H_2O)

tion, unless the concentration of a substance is high, it has little effect. For example, approximately the same concentration of NaCl can be dissolved in 0.1 M sugar solution as in pure water. However, the solubility of NaCl is drastically affected by a solute having an ion in common, such as KCl or NaNO₃.

3. *Temperature.* The solubility of *gases in water* usually decreases as the temperature of the solution increases. The tiny bubbles which form when water is heated are due to the fact that dissolved air becomes less soluble at higher temperatures. The flat taste characteristic of boiled water is largely due to the fact that dissolved air has been expelled. However, in the case of *gases in other liquid solvents* (and, in fact, even in water at higher temperatures) the solubility of the gases need not decrease with increasing temperature. Similarly, there is no general rule for the temperature change of solubility of *liquids* and *solids*. For example, with increasing temperature, lithium carbonate decreases in solubility in water, potassium chloride increases, and sodium chloride shows practically no change. Specific data are given in Figure 8.11 for the solubility of various substances in water.

The change of solubility with temperature is closely related to the heat of solution of the substance. The *heat of solution* is the heat evolved when a solute dissolves to give the saturated solution and can be written as the heat that accompanies the following process:

Solute + solvent ⟶ saturated solution + heat of solution

The heat of solution as experimentally determined can be a positive quantity, in which case heat is evolved to the surroundings, or it can be a negative quantity, in which case heat is absorbed from the surroundings. For example, the heat of solution of lithium carbonate is positive. Heat is evolved and usually appears as a rise in temperature of the solution. The heat of solution of potassium chloride is negative. We can write for the process

$KCl(s) + H_2O \longrightarrow$ solution $-$ heat

or

Heat $+ KCl(s) + H_2O \longrightarrow$ solution

Heat must be supplied, since the process is endothermic. When a substance with negative heat of solution is dissolved, there is usually a drop in the temperature of the solution.

Whether the heat of solution is positive or negative depends on the nature of the solute and the solvent. Specifically, when solids are dissolved in water, the heat of solution depends on the relative magnitude of two energies, the energy required to break up the solid lattice and the energy liberated when the particles are hydrated. In the case of potassium chloride, the overall process can be imagined to occur in two consecutive steps:

$$KCl(s) \longrightarrow K^+(g) + Cl^-(g)$$

$$K^+(g) + Cl^-(g) \xrightarrow[\text{water}]{} K^+(aq) + Cl^-(aq)$$

The first step, vaporizing the solid, requires energy. Work must be done to separate the positive and negative ions from each other. The amount of energy required per mole is called the *lattice energy*. The second step liberates energy. As the water molecules are separated from each other and attracted to the ions, energy is liberated to the surroundings. This energy is called the *hydration energy*.* When the hydration energy is greater than the lattice energy, the overall solution process liberates energy to the surroundings and is exothermic. When less energy is furnished by step (2) than is required by step (1), the overall solution process is endothermic. In a few cases the lattice energy is approximately equal to the hydration energy. For example, the lattice energy of NaCl is 184 kcal mole^{-1} and the hydration energy is 183 kcal mole^{-1}. The heat of solution of NaCl is the difference between these two values and is nearly zero.

We might ask why it is that NaCl dissolves in water, since it takes 184 kcal of heat to break up the lattice whereas only 183 kcal is made available on hydrating the ions. The answer is that although energetically unfavorable, the process still goes because of favorable entropy change. Figure 8.12 shows the quantitative values leading to this conclusion. The overall process, shown in the last line, is the sum of the two preceding steps. For each process, values are listed for ΔH, ΔS, and ΔG at 298°K. ΔH represents the increase in heat content or enthalpy (Section 7.9) and is equal but opposite in sign to the "heat of reaction." Because there is often confusion as to sign convention, we illustrate specifically for the second step of Figure 8.12. The equation

$$Na^+(g) + Cl^-(g) \longrightarrow Na^+(aq) + Cl^-(aq) + 183 \text{ kcal}$$

indicates that 183 kcal is *liberated* by the hydration of the ions. It follows, then, that the heat content of the material has *decreased* by 183 kcal (lost to the surroundings). Therefore, we can write

* Note that the hydration energy actually takes into account both the solvent-solvent interaction (the energy required to make a hole in the water) and the solvent-solute interaction. These are lumped together because experimentally they are hard to separate. In other words, we cannot hydrate an ion without first making room for it any more than we can make a hole in the water without putting something in it.

$$Na^+(g) + Cl^-(g) \longrightarrow Na^+(aq) + Cl^-(aq)$$

$$\Delta H = -183 \text{ kcal mole}^{-1}$$

Similarly, ΔS represents the increase in entropy (Section 7.9); ΔG represents the increase in free energy and is equal to $\Delta H - T\Delta S$. The important point to note is that, for the final overall process, although ΔH is positive, ΔG turns out to be negative; hence, the reaction is favored. The favorable ΔG comes about because the $T\Delta S$ term, which is equal to $(298°)(0.0103 \text{ kcal mole}^{-1} \text{ deg}^{-1}) = 3.07 \text{ kcal mole}^{-1}$, subtracts from the unfavorable ΔH of $+1$ kcal mole^{-1} to give -2 kcal mole^{-1}. The positive ΔS term arises from the fact that ions in the solution, although more restricted than in the gaseous state, have considerably more freedom than in solid NaCl. The overall change is one of increasing disorder and hence of increasing entropy.

Once the appropriate thermodynamic parameters are known, the behavior of a saturated solution with respect to changing temperature can be deduced. Consider, for example, a solute whose solubility is limited by an unfavorable ΔH for dissolving to give the saturated solu-

Process	$\Delta H,$ kcal mole^{-1}	$\Delta S,$ kcal mole^{-1} deg^{-1}	$\Delta G,$ kcal mole^{-1}
NaCl(s) $\longrightarrow$ Na$^+$(g) + Cl$^-$(g)	+184	+0.0543	+168
Na$^+$(g) + Cl$^-$(g) $\longrightarrow$ Na$^+$(aq) + Cl$^-$(aq)	−183	−0.0440	−170
NaCl(s) $\longrightarrow$ Na$^+$(aq) + Cl$^-$(aq)	+1	+0.0103	−2

8.12
Thermodynamic parameters at 298°K

tion. In the equilibrium state, $\Delta G = 0$, i.e., there is no change in free energy per mole if an infinitesimal amount of solute is transferred into or out of the saturated solution. This condition of $\Delta G = 0$ has come about because the unfavorable ΔH is just balanced out by a favorable $T\Delta S$. What happens if T is increased slightly? Assuming ΔH and ΔS stay constant, only T changes. Hence, $T\Delta S$ wins out and more solute can dissolve. Stated differently, in this case where both ΔH and ΔS are positive, an increase of T at equilibrium makes $\Delta H - T\Delta S = \Delta G$ less than zero and so leads to spontaneous dissolving of additional solute.

In some cases solubility is limited not by an unfavorable ΔH but by an unfavorable $T\Delta S$. This happens if ΔH is negative, i.e., the reaction is exothermic in that the heat content decreases, and if ΔS is also negative, i.e., the reaction produces order, as by making an orderly structure of solvent molecules about the solute ions. In this case an increase of T (again assuming ΔH and ΔS constant) increases the unfavorable $T\Delta S$ term, so $\Delta H - T\Delta S = \Delta G$ becomes greater than zero. As a result, precipitation, which is the reverse of dissolving, should occur as the temperature rises.

To summarize, if the saturated solution is one in which ΔH for dissolving is positive (endothermic reaction), the solubility increases with rising temperature; if it is one in which ΔH is negative (exothermic reaction), the solubility decreases with rising temperature. A convenient way of remembering the direction of the effects is in terms of Le Chatelier's principle (Section 7.7). If the dissolving process absorbs heat, the stress of increased temperature can be relieved by favoring the dissolving reaction. If the dissolving process liberates heat, the stress of increased temperature can be relieved by the reverse process, namely, precipitation.

4. Pressure. The solubility of all *gases* is increased as the partial pressure of the gas above the solution is increased. Quantitatively, this is expressed in *Henry's law,* which states that at constant temperature the *ratio of partial pressure of solute gas divided by the mole fraction of the gas in solution is a constant.* For example, the concentration of CO_2 which is dissolved in a carbonated beverage (e.g., champagne) is dependent directly on the partial pressure of CO_2 in the gas phase. When a bottle is opened, the pressure of carbon dioxide drops, its solubility is diminished, and bubbles of carbon dioxide form and escape from the beverage. So far as liquids and solids are concerned, there is essentially no change of solubility with pressure. If there is a change, it can be predicted by Le Chatelier's principle, since it depends on the relative volume of the solution and the component substances. In general, the volume change on solution is so small that the pressure must be made very high, thousands of atmospheres, in order to change the solubility appreciably.

In closing this section on solubility we need to note that it is sometimes possible to prepare solutions which have a higher concentration of solute than that of the saturated solution. Such solutions are *supersaturated* and are unstable with respect to the separation of excess solute. A supersaturated solution of sodium acetate, $NaC_2H_3O_2$, for example, can be made as follows: A saturated solution of $NaC_2H_3O_2$ and H_2O in contact with excess solute is heated until the increase of solubility with temperature is sufficient to dissolve all the excess solute. At sufficiently high temperatures an unsaturated solution results. This unsaturated solution is then cooled very carefully. The system ought to return to its original equilibrium state with the excess solute crystallized out. This, in fact, does happen with most solids. However, with some, such as sodium acetate, cooling can be accomplished without crystallization. The resulting solution has a concentration of solute higher than would correspond to the saturated solution at the lower temperature. It is supersaturated. The situation is reminiscent of that observed in the supercooling of a liquid below its freezing point. Supersaturation can usually be destroyed in the same manner, i.e., by seeding. When a tiny seed crystal of sodium acetate is placed in a supersaturated solution of sodium acetate, excess solute crystallizes on it until the remaining solution is just saturated. Occasionally, a mechanical disturbance such as a sudden shock may suffice to break the supersaturation. Dust particles or even scratches on the inner surface of the container may act as centers on which crystallization can start.

8.8 COLLOIDS

In introducing the topic of solutions it was more or less implied that it is easily possible to distinguish between a homogeneous mixture and a heterogeneous mixture. However, this distinction is not a sharp one. There are systems which are neither obviously homogeneous nor obviously heterogeneous. They are classed as intermediate and are known as *colloids*. In order to get an idea of what a colloid is, we imagine a process in which a sample of solid is placed in a liquid and subdivided. So long as distinct particles of solid are visible to the naked eye, there is no question that the system is heterogeneous. On standing, these visible particles separate out. Depending on the relative density of the solid and the liquid, the solid particles float to the top or settle to the bottom. They can be separated easily by filtration. As the solid is progressively subdivided, a state in which the dispersed particles have been broken down to individual molecules or atoms is eventually reached. In this limit, a solution in which two phases can no longer be distinguished is produced. No matter how powerful a microscope is used, a solution appears uniform throughout, and individual molecules cannot be seen. On standing, the dispersed particles do not separate out, nor can they be separated by filtration.

Between coarse suspensions and true solutions there is a region of change from heterogeneity to homogeneity. In this region dispersed particles are so small that they do not form an obviously separate phase, but they are not so small that they can be said to be in true solution. This state of subdivision is called the *colloidal state*. On standing, the particles of a colloid do not separate out at any appreciable rate; they cannot be seen under a microscope; nor can they be separated by filtration. The dividing lines between colloids and solutions and between colloids and discrete phases are not rigorously fixed, since a continuous gradation of particle size is possible. Usually, however, colloids are defined as a separate class on the basis of size. When the particle size lies between about 10^{-7} and 10^{-4} cm, the dispersion is called a *colloid, a colloidal suspension,* or a *colloidal solution.*

The size of a dispersed particle does not tell anything about the constitution of the particle. The particle may consist of atoms, of small molecules, or of one giant molecule sometimes called a macromolecule. For example, colloidal gold consists of various-sized particles each containing a million or more gold atoms. Colloidal sulfur can be made with particles containing a thousand or so S_8 molecules. An example of a macromolecule is hemoglobin, the protein responsible for the red color of blood. The molecular mass of this molecule is 66800, and the diameter is approximately 3×10^{-7} cm.

Colloids are frequently classified on the basis of the states of aggregation of the component phases, even though the separate phases are not visibly distinguishable once the colloid is formed. The more important classifications are *sols, emulsions, gels,* and *aerosols.* In *sols* a solid is dispersed through a liquid, so that the liquid forms the continuous phase and bits of solid form the discontinuous phase. Milk of

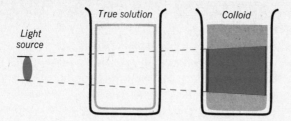

Light source   True solution   Colloid

magnesia is a sol consisting of solid particles of magnesium hydroxide dispersed through water. Sols can be made by breaking down large particles or building up small particles to colloidal dimensions. Colloidal gold can be made by striking an electric arc between two gold electrodes under water. It can also be made by the chemical reduction of chlorauric acid, $HAuCl_4$, by a slow reducing agent such as hydrazine, N_2H_4. Investigation of gold sol by X rays has shown that the particles of gold which are dispersed throughout the water are crystalline in nature.

Emulsions are colloids in which a liquid is dispersed through a liquid. A common example is ordinary milk, which consists of butterfat globules dispersed through an aqueous solution. A *gel* is an unusual type of colloid in which a liquid contains a solid arranged in a fine network extending throughout the system. Both the solid and the liquid phases are continuous. Examples of gels are jellies, gelatin, agar, and slimy precipitates such as aluminum hydroxide. An *aerosol* is a colloid made by dispersing either a solid or a liquid in a gas. The former is called a smoke and the latter a fog.

8.9 LIGHT SCATTERING

When a beam of light is passed through a solution or a pure liquid, the path of the beam is not visible from the side. The dissolved particles are too small to scatter much light. In a colloid the particles are big enough to scatter the light. Therefore, when a beam of light is turned on a colloid, an observer to one side can see the path of the beam. The situation is shown in Figure 8.13. This effect, called the Tyndall effect, can be produced readily by turning a column of light on an aqueous solution of sodium thiosulfate, $Na_2S_2O_3$, and adding a few drops of dilute acid. The ensuing chemical reaction produces elemental sulfur. The light beam is invisible until the sulfur particles aggregate to colloidal dimensions.

By taking into consideration the wave nature of light, information can be obtained from the Tyndall effect about the size and shape of the scattering particles. In an ordinary solution the particles of solute are much smaller than the wavelength of the light. Visible light has a wavelength ranging from 4000 to 7200 Å, or from 4.0×10^{-5} to 7.2×10^{-5} cm. Solute particles that are 5 Å or so in diameter are too small to affect a wave of such length. However, when solute particles are of the order of several thousand angstrom units in diameter, the light beam is scattered or diffracted and becomes visible from the side.

Careful studies of this scattering have been used to determine the size of macromolecules.

When a microscope is focused on a Tyndall beam, light is reflected up into the microscope. Although the colloidal particle itself is too small to be seen, its position may be fixed by noting where the light appears. When observed in this way, colloidal particles are seen to undergo Brownian motion, the rapid, random, zigzag motion previously mentioned in discussing gases (Section 5.10). The smaller the particle size, the more violent the Brownian motion.

Under ordinary circumstances, it is observed that a colloid in an uninsulated container does not settle out. However, when the colloid is kept in a well-insulated container, after a time there will be a gradation in the concentration of colloidal particles from the top to the bottom of the sample. This gradation in concentration develops because there are two opposing effects: (1) the attraction due to gravity, which tends to pull heavier particles down, and (2) the dispersing effect due to Brownian motion. The more massive the particles, the more important is effect 1 and the more pronounced is the concentration gradation.* The main reason no appreciable concentration gradient is observed for colloids in uninsulated containers is that there are convection currents due to nonuniform temperature. These currents keep the colloidal suspension constantly stirred up.

8.10 ADSORPTION

In some colloids the particles adsorb electric charge. For example, ferric oxide sol consists of positively charged aggregates of ferric oxide units. The positive charge enhances the stability of the colloid. Normally, when one particle in its Brownian motion hits another, the two coagulate to form a larger particle. A particle that results from collisions between large particles may be so large that Brownian motion cannot keep it in suspension. However, ferric oxide has great adsorption power for H^+. Presumably the H^+ ions are stuck on oxygen atoms which protrude from the particles. A particle which has H^+ adsorbed on it has a net positive charge and thereby repels any similarly charged particle. The charged ferric oxide particles try to stay as far apart from each other on the average as possible. There is little chance that they will come together to form a large mass which settles out. Arsenious sulfide, As_2S_3, forms a negative sol by adsorbing SH^- or OH^- ions. It is not surprising that mixing a positively charged ferric oxide sol with a negatively charged arsenious sulfide sol coagulates them both.

That some colloidal particles are electrically charged can be shown by studying *electrophoresis, the migration of colloidal particles in an electric field.* Figure 8.14 shows the experimental setup. A U tube is

* Two extreme cases can be imagined. In that of rocks in water the settling is so pronounced that all the rocks are at the bottom. In that of a true solution, such as sugar in water, the gradation in concentration is so slight that only the most careful experiments involving very tall columns and precise temperature control could show any difference in concentration between the top and bottom of the sample.

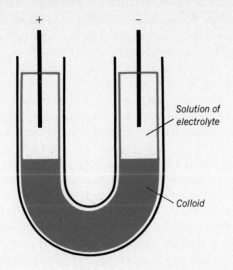

+   −

Solution of
electrolyte

Colloid

partly filled with the colloidal solution. Very carefully, so as not to disturb the colloid, the remainder of the U tube is filled with a solution of an electrolyte. The electrolytic solution needs to be of lower density (so that it will stay on top), different in appearance from the colloid (so that the boundary can be clearly seen), and appreciably electrically conducting. The choice of electrolyte is limited by the fact that many electrolytes coagulate colloids, but usually a salt, such as sodium bromide, which does not affect the colloid can be found. Electrodes are inserted into the solution, with one electrode positively charged and the other negatively charged. After a time that may range from 30 min to 48 hr, the boundaries between the colloid and the electrolyte solution have shifted because of migration of the colloid through the solvent.

From the direction of migration of the colloid the sign of the charge of the colloidal particles can be determined. For example, when the electrophoresis of ferric oxide sol is observed in this cell, the boundary moves toward the negative electrode and away from the positive electrode, suggesting that the colloid is positively charged. By observing the rate at which migration occurs, it is also possible to get information about the size and the shape of the colloidal particles. The study of electrophoresis has been applied with great success to protein molecules. In acid solution protein molecules pick up hydrogen ions to become positively charged. From the migration in an electric field it has been possible to draw inferences about their size and shape. Some, like gamma globulin, seem to be spherical in shape. Others, such as fibrinogen, the blood-clotting agent, are shaped like cigars. Knowledge of the size and shape of protein molecules should help in understanding their behavior.

Some colloidal particles adsorb films of molecules, which shield them from other particles. An example of this adsorption is found in gelatin. Gelatin is a high-molecular-weight protein which has the property of tying to itself a sheath of water. This film of very tightly bound water protects the gelatin particle from coagulating with another gelatin particle. If two gelatin particles collide, they do not coagulate, because the gelatin parts have not been able to get in contact with each other. This property of gelatin is used in stabilizing colloids of silver bromide in preparing photographic film. When finely divided silver bromide is stirred up with water, it settles out. However, if the silver bromide is mixed with gelatin, the gelatin forms a film on the outside of the silver bromide. The gelatin in turn adsorbs a layer of water, so that essentially two protective films have formed on silver bromide to keep it in suspension.

There are two reasons for the high adsorptive properties shown by colloids. One is the extremely large surface area. Subdivision of a solid, for example, may increase its surface area by many factors of 10. One cubic centimeter of sulfur in the form of a cube 1 cm on edge has a surface area of 6 cm^2 or about 1 in.^{2}. However, 1 cc of sulfur ground up into cubes which are 10^{-5} cm on the edge has its surface area increased to 6×10^5 cm^2, or about 700 ft^2. The second reason for great adsorption is that surface atoms have special properties. The valence of surface atoms is usually not satisfied, since the atom is designed to bond in three dimensions, which it cannot do at the surface. The greater the state of subdivision, the greater the fraction of atoms that have unsatisfied valence forces.

Charcoal is a substance in which the surface atoms are an appreciable fraction of the total number. It consists of solid carbon with a fine network of tunnels extending through the specimen. The surface area has been determined to be of the order of 1000 ft^2 g^{-1}. On all this large surface area are carbon atoms which have unsaturated valence. They can attract molecules, especially polar molecules, thus accounting for the high adsorption that is characteristic of charcoal. When a mixture of hydrogen sulfide, H$_2$S, and oxygen is passed over a charcoal surface, the H$_2$S is selectively adsorbed. Because H$_2$S is a polar molecule with the sulfur end more negative than the hydrogen end, it is more strongly adsorbed than the oxygen molecule, which is symmetrical and nonpolar. The charcoal gas mask makes use of this principle of selective adsorption. The charcoal selectively adsorbs poisonous gases, which are usually complicated polar molecules, and lets the oxygen through for respiration.

At higher temperatures molecular motion makes adsorption more difficult. Thus, charcoal with its surface completely covered may be reactivated by heating it up to drive off adsorbed gases. At low temperatures, where molecular motion is slight, adsorption increases. In fact, at very low temperatures selectivity is less pronounced and even nonpolar molecules may be adsorbed, presumably because of van der Waals attraction. At liquid-nitrogen temperatures ($-196°C$) even oxygen gas is strongly adsorbed on charcoal.

QUESTIONS

8.1 Concentration   A given solution of ethanol (C$_2$H$_5$OH) in water is 10.00% alcohol by volume and has a density of 0.9866 g ml^{-1}. If pure ethanol has a density of 0.785 g ml^{-1}, calculate the percent by weight of the above solution.

8.2 Solubility   Other things equal, which will be more soluble: (*a*) A solute with a high lattice energy or one with a low lattice energy? (*b*) A solute with a high hydration energy or one with a low hydration energy? Explain.

8.3 Phase diagram   On the same set of axes sketch the phase diagrams for (*a*) pure water, (*b*) a 1 *m* solution of a nonelectrolyte in water, (*c*) a 1 *m* solution of a strong electrolyte (MX) in water.

8.4 Properties of solutions   A given aqueous solution of nondissociating solute freezes at $-1.30°C$. What is its boiling point?

8.5 Concentration   Figure 8.11 states that, for KCl in H_2O at 20°C, the solubility is 34.0 g KCl per 100 g H_2O. If the density of this solution is 1.17 g ml^{-1}, what is (*a*) the mole fraction of KCl, (*b*) the molality, (*c*) the molarity?

8.6 Heat of solution   For the dissolving of CsF in H_2O, ΔH is -9 kcal $mole^{-1}$. (*a*) Is the dissolving exothermic or endothermic? (*b*) Should the solubility of CsF increase or decrease with rising temperature? (*c*) Which is greater, the lattice energy of CsF or the hydration energy of Cs^+ and F^-?

8.7 Colloids   What should happen to the light-scattering properties of a colloid as the frequency of light is lowered? Explain.

8.8 Boiling-point elevation   A solution of 4.00 g of nonvolatile, nondissociating solute in 180.0 g of CCl_4 raises the boiling point of CCl_4 from 76.8 to 78.5°C. By using the data of Section 8.3, calculate the molecular mass of X.

8.9 Concentration   A solution that is 50.0% by weight of C_2H_5OH in H_2O has a density of 0.914 g ml^{-1}. Calculate for C_2H_5OH in this solution: (*a*) mole fraction, (*b*) molarity, (*c*) molality.

8.10 Concentration   (*a*) What would be the molality of a solution made by mixing equal volumes of 30.0% by weight H_2SO_4 (density 1.218 g ml^{-1}) and 70.0% by weight H_2SO_4 (density 1.610 g ml^{-1})? (*b*) If the density of the resulting solution is 1.425 g ml^{-1}, what is its molarity?

8.11 Macromolecules   Proteins are known to range in molecular mass from 12000 to at least 3 million amu. Assuming spherical particles with a density of 1.4 g cc^{-1}, calculate the range of molecular radii of protein molecules.

8.12 Freezing point of colloids   A typical protein has a molecular mass of 100000 amu. Given an aqueous solution that is 2.0% by weight of this protein, calculate its freezing point.

8.13 Solid solution   Given a solid of formula A_3B that crystallizes with a face-centered cubic arrangement. Two possible situations may arise: (*a*) all the A atoms are on face centers and all the B atoms are at the corners of the cube; (*b*) A and B are distributed at random over both kinds of sites. Which of these situations might properly be called a solution? Which has a higher entropy? Justify your answers.

8.14 Concentration   Which contains a greater mole fraction of solute, a 4.0 *M* solution or a 4.0 *m* solution? Explain.

8.15 Concentration   For which of the concentration units defined in Section 8.2 will concentration of a particular solution not change with temperature?

8.16 Concentration   The concentration of certain solutions of spirits is stated on the label in terms of "proof." In the United States 100 proof is defined as containing one-half its volume of pure alcohol (C_2H_5OH) at 60°F. Pure alcohol at 60°F has a density of 0.793 g ml^{-1}. Calculate the molarity of "Old 86 Proof."

8.17 Raoult's law   A nonvolatile solute X depresses the vapor pressure of ethanol (C_2H_5OH) from 43.9 to 39.3 torr when 1.00 g of X is dissolved in 10.0 g of ethanol. Assuming ideal behavior, calculate the molecular mass of X.

8.18 Raoult's law   At 25°C the equilibrium vapor pressure of pure methanol (CH_3OH) is 96.0 torr and that of pure ethanol (C_2H_5OH) is 43.9 torr. Assuming ideal behavior, what would be the total vapor pressure of a 50.0 weight percent mixture of methanol and ethanol?

8.19 Properties of solutions   A given aqueous solution freezes at −0.672°C and boils at 100.25°C. How might this be explained?

8.20 Freezing point   A solution is prepared from 100 g of H_2O and 2.00 g of compound X. It has a final volume of 101 ml and a freezing point of −0.620°C. Calculate the molality, mole fraction, and molarity of X, assuming it does not dissociate in solution.

8.21 Freezing-point depression   Two elements A and B form compounds having molecular formulas AB_2 and AB_4. When dissolved in 20.0 g of benzene, 1.00 g of AB_2 lowers the freezing point 2.3°C, whereas 1.00 g of AB_4 lowers the freezing point 1.3°C. By using the data of Section 8.3, calculate the atomic masses of A and of B.

8.22 Percent dissociation   A solution prepared by dissolving 0.100 g of HF per 50.0 g of H_2O shows a freezing point of −0.198°C. What is the percent dissociation of HF?

8.23 Solubility   By using the data of Figure 8.11, calculate the mass of $AgNO_3$ that should precipitate when 100.0 g of saturated $AgNO_3$ solution is cooled from 30 to 0°C.

8.24 Thermodynamic parameters   Consider a process in which an infinitesimal amount of solute dissolves in the saturated solution. Suppose that the dissolving is endothermic. At equilibrium, of the three parameters ΔG, ΔH, and ΔS, one is positive, one is negative, and one is zero. Tell which is which and give the meaning of each.

8.25 Gas solubility   For nitrogen the Henry's law constant (ratio of partial pressure, in torr, to mole fraction in aqueous solution) equals 5.75×10^7 at 20°C and 9.20×10^7 at 70°C. (*a*) Calculate the molality of dissolved N_2 at these temperatures when the partial pressure of N_2 in the atmosphere is 600 torr. (*b*) Given 1 kg of water saturated with N_2

at 20°C, what volume of N_2 gas (calculated at 70°C and one standard atmosphere) would be liberated on heating the solution to 70°C?

8.26 Dissociation (a) A solution is prepared by dissolving 0.120 mole of weak acid HX in 200 g of H_2O. If the freezing point of the solution is $-1.30°C$, what is the apparent percent dissociation of the acid in this solution? (b) Is this the actual degree of dissociation? If not, explain briefly. (c) What would happen (qualitatively) to both the percent dissociation and concentration of ions if water were added to the solution?

8.27 Concentration Given a solution whose molarity M is identically equal to its molality m. In terms of these symbols and W for the molecular mass of the solute, derive an expression for the density of the solution.

8.28 Freezing-point depression Glauber's salt is $Na_2SO_4 \cdot 10H_2O$, where the $\cdot 10H_2O$ indicates that 10 moles of H_2O are incorporated in the crystal per mole of Na_2SO_4. Assuming complete dissociation, calculate the expected freezing point of a solution prepared by dissolving 6.00 g of $Na_2SO_4 \cdot 10H_2O$ in 0.100 kg of H_2O.

8.29 Gas solubility At 0°C and 1.00 atm pressure CO_2 dissolves in water to give a mole fraction of 1.37×10^{-3}. Consider a bottle completely filled with an aqueous solution of density 1.00 g ml^{-1} saturated with CO_2 at STP. Imagine all the H_2O molecules to be removed from the bottle, leaving only gaseous CO_2. Assuming ideal behavior, calculate the final pressure inside the bottle.

8.30 Concentration Under what condition could the molality of a solute be less than its molarity?

8.31 Types of solutions A gaseous solution, saturated with respect to one component, corresponds to a solid or liquid with finite vapor pressure. Explain.

8.32 Thermodynamic parameters The changes in heat content (ΔH) for $MI(s) \longrightarrow M^+(aq) + I^-(aq)$ for the alkali iodides are $-15, -2, +5, +7$, and $+9$ kcal mole^{-1} for LiI, NaI, KI, RbI, and CsI, respectively. The corresponding entropy changes (ΔS) are $+0.0114, +0.0170, +0.0257, +0.0276$, and $+0.0269$ kcal mole^{-1} deg^{-1}. Predict which of these iodides should be least soluble at 25°C and which at 100°C. Assume ΔH and ΔS do not change with temperature.

8.33 Surface area Given that the surface area in charcoal is 1000 ft^2 g^{-1}. Imagine a block of carbon (density 2.25 g cc^{-1}) drilled with a square array of round parallel holes that just touch each other. What must be the radius of each hole to account for the observed surface area?

ANSWERS

8.1 7.96%   *8.4* 100.36°C   *8.8* 66 amu   *8.9* (a) 0.281   (b) 9.93 M (c) 21.7 m *8.11* 15 to 95 Å   *8.16* 7.4 M *8.18* 74.6 torr   *8.21* 26 and 43 amu   *8.23* 44.5 g   *8.25* (a) 5.79×10^{-4} m, 3.62×10^{-4} m (b) 6.11 cc   *8.28* $-1.01°C$ *8.29* 1.71 atm   *8.33* 3.5×10^{-6} cm

9 solution reactions

One reason for the heavy emphasis on solutions is that a large fraction of all chemical reactions are carried out in solutions. In this chapter we shall consider in some detail the various kinds of solution reactions. In the discussions we shall give special attention to what species are present and what changes they undergo.

9.1 ACIDS AND BASES

Several definitions of acids and bases are in common use, and there is no general agreement on which is the most useful. It is therefore necessary for a chemist to be familiar with each of the definitions. We shall consider first the simplest one, that due to Arrhenius, the discoverer of electrolytic dissociation. He accounted for the traditional acidic properties (viz., sour taste, makes litmus red, reacts with metals to liberate hydrogen) by postulating that all acids have the formula HX and can dissociate to give H^+ and X^-. It might be noted that X^- itself may contain a dissociable proton and hence could also be an acid. Thus, for Arrhenius, acids would include HCl, HNO_3, H_2SO_4, HSO_4^-, and $HC_2H_3O_2$. Along with this definition of acid, Arrhenius proposed that all bases can be written MOH and can dissociate to give M^+ and OH^-. It follows, then, that, since an acid produces H^+ and a base produces OH^-, a base will neutralize an acid by producing water and also forming the salt MX (in solution as M^+ and X^-). Examples of Arrhenius bases would be NaOH, $Ca(OH)_2$, and $Al(OH)_3$.

The Arrhenius system has the unquestioned virtue of simplicity, and for that reason it is widely used. However, it suffers from lack of generality. For example, it does not cover obviously acidic solutions such as CO_2 in H_2O or basic solutions such as those of NH_3. To handle such cases, the system requires that substances form acids or bases on reaction with water. Thus, for example, it was postulated that CO_2 reacts with H_2O to form H_2CO_3 (carbonic acid) and NH_3 reacts with H_2O to form NH_4OH (ammonium hydroxide). In neither case is the situation so simple as postulated. In aqueous solutions of CO_2 less than 1% exists as H_2CO_3; in aqueous ammonia no discrete NH_4OH species have ever been identified.

By slight modification, the Arrhenius system can be generalized to cover all acidic and basic solutions in water as well as in other solvents. This definition is sometimes referred to as the *general solvent system of acids and bases*. In this system it is recognized that solvents are themselves somewhat dissociated into positive and negative fragments. For example, water conducts electric current to a slight extent even when highly purified. The dissociation of water can be represented as

$$H_2O \longrightarrow H^+ + OH^-$$

Each of the ions is hydrated. Perhaps a better way of describing the dissociation is

$$H:\overset{..}{\underset{..}{O}}: + H:\overset{..}{\underset{..}{O}}: \longrightarrow H:\overset{..}{\underset{..}{O}}:H^+ + :\overset{..}{\underset{..}{O}}:H^-$$
$$\quad H \qquad\quad H \qquad\qquad H$$

$$H_2O + H_2O \longrightarrow H_3O^+ + OH^-$$

The degree of dissociation of water is very small. In pure water the concentration of hydrogen ion is $1.0 \times 10^{-7}\,M$. The concentration of hydroxide ion is, of course, the same, since each time a water molecule is split, one hydrogen ion and one hydroxide ion are formed. In a liter of water at room temperature there are approximately 1000 g, or 55 moles, of H_2O. Thus, the fraction of water dissociated is $1.0 \times 10^{-7}/55$, or 0.0000002%. On the average, only 1 out of 500 million molecules of H_2O is dissociated.

Substances which upset the hydrogen ion–hydroxide ion balance can be added to water. Those substances which increase *the hydrogen-ion concentration* are called *acids;* those substances which increase the *hydroxide-ion concentration* are called *bases.* HCl is a *strong acid,* one which is *completely converted* to hydrogen ions and negative ions; $HC_2H_3O_2$ is a *weak acid,* one which is only *slightly converted* to hydrogen ions and negative ions. Furthermore, CO_2 is an acid because its addition to water increases the hydrogen-ion concentration so that the resulting solution has acidic properties. This can best be represented by the net equation

$$CO_2 + H_2O \longrightarrow H^+ + HCO_3^-$$

where HCO_3^- represents the bicarbonate ion. Similarly, NH_3 is a base because its addition to water increases the hydroxide-ion concentration. This can be represented as

$$NH_3 + H_2O \longrightarrow NH_4^+ + OH^-$$

Other less evident reactions (often called hydrolysis reactions) change the H^+ and OH^- concentrations in water. For example, when certain aluminum compounds are added to water, the solution becomes acidic; when certain sulfides are added to water, the solution becomes basic. For aluminum chloride ($AlCl_3$) dissolved in water the increase of hydrogen-ion concentration can be attributed to the net reaction

$$Al^{+3} + H_2O \longrightarrow H^+ + AlOH^{++}$$

and for sodium sulfide (Na_2S) dissolved in water the increase of hydroxide-ion concentration can be attributed to the net reaction

$$S^{--} + H_2O \longrightarrow OH^- + SH^-$$

In summary, the solvent-system definition of acid would include CO_2 and $AlCl_3$ as well as HCl and $HC_2H_3O_2$, and the definition of base would include NH_3 and Na_2S as well as NaOH, $Ca(OH)_2$, etc.

Solvents other than H_2O may also show self-dissociation. For example, in liquid ammonia there is slight conductivity presumably due to

$$NH_3 + NH_3 \longrightarrow NH_4^+ + NH_2^-$$

In this solvent, compounds such as NH_4Cl would be classified as acids and those such as KNH_2 as bases. The former raise the positive-ion concentration of the solvent; the latter raise the negative-ion concentration of the solvent. Mixing liquid-ammonia solutions of NH_4Cl and of KNH_2, for example, results in neutralization.

A third, commonly used system for defining acids and bases is that proposed in 1923 by J. N. Brønsted of Denmark and independently by T. M. Lowry of England. In the *Brønsted-Lowry system* an acid is defined as a *proton donor* and a base as a *proton acceptor.* So far as acids are concerned, the Brønsted-Lowry definition matches the Arrhenius definition. The new feature is its more general definition of base. For example, not only is OH^- a base in this system but so is H_2O, since it can accept a proton to form H_3O^+. Similarly, NH_3 is a Brønsted-Lowry base in that it can accept a proton to form NH_4^+.

	Conjugate acid	Conjugate base	
Strongest ↑	$HClO_4$	ClO_4^-	Weakest
	H_2SO_4	HSO_4^-	
	HCl	Cl^-	
	H_3O^+	H_2O	
	HSO_4^-	SO_4^{--}	
	HF	F^-	
	$HC_2H_3O_2$	$C_2H_3O_2^-$	
	H_2S	HS^-	
	NH_4^+	NH_3	
	HCO_3^-	CO_3^{--}	
	H_2O	OH^-	
	HS^-	S^{--}	
Weakest	OH^-	O^{--}	Strongest ↓

9.1
Brønsted-Lowry acids and bases

As a general rule, any species that can donate a proton (and hence can be written HX) gives a species X^- that can accept a proton to form HX. Thus, every Brønsted-Lowry acid is paired with a Brønsted-Lowry base, and the two are said to comprise a *conjugate acid-base pair*. To illustrate, HCl is the conjugate acid of Cl^-; Cl^- is the conjugate base of HCl. Other pairs of conjugate acids and bases include the following: $HC_2H_3O_2$, $C_2H_3O_2^-$; H_2SO_4, HSO_4^-; HSO_4^-, SO_4^{--}; NH_4^+, NH_3; H_3O^+, H_2O; H_2O, OH^-. In the Brønsted-Lowry system, "dissociation" of an acid is viewed not as a simple breakup of HX to give H^+ and X^-, but rather as a proton transfer from HX to a molecule of solvent:

$$HX + H_2O \longrightarrow H_3O^+ + X^-$$

In this reaction, for the forward direction, HX is the acid and H_2O is the base; for the reverse direction, H_3O^+ would be the acid and X^- would be the base.

Different acids vary in their tendency to give up a proton. Their relative acid strengths depend on this tendency and also, to a smaller degree, on the solvent in which the reactions occur. Picking H_2O as the common solvent, we can write an ordered list of acids as is done in Figure 9.1. In the left column the acids are arranged by decreasing acid strength, i.e., the strongest acid is at the top. In the right column is shown the conjugate base of each of the acids. Since a strong acid HX necessarily implies a weak conjugate base X^-, the order in the right column is opposite, i.e., the weakest base is at the top and the strongest is at the bottom. From the ordered list it is possible to predict in which direction proton transfer is favored. Any acid has great tendency to transfer its proton to any base *below* it in the table; conversely any acid has small tendency to transfer its proton to any base *above* it. For example, when HF is mixed with Cl^- and NH_3, the proton is transferred from HF to NH_3 and not to Cl^-. Similarly, the table shows that when HF is placed in H_2O, there is but little tendency for the proton to be transferred from HF to H_2O; in other words, HF in H_2O is a weak acid. Of all the acids listed in Figure 9.1, only $HClO_4$, H_2SO_4, and HCl are strong acids. They have great tendency to transfer protons to the base H_2O to form H_3O^+. It might be noted that HSO_4^- in the acid column lies below H_3O^+; hence, HSO_4^- has but little tendency to transfer its proton to H_2O.

Finally, we should note that even though tendencies may be small, reaction can occur to some extent in all cases. Thus, HSO_4^- in H_2O will undergo limited proton transfer to form some H_3O^+ and SO_4^{--}. Similarly, for NH_3 in H_2O there is some proton transfer from H_2O to NH_3 leading to limited formation of OH^- and NH_4^+.

$$H_2O + NH_3 \xrightarrow{\text{slight}} NH_4^+ + OH^-$$

Likewise, solutions of carbonate are basic because of the limited reaction

$$H_2O + CO_3^{--} \xrightarrow{\text{slight}} HCO_3^- + OH^-$$

These cases of limited proton transfer to give slightly basic solutions are to be contrasted with the last two bases in the table. If either S^{--} or O^{--} is placed in water, there is marked production of OH^-:

$$H_2O + S^{--} \longrightarrow HS^- + OH^-$$

$$H_2O + O^{--} \longrightarrow OH^- + OH^-$$

In the last reaction conversion is essentially 100% complete. In the other cases, where the reaction is limited, it is best to treat the problem quantitatively by use of equilibrium constants as done in Section 12.10.

There is yet another commonly used definition of acid and base; it is called the *Lewis definition.* It applies the term "acid" to any species that acts as an electron-pair acceptor in chemical reaction and the term "base" to an electron-pair donor. For instance, in the reaction

$$H^+ + \overset{\textstyle H}{\underset{\textstyle H}{:N:H}} \longrightarrow \left[\overset{\textstyle H}{\underset{\textstyle H}{H:N:H}} \right]^+$$

the Lewis acid H^+ accepts a pair of electrons from the Lewis base NH_3. The great generality of the Lewis definition can be seen from the fact that it covers the reaction

$$\overset{\textstyle :\ddot{F}:}{\underset{\textstyle :\ddot{F}:}{:\ddot{F}:B}} + \overset{\textstyle H}{\underset{\textstyle H}{:N:H}} \longrightarrow \overset{\textstyle :\ddot{F}:H}{\underset{\textstyle :\ddot{F}:H}{:\ddot{F}:B:N:H}}$$

as well as

$$\overset{\textstyle :\ddot{C}l:}{\underset{\textstyle :\ddot{C}l:}{:\ddot{C}l:Al}} + :\ddot{C}l:^- \longrightarrow \overset{\textstyle :\ddot{C}l:}{\underset{\textstyle :\ddot{C}l:}{:\ddot{C}l:Al:\ddot{C}l:^-}}$$

and even

$$:\ddot{Br}:Hg:\ddot{Br}: + 2:\ddot{Br}:^- \longrightarrow \overset{\textstyle :\ddot{Br}:}{\underset{\textstyle :\ddot{Br}:}{:\ddot{Br}:Hg:\ddot{Br}:^{--}}}$$

The choice of definition of acids and bases can be defended equally in the four systems. The Arrhenius system, because of its simplicity, has the widest usage to recommend it. Its minor modification into the general solvent system produces a workable definition of sufficient generality to cover most cases. The Brønsted-Lowry system has great merit owing to its emphasizing the role of the solvent. However, it must be recognized that in almost half a century it has not displaced the older definitions from the chemical literature. The Lewis system also frequently appears in the literature, owing, no doubt, to its great generality. However, this generality in turn is a weakness. For aqueous systems it is doubtful that the Lewis system will ever replace other definitions of acids and bases.

9.2 NEUTRALIZATION

No matter which definition of acids and bases is used, it is generally agreed that acids and bases react with each other. In the Arrhenius system this reaction is called *neutralization*, because, as the H^+ of the acid reacts with the OH^- of the base, the acidic and basic properties of the two disappear. However, even here the term "neutralization" has to be taken with caution, since the acid and base need to be of comparable strength to produce a neutral solution. For example, one mole of acetic acid reacted with one mole of sodium hydroxide produces not a neutral solution, but a slightly basic one. As for the more general definitions, e.g., the Brønsted-Lowry one, the wider range of acid and base reactions makes the term "neutralization" more questionable. Thus, reaction of the acid HCl with the base H_2O can hardly be called a neutralization. Strictly speaking, then, one should define neutralization as the reaction of acids and bases of comparable strength. The following paragraphs consider four possible situations involving reaction between an acid and a base: strong acid–strong base; weak acid–strong base; strong acid–weak base; weak acid–weak base. As noted above, only the first and the last of these should be called neutralization. However, common usage often refers to all four as neutralization reactions.

1. *Strong acid–strong base.* The neutralization of HCl with NaOH is sometimes written as

$$HCl + NaOH \longrightarrow H_2O + NaCl$$

but since HCl, NaOH, and NaCl are all strong electrolytes, the species present in solution are ions. The equation is better written as

$$H^+ + Cl^- + Na^+ + OH^- \longrightarrow H_2O + Na^+ + Cl^-$$

The Na^+ and Cl^- are canceled because they appear on both sides of the equation. The net equation

$$H^+ + OH^- \longrightarrow H_2O$$

is preferred. It does not concern itself with any species not pertinent to the reaction but tells only what disappears and what appears. Because neither the negative ion (Cl⁻) nor the positive ion (Na⁺) appears in it, the net equation is general and applies to the neutralization of any strong acid by any strong base.

In the Brønsted-Lowry system the solution of any strong acid contains the species H_3O^+ and that of any strong base contains OH^-. Therefore, the net equation for the neutralization is

$$H_3O^+ + OH^- \longrightarrow H_2O + H_2O$$

2. *Weak acid–strong base.* For the reaction of a weak acid with a strong base the net equation can be represented as

$$HA + OH^- \longrightarrow H_2O + A^-$$

where HA stands for a weak acid such as acetic acid, $HC_2H_3O_2$. Since weak acids are only slightly dissociated in aqueous solution into H^+ and A^- ions, the original solution of the weak acid contains predominantly HA molecules. In the reaction it is the HA molecules that ultimately disappear, and this must be shown in the net equation. It may well be that the actual mechanism of the reaction involves, first, dissociation of HA into $H^+ + A^-$, with subsequent union of $H^+ + OH^-$ to give H_2O. The net equation represents only the overall reaction. For this particular case, the net equation using the Brønsted-Lowry system coincides exactly with the net equation given above.

3. *Strong acid–weak base.* For the reaction of strong acid by a weak base, the net reaction can be written

$$H^+ + MOH \longrightarrow M^+ + H_2O$$

where MOH represents a weak base such as thallium hydroxide, TlOH. In the Brønsted-Lowry system the strong acid forms H_3O^+, so the equation becomes

$$H_3O^+ + MOH \longrightarrow M^+ + 2H_2O$$

4. *Weak acid–weak base.* For the reaction between a weak acid and a weak base, whether in the Arrhenius system or the Brønsted-Lowry system, the net equation would be

$$HA + MOH \longrightarrow M^+ + A^- + H_2O$$

Comparison of the above net equations shows that the only difference between the Brønsted-Lowry and Arrhenius equations is that the former use H_3O^+ instead of H^+. In subsequent equations, because of the advantage of simplicity, we shall frequently represent the H_3O^+ species as H^+.

9.3 POLYPROTIC ACIDS

The term *polyprotic acid* (sometimes, polybasic acid) is used to describe those acids which can furnish more than one proton per molecule. Two examples of polyprotic acids are H_2SO_4, sulfuric acid, and H_3PO_4, phosphoric acid. In reaction, polyprotic acids usually transfer only one proton at a time. For example, when placed in water, H_2SO_4 transfers a proton to H_2O:

$$H_2SO_4 + H_2O \longrightarrow H_3O^+ + HSO_4^-$$

This reaction is essentially complete; in this sense H_2SO_4 is called a strong electrolyte. When a solution containing one mole of sodium hydroxide is mixed with a solution containing one mole of sulfuric acid, one mole of H_3O^+ neutralizes one mole of OH^-. Evaporation of the resulting solution would give one mole of the salt $NaHSO_4$, sodium hydrogen sulfate. (This salt is also called sodium bisulfate and used to be called primary sodium sulfate.) The ion HSO_4^- is an acid in its own right. Although fairly weak, it can be dissociated to give SO_4^{--}. This reaction can be written

$$HSO_4^- + H_2O \xrightarrow[\text{slight}]{} H_3O^+ + SO_4^{--}$$

It can be considered as the second step in the dissociation of the diprotic acid H_2SO_4 and occurs significantly only when there is a large demand for protons. For example, when one mole of H_2SO_4 is mixed in solution with two moles of sodium hydroxide, the two moles of OH^- neutralize two moles of H^+. Evaporation of the solution would produce the salt Na_2SO_4, sodium sulfate.

The triprotic acid H_3PO_4 undergoes dissociation in three steps:

$$H_3PO_4 + H_2O \xrightarrow[\text{slight}]{} H_3O^+ + H_2PO_4^-$$

$$H_2PO_4^- + H_2O \xrightarrow[\text{slight}]{} H_3O^+ + HPO_4^{--}$$

$$HPO_4^{--} + H_2O \xrightarrow[\text{slight}]{} H_3O^+ + PO_4^{-3}$$

The extent of dissociation is again governed by the demand for protons. It is possible to get three salts from this acid. The following are the net equations for reactions between one mole of H_3PO_4 and one, two, and three moles of NaOH in solution:

$$H_3PO_4 + OH^- \longrightarrow H_2O + H_2PO_4^-$$

$$H_3PO_4 + 2OH^- \longrightarrow 2H_2O + HPO_4^{--}$$

$$H_3PO_4 + 3OH^- \longrightarrow 3H_2O + PO_4^{-3}$$

Evaporation of the solutions would give the salts NaH_2PO_4, monosodium dihydrogen phosphate; Na_2HPO_4, disodium monohydrogen phosphate; and Na_3PO_4, trisodium phosphate. These are sometimes referred to as the primary, secondary, and tertiary sodium phosphates, respectively.

9.4 HYLYROLYSIS

When the salt NaCl is placed in water, the resulting solution is observed to be neutral; i.e., the concentrations of H^+ and OH^- are equal, 1×10^{-7} M, just as in pure H_2O. However, when the salt $NaC_2H_3O_2$ is dissolved in H_2O, the resulting solution is observed to be slightly basic.

Other salts such as ammonium chloride, NH_4Cl, or aluminum chloride, $AlCl_3$, give slightly acid solutions. These interactions between salts and water are called *hydrolysis*.

Hydrolysis is not fundamentally different from any acid-base reaction as viewed in the Brønsted-Lowry system. In the case of sodium acetate, for example, the basic nature of the resulting aqueous solution can be understood from the following reaction:

$$C_2H_3O_2^- + H_2O \xrightarrow{\text{slight}} HC_2H_3O_2 + OH^-$$

Here the Brønsted-Lowry base $C_2H_3O_2^-$ accepts a proton from the Brønsted-Lowry acid H_2O to form the conjugate acid $HC_2H_3O_2$ and the conjugate base OH^-. The basic nature of the solution is due to the formation of OH^-. This reaction goes only slightly from left to right because $C_2H_3O_2^-$ is too weak a base to compete significantly with OH^- for protons (see Figure 9.1).

In principle, any negative ion could act as a base. In practice, however, only a few negative ions compete effectively with OH^- for protons. These include only the very strong bases (for example, O^{--}, S^{--}), so only these solutions are likely to be as basic as solutions prepared from hydroxides. Most negative ions compete only slightly with OH^- for protons, and in these solutions the extent of hydrolysis is small. Thus, solutions of Na_2CO_3, $NaC_2H_3O_2$, NaF, Na_2SO_4, for example, are only slightly basic. Although the extent of hydrolysis increases with dilution, in solutions of the above salts at moderate concentration (order of one molar) the extent of hydrolysis rarely exceeds a percent or so. The extent of hydrolysis of a few negative ions (for example, ClO_4^-, Cl^-, NO_3^-) is so small as to be undetectable. These anions are the weakest of bases, and their conjugate acids are the strongest of acids.

In a few cases the negative ion can act as an acid. For example, HSO_4^- can transfer a proton to H_2O to give an acidic solution containing H_3O^+ and SO_4^{--}. In a similar fashion, HCO_3^- (bicarbonate ion) could transfer a proton to H_2O to form H_3O^+ except that HCO_3^- can also accept a proton (to form ultimately H_2O and CO_2). The two effects occur about equally and so tend to cancel. Solutions of $NaHCO_3$ are very slightly basic in contrast to those of $NaHSO_4$, which are definitely acidic.

Positive ions that hydrolyze generally produce acidic solutions. In some cases, for example, NH_4^+, the source of the proton is obvious:

$$NH_4^+ + H_2O \xrightarrow{\text{slight}} NH_3 + H_3O^+$$

In other cases, e.g., solutions of Al^{+3} salts, the source of the acidity can be attributed to splitting off a proton from the water molecules directly attached to the Al^{+3} in forming a hydrated aluminum ion. Although the configuration of hydrated aluminum ion is not completely known, it is usually assumed to be octahedral; i.e., the aluminum ion is thought to be attached to six H_2O molecules at the corners of an octahedron. The first drawing in Figure 9.2 represents an octahedron having eight faces and six corners. In the hydrated aluminum ion, shown in the second drawing, the oxygen atoms (large circles) are so

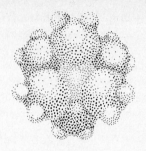

located that their centers describe an octahedron. The transfer of a proton from hydrated aluminum ion to solvent can be written

$$Al(H_2O)_6^{+3} + H_2O \longrightarrow Al(H_2O)_5OH^{++} + H_3O^+$$

The reaction, which leaves a doubly charged complex ion, is represented by Figure 9.3.

The extent of loss of protons from hydrated ions depends on how tightly the protons are held to the oxygen atoms. The effect of the aluminum ion is to pull electrons toward itself away from the water

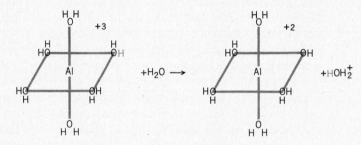

9.3
Acidity of hydrated aluminum ion

molecule, as shown in Figure 9.4. The bond between the hydrogen and the oxygen is thereby weakened, and the proton may dissociate. The higher the charge of the cation, the more pull exerted on the electrons and the more easily the protons dissociate. Thus, most $+1$ ions (for example, Na^+, K^+, Ag^+) show no detectable hydrolysis; most $+2$ ions (for example, Mg^{++}, Zn^{++}, Cu^{++}) are slightly hydrolyzed; $+3$ ions (for example, Al^{+3}, Fe^{+3}, Cr^{+3}) are about as acidic as the moderately weak acetic acid.

In the case of very strong interaction between a positive ion and waters of hydration all the protons from the attached waters may dissociate. The existence of oxyions, such as SO_4^{--}, can be explained in this way. The argument is as follows: In SO_4^{--} the sulfur is assigned an oxidation state of $+6$. Except under extreme conditions of high temperature, S^{+6} is not encountered as a chemical species. However, let us imagine having an S^{+6} ion, which is then placed in water. Molecules of H_2O cluster about it in the usual process of hydration, but S^{+6} has such a high positive charge that electrons are strongly attracted to it. The hydrogen-oxygen bonds in the H_2O are so weakened that the

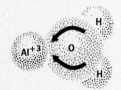

9.4
Effect of Al^{+3} on H_2O

9.4 Hydrolysis

protons split off to leave the oxygen associated with the sulfur. Thus, the formation of SO_4^{--} can be described by the hypothetical reaction

$$S^{+6} + 4H_2O \longrightarrow SO_4^{--} + 8H^+$$

Of the eight dissociating protons, the last one is weakly held, thus accounting for hydrogen sulfate ion, HSO_4^-. The formation of nitrate ion, NO_3^-, can be similarly explained as resulting from the 100% hydrolysis of hypothetical N^{+5}.

9.5 AMPHOTERISM

If a solution of sodium hydroxide is added dropwise to a solution of aluminum nitrate, it is observed that a white precipitate, aluminum hydroxide, is formed. On further addition of base or on addition of acid, the precipitate dissolves. The net equations for the dissolving processes can be written

$$Al(OH)_3(s) + OH^- \longrightarrow Al(OH)_4^-$$

$$Al(OH)_3(s) + 3H^+ \longrightarrow Al^{+3} + 3H_2O$$

These two equations indicate that $Al(OH)_3$ is *amphoteric*, i.e., *is able to neutralize bases and acids.* In other words, aluminum hydroxide is able to act as an acid and also as a base. Zinc hydroxide, $Zn(OH)_2$, lead hydroxide, $Pb(OH)_2$, and chromium hydroxide, $Cr(OH)_3$, are examples of other common amphoteric hydroxides. Oxides may also be classified as amphoteric if they react with water to form amphoteric hydroxides.

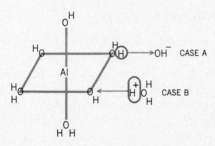

9.5
Amphoteric behavior of
aluminum hydroxide

How can amphoterism be explained? The answer can be seen by writing the above equations in a way that emphasizes Brønsted-Lowry concepts and is more consistent with the best guesses as to the actual species involved.

$$Al(OH)_3(H_2O)_3(s) + OH^- \longrightarrow Al(OH)_4(H_2O)_2^- + H_2O$$

$$Al(OH)_3(H_2O)_3(s) + 3H_3O^+ \longrightarrow Al(H_2O)_6^{+3} + 3H_2O$$

In the first of these reactions, a proton is transferred from $Al(OH)_3(H_2O)_3$ to OH^-; in the second, proton transfer is from H_3O^+ to $Al(OH)_3(H_2O)_3$. Figure 9.5 shows the two possible proton transfers. In case A a proton from an H_2O bound to the central Al transfers to an external OH^-; in case B a proton from an external H_3O^+ transfers to an OH bound to the Al. In both cases, the chemical bond of interest is an

$$\underset{\text{Al}-\text{O-to-H}}{\overset{\text{H}}{|}}$$

bond, broken in case A and formed in case B.

For amphoterism to occur, this bond must be intermediate in strength between an H-to-OH bond and an H-to-OH_2 bond. The strength of the Al(OH)-to-H bond is determined by the electron-pulling ability of Al^{+3}, as shown in Figure 9.4. If the electron pull is too weak, the O-to-H bond is not sufficiently weakened to enhance proton transfer from a bound H_2O of hydration over that from a solvent H_2O. This is the reason why Na^+, Ca^{++}, and even La^{+3} do not give amphoteric hydroxides. These ions do not hydrolyze significantly, which also indicates that the O-to-H bond in the water of hydration has not been weakened sufficiently to show acidic properties. In general, positive ions that do not hydrolyze appreciably are not likely to give amphoteric hydroxides. On the other hand, positive ions that hydrolyze too much (for example, S^{+6}) also do not give amphoteric hydroxides. This arises because a hydrated ion in which the O-to-H bond has been weakened too much (i.e., below the strength of the H-to-OH_2 bond in H_3O^+) will not accept a proton from H_3O^+. A good example is ClOH, which has so little affinity for H^+ that it does not act as a base, but acts only as an acid. The Cl end of the molecule pulls electrons away from the oxygen so strongly that the oxygen has little affinity for an additional proton.

9.6 STOICHIOMETRY OF SOLUTIONS

Labels on reagent bottles specify what the solution was made from, but not necessarily what the solution contains. For example, the label 0.5 M HCl appears on a solution made from 0.5 mole of HCl and sufficient water to give 1 liter of solution. Despite the label, there are no HCl molecules in the solution. HCl is a strong electrolyte and is completely converted to H_3O^+ and Cl^-. For most quantitative considerations, however, it is not necessary to know what species are actually in the solution. It is necessary to know only what is ultimately available. The label 0.5 M $HC_2H_3O_2$ also tells what the solution was made from, but in this case the solution actually contains $HC_2H_3O_2$ molecules, since it is a weak electrolyte and is very slightly dissociated. There is only a trace of H_3O^+ and $C_2H_3O_2^-$ in the solution. However, if this solution is used for a neutralization reaction, not only the trace of H_3O^+ but also the $HC_2H_3O_2$ is neutralized.

The use of solutions for chemical reactions requires a clear distinction between the *number of moles* of solute in a solution and its *concentration*. To illustrate, let us suppose 15.8 g of $KMnO_4$, potassium permanganate, is dissolved to make a 0.100 M $KMnO_4$ solution. The formula weight of $KMnO_4$ is 158; hence 15.8 g is equal to 0.100 mole. To make up the solution, the solute is placed in a graduated container and water is added to it. Not necessarily 1 liter of water is added, but only enough to bring the volume to a liter of solution. (Usually, the volume of solute plus the volume of the solvent is not exactly equal to the volume of the solution.) The solution can now be labeled 0.100 M $KMnO_4$, since it contains 0.100 mole of $KMnO_4$ in 1 liter of solution. The concentration does not depend on how much of this solution is taken. Whether one drop or 200 ml is considered, the solution is still 0.100 M $KMnO_4$. However, the number of moles of $KMnO_4$ taken does depend on the volume of solution. If the volume and the concentration of a sample are known, the number of moles of solute in the sample is the number of moles per liter multiplied by the volume of the sample in liters. In 200 ml of 0.100 M $KMnO_4$, there is (0.200 liter)(0.100 mole liter^{-1}), or 0.0200 mole, of $KMnO_4$.

Solutions are convenient because they permit measuring amounts of solute not by weighing the solute, but by measuring a volume of solution. For example, suppose a given chemical reaction requires 0.0100 mole of $KMnO_4$. This amount of $KMnO_4$ can be provided by 1.58 g of $KMnO_4$ or by 100 ml of 0.100 M $KMnO_4$ solution.

To summarize:

Liters of solution $\times$ molarity of solution = moles of solute in sample

Liters of solution $\times$ normality of solution
$$= \text{gram-equivalents of solute in sample}$$

EXAMPLE 1

To what volume must 50.0 ml of 3.50 M H_2SO_4 be diluted in order to make 2.00 M H_2SO_4?

50.0 ml of 3.50 M H_2SO_4 contains
(0.0500 liter)(3.50 moles liter^{-1}), or 0.175 mole, of H_2SO_4.

We wish the final solution to be 2.00 M.

Therefore, the final volume must be

$$\frac{0.175 \text{ mole}}{2.00 \text{ mole liter}^{-1}} = 0.0875 \text{ liter, or } 87.5 \text{ ml}$$

EXAMPLE 2

To 50.0 ml of 0.50 M H_2SO_4, 75.0 ml of 0.25 M H_2SO_4 is added. What is the concentration of the final solution if its volume is 125 ml?

50.0 ml of 0.50 M H_2SO_4 contains
(0.0500 liter)(0.50 mole liter^{-1}) moles H_2SO_4.

75.0 ml of 0.25 M H_2SO_4 contains
(0.0750 liter)(0.25 mole liter^{-1}) moles H_2SO_4.

Total moles = (0.0500 liter)(0.50 mole liter^{-1})
$$+ (0.0750 \text{ liter})(0.25 \text{ mole liter}^{-1}) = 0.044$$

Final concentration $= \dfrac{0.044 \text{ mole}}{0.125 \text{ liter}} = 0.35 \; M \; H_2SO_4$

EXAMPLE 3

How many milliliters of 0.025 M H_3PO_4 are required to neutralize 25 ml of 0.030 M $Ca(OH)_2$? Assume complete neutralization.

Method 1   Moles:

In 25 ml of 0.030 M $Ca(OH)_2$ there is (0.025 liter)(0.030 mole liter^{-1}), or 0.00075 mole. From the non-net equation

$$3Ca(OH)_2 + 2H_3PO_4 \longrightarrow Ca_3(PO_4)_2 + 6H_2O$$

Three moles of $Ca(OH)_2$ require two moles of H_3PO_4, or 0.00075 mole of $Ca(OH)_2$ requires 0.00050 mole of H_3PO_4.

0.025 M H_3PO_4 means 0.025 mole H_3PO_4 per liter of solution. To get 0.00050 mole of H_3PO_4 as required, we take

$$\frac{0.00050 \text{ mole}}{0.025 \text{ mole liter}^{-1}} = 0.020 \text{ liter, or 20 ml, of 0.025 } M \text{ } H_3PO_4$$

Method 2   Gram-equivalents:

0.030 M $Ca(OH)_2$ is 0.060 N $Ca(OH)_2$, and
0.025 M H_3PO_4 is 0.075 N H_3PO_4.

In 25 ml of 0.030 M $Ca(OH)_2$ there is
(0.025 liter)(0.060 g-equiv liter^{-1}), or 0.0015 g-equiv, of base.

Need 0.0015 g-equiv of acid for neutralization.

Acidic solution has 0.075 g-equiv per liter, or 0.0015 g-equiv in

$$\frac{0.0015 \text{ g-equiv}}{0.075 \text{ g-equiv liter}^{-1}} = 0.020 \text{ liter, or 20 ml}$$

EXAMPLE 4

A solution is made by mixing 10.0 ml of 0.0200 M $Ca(NO_3)_2$ and 15.0 ml of 0.0300 M $NaNO_3$. Assuming the final volume is 25.0 ml and that dissociation is complete, calculate the concentrations of Ca^{++}, Na^+, and NO_3^- in the final solution.

$$Ca^{++} = (0.0100 \text{ liter})(0.0200 \text{ mole liter}^{-1}) = 0.000200 \text{ mole}$$

$$= \frac{0.000200 \text{ mole}}{0.0250 \text{ liter}} = 0.00800 \text{ } M$$

$$Na^+ = (0.0150 \text{ liter})(0.0300 \text{ mole liter}^{-1}) = 0.000450 \text{ mole}$$

$$= \frac{0.000450 \text{ mole}}{0.0250 \text{ liter}} = 0.0180 \text{ } M$$

$$NO_3^- = (0.0100 \text{ liter})(2 \times 0.0200 \text{ mole liter}^{-1})$$
$$+ (0.01500 \text{ liter})(0.0300 \text{ mole liter}^{-1})$$

$$= 0.000400 \text{ mole} + 0.000450 \text{ mole} = 0.000850 \text{ mole}$$

$$= \frac{0.000850 \text{ mole}}{0.0250 \text{ liter}} = 0.0340 \text{ } M$$

In the quantitative consideration of oxidation-reduction reactions in aqueous solution, electrolytic dissociation simplifies the consideration. Only the net reaction need be considered; other ions present in the solution can be ignored. As a specific case we consider the reaction of an acidified solution of $KMnO_4$ with a solution of ferrous sulfate, $FeSO_4$. Before reaction occurs, the mixture contains K^+, MnO_4^-, H^+, HSO_4^-, Fe^{++}, and SO_4^{--}. After the reaction is complete, the mixture contains K^+, HSO_4^-, Mn^{++}, Fe^{+3}, and SO_4^{--}. The K^+, HSO_4^-, and SO_4^{--} are present at the initial concentration in the final mixture and can be ignored. The net reaction shows the disappearance of MnO_4^-, Fe^{++}, and H^+ and the appearance of Mn^{++}, Fe^{+3}, and H_2O. It can be written

$$5Fe^{++} + MnO_4^- + 8H^+ \longrightarrow 5Fe^{+3} + Mn^{++} + 4H_2O$$

Net equations show both the species involved in the reactions and the stoichiometry. The number of moles of reactants can be calculated from the equation. The volumes of solutions necessary for complete reaction are thus specified. In general, principal interest is focused on the oxidizing agent and the reducing agent, since the acidic or basic nature of the solution is usually provided by an excess of an acid or base.

EXAMPLE 5

How many milliliters of 0.20 M $KMnO_4$ are required to oxidize 25.0 ml of 0.40 M $FeSO_4$ in acidic solution? The reaction which occurs is the oxidation of Fe^{++} by MnO_4^- to give Fe^{+3} and Mn^{++}.

Method 1   Moles:

The balanced net equation is

$$5Fe^{++} + MnO_4^- + 8H^+ \longrightarrow 5Fe^{+3} + Mn^{++} + 4H_2O$$

25.0 ml of 0.40 M $FeSO_4$ supplies (0.0250 liter)(0.40 mole liter^{-1}), or 0.010 mole Fe^{++}.

From the equation, five moles of Fe^{++} require one mole of MnO_4^-.

Hence 0.010 mole Fe^{++} requires 0.0020 mole MnO_4^-, or

$$\frac{0.0020 \text{ mole}}{0.20 \text{ mole liter}^{-1}} = 0.010 \text{ liter} = 10 \text{ ml}$$

The problem can also be solved by using gram-equivalents as defined in Section 4.10. In this reaction the reducing agent Fe^{++} changes to Fe^{+3}. Each Fe^{++} loses one electron to the oxidizing agent. The Avogadro number of Fe^{++} ions, or one mole of Fe^{++}, can furnish the Avogadro number of electrons. For this reaction, one mole of $FeSO_4$ is equal to one gram-equivalent of $FeSO_4$, and 0.40 M $FeSO_4$ is 0.40 N. The oxidizing agent, MnO_4^-, changes to Mn^{++} in the course of the reaction. As the manganese changes oxidation state from +7 to +2, each MnO_4^- appears to gain five electrons. One mole of MnO_4^- requires five times the Avogadro number of electrons and so is equal to five gram-equivalents. Therefore, 0.20 M $KMnO_4$ is 1.0 N. In general, the *normality of a solution of an oxidizing or reducing agent is equal to the molarity times the electron change per formula-unit.*

Example 5 can be rephrased by using normality instead of molarity: How many milliliters of 1.0 N $KMnO_4$ are required to oxidize 25.0 ml of 0.40 N $FeSO_4$ in acidic solution?

Method 2   Gram-equivalents:

25.0 ml of 0.40 N $FeSO_4$ supplies (0.0250 liter)(0.40 g-equiv liter^{-1}), or 0.010 g-equiv of reducing agent.

One gram-equivalent of any reducing agent requires one gram-equivalent of any oxidizing agent.

0.010 g-equiv of reducing agent requires 0.010 g-equiv of oxidizing agent, or 0.010 g-equiv/1.0 g-equiv liter^{-1} = 0.010 liter, or 10 ml.

In some cases a given oxidizing agent can be reduced to different products depending on conditions. For example, MnO_4^- can be reduced to Mn^{++}, MnO_2, or MnO_4^{--} if the medium is acid, neutral, or basic, respectively. In these reactions the number of electrons transferred is five, three, and one. A solution that is 1 M $KMnO_4$ is 5 N $KMnO_4$, 3 N $KMnO_4$, or 1 N $KMnO_4$, depending on which product is formed. Thus, the normality given for a particular solution may be ambiguous unless the reaction for which the solution is to be used is specified.

QUESTIONS

9.1 Polyprotic acids   Write the eight net equations for the stepwise dissociation and for the stepwise neutralization by OH^- of $H_4P_2O_7$.

9.2 Acids and bases   State whether each of the following is an acid, a base, or both in the Brønsted-Lowry system: HCl, HSO_4^-, NH_3, OH^-, Cl^-.

9.3 Stoichiometry   An unknown solution of H_2SO_4 neutralizes 4.06 ml of 0.136 M $NaOH$ per ml. What is its normality?

9.4 Acids and bases   Compare and contrast the Brønsted-Lowry, Arrhenius, and Lewis definitions of acids and bases.

9.5 Amphoterism   Assuming that zinc ion is four-coordinate (i.e., binds to four neighboring atoms), write equations that demonstrate the amphoteric behavior of zinc hydroxide.

9.6 Stoichiometry   To what volume must 0.125 liter of 0.360 M H_2SO_4 be diluted to prepare each of the following: (*a*) 0.100 M H_2SO_4, (*b*) 0.100 N H_2SO_4?

9.7 Neutralization   Write net equations for each of the following "neutralizations": (*a*) strong acid HX with weak base MOH, (*b*) strong base NOH with weak acid HY, (*c*) HX with NOH, (*d*) MOH with HY.

9.8 Conjugate acids and bases   From the following list pick out all the pairs of conjugate acids and bases. *Note:* each species may be used more than once. H_3O^+, H_2O, OH^-, O^{--}, NH_4^+, NH_3, NH_2^-, NH^{--}, N^{-3}, $H_3SO_4^+$, H_2SO_4, HSO_4^-, SO_4^{--}, SO_3^{--}, SO_2^{--}, SO^{--}, S^{--}, HS^-, H_2S.

9.9 Neutralization Why is there ambiguity in describing as a "neutralization" the reaction of acetic acid with sodium hydroxide?

9.10 Acid-base reactions By reference to Figure 9.1, decide which of the following reactions occurs to the greatest extent:

$$H_3O^+ + F^- \longrightarrow HF + H_2O$$
$$HF + H_2O \longrightarrow H_3O^+ + F^-$$
$$H_3O^+ + NH_3 \longrightarrow NH_4^+ + H_2O$$
$$NH_4^+ + H_2O \longrightarrow NH_3 + H_3O^+$$
$$HF + NH_3 \longrightarrow NH_4^+ + F^-$$

9.11 Brønsted-Lowry By using Figure 9.1 predict what species will be present in significant concentration when the following pairs are added in equal molar amounts to H_2O: (*a*) H_2SO_4 and HCl, (*b*) HCl and HF, (*c*) HF and NH_4^+, (*d*) $HClO_4$ and SO_4^{--}, (*e*) H_2SO_4 and Cl^-, (*f*) HCO_3^- and OH^-.

9.12 Acids and bases Consider the species H^+, H_3O^+, HCl, Al^{+3}, F^-, NaOH, H_2O. (*a*) Tell which of these in aqueous solution is an acid and which is a base in the general solvent system of acids and bases. (*b*) Tell which is an acid and which is a base in the Brønsted-Lowry system. (*c*) Tell which is an acid and which is a base in the Lewis system.

9.13 Stoichiometry (*a*) In basic solution CrO_4^{--} oxidizes $S_2O_3^{--}$ to form $Cr(OH)_4^-$ and SO_4^{--}. How many milliliters of 0.154 M Na_2CrO_4 are required just to react with 40.0 ml of 0.246 M $Na_2S_2O_3$? (*b*) Assuming additive volumes, what would be the SO_4^{--} concentration after reaction?

9.14 Stoichiometry Calculate the concentration of the final solution made by mixing 25.0 ml of 0.126 M H_2SO_4 with each of the following (assume volumes are additive): (*a*) 35.0 ml of H_2O, (*b*) 10.0 ml of 0.126 M H_2SO_4, (*c*) 45.0 ml of 0.0630 M H_2SO_4.

9.15 Hydrolysis (*a*) With reference to Figure 9.1, tell what is meant by hydrolysis and how it comes about. (*b*) Which should hydrolyze in water more, S^{--} or $C_2H_3O_2^-$?

9.16 Stoichiometry How many moles of H_2SO_4 are required (*a*) to make 96.0 ml of 0.124 M H_2SO_4, (*b*) to make 12.4 ml of 0.0960 N H_2SO_4, (*c*) to neutralize 48.6 ml of 0.0644 M $Ba(OH)_2$, (*d*) to neutralize 23.6 ml of 0.0416 N $Ba(OH)_2$, (*e*) to be added to 25.0 ml of 0.30 N H_2SO_4 to make it 0.45 M if volume remains constant?

9.17 Hydrolysis Account for the fact that $AlCl_3$ gives a more acidic aqueous solution than $CaCl_2$ gives.

9.18 Stoichiometry In acidic solution IO_3^- reacts with I^- to form I_2. What will be the final concentration of IO_3^-, I^-, and I_2 in a solution prepared by mixing 64.8 ml of 1.00×10^{-3} M KIO_3 with 35.2 ml of 6.00×10^{-3} M KI?

9.19 Hydrolysis Criticize the following: "Aqueous solutions of sodium acetate are basic because the activity of sodium hydroxide is strong and the activity of acetic acid is weak."

9.20 Hydrolysis Rank the following equimolar aqueous solutions in order of increasing acidity: NaCl, $NaC_2H_3O_2$, $CaCl_2$, $GaCl_3$, $BaCl_2$.

9.21 Stoichiometry In acidic solution $H_2C_2O_4$ is oxidized by MnO_4^- to form CO_2. What is the normality (*a*) as a reducing agent and (*b*) as an acid of a solution made by dissolving 4.20 g of $H_2C_2O_4 \cdot 2H_2O$ in enough water to make 0.360 liter of solution?

9.22 Acids and bases In liquid ammonia as a solvent HF is a strong acid, but in water it is a weak acid. Explain.

9.23 Hydrolysis (*a*) Why is it that highly charged positive ions hydrolyze more than those of lower charge? (*b*) Why is it that small ions hydrolyze more than large ions?

9.24 Acid normality With respect to reaction with OH^-, what would be the normality of each of the following solutions: (*a*) 0.100 *M* H_2SO_4, (*b*) 0.200 *M* $NaHSO_4$, (*c*) 0.240 *M* Na_2HPO_4, (*d*) 0.024 *M* $Ca(HSO_4)_2$, (*e*) 0.021 *M* $Ca(H_2PO_4)_2$?

9.25 Neutralization By reference to Figure 9.1, write net equations for each of the following "neutralizations" in aqueous solution: (*a*) $HClO_4$ with NH_3, (*b*) HCl with NaOH, (*c*) H_2SO_4 with NaOH, (*d*) CaO with $HC_2H_3O_2$, (*e*) Na_2S with NH_4Cl.

9.26 Hydrolysis Which aqueous solution would you predict to be more acidic: 0.1 *M* $Cr(H_2O)_6^{+3}$ or 0.1 *M* $Cr(NH_3)_6^{+3}$? Explain.

9.27 Stoichiometry Compute the final concentration of each ion in a solution made by mixing 0.100 mole $La(OH)_3$, 30.0 ml of 2.40 *M* $La(NO_3)_3$, 40.0 ml of 15.7 *M* HNO_3, and enough water to bring the total volume to 125 ml.

9.28 Stoichiometry How many milliliters of 0.250 *M* HCl can you make from no more than 250 ml of H_2O and 350 ml of 0.640 *M* HCl? (Assume additive volumes.)

9.29 Hydrolysis Develop a hydrated-anion scheme to account for hydrolysis of negative ions.

9.30 Stoichiometry A solution is made by mixing 0.100 liter of 2.00 *M* HNO_3, 50.0 ml of 0.200 *M* $K_2Cr_2O_7$, and 100.0 ml of 0.240 *M* $H_2C_2O_4$ to give 0.250 liter of solution. Reaction occurs between $Cr_2O_7^{--}$ and $H_2C_2O_4$ to produce Cr^{+3} and $CO_2(g)$. Note that $H_2C_2O_4$ is a weak electrolyte. (*a*) Calculate the concentrations of H_3O^+, NO_3^-, K^+, $Cr_2O_7^{--}$, $H_2C_2O_4$, and Cr^{+3} in the final solution. (*b*) If the CO_2 from this reaction is bubbled off and absorbed in 200.0 ml of 1.00 *M* KOH, calculate the final concentration of OH^-, assuming the $CO_2(g)$ reacts with OH^- to produce CO_3^{--}.

ANSWERS

9.3 0.552 *N*   *9.6* (*a*) 0.450 liter   (*b*) 0.900 liter   *9.13* (*a*) 170 ml   (*b*) 0.0937 *M*   *9.16* (*a*) 0.0119   (*b*) 0.000595   (*c*) 0.00313   (*d*) 0.000491   (*e*) 0.0075   *9.21* 0.185 *N*   *9.27* 1.38 *M* La^{+3}, 6.75 *M* NO_3^-, 2.62 *M* H_3O^+ *9.30* (*a*) 0.544 *M* H_3O^+, 0.800 *M* NO_3^-, 0.0800 *M* K^+, 0.0080 *M* $Cr_2O_7^{--}$, 0.0640 *M* Cr^{+3} (*b*) 0.520 *M*

10 chemical kinetics

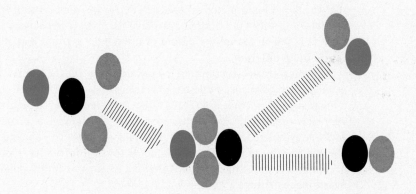

Chemical kinetics is the branch of chemistry concerned with the velocity of chemical reactions and the mechanism by which chemical reactions occur. The term *reaction velocity* is used to describe the rate at which chemical change occurs. The term *reaction mechanism* is used to describe the sequence of stepwise reactions by which the overall change occurs. In most reactions it is only the disappearance of starting materials and the appearance of final products that can be detected; i.e., only the net reaction is observable. In general, however, the net reaction is not the whole story, but simply represents a summation of all the changes that occur. The net change may actually consist of several consecutive reactions, each of which constitutes a step in the formation of final products. In discussing chemical reactions it is important to keep clear the distinction between a net reaction and one step in that reaction.

When a reaction occurs in steps, intermediate species are probably formed, and they may not be detectable because they may be promptly used up in a subsequent step. However, by investigating the influence that various factors have on the rate at which the net change occurs, it is sometimes possible to elucidate what the intermediates are and how they are involved in the mechanism of the reaction.

What factors influence the rate of chemical reaction? Experiments show that four important ones are (1) nature of reactants, (2) concentration of reactants, (3) temperature, and (4) catalysis.

10.1 NATURE OF REACTANTS

In a chemical reaction, bonds are formed and bonds are broken. The rate should therefore depend on the specific bonds involved. Experimentally, the reaction velocity depends on the specific substances brought together in reaction. For example, the reduction of permanganate ion in acidic solution by ferrous ion is practically instantaneous. MnO_4^- disappears as fast as ferrous sulfate solution is added; the limiting factor is the rate of mixing the solutions. On the other hand, the reduction of permanganate ion in acidic solution by oxalic acid, $H_2C_2O_4$, is not instantaneous. The violet color characteristic of MnO_4^- persists long after the solutions are mixed. In these two reactions everything is identical except the nature of the reducing agent, but still the rate is quite different.

The rates observed in different reactants vary widely. There are reactions, such as occur in acid-base neutralization, which may be over in a microsecond, so that the rate is difficult to measure. There are also very slow reactions, such as those occurring in geological processes, which may not reach completion in a million years. The changes in a lifetime may be too small to be detected. Most information has been accumulated about the reactions that occur at rates intermediate between these extremes.

10.2 CONCENTRATION OF REACTANTS

It is found by experiment that the rate of a homogeneous chemical reaction depends on the concentration of the reactants. A homogeneous reaction is one which occurs in only one phase. Heterogeneous reactions involve more than one phase. It is found that the rate of a *heterogeneous* reaction is proportional to the area of contact between the phases. An example is the rusting of iron, a heterogeneous reaction involving a solid phase, iron, and a gas phase, oxygen. Rusting is slow when the surface of contact is small, as in the case with a bar of iron. If the bar is ground into powder, rusting is more rapid because of greater area of contact.

The rate of a *homogeneous* reaction depends on the concentration (amount per unit volume) of the reactants in solution. The solution may

Experiment	Initial molar concentration × 10³*		Initial rate, torr min⁻¹
	NO	H₂	
I	6.00	1.00	20
II	6.00	2.00	40
III	6.00	3.00	60
IV	1.00	6.00	3
V	2.00	6.00	12
VI	3.00	6.00	27

* "Initial molar concentration $\times 10^3$" means that the values of molar concentration have been multiplied by 10^3 before being entered in the table. Hence in experiment I, the concentration of NO is 6.00×10^{-3} M and that of H_2 is 1.00×10^{-3} M.

be liquid or gaseous. In a liquid solution the concentration of a reactant can be changed either by its addition or removal or by changing the volume of the system, as by addition or removal of solvent. The specific effect has to be determined by experiment. Thus, in the reaction of substance A with substance B, the addition of A may cause an increase, a decrease, or no change in rate depending on the particular reaction. Quantitatively, the rate may double, triple, become half as great, etc. A priori, it is not possible to look at the net equation for a chemical reaction and tell how the rate is affected by a change of concentration of reactants. The quantitative influence of concentration on the rate can be found only by experiment.

The determination of how the rate of reaction changes with concentration of reactants is an experimental problem beset by many difficulties. The usual procedure is to keep everything constant except the concentration of one reactant. As the concentration of the one reactant is systematically changed, the reaction rate is measured. This may be done by noting the rate of disappearance of a reactant or the rate of formation of a product. Experimental difficulties usually come in determining the instantaneous concentration of a component as it changes.

The reaction between hydrogen and nitric oxide

$$2H_2(g) + 2NO(g) \longrightarrow 2H_2O(g) + N_2(g)$$

is a homogeneous reaction which can be investigated kinetically by following the change in pressure of the gaseous mixture as the reaction proceeds. The pressure drops because four moles of gas are converted to three moles of gas. Typical data for several experiments at 800°C are given in Figure 10.1. Since reactants are being used up during the course of the reaction, their concentrations and their rate of reaction are constantly changing. The concentrations and rates listed are those at the very beginning of the reaction when little change has occurred. The first three experiments have the same initial concentration of NO but different initial concentrations of H_2. The last three experiments have the same initial concentration of H_2 but different initial concentrations of NO.

The data for experiments I and II show that, when the initial concentration of NO is constant, doubling the concentration of H_2 doubles the rate; I and III show that tripling the concentration of H_2 triples the rate. The rate of reaction is therefore found to be directly proportional to the concentration of H_2. The data for experiments IV and V show that, when the initial concentration of H_2 is constant, doubling the concentration of NO quadruples the rate; IV and VI show that tripling the concentration of NO triply triples the rate. The rate of reaction is therefore found to be proportional to the square of the concentration of NO. Quantitatively, the data can be summarized by stating that the reaction rate is proportional to (concentration of H_2) $\times$ (concentration of NO)^2. This can be written mathematically as

Rate $= k[H_2][NO]^2$

The equation, known as the *rate law* for the reaction, states that the rate is equal to a proportionality constant times the concentration of H_2 to the first power times the concentration of NO to the second power. Square brackets represent concentration of a substance in moles per liter. The proportionality constant k, called the *specific rate constant,* is characteristic of a given reaction but varies with temperature.

The general form of any rate law is

Rate $= k[A]^n[B]^m \cdots$

where n is the appropriate power to which the concentration of A must be raised and m is the appropriate power to which the concentration of B must be raised in order to summarize the data. The three dots represent other reactants which may be involved in the rate law. The exponents n and m may be fractions and, in fact, may be negative. Negative exponents express inverse proportionality. The important thing to note is that the rate law is determined by experiment. A common error is to assume that the coefficients in the balanced net equation are the exponents in the rate law. This, in general, is not true. For example, in the reaction between H_2 and NO the exponents in the rate law are 1 and 2, whereas the coefficients in the balanced equation are 2 and 2. The only way to determine the exponents in the rate law unambiguously is to do the experiment.

In our discussion of rate laws we have so far been limited to the *initial* rate, i.e., the reaction rate at the very beginning of reaction before any significant changes of concentration have occurred. What happens as time goes on? The concentrations change, and the rate will change in accord with the rate law. To describe such a system, it is most convenient to use the formalism of calculus. In brief, the treatment goes as follows. Suppose Figure 10.2 represents what happens as time passes to the concentration of A and to the concentration of B in a particular reaction in which a molecule of A converts to a molecule of B. Since A and B are stoichiometrically related, the rate of conversion can be expressed either as the rate of disappearance of A or as the rate of formation of B. Referring to the change of concentration of A, we can see from the two triangles drawn adjacent to the curve for A in Figure 10.2 that the rate is not constant with time. For equal time

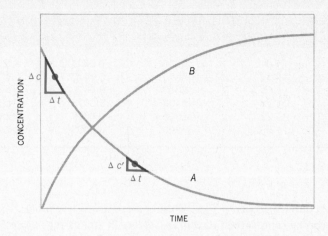

10.2
Change of concentration
during chemical reaction
in which one mole of A is
completely converted to
one mole of B

intervals Δt, near the start of reaction the concentration of A changes by an amount ΔC_A but later in the reaction by a smaller amount $\Delta C_A'$. This can also be expressed by saying the slope (i.e., the tangent) of the curve decreases as time goes on. Mathematically the slope is expressed as

$$-\frac{dC_A}{dt} = \lim_{\Delta t \to 0}\left(-\frac{\Delta C_A}{\Delta t}\right)$$

The minus sign indicates that the concentration of A, C_A, is decreasing with time. ΔC_A is the difference between C_A at some time $t + \Delta t$ and C_A at time t. Therefore, ΔC_A is a negative number. The equation merely states that, if Δt's are picked shorter and shorter ($\Delta t \longrightarrow 0$), then, as Δt approaches zero, the limiting ratio ($-\Delta C_A/\Delta t$) is ($-dC_A/dt$). With reference to Figure 10.2, we can imagine the base of the colored triangle as shrinking to zero so that the tangent line (hypotenuse of the triangle) shrinks to the point shown. The term dC/dt, called the derivative of C with respect to t, expresses the rate at which C changes with t at a point. For a straight line, dC/dt would be a constant; for a curve falling off to zero, dC/dt continually decreases. If the rate of reaction A $\longrightarrow$ B is dependent on the first power of the A concentration (i.e., is a first-order reaction), then the rate law can be written

$$-\frac{d[A]}{dt} = k[A] \qquad \text{or} \qquad \frac{d[B]}{dt} = k[A]$$

In summary, the reaction rate can be expressed in terms of either the disappearance of a reactant or the formation of a product. The two derivatives are of opposite sign, and both change with time so long as the concentration of reactant is changing.

In order to get at the specific rate constant k, the above equation for $-d[A]/dt$ can be rearranged to give

$$\frac{d[A]}{[A]} = -k \, dt$$

Time, sec	$[N_2O_5]$	$-\ln [N_2O_5]$	Time, sec	$[N_2O_5]$	$-\ln [N_2O_5]$
0	0.0176	4.04	3600	0.0029	5.84
600	0.0124	4.39	4200	0.0022	6.12
1200	0.0093	4.68	4800	0.0017	6.38
1800	0.0071	4.95	5400	0.0012	6.73
2400	0.0053	5.24	6000	0.0009	7.01
3000	0.0039	5.55	7200	0.0005	7.60

10.3
Rate data for decomposi-
tion of nitrogen pentoxide
at 45°C

It turns out that $d[A]/[A]$, which represents the fractional change of $[A]$, can be represented as $d \ln [A]$, where ln stands for natural logarithm (see Appendix 2.2). Therefore, we can write

$$d \ln [A] = -k \, dt$$

or, again rearranging,

$$\frac{d \ln [A]}{dt} = -k$$

This last equation says that, for a first-order reaction, the natural logarithm of the concentration when plotted against time gives a straight line whose slope is a constant equal to $-k$. Figure 10.3 shows some data for the reaction

$$N_2O_5(g) \longrightarrow 2NO_2(g) + \tfrac{1}{2}O_2(g)$$

which shows typical first-order behavior. As shown in Figure 10.4, although the plot of concentration of N_2O_5 versus time is not a straight line (i.e., not a constant rate of change), that of the negative natural logarithm is. The specific rate constant k from the slope of the line has a value of 4.8×10^{-4} sec^{-1} for this decomposition. In general, for any first-order reaction the plot of the logarithm of the concentration vs. time will be a straight line indicating that the *fractional* decrease of re-actant concentration with time is constant. For example, the time required to use up half of the remaining reactant is the same at any time during the course of the reaction. Thus, for first-order reactions the rate can be specified by giving either a specific rate constant k or the *half-life* of the reaction $t_{1/2}$. The relation between these two quantities is

$$t_{1/2} = \frac{0.693}{k}$$

A *second-order reaction* is one in which the rate is proportional to the square of a reactant concentration or to the product of two reactant concentrations. (In general, the *order of a reaction* is defined as the sum of the exponents in the rate law. The *order with respect to one reactant* is just its exponent in the rate law.) An example of a second-order reaction is

10.2 Concentration of reactants

224

$$2HI \longrightarrow H_2 + I_2$$

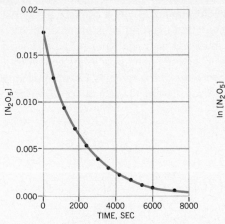 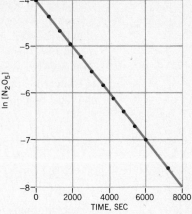

For this reaction a plot of log concentration vs. time will not give a straight line. Instead, to get a straight line, it is necessary to plot the reciprocal of the concentration, $[HI]^{-1}$, against time. That such a plot will give a straight line can be seen as follows: Since the reaction is second order, the rate law is

$$ -\frac{d[HI]}{dt} = k[HI]^2 $$

which can be rewritten

$$ -\frac{d[HI]}{[HI]^2} = k\,dt $$

From differential calculus, $dx/x^2 = -d(1/x)$, and therefore

$$ d\left(\frac{1}{[HI]}\right) = k\,dt $$

or

$$ \frac{d(1/[HI])}{dt} = k $$

The last equation states that, for this second-order reaction, a plot of $1/[HI]$ versus t is a straight line of slope k. Thus, k is readily obtained from the experimental data.

Another example of a second-order reaction is the reverse of the above change, namely,

$$ H_2 + I_2 \longrightarrow 2HI $$

In this case a straight line will be obtained by plotting the reciprocal concentration of either H_2 or I_2 versus time but *only* if these two concentrations are equal. If $[H_2]$ and $[I_2]$ are equal, each can be set equal to x, and the calculus is the same as above. However, if $[H_2]$ and $[I_2]$ are not equal, this cannot be done. To appreciate the difference, we consider the situation where H_2, for example, is present in such great excess that all the I_2 can react with some of it without appreciably changing the concentration of H_2. As a consequence, $[H_2]$ can be considered as a constant and the reaction is pseudo-first order, i.e., a plot of $\ln [I_2]$ versus time gives a straight line. To see this, we can let x represent the concentration of I_2 and $x + a$, the concentration of H_2. As time goes on, x decreases but a remains constant because the excess of H_2 over I_2 stays fixed. Letting the rate be dx/dt, we can write for the chemical reaction

$$H_2 + I_2 \longrightarrow 2HI$$

the rate law

$$-\frac{d[I_2]}{dt} = k[H_2][I_2]$$

or, substituting,

$$-\frac{dx}{dt} = k(x + a)(x)$$

If a is zero, this is a simple second-order case; if a is much greater than x, then

$$-\frac{dx}{dt} \cong k(a)(x)$$

$$-\frac{d \ln x}{dt} \cong k(a)$$

From the last equation it follows that a plot of $\ln [I_2]$ versus t gives a straight line of slope $-ka$, where k is the second-order rate constant and a is the excess H_2 concentration. In general, for rate analysis involving more than one reactant, it is convenient to use excess concentrations for all but one reactant and thus determine the order of the reaction with respect to that reactant. Successive experiments then can tell about the other reactants.

In summary, the dependence of rate on concentration must be obtained from experimental data giving concentration as a function of time. By trial and error, the data for one limiting reactant can be plotted to give the best straight line. If $\ln C$ versus t gives a straight line, the reaction is first order in that reactant; if C^{-1} versus t is linear, the reaction is second order in that reactant. For higher orders a plot of $1/C^n$ versus t, if linear, indicates the reaction to be of order $n + 1$ for the reactant in question.

10.3 TEMPERATURE

How does the temperature of a reaction affect the reaction rate? Observations on rate experiments like those described in the preceding section indicate that a rise in temperature almost invariably increases the rate of any reaction. Furthermore, a decrease in temperature decreases the rate independently of whether the reaction is exothermic or endothermic. The change of rate with temperature is expressed by a change in the specific rate constant k. For every reaction, k increases with increasing temperature.* As to the magnitude of the effect, no generalization can be made. The magnitude varies from one reaction to another and also from one temperature range to another. A rule, which must be used with great caution, is that a 10°C rise in temperature approximately doubles or triples the reaction rate. For each specific reaction it is necessary to determine from experiment the quantitative effect of a rise in temperature.

The relation between the specific rate constant k and the temperature T (°K) is usually expressed as

$$k = Ae^{-E/RT}$$

where A is a constant characteristic of the reaction; e is the number 2.718 . . . , that is, the base of natural logarithms (Appendix 2.2); E is an energy called the activation energy of the reaction; R is the gas constant equal to 1.987 cal mole^{-1} deg^{-1}. The dependence of k on T is not a linear one, but is instead an exponential one; that is, T appears in the exponent. Consequently, small changes in T may produce relatively large changes in k. However, the connection is not a simple one. It can perhaps best be seen by taking the natural logarithm of both sides of the above equation. This gives

$$\ln k = \ln A - \frac{E}{RT}$$

Since 2.303 times log (base 10) equals ln, the last equation can be rewritten

$$\log k = \log A - \frac{E}{2.303RT}$$

For a typical first-order reaction, A might be 1.0×10^{14} sec^{-1} and E might be 20 kcal mole^{-1}. At room temperature ($T = 300°$K)

$$\log k = \log (1.0 \times 10^{14}) - \frac{20000}{(2.303)(1.986)(300)} = -0.58$$

which means that log $k = -1 + 0.42$, or that $k = 2.6 \times 10^{-1}$ sec^{-1}. But if the temperature is 10° higher ($T = 310°$ K), it turns out that log $k = -0.12$, or that $k = 7.6 \times 10^{-1}$ sec^{-1}. In other words, in this case a 10° rise near room temperature roughly triples the rate.

What if we have a reaction the same as the above one except that E is 40 kcal mole^{-1} instead of 20 kcal mole^{-1}? In that case k will be 6.8×10^{-16} sec^{-1} at 300°K and 5.8×10^{-15} sec^{-1} at 310°K. In other words, a 10° rise near room temperature has increased k roughly 9 times. Finally, it might be noted that the effect of a 10° rise will be greater at low temperature than at high.

The value of the activation energy E for a particular reaction is de-

* There are a few extraordinary cases in which a reaction rate apparently decreases with an increase of temperature. Such odd behavior can arise when there is a sequence of forward and backward steps in which the rate of a backward step increases more rapidly with a rise in temperature than does the rate of the subsequent forward step. By allowing for enough steps in a reaction sequence, any observation, no matter how strange, can be explained away—fortunately!

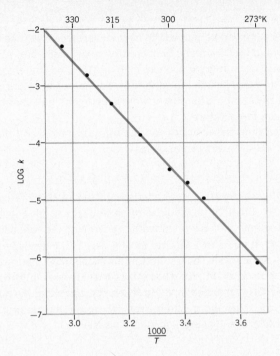

10.5
Rate of decomposition of
N₂O₅ at various
temperatures

termined from experimental data by plotting the logarithm of k against $1/T$. The slope of the line is $-E/2.303R$. Figure 10.5 shows some typical data for the decomposition of N_2O_5 to NO_2 and O_2 at various temperatures. The slope of the line is -5400, which corresponds to an activation energy of 25000 cal mole^{-1}.

10.4 CATALYSIS

It is found by experiment that some reactions can be speeded up by the presence of substances which themselves remain unchanged after the reaction has ended. Such substances are known as *catalysts,* and their effect is known as *catalysis.* Often only a trace of catalyst is sufficient to accelerate the reaction. However, there are many reactions in which the rate of reaction is proportional to some power of the concentration of catalyst. The actual dependence of rate on catalyst concentration must be determined by experiment. If the experiments show there is such a dependence, then the catalyst concentration to the appropriate power becomes part of the rate law in the same way as the reactants become a part of it.

There are numerous examples of catalysis. For instance, when $KClO_3$ is heated so that it decomposes into KCl and oxygen, it is observed that manganese dioxide, MnO_2, considerably accelerates the reaction. At the end of the reaction the $KClO_3$ is gone, but all the MnO_2 remains. It appears that the catalyst is not involved in the reaction, because the starting amount can be recovered. However, the catalyst must take some part in the reaction, or else it could not change the rate.

When hydrogen gas escapes from a cylinder into the air, no change is visible. If the escaping hydrogen is directed at finely divided platinum, it is observed that the platinum glows and eventually ignites the hydrogen. In the absence of platinum, the rate of reaction is too small to observe. In contact with platinum, hydrogen reacts with oxygen from the air to form water. As they react, they give off energy which heats the platinum. As the platinum gets hotter, it heats the hydrogen and oxygen, so that their rate of reaction increases until ignition eventually occurs and the reaction of hydrogen with oxygen becomes self-sustaining.

Enzymes are complex substances in biological systems which act as catalysts for biochemical processes. Pepsin in the gastric juice and ptyalin in the saliva are examples. Ptyalin is the catalyst which accelerates the conversion of starch to sugar. Although starch will react with water to form sugar, it takes weeks for the conversion to occur. A trace of ptyalin is enough to make the reaction proceed at a biologically useful rate.

A special type of catalysis occasionally encountered is *autocatalysis,* or *self-catalysis.* As the name implies, this is catalysis in which one of the products of the reaction is a catalyst for the reaction. For example, in the reaction of permanganate and oxalic acid

$$2MnO_4^- + 5H_2C_2O_4 + 6H^+ \longrightarrow 2Mn^{++} + 10\ CO_2 + 8H_2O$$

Violet   Colorless

the product Mn^{++} catalyzes the reaction. This can readily be observed by mixing solutions of potassium permanganate, sulfuric acid, and oxalic acid. No appreciable decolorization occurs until a tiny crystal of manganous sulfate, $MnSO_4$, is dropped into the reaction mixture. The uncatalyzed reaction is quite slow. Until some Mn^{++} is formed, the reaction does not proceed at an appreciable speed. Addition of a trace of Mn^{++} enables the reaction to start. More Mn^{++} is produced and speeds the reaction further.

Interesting catalysis is observed in the case of hydrogen peroxide. Hydrogen peroxide decomposes to water and oxygen. The reaction is rapid enough that solutions of hydrogen peroxide are difficult to keep without decomposition. It is observed that there are certain substances, such as phosphates, which can be added in trace amounts to slow down the rate of decomposition. This looks like the reverse of catalysis, and, in fact, substances which slow down the rate have been called negative catalysts. The name is misleading, since the function of the phosphate in hydrogen peroxide is probably to destroy the action of catalysts already present in the hydrogen peroxide. For example, it is found by experiment that the decomposition of hydrogen peroxide is catalyzed by traces of Fe^{+3} ion. When phosphate is added, it combines with the Fe^{+3} and prevents the Fe^{+3} from functioning as a catalyst.

10.5 COLLISION THEORY

Many of the observed facts of chemical kinetics have been interpreted in terms of the *collision theory*. This theory makes the basic assumption that, for a chemical reaction to occur, particles must collide. For substance A to react with substance B, it is necessary that the particles A, be they molecules, ions, or atoms, collide with particles B. In the collision, atoms and electrons are rearranged. There is a reshuffling of chemical bonds leading to the production of other species.

According to collision theory, the rate of any step in a reaction is directly proportional to (1) the *number of collisions per second* between the reacting particles involved in that step and (2) the *fraction of these collisions that are effective*. That the rate should depend on the number of collisions per second seems obvious. For instance, in a box that contains A molecules and B molecules there is a certain frequency of collision between A and B molecules. If more A molecules are placed in the box, the collision frequency between A molecules and B molecules is increased. With more collisions between reacting molecules, the reaction between A and B should go faster. However, this cannot be the full story. Calculations of the number of collisions between particles indicate that the collision frequency is very high. In a mixture containing 1 mole of A molecules and 1 mole of B molecules as gases at STP, the number of collisions is more than 10^{30} sec^{-1}. If every one of these collisions led to reaction, the reaction would be over in an instant, and all reactions would be very fast. By observation, this is not true. It must be that only some of the collisions lead to reaction.

Collisions between A molecules and B molecules may be so gentle that there is no change in the identity of the molecules after collision. The colliding particles separate to resume their original identity. The electron cloud associated with A and the electron cloud associated with B repel each other because they are similarly charged. In a gentle collision the repulsion between the electron clouds may simply cause the molecules to bounce apart. However, if A or B or both A and B have much kinetic energy before collision, they can easily use that kinetic energy to do work against the repulsive forces. In the collision the molecules may penetrate each other far enough that electron repulsion is overcome and electron rearrangement ensues. One or more new species may be formed.

The extra amount of energy required in a collision to produce chemical reaction is the *energy of activation*. Its magnitude depends on the nature of the reactants. Some reactions have a large energy of activation. These reactions are slow, since only a small fraction of the reactant particles have enough kinetic energy to furnish the required energy of activation. Other reactions have a small energy of activation. These reactions are fast, since a greater fraction of the collisions are effective. More of the particles have sufficient kinetic energy to furnish the required energy of activation.

Qualitatively, the collision theory quite satisfactorily accounts for the four factors which influence reaction rates: (1) The rate of chemical reaction depends on the *nature of the chemical reactants,* because the energy of activation differs from one reaction to another. (2) The rate of reaction depends on the *concentration of reactants,* because the number of collisions increases as the concentration is increased. (3) The rate of reaction depends on the *temperature,* because an increase of temperature makes molecules move faster. They collide more frequently with other molecules, and, what is more important, the collisions are more violent and more likely to cause reaction. In any collection of molecules there is a distribution of energies. According to collision theory only the highly energetic molecules have enough energy to react. As the temperature is raised, the whole distribution curve is shifted to higher energies (Figure 5.14), so that a larger fraction of the molecules are highly energetic. More of the collisions are therefore effective at high temperatures than at low temperatures. (4) The rate of reaction depends on the presence of *catalysts,* because somehow, in catalysis, collisions are made more effective. This may be done by a preliminary step involving reaction between one or more of the reactants and the catalyst. New reactants which react more rapidly may be produced.

One of the trickiest aspects of chemical kinetics is to account for the quantitative dependence of rate on concentration. For simplicity, let us consider one step of a reaction. Suppose that in this step one molecule of A reacts with one molecule of B to form a molecule AB. The balanced equation for *this step* is

$$A + B \longrightarrow AB$$

According to collision theory, the rate of formation of AB is proportional to the rate at which A and B collide. Let us imagine that we have a box that contains some B molecules and a single A molecule. The rate at which the A molecule collides with B molecules is directly proportional to the number of B molecules in the box. (If we should double the number of B molecules in the box, we would then have twice as many A-B collisions per second.) Suppose now we place a second A molecule in the box. We now have twice as many A molecules in the box, so that the total number of A-B collisions per second is doubled. In other words, the rate at which A and B molecules collide is directly proportional to the concentration of A and to the concentration of B. The rate of formation of AB should therefore be directly proportional to the concentration of A and to that of B. Thus, the rate law for this step is

$$Rate = \frac{d[AB]}{dt} = k[A][B]$$

It should be noted that the exponents of [A] and of [B] in the rate law are unity, just as the two coefficients are in the balanced equation for the step.

What is the situation if the balanced equation for a step involves coefficients larger than 1? Consider the reaction

$$2A \longrightarrow A_2$$

In this step an A molecule must collide with another A molecule to form A_2. The rate at which A_2 forms is thus proportional to the rate at which two A molecules collide. Again we imagine a box, this time containing only molecules of type A. The rate at which *any one* A molecule collides with any other A molecule is proportional to the number of other A molecules in the box. If we should double the number of other A molecules in the box, we would then double the rate at which collisions occur with the one molecule under observation. Now suppose we extend our observation to all the molecules in the box. The total number of collisions per second is proportional to the number of collisions per second made by one A molecule times the total number of A molecules in the box. Another way of saying the same thing is that the rate of collisions is proportional to the number of molecules hitting multiplied by the number of molecules being hit. In any event, we can say that the rate at which two A molecules collide is proportional to the concentration of A times the concentration of A, or to the square of the concentration of A. Consequently, for the step

$$2A \longrightarrow A_2$$

we can write the rate law

$$\text{Rate} = \frac{d[A_2]}{dt} = k[A]^2$$

It might be noted that the exponent of the concentration of A in the rate law is 2, just as the coefficient of A in the balanced equation for the step is 2.

For the general case of a step for which the balanced equation shows the disappearance of n molecules of A and m molecules of B to form P, we can write the rate law

$$\text{Rate} = \frac{d[P]}{dt} = k[A]^n[B]^m$$

indicating that the rate of that step is proportional to the concentration of A taken to the n power times the concentration of B taken to the m power. We should note again that a net chemical change may consist of several consecutive steps, and a knowledge of only the overall balanced equation does not permit us to predict what the experimentally observed rate law will be. For example, in the reaction between NO and H_2, discussed in Section 10.2, the rate law obtained experimentally states that the reaction rate is proportional to the first power of the H_2 concentration times the second power of the NO concentration. Yet the balanced equation for the reaction is

$$2H_2(g) + 2NO(g) \longrightarrow N_2(g) + 2H_2O(g)$$

From collision theory, it appears that reaction could occur by a collision between two H_2 molecules and the two NO molecules. The number of such collisions per second is proportional to the molar concentration of H_2 squared times the molar concentration of NO squared. This means that doubling the H_2 concentration ought to quadruple the number of collisions per second and therefore quadruple the rate. This does not agree with experiment. The collisions that determine the rate cannot be between two H_2 molecules and two NO molecules.

To account for the observed rate law, collision theory assumes that this reaction, like many others, occurs in steps. In stepwise reactions, the slow step is the one which determines the rate. It is the bottleneck and determines the rate law for the reaction. The following example shows a two-step reaction:

$$A(g) + B(g) \longrightarrow \text{[intermediate]} \tag{1}$$

$$\text{[intermediate]} + B(g) \longrightarrow C(g) \tag{2}$$

Net reaction:

$$A(g) + 2B(g) \longrightarrow C(g)$$

In step (1) a molecule of A collides with a molecule of B to form a short-lived intermediate. In step (2) the intermediate reacts with a molecule of B to form a molecule of C. If the first step is slow and if the second step is fast, the rate at which the product C forms depends only on the rate at which the intermediate forms. As soon as the intermediate appears, it is used up in the second reaction. The rate at which the intermediate is produced is determined by the collision of A and B. Thus, the rate of the slow step is proportional to the concentration of A times the concentration of B. Since the slow step is the rate-determining step in the overall change, the rate law for the net change is

$$\text{Rate} = \frac{d[C]}{dt} = k[A][B]$$

The net change is determined by adding steps (1) and (2):

$$A(g) + B(g) + B(g) \longrightarrow C(g)$$

The intermediate cancels out because it occurs on both sides of the equation. The coefficients which appear in the net equation are different from the exponents in the rate law.

For the specific reaction

$$2H_2(g) + 2NO(g) \longrightarrow N_2(g) + 2H_2O(g)$$

the rate law is determined by experiment to be

$$\text{Rate} = \frac{d[N_2]}{dt} = k[H_2][NO]^2$$

The reaction must occur in steps. One possible set of steps is

$$H_2(g) + NO(g) + NO(g) \longrightarrow N_2O(g) + H_2O(g) \tag{3}$$

$$H_2(g) + N_2O(g) \longrightarrow N_2(g) + H_2O(g) \tag{4}$$

The first step [Equation (3)] must be the slower and therefore must determine the rate law. However, many people object to this mechanism because Equation (3) requires a simultaneous collision of three molecules. As any billiard player knows, three-body collisions are quite improbable. An alternative series of steps without three-body collision is

$$2NO(g) \longrightarrow N_2O_2(g) \tag{5}$$

$$N_2O_2(g) + H_2(g) \longrightarrow N_2O(g) + H_2O(g) \tag{6}$$

$$N_2O(g) + H_2(g) \longrightarrow N_2(g) + H_2O(g) \tag{7}$$

with Equation (6) rate-determining. Since the N_2O_2 for Equation (6) is formed by collision of two NO molecules, the concentration of N_2O_2 is proportional to the square of the concentration of NO. The rate of the second step thus depends on the square of the concentration of NO times the concentration of H_2. On the basis of the observed rate law, it is not possible to distinguish between these two mechanisms. In fact, it may be that neither is right and that the actual mechanism is much more complicated.

10.6 ABSOLUTE-REACTION-RATE THEORY

The collision theory of chemical kinetics is the basis of the *absolute-reaction-rate theory,* which assumes that reaction rate can be calculated by applying the equations of wave mechanics (Section 2.3) to the colliding particles. The calculations are complicated and have been done only for a few simple cases. However, some of the basic ideas are useful and easily applied qualitatively.

For simplicity, we consider the one-step reaction in which one molecule of A collides with one molecule of B to form one molecule each of C and D. The collision is assumed to consist of the approach of an A molecule to a B molecule to form some kind of a transient complex particle. This complex particle, which is called the *activated complex,* can split apart to restore the A and B molecules, or it can split in some other way to give the new particles C and D. The absolute-reaction-rate theory calculates the potential-energy change of the system as A and B molecules come together to form the activated complex and then separate to give C and D molecules. A typical potential-energy curve is shown in Figure 10.6. On the vertical axis is plotted the potential energy of the system; on the horizontal axis is plotted a coordinate which tells how far the reaction has gone from the initial state toward the final state. In the initial state, A and B molecules are far enough apart not to affect each other. The potential energy is the sum of the potential energy of A by itself plus that of B by itself. It makes no difference what the actual value is, since potential energy is relative. As A and B come together, the forces of repulsion between the electron clouds become appreciable. Work must be done on the system to squash the particles together. This means the potential energy must increase. It increases until it reaches a maximum that corresponds to the activated complex. The activated complex then splits into C and D molecules, and the potential energy drops as C and D go apart.

The difference (shown by the arrow) between the potential energy of the initial state A plus B and the potential energy of the activated com-

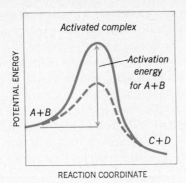

10.6
Potential-energy change
during a reaction (Dotted
line refers to catalyzed
reaction.)

plex is a measure of the energy which must be added to the particles in order to get them to react. This is the activation energy of the reaction. It usually is supplied by converting some of the kinetic energy of the particles into potential energy. If A and B molecules do not have much kinetic energy, on collision they are able to go only part way up the side of the hump. All the kinetic energy may be converted into potential energy without getting the pair distorted into the activated complex. In such case, A and B slide back down the hump and fly apart unchanged. The situation is similar to that of a ball rolled up the side of a hill. If the ball is rolled slowly, it goes part way up, stops, and rolls back again. If the ball is rolled rapidly, it goes completely to the top of the hill and down the other side. Similarly, if A and B molecules have high enough kinetic energy, they can attain the activated complex and get over the hump from A and B to C and D. In a reaction at higher temperatures more molecules get over the potential-energy hump per unit time, and the reaction occurs faster.

Two other aspects of Figure 10.6 are of interest. For the case represented, the final state C and D has lower potential energy than the initial state A and B. There is a net decrease in potential energy as the reaction proceeds. This energy usually shows up as heat, so the particular change

$$A + B \longrightarrow C + D$$

is exothermic. The amount of energy required to distort A and B into the activated complex is more than made up for when the activated complex springs apart to form C and D. However, since the activation energy is large, the reaction is slow, even though the system goes to a lower potential-energy state. An example of a slow, exothermic reaction is

$$2H_2(g) + O_2(g) \longrightarrow 2H_2O(g) + 116 \text{ kcal}$$

Figure 10.6 is a potential-energy diagram for the reaction of A and B to produce C and D. It can also be read from right to left as a diagram for the reaction of C and D to produce A and B; that is, the reaction is reversible. As can be seen from the diagram, the reaction C and D to give A and B is endothermic. Also, reaction between C and D has a higher activation energy than reaction between A and B.

When a reaction is catalyzed, there is a change of path or mechanism. Since the rate is now faster, the activation energy for the new path must be lower than for the old path. The dotted curve in Figure 10.6 shows what the potential-energy curve might look like for the new path. Since the barrier is lower, at any given temperature and concentration more particles per second can get over the hump; hence the reaction goes faster. As an example, the reaction between hydrogen and oxygen to form water is catalyzed by the presence of platinum. It has been sug- gested that the effect of the platinum is to react with H_2 molecules to produce H atoms. The oxygen molecules then collide with H atoms in- stead of with H_2 molecules. The new path has a lower activation energy in the rate-determining step.

QUESTIONS

10.1 *Rate law*   The kinetic data listed in the accompanying table were obtained at 25°C for the reaction

$$A(g) + B(g) \longrightarrow C(g)$$

Experiment	[A], M	[B], M	Initial rate of C formation, mole liter^{-1} min^{-1}
1	0.10	0.10	0.25
2	0.20	0.20	2.0
3	0.10	0.20	1.0
4	0.20	0.40	8.0

(*a*) Write the rate law for the reaction. (*b*) What is the rate-determining step for the reaction? (*c*) What is the numerical value for the specific rate constant k at 25°C? (*d*) What will be the initial rate of formation of C if the initial concentration of A is 0.15 M and that of B is 0.35 M at 25°C? (*e*) What would be the initial rate of formation of C if the pres- sure in (*d*) were increased by addition of 0.50 M neon? (*f*)What would be the initial rate of formation of C if the pressure in (*d*) were increased by halving the container volume?

10.2 *Reaction rate*   Assume for the reaction $2H_2 + 2NO \longrightarrow 2H_2O + N_2$ that the activated complex is derived from one H_2 and two NO molecules. How will the rate of activated-complex formation be af- fected by each of the following changes? (*a*) Halving the H_2 concentra- tion. (*b*) Halving the NO concentration. (*c*) Raising the temperature.

10.3 *Reaction rate*   When $PCl_3(g)$ and $Cl_2(g)$ are mixed at 500°K, they react to form some $PCl_5(g)$. The rate of formation of PCl_5 is first order with respect to PCl_3 and first order with respect to Cl_2. Suppose, at time $t = 0$, one mole of PCl_3 and one mole of Cl_2 are simultaneously injected into a 20-liter box. One second later, before reaction is com- plete, the contents of the box are examined for the number of moles of PCl_5. What effect on the number of moles of PCl_5, at $t = 1$ sec, would there be if each of the following changes were made in initial conditions? Answer *increase, decrease, no change,* or *can't tell*. (*a*) More moles of PCl_3 had been added. (*b*) More moles of Cl_2 had been added. (*c*) Some helium had been added. (*d*) The volume of the box had been decreased. (*e*) The temperature had been raised. (*f*) One cc of finely divided platinum had been added.

10.4 Rate calculations Consider the data given for experiment VI in Figure 10.1. (*a*) What is the total initial pressure before any reaction has occurred? (*b*) What is the initial H_2 pressure before reaction? (*c*) What will the total pressure be after 6 sec has elapsed, assuming that the reaction progresses at the initial rate indicated? (*d*) Noting that two moles of H_2 disappear for each one-mole decrease of the total, what will the H_2 pressure be after 6 sec has elapsed? (*e*) Compute the fraction of H_2 used up in the first 6 sec of reaction.

10.5 Rate plots (*a*) By using the data of Figure 10.3, show that $d[A]/[A]$ is equivalent to $d \ln [A]$ by plotting for each time t the change of $[N_2O_5]$ in each 600-sec interval divided by the value of $[N_2O_5]$ at the end of that interval against time. Compare your plot with the plots given in Figure 10.4. (*b*) Make a plot of $1/[N_2O_5]$ versus time to show that this decomposition can be demonstrated graphically not to be second order.

10.6 Radioactive decay The spontaneous decomposition of radioactive nuclei is a first-order rate process. I^{136} disintegrates with the emission of a beta particle (i.e., electron) with a half-life of 86 sec. (*a*) Write the rate law for this process. (*b*) Calculate the specific rate constant k. (*c*) Given 6.0×10^{20} I^{136} nuclei at time $t = 0$, calculate how many I^{136} nuclei will be left after one half-life; after two half-lives; after three half-lives. (*d*) Plot the number of I^{136} nuclei as a function of time. Plot also the log of this number of I^{136} nuclei as a function of time. (*e*) Calculate the rate (disintegrations of I^{136} sec^{-1}) at each of the four times mentioned in (*c*).

10.7 Activation energy The reaction between H_2 and I_2 to form HI is exothermic and reversible. (*a*) Does the forward or the reverse reaction have the greater activation energy? Explain with a diagram. (*b*) Will the forward or reverse reaction be increased more by raising the temperature? Explain.

10.8 Rate law (*a*) What is meant by a "rate law"? Give an example. (*b*) If the rate-law exponents do not match the coefficients in the balanced overall equation, what can you deduce about the mechanism? (*c*) Suppose the given reaction is catalyzed by a soluble substance. Predict whether this catalyst appears or not (1) in the rate law and (2) in the balanced overall equation.

10.9 Rate law Given the balanced equation

$$A + B_2 \longrightarrow AB + B$$

The rate of formation of AB is found to be directly proportional to the concentration of B_2, independent of A, and proportional to the concentration of C. (*a*) Write the rate law. (*b*) Write a mechanism consistent with the facts. (c) Tell how catalysis is involved in this reaction by noting what the catalyst is, how it speeds the reaction, and how it is that it is not destroyed.

10.10 Mechanism (a) Complete and balance for acid solution

$$As(OH)_3 + HCrO_4^- \longrightarrow Cr^{+3} + H_3AsO_4$$

(b) The rate of $HCrO_4^-$ reduction doubles if either $As(OH)_3$ or $HCrO_4^-$ concentration is doubled. Other things equal, the rate is nine times as fast in 0.030 M acid as at 0.010 M acid. Write the rate law. (c) Assuming the rate-limiting step is first in the mechanism, tell what oxidation state the Cr is in just after this first step if As is as H_3AsO_4.

10.11 Effect of temperature Given a reaction for which $A = 2.0 \times 10^{14}$ sec^{-1} and $E = 15$ kcal mole^{-1} in the relation $k = Ae^{-E/RT}$. Assuming A and E to be independent of temperature, show that a 10° rise in temperature changes k by a larger factor at 100°K than at 400°K.

10.12 Half-life (using calculus) By methods of integration, show that, for a first-order reaction, the half-life $t_{1/2}$ is equal to $0.693/k$.

10.13 Rate law (with calculus) By using the calculus, show that, for a reaction which follows the rate law $-dC/dt = kC^n$, a straight-line plot will be obtained for $C^{-(n-1)}$ versus t.

10.14 Activation energy (using calculus) (a) From the relation $k = Ae^{-E/RT}$ find expressions for $d \log k/dT$ and $d \log k/d(1/T)$. (b) Find expressions for dk/dT and $dk/d(1/T)$.

10.15 Reaction order Suppose you have a one-step reaction that is first order in A and second order in B. What function of concentration of the limiting reagent would you need to plot vs. time to get a straight line in each of the following experiments? (a) Initial concentration of A is 100 times that of B. (b) Initial concentration of B is 100 times that of A. (c) Initial concentration of B is twice that of A.

10.16 Integrated rate law (using calculus) For the decomposition of $N_2O_5 \longrightarrow 2NO_2 + \frac{1}{2}O_2$ the rate law is

$$-d[N_2O_5]/dt = 4.8 \times 10^{-4} [N_2O_5]$$

for time expressed in seconds. (a) By the methods of integral calculus, show that at any time t the concentration of N_2O_5 is related to the initial concentration by the expression

$$\log \frac{[N_2O_5]_{initial}}{[N_2O_5]_{final}} = 2.1 \times 10^{-4} t$$

(b) How long would it take for 80% of the initial N_2O_5 to decompose?

ANSWERS

10.4 (a) 602 torr   (b) 401 torr   (c) 599 torr   (d) 396 torr
(e) 0.013   10.15 (a) 1/[B]   (b) log [A]   (c) 1/[A]² or 1/[B]²
10.16 (b) 3300 sec

11 chemical equilibrium

It is found by experiment that, when reacting species are brought together so as to undergo chemical reaction, the conversion of reactants
to products is often incomplete, no matter how long the reaction is
allowed to continue. In the initial state the reactants are present at a
definite concentration. As the reaction proceeds, the concentrations of
reactants decrease. Sooner or later, however, they level off and become
constant. A state in which the concentrations no longer change is
established. This state is known as the state of *chemical equilibrium*.

11.1 THE EQUILIBRIUM STATE

As an example of the attainment of equilibrium, we consider a reaction

$$A(g) + B(g) \longrightarrow C(g) + D(g)$$

in which one molecule of A reacts with one molecule of B to form molecules of C and D. For simplicity, all the substances are assumed to be gases. At the start of the experiment, A and B are mixed in a box. The concentration of A and the concentration of B are measured as time passes. Results of the measurements are plotted in Figure 11.1, where concentration is the vertical axis and time is the horizontal axis. The initial concentration of A is some definite number, depending on the number of moles of A and the volume of the box. As time goes on, the concentration of A diminishes, at first quite rapidly but later less rapidly. Eventually, the concentration of A levels off and becomes constant. The concentration of B changes in similar fashion, even though, at the start, it may not be the same as A. The initial concentrations of C and D are zero. As time goes on, C and D are produced. Their concentrations increase quite rapidly at first but then level off. At time t_e each of the concentrations becomes essentially constant. Once this equilibrium state has been established, it persists indefinitely and, if undisturbed, will last forever.

The constant state that characterizes equilibrium vapor pressure (Section 7.2) is due to equality of opposing reactions. Similarly, the constant state that characterizes chemical equilibrium is due to equality of opposing reactions. A and B molecules react to form C and D molecules. So long as A and B are present, this reaction continues. Reaction does not stop at time t_e. As soon as an appreciable number of C and D molecules form, they react with each other to produce A and B. After time t_e, the forward and reverse changes occur at the same rate. The equality of opposing reactions is indicated by writing

$$A(g) + B(g) \rightleftharpoons C(g) + D(g)$$

or

$$A(g) + B(g) = C(g) + D(g)$$

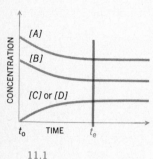

11.1

Approach to equilibrium

11.2 MASS ACTION

It is found by experiment that every particular reaction has its own specific equilibrium state in which there is a definite relation between the concentrations of the materials. To illustrate the relation, we consider the reaction between A and B to produce C and D. In a series of experiments, all done at the same temperature but *differing in initial concentrations* of A and B, the results shown in Figure 11.2 are obtained. The concentrations given, in moles per liter, are those in the equilibrium state, and they are called equilibrium concentrations. Although the equilibrium concentrations change from experiment to experiment, there is a single relationship which holds for all the experiments. If the concentration of C times the concentration of D is divided by the con-

11.2 Mass action

240

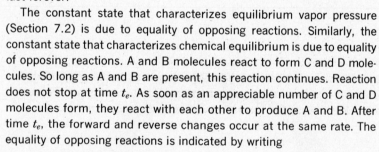

Experiment	Equilibrium concentrations, moles liter^{-1}			
	A	B	C	D
1	3.00	2.00	1.00	1.00
2	9.60	10.0	4.00	4.00
3	0.500	3.00	0.500	0.500
4	21.9	1.22	2.11	2.11

centration of A times the concentration of B, the number 0.167 is obtained in every case. This number, *the equilibrium constant,* is characteristic of this specific reaction and varies only with changes in temperature. Whenever A, B, C, and D are present together in equilibrium, the concentrations must be such that they satisfy the expression

$$\frac{[C][D]}{[A][B]} = 0.167$$

The balanced general equation

$$nA(g) + mB(g) + \cdots \rightleftharpoons pC(g) + qD(g) + \cdots$$

can be read as n molecules of A plus m molecules of B react to form p molecules of C and q molecules of D. The three dots represent other reactants or products, so that this equation applies to any reaction. The letters n, m, p, and q represent numbers that are the coefficients of the chemical equation. The letters A, B, C, and D represent the formulas of the various reactants and products. If the balanced equation is written in this way, the relationship that is constant at equilibrium is

$$\frac{[C]^p[D]^q \cdots}{[A]^n[B]^m \cdots}$$

This fraction is called the *mass-action expression.** The square brackets designate concentrations, in moles per liter, and the exponents are the powers to which these concentrations must be raised. In the mass-action expression, by convention, concentrations of the materials on the right-hand side of the chemical equation appear in the numerator and concentrations of the materials on the left-hand side of the equation in the denominator. At equilibrium the expression is numerically equal to the equilibrium constant K for the particular reaction:

$$\frac{[C]^p[D]^q \cdots}{[A]^n[B]^m \cdots} = K$$

* The term "mass action" derives from the original work of Cato Maximilian Guldberg and Peter Waage, Norwegian chemists, who in 1864 proposed that the reaction A + B = C + D could be treated as follows: The "action force" between A and B is proportional to the "active mass" of A and that of B. This is called the law of mass action. Similarly, the action force between C and D is proportional to the active masses of C and D. At equilibrium the action force between A and B equals the action force between C and D. Although Guldberg and Waage were not clear in what was meant by "action force" and "active mass," their work was a milestone in the development of a suitable description of chemical equilibrium.

This equilibrium condition is called the *law of chemical equilibrium.* The law states that, in a system at chemical equilibrium, the concentrations of the materials which participate in the reaction must satisfy the condition expressed by the constancy of the mass-action expression. There is no other restriction on the individual concentrations.

The law of chemical equilibrium is an experimental fact. It can, however, be justified by using the principles of chemical kinetics and requiring at equilibrium the equality of the rates of forward and reverse reactions. For example, in the equilibrium

$$A(g) + B(g) \rightleftharpoons C(g) + D(g)$$

reaction may proceed in a single step or in a series of steps. The mass-action expression is the same in either case and can be written without any knowledge of the kinetics of the reaction. That the mass-action expression is independent of the mechanism is shown as follows:

1. Suppose the reaction proceeds through a single reversible step.

$$A(g) + B(g) \rightleftharpoons C(g) + D(g) \tag{1}$$

For the forward reaction,

$$\text{Rate} = k[A][B]$$

where k is the rate constant of the forward reaction. For the reverse reaction

$$\text{Rate} = k'[C][D]$$

where k' is the rate constant of the reverse reaction. At equilibrium, the rate of the forward reaction is equal to the rate of the reverse reaction. Thus,

$$k[A][B] = k'[C][D]$$

or

$$\frac{[C][D]}{[A][B]} = \frac{k}{k'}$$

This proves that in this case the mass-action expression is equal to a constant.

2. Suppose the reaction proceeds through more than one reversible step. For example, the steps

$$A(g) + A(g) \rightleftharpoons C(g) + Q(g) \tag{2}$$

$$Q(g) + B(g) \rightleftharpoons A(g) + D(g) \tag{3}$$

add up to give

$$A(g) + B(g) \rightleftharpoons C(g) + D(g)$$

which is the same net equation as Equation (1). For the first step [Equation (2)] k_1 and k_1' are the rate constants for the forward and reverse directions. For Equation (3), k_2 and k_2' apply to the forward and reverse directions. At equilibrium, forward and reverse reactions must be equal for each step. Thus, for the first step,

$$k_1[A][A] = k_1'[C][Q]$$

For the second step

$$k_2[Q][B] = k_2'[A][D]$$

These simultaneous equations can be combined by eliminating the chemical intermediate Q to give

$$\frac{k_1}{k_1'}\frac{[A][A]}{[C]} = \frac{k_2'}{k_2}\frac{[A][D]}{[B]}$$

Rearranging and simplifying gives

$$\frac{[C][D]}{[A][B]} = \frac{k_1 k_2}{k_1' k_2'}$$

Again, the mass-action expression is shown to be equal to a constant.

11.3 EQUILIBRIUM CONSTANT

The numbers observed for equilibrium constants vary from very large numbers to extremely small numbers, depending on the specific reaction. If the equilibrium constant is small ($K < 1$), the numerator of the mass-action expression is smaller than the denominator. This means that, in the equilibrium state, the concentration of at least one of the materials on the right of the chemical equation is small. Therefore, a small equilibrium constant implies that the reaction does not proceed far from left to right. For example, if for

$$A(g) + B(g) \rightleftharpoons C(g) + D(g) \qquad K = 1.0 \times 10^{-5}$$

then the mixing of A and B does not result in the production of much C and D at equilibrium. If the equilibrium constant is large ($K > 1$), the denominator of the mass-action expression is smaller than the numerator. This means that, in the equilibrium state, the concentration of at least one of the materials on the left of the chemical equation is small. Therefore, a large equilibrium constant implies that the reaction proceeds from left to right essentially to completion. For example, if for

$$E(g) + F(g) \rightleftharpoons G(g) + H(g) \qquad K = 1.0 \times 10^{5}$$

then the mixing of E and F results in practically complete conversion of E and F to G and H.

The equilibrium constant is determined by experiment. For example, measurements have been made of the equilibrium involving hydrogen, iodine, and hydrogen iodide. The equilibrium is described by

$$H_2(g) + I_2(g) \rightleftharpoons 2HI(g)$$

In the equilibrium state all three components are present. The equilibrium condition is

$$\frac{[HI]^2}{[H_2][I_2]} = K$$

The number K can be determined by measuring all three concentrations in the equilibrium state. In an experiment at 490°C the following results might be obtained:

Concentration of H_2 = 0.000862 mole liter^{-1}

Concentration of I_2 = 0.00263 mole liter^{-1}

Concentration of HI = 0.0102 mole liter^{-1}

Since these concentrations are equilibrium concentrations, they satisfy the equilibrium condition

$$\frac{[HI]^2}{[H_2][I_2]} = \frac{(0.0102)^2}{(0.000862)(0.00263)} = 45.9$$

For any equilibrium system at 490°C containing H_2, I_2, and HI, the mass-action expression must be equal to 45.9. If this condition is not satisfied, the system is not at equilibrium, and changes will occur until equilibrium is established.

In the above examples it happens that the numbers of moles of gas on the two sides of the equation are equal and, therefore, the final equilibrium constant is dimensionless. However, in other cases, for example, $PCl_5(g) \rightleftharpoons PCl_3(g) + Cl_2(g)$, there are different numbers of moles on the two sides and so K would appear to have units. At 546°K

$$K = \frac{[PCl_3][Cl_2]}{[PCl_5]} = 0.073 \text{ mole liter}^{-1}$$

Clearly, a different numerical value would apply if concentration were measured in different units, e.g., in terms of atmospheres pressure. To avoid such complications, concentration may be replaced by a dimensionless quantity called "chemical activity," or simply "activity." Activity can be evaluated by dividing the actual concentration by the concentration of the material in a standard reference state; hence, the units cancel out. Activity can be considered to specify how many times as effective as the standard state is the actual concentration of the material. In some cases the true activity is not exactly proportional to concentration, but instead needs to include correction factors for nonideal behavior. We shall assume behavior is ideal and neglect such correction factors.

11.4 EQUILIBRIUM CALCULATIONS

Once the equilibrium constant of a reaction has been determined, it can be used to describe any system containing the chemical components of that reaction at equilibrium. Thus, the value 45.9 can be used to describe any system containing H_2, I_2, and HI in chemical equilibrium at 490°C.

EXAMPLE 1

One mole of H_2 and one mole of I_2 are introduced into a 1-liter box at a temperature of 490°C. What will be the final concentrations in the box when equilibrium has been established?

Initially, there is no HI in the box. The system is not at equilibrium, since the mass-action expression is zero instead of 45.9. In order to establish equilibrium, changes must occur to produce HI. HI can come only from the reaction

$$H_2(g) + I_2(g) \rightleftharpoons 2HI(g)$$

This reaction proceeds to produce enough HI to satisfy the equilibrium condition.

Let n equal the number of moles of hydrogen that must disappear in order to establish equilibrium. Every time one mole of hydrogen disappears, one mole of iodine also disappears. So, n also represents the number of moles of iodine that disappear in order to establish equilibrium. According to the balanced equation, if one mole of hydrogen disappears, two moles of HI must be formed. If n moles of hydrogen disappear, $2n$ moles of HI must appear. Therefore, $2n$ is equal to the number of moles of HI formed in order to establish equilibrium. The situation is summarized as follows:

Initially	At equilibrium
$[H_2] = 1.000$ mole liter^{-1}	$[H_2] = (1.000 - n)$ moles liter^{-1}
$[I_2] = 1.000$ mole liter^{-1}	$[I_2] = (1.000 - n)$ moles liter^{-1}
$[HI] = 0$	$[HI] = 2n$ moles liter^{-1}

Since the volume of the box is 1 liter, the concentration of each component is identical with the number of moles of that component in the box. The equilibrium concentrations must satisfy the condition

$$\frac{[HI]^2}{[H_2][I_2]} = 45.9$$

Substitution gives

$$\frac{(2n)^2}{(1.000 - n)(1.000 - n)} = 45.9$$

for which

$$n = 0.772*$$

Therefore, at equilibrium

$$[H_2] = (1.000 - n) = 0.228 \text{ mole liter}^{-1}$$

$$[I_2] = (1.000 - n) = 0.228 \text{ mole liter}^{-1}$$

$$[HI] = 2n = 1.544 \text{ moles liter}^{-1}$$

That these values represent equilibrium concentrations can be checked by calculating the value of the mass-action expression

* This particular equation can be solved by taking the square root of both sides of the equation. For a more general case we can use the ordinary algebraic methods for solving quadratic equations (see Appendix 2.3). Of the two roots necessarily obtained for the quadratic equation, one can be discarded as physically impossible. In this case the root $n = 1.42$ corresponds to more than 100% reaction.

$$\frac{[HI]^2}{[H_2][I_2]} = \frac{(1.544)^2}{(0.228)(0.228)}$$

It must be 45.9 at 490°C.

To emphasize the fact that it makes no difference from which side of the equation equilibrium is approached, we consider what happens when only HI is placed in the box at 490°C. Since initially there is no hydrogen or iodine in the system, decomposition of HI must occur in order to establish equilibrium.

EXAMPLE 2

Two moles of HI are injected into a box of 1-liter volume at 490°C. What will be the concentration of each species in the box at equilibrium?

The equilibrium is

$$H_2(g) + I_2(g) \rightleftharpoons 2HI(g)$$

Let x equal the number of moles of HI that must decompose in order to establish equilibrium. In the reverse reaction, for each two moles of HI that disappear, one mole of hydrogen and one mole of iodine are formed. If x moles of HI disappear, $x/2$ moles of hydrogen and $x/2$ moles of iodine appear. The initial and final concentrations are summarized:

Initially	At equilibrium
$[HI] = 2.000$ moles liter^{-1}	$[HI] = (2.000 - x)$ moles liter^{-1}
$[H_2] = 0$ mole liter^{-1}	$[H_2] = (x/2)$ moles liter^{-1}
$[I_2] = 0$ mole liter^{-1}	$[I_2] = (x/2)$ moles liter^{-1}

At equilibrium

$$\frac{[HI]^2}{[H_2][I_2]} = 45.9 = \frac{(2.000 - x)^2}{(x/2)(x/2)}$$

for which

$$x = 0.456$$

Therefore, at equilibrium

$[H_2] = x/2 = 0.228$ mole liter^{-1}

$[I_2] = x/2 = 0.228$ mole liter^{-1}

$[HI] = 2.000 - x = 1.544$ moles liter^{-1}

Examples 1 and 2 show that it makes no difference whether the equilibrium state is produced from the material on the left-hand side of the chemical equation or from the material on the right-hand side. Change occurs so as to produce the missing material in sufficient concentration to establish equilibrium. Sometimes the initial nonequilibrium system contains all the components, in which case the change necessary to establish equilibrium is not obvious. In the following example, it is not immediately clear whether the concentration of HI must increase or decrease in order to establish equilibrium.

EXAMPLE 3

One mole of H_2, two moles of I_2, and three moles of HI are injected into a one-liter box. What will be the concentration of each species at equilibrium at 490°C?

The equilibrium is

$$H_2(g) + I_2(g) \rightleftharpoons 2HI(g)$$

Let x be the number of moles of H_2 that must be used up in order to establish equilibrium. (If it turns out that *more* H_2 must be formed, x will be a negative number.) According to the stoichiometry of the reaction, x is also the number of moles of I_2 that must be used up and $2x$ is the number of moles of HI that must be formed. At equilibrium the concentration of H_2 is reduced by the amount x, the concentration of I_2 is reduced by the amount x, and the concentration of HI is increased by $2x$.

Initially	At equilibrium
$[H_2] = 1.000$ mole liter^{-1}	$[H_2] = (1.000 - x)$ moles liter^{-1}
$[I_2] = 2.000$ moles liter^{-1}	$[I_2] = (2.000 - x)$ moles liter^{-1}
$[HI] = 3.000$ moles liter^{-1}	$[HI] = (3.000 + 2x)$ moles liter^{-1}

At equilibrium

$$\frac{[HI]^2}{[H_2][I_2]} = 45.9 = \frac{(3.000 + 2x)^2}{(1.000 - x)(2.000 - x)}$$

for which

$$x = 0.684$$

Therefore, at equilibrium

$$[H_2] = 1.000 - x \ = 0.316 \text{ mole liter}^{-1}$$

$$[I_2] = 2.000 - x \ = 1.316 \text{ moles liter}^{-1}$$

$$[HI] = 3.000 + 2x = 4.368 \text{ moles liter}^{-1}$$

11.5 HETEROGENEOUS EQUILIBRIUM

Heterogeneous equilibria are those equilibria which involve two or more phases. For example, the equilibrium

$$2C(s) + O_2(g) \rightleftharpoons 2CO(g)$$

involves both gaseous and solid phases. The solid phase consists of pure carbon, and the gas phase consists of a mixture of oxygen and carbon monoxide. In mass-action expressions, the concentrations must apply to the phase specified by the equation. For example, for the above equilibrium the equilibrium condition is

$$K' = \frac{[CO(g)]^2}{[C(s)]^2[O_2(g)]}$$

where $[CO(g)]$ refers to the concentration of CO in the gas phase, $[C(s)]$ refers to the concentration of C in the solid phase, and $[O_2(g)]$ refers to the concentration of O_2 in the gas phase.

A simplification of the equilibrium condition is possible because, although the concentration of carbon monoxide and the concentration of oxygen in the gas phase are variable, the concentration of carbon in the solid cannot be changed. The concentration of carbon monoxide in the gas phase can be changed, e.g., by the addition of CO. Since the volume remains constant and more CO has been added, the concentration of CO is increased. Similarly, the concentration of O_2 can be changed, but for solid carbon this is not possible. If more solid carbon is added, the concentration is not changed, because as the number of moles of carbon increases, the volume of carbon also increases. The *number of moles per liter of solid carbon* is the same number, no matter how much carbon is present.

In the general case, at constant temperature, the concentration of any substance as a pure solid or a pure liquid cannot be changed and is a constant. The constant concentration can be combined with the original equilibrium constant to give a new equilibrium constant for which the mass-action expression does not include the pure condensed phase. Thus, for the equilibrium

$$2C(s) + O_2(g) \rightleftharpoons 2CO(g)$$

$$K'[C(s)]^2 = \frac{[CO]^2}{[O_2]}$$

where $[C(s)]$ is a constant. Therefore,

$$K'[C(s)]^2 = K$$

$$K = \frac{[CO]^2}{[O_2]}$$

The last equation expresses the requirement that a system containing $CO(g)$, $O_2(g)$, and $C(s)$ is in equilibrium no matter how much $C(s)$ is present, provided that $[CO]^2/[O_2]$ has the proper value. The simple rule is that for heterogeneous equilibria pure solids and pure liquids are omitted from the mass-action expression. Further examples are given below:

At 1000°C $\quad H_2(g) + S(g) \rightleftharpoons H_2S(g) \qquad K_1 = \dfrac{[H_2S]}{[H_2][S]}$

At 200°C $\quad H_2(g) + S(l) \rightleftharpoons H_2S(g) \qquad K_2 = \dfrac{[H_2S]}{[H_2]}$

At −100°C $\quad H_2(g) + S(s) \rightleftharpoons H_2S(s) \qquad K_3 = \dfrac{1}{[H_2]}$

When a system at equilibrium is disturbed, chemical reaction occurs and equilibrium is reestablished. As an example, we consider the equilibrium system consisting of H_2, I_2, and HI in a sealed box.

$$H_2(g) + I_2(g) \rightleftharpoons 2HI(g)$$

$$K = \frac{[HI]^2}{[H_2][I_2]}$$

At 490°C, K is 45.9. The concentrations of HI, H_2, and I_2 do not change until conditions are changed. Several kinds of changes are possible. (1) H_2, I_2, or HI can be injected into the box. (2) H_2, I_2, or HI can be removed from the box. (3) The volume of the box can be changed. (4) The temperature of the system can be changed. (5) A catalyst can be added. How is the equilibrium state affected by each of these changes?

1. *The concentration of one of the components is changed by addition.* For example, more H_2 is added to a box which contains H_2, I_2, and HI in equilibrium at 490°C. What effect does this concentration increase have on the other components? The problem can be explored three ways:

a. *The equilibrium constant.* The equilibrium condition is of the form

$$\frac{[HI]^2}{[H_2][I_2]} = 45.9$$

By increasing the concentration of hydrogen, the denominator is made bigger. If everything else stays the same, the fraction becomes less than 45.9; therefore, the system is no longer at equilibrium. To reestablish equilibrium, two things could happen. There could be a decrease in the concentration of I_2, so that the denominator would be restored to its original value. Or there could be an increase in the concentration of HI, so that the numerator would increase to compensate for the increased denominator. Since iodine atoms must exist either as I_2 or HI molecules, the decrease of I_2 and the increase of HI occur simultaneously.

b. *Le Chatelier's principle.* According to the principle of Le Chatelier (Section 7.7), any equilibrium system subjected to a stress tends to change so as to relieve the stress. For a system in chemical equilibrium, changing the concentration of one of the components constitutes a stress. If in the present case hydrogen is added to the box, the equilibrium system

$$H_2(g) + I_2(g) \rightleftharpoons 2HI(g)$$

adjusts itself to absorb the effect of the added hydrogen. The system can absorb the stress if some hydrogen molecules combine with iodine molecules to form HI. This means that the concentration of HI increases and the concentration of I_2 decreases. Le Chatelier's principle leads to the same prediction as does the equilibrium constant.

c. *Kinetics.* The effect of added H_2 can be predicted from a consideration of reaction rates. The argument here is relatively simple because the reaction proceeds by one step. In the equilibrium state, collisions between H_2 and I_2 molecules form HI, and simultaneously collisions between HI molecules form H_2 and I_2. These two rates are equal. By adding H_2 to the box, the chance for collision between H_2 and I_2 molecules is increased. The more collisions there are between H_2 and I_2, the faster HI is formed. The instantaneous effect of adding hydrogen is therefore to increase the rate of HI formation. When hydrogen is added, there is no instantaneous effect on the decomposition rate of HI. For a time, HI is forming faster than it is decomposing, and so its concentration increases. Eventually, the concentration of HI increases to the point that there are more collisions between HI molecules, and the reverse reaction, the decomposition of HI, then begins to speed up. It continues to speed up until it equals the increased rate of formation. Equilibrium is reestablished with a net increase in HI and H_2 and a decrease in I_2.

2. *The concentration of one of the components is changed by removal.* For example, H_2 is removed from the box.

a. *The equilibrium condition*

$$\frac{[HI]^2}{[H_2][I_2]} = 45.9$$

predicts that a decrease in the concentration of hydrogen must be compensated for by an increase in the concentration of iodine and a decrease in the concentration of HI.

b. *Le Chatelier's principle* predicts that the system will adjust to relieve the stress caused by the removal of H_2. Some HI decomposes to form H_2 to replace some of that removed. The effect is to reduce the concentration of HI and to increase the concentration of I_2.

c. *Kinetics* predicts that the removal of hydrogen from the container reduces the rate at which H_2 and I_2 combine to form HI. This means that, instantaneously, HI is forming from H_2 and I_2 more slowly than it is decomposing to H_2 and I_2. The result is a net decrease in HI concentration and a net increase in I_2 concentration.

3. *The volume of the box is decreased.* In cases 1 and 2 the volume of the box is kept constant, and therefore the change in concentration and the change in number of moles are parallel. When the volume of the box is decreased, the *concentration* of all species is increased. However, a detailed analysis of the specific problem is required to determine how the *number of moles* of each species changes.

a. *The equilibrium condition*

$$\frac{[HI]^2}{[H_2][I_2]} = 45.9$$

can be considered in terms of concentration. For each component, the concentration is equal to the number of moles, n, of that component divided by the volume of the box, V. By substitution of n/V for concentration, the equilibrium condition becomes

$$\frac{[HI]^2}{[H_2][I_2]} = \frac{(n_{HI}/V)^2}{(n_{H_2}/V)(n_{I_2}/V)} = \frac{(n_{HI})^2}{(n_{H_2})(n_{I_2})} = 45.9$$

and V cancels out. No matter what the volume of the box, the number of moles of HI squared divided by the number of moles of H_2 and the number of moles of I_2 must equal 45.9. Changing the volume of the box in this case cannot change the number of moles of each species. For the particular case

$$H_2(g) + I_2(g) \rightleftharpoons 2HI(g)$$

the number of gas molecules on the left-hand side of the equation is the same as the number of gas molecules on the right-hand side of the equation. If this condition is not true, the volume does not cancel out of the mass-action expression. An example of such a case is the equilibrium between nitrogen, hydrogen, and ammonia:

$$N_2(g) + 3H_2(g) \rightleftharpoons 2NH_3(g)$$

The equilibrium expression is

$$K = \frac{[NH_3]^2}{[N_2][H_2]^3}$$

Substituting n/V for concentration gives

$$K = \frac{(n_{NH_3}/V)^2}{(n_{N_2}/V)(n_{H_2}/V)^3} = \frac{(n_{NH_3})^2}{(n_{N_2})(n_{H_2})^3} V^2$$

In this case the volume does not cancel out, and a change in V must be compensated for by a change in the number of moles. Specifically, when the volume is decreased, the fraction $(n_{NH_3})^2/(n_{N_2})(n_{H_2})^3$ must increase in order to maintain K constant. There must be an increase in the number of moles of ammonia at the expense of the moles of nitrogen and hydrogen. However, the *concentrations* of NH_3, N_2, and H_2 all increase. In the case of N_2 and H_2 this can come about only because the volume decreases more than the number of moles decreases. In commerce, when ammonia is made from nitrogen and hydrogen, it is done in as small a volume as possible in order to get maximum conversion to ammonia.

   b. The Le Chatelier principle predicts the effect of reduced volume more simply. For the system H_2, I_2, and HI at equilibrium, the Le Chatelier principle is applied as follows: When the volume of the box is reduced, the molecules are crowded closer together. The stress can be relieved if the molecules are reduced in number. In the case

$$H_2(g) + I_2(g) \rightleftharpoons 2HI(g)$$

there is no device by which this can be accomplished. If one molecule of hydrogen and one molecule of iodine disappear, two molecules of HI are produced. There can be no change in the total number of molecules in the box. Neither the forward nor reverse reaction can absorb the stress of a decreased volume. There is no net change; the number of moles of H_2, I_2, and HI stay constant. Of course, since the volume is diminished, the *concentration* of each component is increased. In the ammonia equilibrium the situation is different. When one molecule of N_2 reacts with three molecules of H_2, two molecules of NH_3 are formed. A decrease of the volume of the box can be compensated for by forming fewer molecules, i.e., by favoring the formation of ammonia. It is a general principle that, for reactions in which there is a change in the number of gas molecules, a decrease in the volume favors the reaction which produces fewer molecules.

c. Kinetics predicts the effect of a decrease in volume on an equilibrium system by considering the effects on the rates of the forward and reverse reactions. For example, in the equilibrium system containing H_2, I_2, and HI, a decrease of the volume forces H_2 and I_2 molecules closer together, and they collide more frequently. There is an increase in the rate of the forward reaction. At the same time, HI molecules are closer together, and they also collide more frequently. The back reaction is also increased. If the number of gas molecules is the same on the left and the right of the equation, the rate of the forward reaction is increased just as much as that of the back reaction. There is no net change in the number of molecules. If there is a change in the number of gas molecules, the situation is more complicated. For example, in the case

$$N_2(g) + 3H_2(g) \rightleftharpoons 2NH_3(g)$$

it turns out that a decrease of the volume increases the rate of ammonia formation to a greater extent than the rate of ammonia decomposition. The net effect is to increase the number of ammonia molecules present at equilibrium.

   4. The temperature of the system is changed.

   a. The equilibrium constant has a specific value at a given temperature. If the temperature is changed, K may change. For reactions which are endothermic, experiments show that raising the temperature causes K to increase. For those reactions which are exothermic, experiments show that raising the temperature causes K to decrease. The reaction

$$H_2(g) + I_2(g) \rightleftharpoons 2HI(g) + 3 \text{ kcal}$$

is exothermic as written, and K decreases as the temperature increases. Therefore, with an increase of the temperature, the concentration of HI at equilibrium diminishes while the concentrations of H_2 and I_2 increase. This is another way of saying that HI is less stable at higher temperatures.

   b. The Le Chatelier principle predicts that a rise in temperature favors the change that uses up heat. When one mole of H_2 and one mole of I_2 disappear, two moles of HI and 3 kcal of heat are liberated. The reverse process absorbs heat. At equilibrium the liberation of heat by the forward reaction is compensated for by the absorption of heat by the back reaction. If the temperature is increased, the system tries to relieve the stress by absorbing the added heat. Since the back reaction uses heat, it is favored. Favoring the back reaction causes a net decrease in the concentration of HI and a net increase in the concentration of I_2 and H_2.

   c. Kinetics. It is a principle of kinetics that the rate of a reaction is increased by an increase in temperature (Section 10.3). Furthermore, for a given equilibrium it is always found that the rate of endothermic

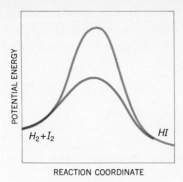

11.3
Potential-energy diagram
showing effect of catalyst

POTENTIAL ENERGY

H_2+I_2

HI

REACTION COORDINATE

reaction (having larger activation energy) is increased more than the rate of the exothermic reaction (having smaller activation energy). For the HI equilibrium, the rate of HI decomposition is increased more than the rate of HI formation is. The result is a net decrease in the concentration of HI.

    5. *What effect does a catalyst have on an equilibrium system?*

      a. The equilibrium constant is concerned only with the materials in the net equation. Intermediates may be involved, but the net equation ignores them. Although the catalyst affects intermediates, it does not appear in the net equation or in the equilibrium-constant expression. Insertion of a catalyst into an equilibrium system has no effect on equilibrium concentrations.

      b. The Le Chatelier principle ignores the presence of a catalyst.

      c. Kinetics gives the best argument for the fact that a catalyst does not affect the composition of the equilibrium system. According to reaction-rate theory, the rate of chemical reaction depends on how fast particles can get over the potential-energy barrier between the initial and final states. For example, Figure 11.3 shows the potential-energy barrier for the reaction

$$H_2(g) + I_2(g) \rightleftharpoons 2HI(g)$$

The colored line represents the path in the presence of catalyst. The rate of the forward reaction depends on the height of the barrier between the initial and final states. Since the catalyst reduces the height of the barrier, it speeds up the rate of the forward reaction. However, if the potential-energy barrier is lowered for the change in the forward direction, it is likewise lowered for the change in the reverse direction. Thus, the reverse change is also accelerated. The increase in the rates of the forward and reverse reactions is the same; hence, the equilibrium concentrations are unchanged.

Quantitatively, we can see this last point by considering the equation of Section 10.3

$$k = Ae^{-E/RT}$$

where E is the activation energy. For the case shown in Figure 11.3, the activation energy of the forward process is 40 kcal per mole of H_2

or I_2 used, whereas the activation energy of the reverse process is 43 kcal per mole of H_2 or I_2 formed. Suppose the catalyst acts to lower the activation barrier by 20 kcal mole^{-1}. For the forward process we can write

$$k_f = A_f e^{-40/RT} \qquad \text{uncatalyzed}$$

$$k_f' = A_f e^{-(40-20)/RT} \qquad \text{catalyzed}$$

$$= A_f e^{-40/RT} e^{20/RT}$$

For the reverse process we can similarly write

$$k_r = A_r e^{-43/RT} \qquad \text{uncatalyzed}$$

$$k_r' = A_r e^{-(43-20)/RT} \qquad \text{catalyzed}$$

$$= A_r e^{-43/RT} e^{20/RT}$$

It should be noted that the effect of the catalyst dropping the activation energy by 20 kcal mole^{-1} is to multiply each rate by the same factor $e^{20/RT}$. Clearly, the equilibrium constant, which is the ratio of k_f to k_r, is unchanged.

QUESTIONS

11.1 Equilibrium calculation   For the equilibrium

$$COCl_2(g) \rightleftharpoons CO(g) + Cl_2(g)$$

the equilibrium constant at 1000°K is 0.329. To what value must the equilibrium concentration of Cl_2 be adjusted so that half of the carbon atoms exist as $COCl_2$?

11.2 Equilibrium changes   It is commonly stated that an increase of pressure favors the formation of ammonia in the equilibrium

$$N_2(g) + 3H_2(g) \rightleftharpoons 2NH_3(g)$$

Show with an algebraic equation that it would be more to the point to say that a decrease of volume favors formation of NH_3.

11.3 Equilibrium concentrations   For each of the following systems, which of the concentrations should increase, which decrease, and which stay the same as equilibrium is approached?

(a) $N_2(g) + 3H_2(g) \rightleftharpoons 2NH_3(g)$ $K_{1000°K} = 2.37 \times 10^{-3}$
One mole N_2, one mole H_2, one mole NH_3 in 2-liter box at 1000°K.

(b) $2NO(g) + O_2(g) \rightleftharpoons 2NO_2(g)$ $K_{500°K} = 6.45 \times 10^5$
One mole NO, one mole O_2, one mole NO_2 in 2-liter box at 500°K.

11.4 Mass-action expressions   (a) Set up the mass-action expression for each of the following:

(1) $2SO_2(g) + O_2(g) \rightleftharpoons 2SO_3(g)$
(2) $2SO_3(g) \rightleftharpoons 2SO_2(g) + O_2(g)$
(3) $SO_2(g) + \frac{1}{2}O_2(g) \rightleftharpoons SO_3(g)$
(4) $SO_3(g) \rightleftharpoons SO_2(g) + \frac{1}{2}O_2(g)$

(b) Given that K for Equation (1) in (a) has the value 261 at 1000°K. Calculate the numerical value of K for the other equations in (a).

11.5 Equilibrium calculations (a) Write a balanced equation and the mass-action-constant expression for the formation of $NH_3(g)$ from $N_2(g)$ and $H_2(g)$. (b) A hundred-liter container at 600°K contains at equilibrium 2.5×10^{-2} moles of NH_3 and 1.00 mole each of N_2 and H_2. Calculate the numerical value of K. (c) What concentration of NH_3 would be in equilibrium at 600°K with 1.0×10^{-3} M N_2 and 2.0×10^{-3} M H_2?

11.6 Equilibrium changes Given a 20-liter box containing $NH_3(g)$, $N_2(g)$, and $H_2(g)$ at equilibrium at 1000°K. The equilibrium constant for

$$N_2(g) + 3H_2(g) \rightleftharpoons 2NH_3(g) + 22 \text{ kcal}$$

is $K = 2.4 \times 10^{-3}$ at 1000°K. What would be the effect on the number of moles of NH_3 in the box at equilibrium of each of the following? Answer *increase, decrease, no change,* or *can't tell.* (a) Add N_2. (b) Add H_2. (c) Add NH_3. (d) Raise temperature. (e) Add neon. (f) Increase the volume of the box. (g) Add 1 cc of finely divided platinum.

11.7 Temperature change For the system $PCl_5(g) \rightleftharpoons PCl_3(g) + Cl_2(g)$ the equilibrium constant is 0.0224 at 500°K and 33.3 at 760°K. (a) Tell whether PCl_5 is more stable to decomposition at high or low temperature. (b) Is the decomposition exothermic or endothermic? (c) Assuming a single-step reaction mechanism, tell whether the decomposition of PCl_5 or its formation has the greater activation energy.

11.8 Equilibrium calculation At 2000°K the equilibrium constant for the reaction

$$H_2(g) + CO_2(g) \rightleftharpoons H_2O(g) + CO(g)$$

has the value 4.40. Calculate the final concentrations in a ten-liter container initially charged with 1.50 mole H_2 plus 1.50 mole CO_2 at 2000°K.

11.9 Equilibrium calculations For the equilibrium

$$CO(g) + H_2O(g) \rightleftharpoons H_2(g) + CO_2(g)$$

the equilibrium constant at 2000°K is 0.227. (a) Calculate the equilibrium concentrations that result when 1.00 mole of CO and 1.00 mole of H_2O are equilibrated at 2000°K in a two-liter volume. (b) Suppose 1.00 mole of CO_2 and 1.00 mole of H_2 are subsequently added to the result from (a). Calculate the final concentrations.

11.10 Equilibrium calculation For the equilibrium

$$COCl_2(g) \rightleftharpoons CO(g) + Cl_2(g)$$

the equilibrium constant at 1000°K is 0.329. Suppose that x moles of $COCl_2$ are allowed to come to equilibrium in a one-liter box at 1000°K. What value of x must be used in order that half the chlorine atoms remain as $COCl_2$?

11.11 Equilibrium concentrations For the system $2NO(g) + O_2(g) \rightleftharpoons 2NO_2(g)$ the value of K is 6.45×10^5 at 500°K. In each of the following cases tell which concentration should increase and which decrease as equilibrium is approached. (a) 0.10 mole NO, 0.10 mole O_2, 0.10 mole NO_2 in a 10-liter box at 500°K. (b) 6.0×10^{-3} mole NO, 3.9×10^2 mole O_2, 1.0 mole NO_2 in a 2.5-liter box at 500°K. (c) 6.0×10^{-3} mole NO, 3.9×10^{-2} mole O_2, 10.0 mole NO_2 in a 25-liter box at 500°K.

11.12 Combined equilibrium constants Given the following equilibrium constants at 1000°K

$$COCl_2(g) \rightleftharpoons CO(g) + Cl_2(g) \qquad K = 0.329$$
$$2CO(g) + O_2(g) \rightleftharpoons 2CO_2(g) \qquad K = 2.24 \times 10^{22}$$

calculate the K at 1000°K for

$$2COCl_2(g) + O_2(g) \longrightarrow 2CO_2(g) + Cl_2(g)$$

11.13 Equilibrium calculations (*a*) 1.00 mole of H_2 and 2.00 moles of I_2 are put in a ten-liter container at 490°C. If $K = 45.9$, what are the equilibrium concentrations of H_2, I_2, and HI? (*b*) What would happen to the equilibrium concentrations if the volume of the container were compressed to five liters?

11.14 Mass-action expression In examining the equilibrium for the reaction x moles of A give one mole each of B and C it is found that the fraction of A decomposed at equilibrium is independent of the initial concentration of A. What is x?

11.15 Pressure constant For the reaction $N_2(g) + 3H_3(g) \rightleftharpoons 2NH_3(g)$, K has the value 2.37×10^{-3} at 1000°K when expressed in moles per liter concentrations. What will be the value of K_p, in which concentrations are given as partial pressures in atmospheres? Assume ideal-gas behavior.

11.16 Combined equilibrium constants Given:

$$H_2(g) + CO_2(g) \rightleftharpoons H_2O(g) + CO(g) \qquad K_{2000°K} = 4.40$$
$$2H_2O(g) \rightleftharpoons 2H_2(g) + O_2(g) \qquad K_{2000°K} = 5.31 \times 10^{-10}$$
$$2CO(g) + O_2(g) \rightleftharpoons 2CO_2(g) \qquad K_{1000°K} = 2.24 \times 10^{22}$$

From these data, show whether the last reaction is exothermic or endothermic.

11.17 Equilibrium calculations For the decomposition of phosgene, $COCl_2(g) \rightleftharpoons CO(g) + Cl_2(g)$, the equilibrium constant is 0.329 at 1000°K. What fraction of a mole of $COCl_2$ would be decomposed if placed in a ten-liter tank at 1000°K?

11.18 Equilibrium calculations For the equilibrium

$$COCl_2(g) \rightleftharpoons CO(g) + Cl_2(g)$$

the equilibrium constant at 1000°K is 0.329. (*a*) Calculate the fraction of $COCl_2$ left undecomposed when 1.00 mole of $COCl_2$ is allowed to reach equilibrium at 1000°K in a two-liter container. (*b*) How would your answer to (*a*) be changed if 1.00 mole of Cl_2 were also originally present in the container?

11.19 Equilibrium calculation For the equilibrium

$$PCl_5(g) \rightleftharpoons PCl_3(g) + Cl_2(g)$$

the equilibrium constant at 500°K is 0.0224. Suppose that some PCl_5 is injected into an empty container and allowed to come to equilibrium at 500°K. What must be the total pressure in the container in order that 75% of the chlorine atoms be bound to phosphorus? Assume ideal-gas behavior.

11.20 Equilibrium calculation   Calculate the percent dissociation of I_2 at 1000°K at total pressures of (a) 1.00 atm, (b) 0.100 atm, (c) 0.0100 atm. At 1000°K the equilibrium constant for

$$I_2(g) \rightleftharpoons 2I(g)$$

is 3.76×10^{-5}.

ANSWERS

11.1 0.329   *11.4* (2) 3.84×10^{-3}, (3) 16.1, (4) 0.0620   *11.8* 0.102 M H_2O, 0.102 M CO, 0.048 M H_2, 0.048 M CO_2 *11.10* 0.658 mole   *11.12* $K = 2.43 \times 10^{21}$ *11.15* 3.52×10^{-7} *11.17* 0.80   *11.19* 1.43 atm   *11.20* (a) 2.78%   (b) 8.74%   (c) 26.7%

12 aqueous solution equilibria

Perhaps the most common application of chemical-equilibrium principles is to reactions in aqueous solutions. The solute species in such
solutions are susceptible to concentration variation in the same way as
gases are. Therefore, the principles developed in the preceding chapter
for defining and describing an equilibrium state are directly applicable
to solutions. Since reactions are reversible and tend toward the equilibrium state, the principles of equilibrium give the key to understanding
the many reactions that may occur in solution. In this chapter we consider equilibria in aqueous solutions and how they are related to the
reactions that are observed. The important equilibria to be considered
are of two fundamental types: *dissociation,* an equilibrium between a
dissolved undissociated species and its component parts, e.g., acetic

Acid	Reaction	K_{diss} (25°C)
Acetic	$HC_2H_3O_2 \rightleftharpoons H^+ + C_2H_3O_2^-$	1.8×10^{-5}
Nitrous	$HNO_2 \rightleftharpoons H^+ + NO_2^-$	4.5×10^{-4}
Hydrofluoric	$HF \rightleftharpoons H^+ + F^-$	6.7×10^{-4}
Hydrocyanic	$HCN \rightleftharpoons H^+ + CN^-$	4.0×10^{-10}
Sulfurous	$H_2SO_3 \rightleftharpoons H^+ + HSO_3^-$	1.3×10^{-2}

12.1
Dissociation of weak acids

acid molecules in equilibrium with hydrogen ions and acetate ions, and *solubility,* an equilibrium between a pure phase, usually a solid, and its characteristic species in solution, e.g., solid barium sulfate in equilibrium with barium ions and sulfate ions. In addition, we shall consider the simultaneous establishment of two or more equilibria in the same solution.

12.1 DISSOCIATION

When a substance in aqueous solution can dissociate into simpler fragments, an equilibrium is established between the undissociated species and the component parts. Thus, for example, when the weak acid HX is placed in water, some of it dissociates to give H^+ and X^-. When equilibrium is established, the association of H^+ with X^- to form HX occurs at a rate just sufficient to balance the dissociation. The equilibrium can be represented by the reversible equation

$$HX \rightleftharpoons H^+ + X^-$$

and the equilibrium condition can be expressed as

$$\frac{[H^+][X^-]}{[HX]} = K$$

(Recall that square brackets indicate concentration, in moles per liter.) This equilibrium constant is called a *dissociation constant* and is often designated as K_{diss} or K_{HX}. The mass-action expression is constant only in quite dilute solutions. In more concentrated solutions, interionic attraction must be considered; because of their complexity, we shall, however, ignore such considerations.* Typical experimental values of the dissociation constants of various weak acids are given in Figure 12.1. Others may be found in Appendix 7. Values are quoted for 25°C. The smaller the value of K_{diss}, the weaker the acid. Thus, HCN is a weaker acid than HF, and it is much less dissociated for a given concentration. When K_{diss} is 1 or greater, the acid is extensively dissociated, even in 1 M solution, and is classified as moderately strong. When K_{diss} is 10 or greater, the acid is essentially 100% dissociated in

12.1 Dissociation

260

* The mass-action expression is strictly constant only if we use the chemical activity of the various species in the expression. Just as for gases (page 244), the true chemical activity of a species in the mass-action expression is frequently approximated by its concentration.

all except very concentrated solutions. For example, perchloric acid, $HClO_4$, is one of our strongest acids and has K_{diss} greater than 10. Similarly, HNO_3, HCl, and H_2SO_4 are common acids with high dissociation constants.

Strictly speaking, the dissociation of an acid, as explained in Section 9.1, is better written as

$$H_2O + HX \rightleftharpoons H_3O^+ + X^-$$

However, this leads to the same equilibrium condition as above, as can be seen from the following: The equilibrium condition for the reaction that includes water is

$$\frac{[H_3O^+][X^-]}{[H_2O][HX]} = K'$$

but, in those dilute solutions for which K' applies without correction for interionic attractions, the concentration of H_2O is essentially constant. (In dilute solutions the concentration of H_2O is so great that it changes little as the concentration of other species changes.) Therefore, the equilibrium condition is

$$\frac{[H_3O^+][X^-]}{[HX]} = K'[H_2O] = K$$

By ignoring the water of hydration, $[H_3O^+]$ can be replaced by $[H^+]$, giving the same equilibrium condition as that for the reaction written without water.

The dissociation constant can also be applied to ions which dissociate as acids. For example, the hydrogen sulfate ion, HSO_4^-, can dissociate into H^+ and SO_4^{--} and must be in equilibrium with these ions.

$$HSO_4^- \rightleftharpoons H^+ + SO_4^{--}$$

$$K_{HSO_4^-} = \frac{[H^+][SO_4^{--}]}{[HSO_4^-]} = 1.3 \times 10^{-2}$$

This dissociation constant of HSO_4^- can be considered the second dissociation constant of H_2SO_4, since it applies to the second step of its dissociation.

$$H_2SO_4 \rightleftharpoons H^+ + HSO_4^- \qquad K_I > 10$$

$$HSO_4^- \rightleftharpoons H^+ + SO_4^{--} \qquad K_{II} = 1.3 \times 10^{-2}$$

K_I and K_{II} are respectively the first and second dissociation constants of sulfuric acid. The large value of K_I means that H_2SO_4 is essentially completely dissociated into H^+ and HSO_4^-. The moderate value of K_{II} means that a modest amount of the HSO_4^- (about 10% in 0.1 M H_2SO_4) is in turn dissociated into H^+ and SO_4^{--}. In a given solution of H_2SO_4 both equilibria exist simultaneously, and both constants must be

satisfied by the concentration of undissociated H_2SO_4, H^+, HSO_4^-, and SO_4^{--}.

For weak bases the dissociation equilibria are treated in much the same way. If the base can be written as MOH, then its dissociation can be represented as

$$MOH \rightleftharpoons M^+ + OH^-$$

The equilibrium condition is

$$\frac{[M^+][OH^-]}{[MOH]} = K_{diss}$$

However, most weak bases are more complicated than this. For example, aqueous ammonia* is best described by the equilibrium

$$NH_3 + H_2O \rightleftharpoons NH_4^+ + OH^-$$

for which the equilibrium condition is

$$\frac{[NH_4^+][OH^-]}{[NH_3]} = K = 1.8 \times 10^{-5}$$

In the mass-action expression, the concentration of H_2O does not appear, because it is essentially invariant. The constant K is often referred to as the dissociation constant for aqueous ammonia. The value given refers to 25°C, but its change with temperature is small.

Besides acids and bases there are in chemistry a few salts that are weak electrolytes; i.e., they are only slightly dissociated in solution. An example is mercuric chloride, $HgCl_2$, which dissociates

$$HgCl_2 \rightleftharpoons HgCl^+ + Cl^-$$

for which

$$\frac{[HgCl^+][Cl^-]}{[HgCl_2]} = K_{diss} = 3.3 \times 10^{-7}$$

The second dissociation is

$$HgCl^+ \rightleftharpoons Hg^{++} + Cl^-$$

for which

$$\frac{[Hg^{++}][Cl^-]}{[HgCl^+]} = K_{II} = 1.8 \times 10^{-7}$$

Mercuric chloride is an exception to the usual rule that salts are 100% dissociated in solution. However, $HgCl_2$ is not unique. For instance, cadmium sulfate, $CdSO_4$, has a dissociation constant of 5×10^{-3}.

As pointed out in Section 11.4, it makes no difference whether an equilibrium state is produced from the material on the left-hand side of the chemical equation or from the material on the right-hand side. Change occurs to form material in sufficient concentration to establish equilibrium. This means that the same equilibrium state is produced by having a weak electrolyte dissociate as is produced by having the ions associate. Specifically, the same final solution results from placing either one mole of acetic acid or one mole of H^+ plus one mole of

* Before the facts were known, these weakly basic solutions were forced to fit the formulation $MOH \rightleftharpoons M^+ + OH^-$ by postulating that NH_3 plus H_2O formed the hypothetical species NH_4OH. The name "ammonium hydroxide" still survives, though all experiments designed to show the presence of such a species have proved negative. *Sic transit gloria mundi.*

$C_2H_3O_2^-$ in a liter of water. In either case, the condition for equilibrium is

$$\frac{[H^+][C_2H_3O_2^-]}{[HC_2H_3O_2]} = 1.8 \times 10^{-5}$$

Since $HC_2H_3O_2$ is a weak acid, the concentration of H^+ and of $C_2H_3O_2^-$ in the final solutions must be small.

When ions are mixed and association occurs, a chemical equation can be written to stress the direction of the net reaction. For example, when solutions of HCl and $NaC_2H_3O_2$ are mixed, the equation can be written

$$H^+ + C_2H_3O_2 \rightleftharpoons HC_2H_3O_2$$

for which

$$\frac{[HC_2H_3O_2]}{[H^+][C_2H_3O_2^-]} = K_{assoc}$$

The numerical value of K_{assoc} is 5.6×10^4, which is the reciprocal of K_{diss} for acetic acid.

Association occurs whenever the constituent parts of a weak electrolyte are mixed. Thus, when solutions of NH_4Cl and NaOH are mixed, NH_4^+ ions associate with OH^- ions to form NH_3 and H_2O. Likewise, when solutions of $Hg(NO_3)_2$ and NaCl are mixed, Hg^{++} ions associate with Cl^- ions to form $HgCl_2$.

12.2 CALCULATIONS USING K_{diss}

The methods of equilibrium calculation described in Section 11.4 apply to dissociation equilibria in aqueous solution. Like any equilibrium constant, K_{diss} must be experimentally determined. Once its value is known at a given temperature, it can be used for all calculations involving that equilibrium at the same temperature.

EXAMPLE 1

What is the concentration of all solute species in a solution labeled 1.00 M $HC_2H_3O_2$? What percent of the acid is dissociated?

$$HC_2H_3O_2 \rightleftharpoons H^+ + C_2H_3O_2^- \qquad K_{diss} = 1.8 \times 10^{-5}$$

Let x equal the moles per liter of $HC_2H_3O_2$ that dissociate to establish equilibrium. According to the dissociation equation, each mole of $HC_2H_3O_2$ that dissociates produces one mole of H^+ and one mole of $C_2H_3O_2^-$. If x moles of $HC_2H_3O_2$ dissociate, then x moles of H^+ and x moles of $C_2H_3O_2^-$ must be formed. The initial and equilibrium concentrations are summarized as follows:

Initially	At equilibrium
$[HC_2H_3O_2] = 1.00$ mole liter^{-1}	$[HC_2H_3O_2] = (1.00-x)$ moles liter^{-1}
$[H^+] = 0$ mole liter^{-1}	$[H^+] = x$ moles liter^{-1}
$[C_2H_3O_2^-] = 0$ mole liter^{-1}	$[C_2H_3O_2^-] = x$ moles liter^{-1}

At equilibrium

$$\frac{[H^+][C_2H_3O_2^-]}{[HC_2H_3O_2]} = 1.8 \times 10^{-5} = \frac{(x)(x)}{(1.00 - x)}$$

Solving this equation by use of the quadratic formula (Appendix 2.3) gives $x = 0.0042$. Therefore, at equilibrium (with due regard for significant figures)

$$[HC_2H_3O_2] = 1.00 - x = 1.00 \ M$$

$$[H^+] = x = 0.0042 \ M$$

$$[C_2H_3O_2^-] = x = 0.0042 \ M$$

The percent dissociation is defined as 100 times the number of moles of $HC_2H_3O_2$ dissociated divided by the number of moles of $HC_2H_3O_2$ originally available.

$$\text{Percent dissociation} = \frac{0.0042 \times 100}{1.00} = 0.42\%$$

It might be noted here that much of the algebraic work involved in solving equilibrium problems can be avoided by judicious attention to chemical facts which may suggest laborsaving approximations. Thus, in Example 1, since $HC_2H_3O_2$ is a weak acid, it cannot be much dissociated. In other words, x must be small compared to 1.00 and may be neglected when added to or subtracted from 1.00. Thus, instead of solving the exact equation

$$1.8 \times 10^{-5} = \frac{(x)(x)}{(1.00 - x)}$$

we can solve the approximate equation

$$1.8 \times 10^{-5} \cong \frac{(x)(x)}{(1.00)}$$

obtained by assuming that $1.00 - x \cong 1.00$. From

$$1.8 \times 10^{-5} \cong x^2$$

we get

$$x \cong \sqrt{1.8 \times 10^{-5}} = \sqrt{18 \times 10^{-6}} = 4.2 \times 10^{-3}$$

Checking the approximation and paying due attention to significant figures, we find that $1.00 - x = 1.00 - (4.2 \times 10^{-3}) = 1.00$, as assumed.

EXAMPLE 2

Suppose that 1.00 mole of HCl and 1.00 mole of $NaC_2H_3O_2$ are mixed in enough water to make a liter of solution. What will be the concentration of H^+ in the final solution?

Since HCl and $NaC_2H_3O_2$ are strong electrolytes, they are 100% dissociated in solution. The Na^+ and Cl^- do not associate and so can be ignored. The problem is thus one of associating H^+ and $C_2H_3O_2^-$ to form $HC_2H_3O_2$ in sufficient concentration to satisfy the equilibrium

$$HC_2H_3O_2 \rightleftharpoons H^+ + C_2H_3O_2^-$$

which is described by $K_{\text{diss}} = 1.8 \times 10^{-5}$. The initial and equilibrium concentrations can be summarized as follows, where y is the moles of H^+ and of $C_2H_3O_2^-$ that associate per liter to form y moles of $HC_2H_3O_2$:

Initially	At equilibrium
$[H^+] = 1.00\ M$	$[H^+] = (1.00 - y)\ M$
$[C_2H_3O_2^-] = 1.00\ M$	$[C_2H_3O_2^-] = (1.00 - y)\ M$
$[HC_2H_3O_2] = 0\ M$	$[HC_2H_3O_2] = y\ M$

At equilibrium

$$\frac{[H^+][C_2H_3O_2^-]}{[HC_2H_3O_2]} = 1.8 \times 10^{-5} = \frac{(1.00 - y)(1.00 - y)}{(y)}$$

This equation can be solved by applying the quadratic formula (see Appendix 2.3), giving $y = 0.996$. Since y is not small compared to 1.00, the approximation made in solving Example 1 cannot be used.

A better way to solve this problem is to note that, when 1.00 mole of H^+ and 1.00 mole of $C_2H_3O_2^-$ are mixed, the resulting system is exactly the same as if H^+ and $C_2H_3O_2^-$ first completely react to form 1.00 mole of $HC_2H_3O_2$, which then dissociates to establish equilibrium. If x is defined as the moles per liter that dissociate of this hypothetical 1.00 mole of $HC_2H_3O_2$, the problem becomes identical with Example 1. We can therefore write down directly the equilibrium concentrations:

$$[H^+] = 4.2 \times 10^{-3}\ M$$

$$[C_2H_3O_2^-] = 4.2 \times 10^{-3}\ M$$

$$[HC_2H_3O_2] = 1.00\ M$$

$$[Na^+] = 1.00\ M$$

$$[Cl^-] = 1.00\ M$$

EXAMPLE 3

What are the concentrations of species and the percent dissociation in $0.10\ M\ HC_2H_3O_2$?

Let x = moles of $HC_2H_3O_2$ that dissociate per liter

Then x = final concentration of H^+

x = final concentration of $C_2H_3O_2^-$

$0.10 - x$ = final concentration of $HC_2H_3O_2$

At equilibrium

$$\frac{[H^+][C_2H_3O_2^-]}{[HC_2H_3O_2]} = 1.8 \times 10^{-5} = \frac{(x)(x)}{(0.10 - x)}$$

Assuming that x is small compared to 0.10,

$$\frac{x^2}{0.10} \cong 1.8 \times 10^{-5}$$

$$x^2 \cong 1.8 \times 10^{-6}$$

$$x \cong 1.3 \times 10^{-3}$$

Therefore, at equilibrium

$$[H^+] = x = 1.3 \times 10^{-3}\ M$$

$$[C_2H_3O_2^-] = x = 1.3 \times 10^{-3}\ M$$

$$[HC_2H_3O_2] = 0.10 - x = 0.10\ M$$

$$\text{Percent dissociation} = \frac{1.3 \times 10^{-3}}{0.10}\ 100 = 1.3\%$$

Comparison of Examples 1 and 3 indicates the general fact that, when a solution of a weak electrolyte is diluted, the concentration of each species *decreases* and the percent dissociation *increases*. It should be noted that, although there is a tenfold dilution in going from 1.00 M $HC_2H_3O_2$ to 0.10 M $HC_2H_3O_2$, the concentration of H^+ does not decrease tenfold, but decreases only from $4.2 \times 10^{-3}\ M$ to $1.3 \times 10^{-3}\ M$. This, of course, is consistent with the fact that in the more dilute solution a greater percentage of the acid is dissociated to counterbalance partially the tenfold dilution.

12.3 DISSOCIATION OF WATER; pH

In the preceding section we have ignored the fact that water is a weak electrolyte and is dissociated according to the equation

$$H_2O \rightleftharpoons H^+ + OH^-$$

In pure water and in all aqueous solutions, this equilibrium exists and must satisfy the condition

$$\frac{[H^+][OH^-]}{[H_2O]} = K$$

In all dilute solutions the concentration of H_2O can be considered constant and combined with the constant K to give K_w as follows:

$$K[H_2O] = K_w = [H^+][OH^-]$$

K_w is usually called the dissociation constant, or *ion product*, of water. It has the value of 1.0×10^{-14} at 25°C.

In pure water all the H^+ and the OH^- must come from the dissociation of water molecules. If x moles of H^+ are produced per liter, x moles of OH^- must be simultaneously produced.

$$[H^+][OH^-] = 1.0 \times 10^{-14}$$

$$(x)(x) = 1.0 \times 10^{-14}$$

$$x^2 = 1.0 \times 10^{-14}$$

$$x = 1.0 \times 10^{-7}$$

Thus, in pure H_2O the concentrations of H^+ and OH^- are each 1.0×10^{-7} M. This very small concentration is to be compared with H_2O concentration of approximately 55.4 moles liter^{-1}. (A liter of H_2O at 25°C weighs 997 g, and a mole of H_2O weighs 18.0 g; therefore, 1 liter contains 997/18.0, or 55.4, moles.) This means that on the average there is one H^+ ion and one OH^- ion for every 554 million H_2O molecules.

If an acid is added to water, the hydrogen-ion concentration increases above $1.0 \times 10^{-7} M$. The ion product must remain equal to 1.0×10^{-14}; consequently, the hydroxide-ion concentration decreases below $1.0 \times 10^{-7} M$. Similarly, when a base is added to water, the concentration of OH^- increases above $1.0 \times 10^{-7} M$ and the concentration of H^+ decreases below $1.0 \times 10^{-7} M$. As a convenience for working with small concentrations, the pH scale has been devised to express the concentration of H^+. By definition,

$$pH = -\log [H^+] \qquad \text{or} \qquad [H^+] = 10^{-pH}$$

For example, in pure water, where the concentration of H^+ is 1.0×10^{-7} M, the pH is 7. All neutral solutions have a pH of 7. Acid solutions have pH less than 7; basic solutions have pH greater than 7. (For a review of logarithms, see Appendix 2.2.)

EXAMPLE 4

What is the pH of 0.20 M HCl?

In 0.20 M HCl, practically all the H^+ comes from the 100% dissociation of the strong electrolyte HCl. H_2O is such a weak electrolyte in comparison that it contributes a negligible amount of H^+.

$$[H^+] = 0.20 M = 2.0 \times 10^{-1} M$$

$$pH = -\log (2.0 \times 10^{-1}) = 1 - 0.30 = 0.70$$

EXAMPLE 5

What is the pH of 0.10 M NaOH?

NaOH is a strong electrolyte and accounts for essentially all the OH^- in the solution.

$$[OH^-] = 0.10 M$$

$$[H^+] = \frac{K_w}{[OH^-]} = \frac{1.0 \times 10^{-14}}{0.10} = 1.0 \times 10^{-13} M$$

$$pH = -\log (1.0 \times 10^{-13}) = 13$$

In Examples 4 and 5 the contributions from H_2O dissociation to $[H^+]$ in the acidic solution and to $[OH^-]$ in the basic solution are negligible. This is true because acids and bases repress the dissociation of water. To illustrate, in Example 5, the added OH^- represses the dissociation of

H_2O so that only 1.0×10^{-13} mole of H^+ per liter is produced. This means that only 1.0×10^{-13} mole of OH^- per liter comes from the H_2O dissociation, an amount that is indeed negligible compared to that from 0.10 M NaOH.

12.4 TITRATION

So far, we have emphasized the dissociation of water to give ions. However, since equilibrium may be approached from the left or the right side of an equation, the same equilibrium constant that describes the dissociation of water also describes the association of H^+ and OH^- to form water. Such association occurs in neutralization reactions, as discussed in Section 9.2, and is the basis of the process of *titration*, the progressive addition of an acid to a base or vice versa. At each step in the titration the expression $[H^+][OH^-] = 1.0 \times 10^{-14}$ must be satisfied in the solution. Figure 12.2 represents what happens to the concentration of H^+ and OH^- as solid NaOH is added stepwise to 0.010 mole of HCl in a liter of water. As NaOH is progressively added, the original solution changes from acid (pH less than 7) to basic (pH greater than 7). The titration can be represented graphically by plotting the concentration of H^+ against the moles of added NaOH. However, since the H^+ concentration changes by a factor of 10 billion during the experiment, it is hard to get all the values on the same scale. Not so with the pH. It changes only by a factor of 6 and is a convenient representation of what happens to the solution during the titration.

12.2

Progressive addition of
solid NaOH to one liter of
0.010 M HCl

Moles of NaOH added	$[H^+]$	$[OH^-]$	pH
None	0.010	1.0×10^{-12}	2.00
0.001	0.009	1.1×10^{-12}	2.04
0.002	0.008	1.3×10^{-12}	2.10
0.003	0.007	1.4×10^{-12}	2.15
0.004	0.006	1.7×10^{-12}	2.23
0.005	0.005	2.0×10^{-12}	2.30
0.006	0.004	2.5×10^{-12}	2.40
0.007	0.003	3.3×10^{-12}	2.52
0.008	0.002	5.0×10^{-12}	2.70
0.009	0.001	1.0×10^{-11}	3.00
0.010	1.0×10^{-7}	1.0×10^{-7}	7.00
0.011	1.0×10^{-11}	0.001	11.00
0.012	5.0×10^{-12}	0.002	11.30
0.013	3.3×10^{-12}	0.003	11.48
0.014	2.5×10^{-12}	0.004	11.60
0.015	2.0×10^{-12}	0.005	11.70
0.016	1.7×10^{-12}	0.006	11.77
0.017	1.4×10^{-12}	0.007	11.85
0.018	1.3×10^{-12}	0.008	11.90
0.019	1.1×10^{-12}	0.009	11.96
0.020	1.0×10^{-12}	0.010	12.00

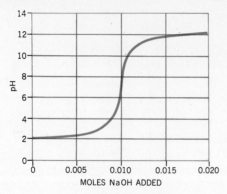

12.3
Titration curve of one liter
of 0.010 M HCl

Figure 12.3 represents the change of pH as solid NaOH is added to a liter of 0.010 M HCl. The pH first rises very slowly, then rapidly through the neutral point, and finally very slowly as the solution gets more basic. Such a pH curve is typical of the titration of any strong acid with any strong base. The important thing to note is that, as the neutral point is approached, there is a sharp rise in pH. At this point even a trace of NaOH adds enough moles of base to increase the pH greatly. Thus, any method which locates the point at which the pH changes rapidly can be used to detect the *equivalence point* of a titration, i.e., the point at which equivalent amounts of base and acid have been mixed.

One method for determining the equivalence point makes use of the fact that many dyes have colors that are sensitive to hydrogen-ion concentration. Such dyes can be used as *indicators* to give information about the pH of a solution. Indicators can be considered to be weak acids, HIn, which dissociate to give H^+ and In^-. As weak acids, they must satisfy the condition

$$\frac{[H^+][In^-]}{[HIn]} = K \qquad \text{or} \qquad \frac{[In^-]}{[HIn]} = \frac{K}{[H^+]}$$

from which it is evident that the ratio $[In^-]/[HIn]$ is inversely proportional to the hydrogen-ion concentration of the solution. If the species In^- and HIn have different colors, the color of the solution depends on which species is predominant. For phenolphthalein, HIn is colorless, but In^- is red. In solutions of high hydrogen-ion concentration, the ratio $[In^-]/[HIn]$ is small, and the colorless species HIn is dominant. Conversely, when $[H^+]$ is small, the red species In^- is dominant. Figure 12.4 lists the characteristic colors of some common indicators.

In Figure 12.3 the pH rises so sharply at the equivalence point that any one of the indicators of Figure 12.4, except possibly alizarin yellow, could be used to tell when enough NaOH had been added to neutralize 1 liter of 0.010 M HCl.

The titration curve of Figure 12.3 is general for strong acids and strong bases but does not apply when a strong acid is titrated with a weak base, when a strong base is titrated with a weak acid, or when a weak acid is titrated with a weak base. In the latter cases the shapes of the titration curves are quite different and require individual considera-

Indicator	pH at which color changes	Color at lower pH	Color at higher pH
Methyl orange	4	Red	Yellow
Methyl red	5	Red	Yellow
Litmus	7	Red	Blue
Bromthymol blue	7	Yellow	Blue
Phenolphthalein	9	Colorless	Red
Alizarin yellow	11	Yellow	Red

12.4
Indicator colors

tion before an indicator is chosen. It turns out that, in titrating acetic acid with NaOH, phenolphthalein is satisfactory but methyl orange is not.

12.5 BUFFER SOLUTIONS

In practically all biological processes, as well as in many other chemical processes, it is important that the pH not deviate very much from a fixed value. For example, the proper functioning of human blood in carrying oxygen to the cells from the lungs is dependent on maintaining a pH very near to 7.4. In fact, for a particular individual, there is a difference of but 0.02 pH unit between venous and arterial blood in spite of numerous acid-and base-producing reactions in the cells.

The near constancy of pH in a system to which acid or base is added is due to a buffering action of an acid-base equilibrium. Let us consider, for example, a solution that contains acetic acid molecules and acetate ions (plus other ions, of course). The principal equilibrium in this solution can be written

$$HC_2H_3O_2 \rightleftharpoons H^+ + C_2H_3O_2^-$$

for which

$$\frac{[H^+][C_2H_3O_2^-]}{[HC_2H_3O_2]} = K$$

Solving this expression for $[H^+]$, we get

$$[H^+] = K \frac{[HC_2H_3O_2]}{[C_2H_3O_2^-]}$$

which indicates that the hydrogen-ion concentration of the solution depends on K and on the ratio of the concentrations of undissociated acetic acid to acetate ion. Taking the negative logarithm of both sides, we get

$$pH = -\log K - \log \frac{[HC_2H_3O_2]}{[C_2H_3O_2^-]}$$

In a particular solution (made by dissolving equal numbers of moles of $HC_2H_3O_2$ and $NaC_2H_3O_2$) where the ratio $[HC_2H_3O_2]/[C_2H_3O_2^-]$ is equal to unity, pH is just equal to $-\log K$, since log 1 equals zero. In any solution where the ratio $[HC_2H_3O_2]/[C_2H_3O_2^-]$ is not far from unity, the pH will not differ much from $-\log K$ (sometimes called pK). Thus, a mixture of acetic acid and acetate ion is said to be a *buffer* for pH of $-\log$ (1.8×10^{-5}), or 4.74. If a small amount of strong acid is added to such a solution, some of the acetate ion is converted to acetic acid; if base is added, some of the acetic acid is converted to acetate ion. In either case the ratio $[HC_2H_3O_2]/[C_2H_3O_2^-]$ changes slightly from unity and the pH changes even less—not nearly so much as in the absence of the buffer.

EXAMPLE 6

Calculate the pH of a solution made by adding 0.0010 mole of NaOH to 100 ml of 0.50 M $HC_2H_3O_2$ and 0.50 M $NaC_2H_3O_2$.

Assume that in the 100 ml there are originally 0.050 mole $HC_2H_3O_2$ and 0.050 mole of $C_2H_3O_2^-$ and that the added 0.0010 mole of OH^- converts an equivalent amount of $HC_2H_3O_2$ into $C_2H_3O_2^-$. This gives 0.049 mole $HC_2H_3O_2$ and 0.051 mole $C_2H_3O_2^-$ in the final solution. Since the volume of the solution is 0.100 liter, the respective concentrations are 0.49 M and 0.51 M, and the pH is

$$pH = -\log(1.8 \times 10^{-5}) - \log \frac{(0.49)}{(0.51)} = +4.74 + 0.017 = +4.76$$

In contrast, when 0.0010 mole of NaOH is added to 100 ml of water, the pH becomes 10.0.

In general, any solution of a weak acid which also contains a salt of that acid can function as a buffer. The buffer region—i.e., the region in which the pH changes most slowly—is centered about the pK of the acid. In a similar way, a solution of a weak base plus a salt of that base can function as a buffer to keep the OH^- concentration equal to $K[MOH]/[M^+]$:

$$MOH \rightleftharpoons M^+ + OH^-$$

$$\frac{[M^+][OH^-]}{[MOH]} = K$$

$$[OH^-] = \frac{K[MOH]}{[M^+]}$$

$$[H^+] = \frac{K_w}{[OH^-]} = \frac{K_w}{K} \frac{[M^+]}{[MOH]}$$

$$pH = -\log \frac{K_w}{K} - \log \frac{[M^+]}{[MOH]}$$

Thus, there are as many possible buffers as there are weak acids and weak bases. In human blood there are a number of buffers acting simultaneously. These include (1) dissolved CO_2 and HCO_3^-, (2) $H_2PO_4^-$ and HPO_4^{--}, and (3) the various proteins which can accept hydrogen ions.

Complex ion	Reaction	K_{diss}
Copper-ammonia	$Cu(NH_3)_4^{++} \rightleftharpoons Cu^{++} + 4NH_3$	1.0×10^{-12}
Cobaltous-ammonia	$Co(NH_3)_6^{++} \rightleftharpoons Co^{++} + 6NH_3$	4.0×10^{-5}
Cobaltic-ammonia	$Co(NH_3)_6^{+3} \rightleftharpoons Co^{+3} + 6NH_3$	6.3×10^{-36}
Silver-ammonia	$Ag(NH_3)_2^{+} \rightleftharpoons Ag^{+} + 2NH_3$	6×10^{-8}
Silver-thiosulfate	$Ag(S_2O_3)_2^{-3} \rightleftharpoons Ag^{+} + 2S_2O_3^{--}$	6×10^{-14}
Silver-cyanide	$Ag(CN)_2^{-} \rightleftharpoons Ag^{+} + 2CN^{-}$	1.8×10^{-19}
Ferric-thiocyanate	$FeNSC^{++} \rightleftharpoons Fe^{+3} + SCN^{-}$	1×10^{-3}
Mercuric-cyanide	$Hg(CN)_4^{--} \rightleftharpoons Hg^{++} + 4CN^{-}$	4×10^{-42}

12.5
Dissociation of complex ions

12.6 COMPLEX IONS

The term *complex ion* refers to a charged particle which contains more than one atom. Certain complex ions, e.g., sulfate, SO_4^{--}, are little different from simple ions in that for all practical purposes they do not dissociate into smaller fragments. Others, however, may dissociate to establish an equilibrium between the complex ion and its component pieces. Thus, for example, in a solution containing the silver-ammonia complex ion, $Ag(NH_3)_2^{+}$, there is an equilibrium between the complex ion, silver ion, and ammonia molecules. For

$$Ag(NH_3)_2^{+} \rightleftharpoons Ag^{+} + 2NH_3$$

the equilibrium condition is

$$\frac{[Ag^{+}][NH_3]^2}{[Ag(NH_3)_2^{+}]} = 6 \times 10^{-8}$$

When silver nitrate, $AgNO_3$, and aqueous ammonia are mixed, enough silver-ammonia complex ion is formed to satisfy this equilibrium condition. Furthermore, as the concentration of NH_3 in the solution is increased by addition of more NH_3, the concentration of Ag^{+} decreases, as required by constancy of the mass-action expression.

Figure 12.5 lists some common complex ions and their equilibrium constants. The dissociation constant of a complex ion gives a measure of its stability with respect to dissociation. Of the three complex ions of silver in Figure 12.5, the silver-cyanide complex is least dissociated and is said to be most stable. For example, in a solution containing silver ion, cyanide ion, thiosulfate ion, and ammonia, the silver-cyanide complex is preferentially formed since it is the least dissociated, i.e., since it is the most stable.

12.7 SOLUBILITY OF IONIC SOLIDS

When an ionic solid is placed in water, an equilibrium is established between the ions in the saturated solution and the excess solid phase. For example, with excess solid silver chloride in contact with a saturated solution of silver chloride, the equilibrium is

$$AgCl(s) \rightleftharpoons Ag^{+} + Cl^{-}$$

for which

$$\frac{[Ag^+][Cl^-]}{[AgCl(s)]} = K$$

The concentration of a pure solid is a constant number. Thus, the concentration of silver chloride *in the solid phase* is fixed and cannot change, no matter how much solid there is in contact with the solution. It follows that

$$[Ag^+][Cl^-] = K[AgCl(s)] = K_{sp}$$

The constant K_{sp} is called the *solubility product,* and the expression $[Ag^+][Cl^-]$ the *ion product.* The equation states that the ion product must equal K_{sp} when the saturated solution is in equilibrium with excess solid. It should be noted that there is no separate restriction on what the concentrations of Ag^+ and Cl^- must be. The concentration of Ag^+ can have any value, so long as the concentration of Cl^- is such that the product of Ag^+ concentration and Cl^- concentration is equal to K_{sp}.

The numerical value of K_{sp}, as of any equilibrium constant, must be determined by experiment. Once determined, it can be tabulated for future use. (Appendix 7 contains some typical values.) The kind of experiment that can be done is illustrated as follows, for the case of barium sulfate: A weighed amount of solid $BaSO_4$ is ground up and thoroughly agitated with a liter of water at 25°C until the saturated solution is formed. The saturated solution is then filtered, and the residual solid $BaSO_4$ is dried and weighed. The loss in weight corresponds to the amount dissolved in a liter of H_2O at 25°C. The solubility of $BaSO_4$ thus determined is 3.9×10^{-5} mole per liter.

Like practically all salts, $BaSO_4$ is a strong electrolyte and so is 100% dissociated into ions. Therefore, when 3.9×10^{-5} mole of $BaSO_4$ dissolves, it forms 3.9×10^{-5} mole of Ba^{++} and 3.9×10^{-5} mole of SO_4^{--}. In the saturated solution the concentration of Ba^{++} is 3.9×10^{-5} M and the concentration of SO_4^{--} is 3.9×10^{-5} M. Therefore, for the equilibrium

$$BaSO_4(s) \rightleftharpoons Ba^{++} + SO_4^{--}$$

we have the condition

$$K_{sp} = [Ba^{++}][SO_4^{--}] = (3.9 \times 10^{-5})(3.9 \times 10^{-5}) = 1.5 \times 10^{-9}$$

This means that, in any solution containing Ba^{++} and SO_4^{--} in equilibrium with solid $BaSO_4$, the product of the concentrations of Ba^{++} and SO_4^{--} is equal to 1.5×10^{-9}. Since K_{sp} is a very small number, $BaSO_4$ may be called an insoluble salt. If $[Ba^{++}]$ multiplied by $[SO_4^{--}]$ is less than 1.5×10^{-9}, the solution is unsaturated, and $BaSO_4$ must dissolve to increase the concentrations of Ba^{++} and SO_4^{--}. If the product of $[Ba^{++}]$ and $[SO_4^{--}]$ is greater than 1.5×10^{-9}, the system is not at equilibrium. $BaSO_4$ precipitates in order to decrease the concentrations of Ba^{++} and SO_4^{--}.

When $BaSO_4$ is placed in pure water, the concentrations of Ba^{++} and SO_4^{--} must be equal. On the other hand, it is possible to prepare a solution in which unequal concentrations of Ba^{++} and SO_4^{--} are in equilibrium with solid $BaSO_4$. As an illustration, unequal amounts of barium chloride and sodium sulfate might be added to water. A precipitate of $BaSO_4$ forms if K_{sp} of $BaSO_4$ is exceeded. However, there is no requirement that $[Ba^{++}] = [SO_4^{--}]$, since the two ions come from different salts. Alternatively, barium sulfate solid might be added to a $NaSO_4$ solution. Some barium sulfate would dissolve, but in the final solution the concentration of SO_4^{--} would be greater than the concentration of Ba^{++}.

EXAMPLE 7

Given that the K_{sp} of radium sulfate, $RaSO_4$, is 4×10^{-11}. Calculate its solubility in (a) pure water and (b) 0.10 M Na_2SO_4.

(a) Let $x =$ moles of $RaSO_4$ that dissolve per liter of water. Then, in the saturated solution,

$[Ra^{++}] = x$ moles liter^{-1}

$[SO_4^{--}] = x$ moles liter^{-1}

$RaSO_4(s) \rightleftharpoons Ra^{++} + SO_4^{--}$

$[Ra^{++}][SO_4^{--}] = K_{sp} = 4 \times 10^{-11}$

$(x)(x) = 4 \times 10^{-11}$

$x = 6 \times 10^{-6}$ mole liter^{-1}

Thus, the solubility of $RaSO_4$ is 6×10^{-6} mole liter^{-1} of water, giving a solution containing 6×10^{-6} M Ra^{++} and 6×10^{-6} M SO_4^{--}.

(b) Let $y =$ moles of $RaSO_4$ that dissolve per liter of 0.10 M Na_2SO_4. This dissolving produces y moles of Ra^{++} and y moles of SO_4^{--}. The solution already contains 0.10 M SO_4^{--}. Thus, in the final saturated solution,

$[Ra^{++}] = y$ moles liter^{-1}

$[SO_4^{--}] = (y + 0.10)$ moles liter^{-1}

where

$[Ra^{++}][SO_4^{--}] = (y)(y + 0.10) = K_{sp} = 4 \times 10^{-11}$

Since K_{sp} is very small, not much $RaSO_4$ dissolves, and y is so small that it is negligible compared to 0.10.

$(y + 0.10) \cong 0.10$

$[Ra^{++}][SO_4^{--}] \cong (y)(0.10) \cong 4 \times 10^{-11}$

$y \cong \dfrac{4 \times 10^{-11}}{0.10} = 4 \times 10^{-10}$ mole liter^{-1}

Thus, the solubility of $RaSO_4$ in 0.10 M Na_2SO_4 is 4×10^{-10} mole liter^{-1}, giving a solution in which the concentration of Ra^{++} is 4×10^{-10} M and that of SO_4^{--} is 0.10 M.

It is interesting to note that $RaSO_4$ is less soluble in a Na_2SO_4 solution than in pure water. This is an example of the common-ion effect, by which the solubility of an ionic salt is generally decreased by the presence of another solute that furnishes one of its ions. Thus, radium sulfate is less soluble in any solution containing either radium ion or sulfate ion than it is in water. The greater the concentration of the common ion, the less radium sulfate can dissolve. Of course, if the common ion is present in negligible concentration, it has no appreciable effect on the solubility. This is illustrated in the following example.

EXAMPLE 8

Given that magnesium hydroxide, $Mg(OH)_2$, is a strong electrolyte and has a solubility product of 8.9×10^{-12}, calculate the solubility of $Mg(OH)_2$ in water.

Let x = moles of $Mg(OH)_2$ that dissolve per liter. According to the equation

$$Mg(OH)_2(s) \rightleftharpoons Mg^{++} + 2OH^-$$

x moles of $Mg(OH)_2$ dissolve to give x moles of Mg^{++} and $2x$ moles of OH^-. Some hydroxide ion is also furnished by the dissociation of water. Since H_2O is a very weak electrolyte, we assume as in Example 5 that it contributes only a negligible amount of OH^- compared to that furnished by the dissolving of $Mg(OH)_2$. Thus at equilibrium

$[Mg^{++}] = x$ moles liter^{-1}

$[OH^-] \cong 2x$ moles liter^{-1}

For the saturated solution the equilibrium is

$$Mg(OH)_2(s) \rightleftharpoons Mg^{++} + 2OH^-$$

and $K_{sp} = 8.9 \times 10^{-12} = [Mg^{++}][OH^-]^2$.

Substituting, we get

$(x)(2x)^2 = 8.9 \times 10^{-12}$

$4x^3 = 8.9 \times 10^{-12}$

$x = \sqrt[3]{2.2 \times 10^{-12}} = 1.3 \times 10^{-4}$ mole liter^{-1}

Thus, 1.3×10^{-4} mole of $Mg(OH)_2$ dissolves per liter of water. The saturated solution contains 1.3×10^{-4} M Mg^{++} and 2.6×10^{-4} M OH^-.

As noted in Section 11.2, the mass-action expression for a given reaction contains concentrations raised to powers that correspond to the coefficients in the chemical equation. Since the ion product is a mass-action expression, it must be formed by raising the concentrations of ions to powers that correspond to the coefficients in the solubility equation. An exponent applies to the concentration of the specified ion, no matter where that ion comes from. For example, in the following problem essentially all the OH^- comes from NaOH, but its concentration still must be squared.

EXAMPLE 9

Calculate the solubility of $Mg(OH)_2$ in 0.050 M NaOH.

Let $x =$ moles of $Mg(OH)_2$ that dissolve per liter. This forms x moles of Mg^{++} and $2x$ moles of OH^-. Since the solution already contains 0.050 mole of OH^-, equilibrium concentrations are

$[Mg^{++}] = x$ moles liter^{-1}

$[OH^-] = (2x + 0.050)$ moles liter^{-1}

$[Mg^{++}][OH^-]^2 = (x)(2x + 0.050)^2 = K_{sp}$

$(x)(2x + 0.050)^2 = 8.9 \times 10^{-12}$

Assuming that x is a very small number and that $2x$ can be neglected when added to 0.050, we have approximately

$(x)(0.050)^2 \cong 8.9 \times 10^{-12}$

$x = 3.6 \times 10^{-9}$ mole liter^{-1}

Since x is small compared to 0.050, the assumption is valid. The calculation indicates that 3.6×10^{-9} mole of $Mg(OH)_2$ can dissolve in 1 liter of 0.050 M NaOH to give a saturated solution containing 3.6×10^{-9} M Mg^{++} and 0.050 M OH^-.

12.8 PRECIPITATION

One of the most useful applications of the solubility product is to predict whether precipitation will occur when two solutions are mixed. In the saturated solution of a salt, the ion product equals K_{sp}. If two solutions containing the ions of a salt are mixed and if the ion product then exceeds K_{sp}, precipitation should occur.

EXAMPLE 10

Should precipitation occur when 50 ml of 5.0×10^{-4} M $Ca(NO_3)_2$ is mixed with 50 ml of 2.0×10^{-4} M NaF to give 100 ml of solution? The K_{sp} of CaF_2 is 1.7×10^{-10}.

In order to solve such a problem, it is convenient to calculate first the concentration of the ions in the mixture, assuming that no precipitation occurs. Thus, the Ca^{++} from the 5.0×10^{-4} M $Ca(NO_3)_2$ solution is made 2.5×10^{-4} M in the final mixture because of the twofold dilution. Likewise, the F^- is diluted to $1.0 \times 10^{-4}\ M$ in the final mixture. Therefore, if no precipitation occurs, the final solution would have

$$[Ca^{++}] = 2.5 \times 10^{-4}\ M \qquad \text{and} \qquad [F^-] = 1.0 \times 10^{-4}\ M$$

To determine whether precipitation should occur, it is necessary to see whether the ion product exceeds the solubility product. For a saturated solution of CaF_2 the equilibrium would be

$$CaF_2(s) \rightleftharpoons Ca^{++} + 2F^-$$

for which the ion product is $[Ca^{++}][F^-]^2$. In the present mixture the ion product has the numerical value

$$[Ca^{++}][F^-]^2 = (2.5 \times 10^{-4})(1.0 \times 10^{-4})^2 = 2.5 \times 10^{-12}$$

Since this number does not exceed 1.7×10^{-10}, the K_{sp} of CaF_2, precipitation does not occur. The solution obtained as the final mixture is unsaturated with respect to precipitation of CaF_2.

In order to precipitate a salt, the ion product must be made to exceed the K_{sp} of that salt. This gives a method for driving ions out of solution. For example, given a solution of $RaCl_2$, the Ra^{++} can be made to precipitate as $RaSO_4$ by addition of Na_2SO_4. The more the concentration of SO_4^{--} is increased in the solution, the lower the concentration of Ra^{++} becomes. Essentially all the valuable Ra^{++} can be recovered from the solution in this way by adding a large excess of SO_4^{--} ions.

12.9 SIMULTANEOUS EQUILIBRIA

In the preceding discussion only one equilibrium has been considered at a time. This is an idealized situation, since usually aqueous solutions have two or more equilibria which must be satisfied simultaneously. For example, in a solution containing the weak acid $HC_2H_3O_2$ there are two dissociation equilibria:

$$HC_2H_3O_2 \rightleftharpoons H^+ + C_2H_3O_2^- \qquad \frac{[H^+][C_2H_3O_2^-]}{[HC_2H_3O_2]} = K_{diss}$$

and

$$H_2O \rightleftharpoons H^+ + OH^- \qquad [H^+][OH^-] = K_w$$

The solution of acetic acid has a characteristic concentration of H^+ which simultaneously satisfies K_{diss} and K_w. Strictly speaking, this H^+ comes partly from the dissociation of $HC_2H_3O_2$ and partly from the dissociation of H_2O. However, H_2O is so slightly dissociated compared with $HC_2H_3O_2$ that it is justified to consider the H^+ as coming entirely from the $HC_2H_3O_2$. This assumption was implicitly made in the calculations of Section 12.2. The H^+ concentration of $1M\ HC_2H_3O_2$ was calculated by assuming that negligible H^+ is contributed by dissociation of H_2O. Since the OH^- comes exclusively from H_2O dissociation, its concentration is calculated by using K_w.

EXAMPLE 11

Calculate the concentrations of H^+ and OH^- in a solution made by mixing 0.50 mole of $HC_2H_3O_2$ and 0.50 mole of HCN with enough water to make a liter of solution.

There are three simultaneous equilibria in the final solution:

$$HC_2H_3O_2 \rightleftharpoons H^+ + C_2H_3O_2^- \qquad K_{HC_2H_3O_2} = 1.8 \times 10^{-5} \qquad (1)$$

$$HCN \rightleftharpoons H^+ + CN^- \qquad K_{HCN} = 4 \times 10^{-10} \qquad (2)$$

$$H_2O \rightleftharpoons H^+ + OH^- \qquad K_w = 1.0 \times 10^{-14} \qquad (3)$$

Only acetic acid contributes an appreciable concentration of H^+, because it has much the largest dissociation constant. Ignoring the other dissociations, let x = moles of $HC_2H_3O_2$ that dissociate per liter. Then, at equilibrium

$$[HC_2H_3O_2] = (0.50 - x) \text{ moles liter}^{-1}$$

$$[H^+] = x \text{ moles liter}^{-1}$$

$$[C_2H_3O_2^-] = x \text{ moles liter}^{-1}$$

$$\frac{[H^+][C_2H_3O_2^-]}{[HC_2H_3O_2]} = \frac{(x)(x)}{(0.50 - x)} = 1.8 \times 10^{-5}$$

$$x = 3.0 \times 10^{-3} M$$

Thus, the final solution has a hydrogen-ion concentration of 3.0×10^{-3} M. Substituting this value in the equilibrium condition for equilibrium (3),

$$K_w = [H^+][OH^-] = 1.0 \times 10^{-14}$$

$$(3.0 \times 10^{-3})[OH^-] = 1.0 \times 10^{-14}$$

$$[OH^-] = 3.3 \times 10^{-12} M$$

Another common example of simultaneous equilibrium occurs in solutions of polyprotic acids (Section 9.3). For example, in a solution of hydrogen sulfide, besides the water equilibrium, there are the two equilibria that correspond to the stepwise dissociation of H_2S.*

$$H_2S \rightleftharpoons H^+ + HS^- \qquad K_I = 1.1 \times 10^{-7}$$

$$HS^- \rightleftharpoons H^+ + S^{--} \qquad K_{II} = 1 \times 10^{-14}$$

Since H_2S is a weak acid, a solution of H_2S is slightly acidic. In order to calculate the acidity of the solution, is it necessary to consider both steps of the dissociation? The case is exactly analogous to that of acetic acid

* There is considerable disagreement as to the value of the second dissociation constant of H_2S. The old accepted value was 1×10^{-15}; more recent values range as high as 1×10^{-12}. It is not very probable that HS^- is becoming a stronger acid with the years. We have chosen the intermediate value 1×10^{-14}, as given by W. M. Latimer in *Oxidation Potentials*, 2d ed., Prentice-Hall, Englewood Cliffs, N.J., 1952.

in water, where the H_2O dissociation contributes a negligible concentration of H^+. In H_2S the dissociation of HS^- contributes a negligible concentration of H^+. Using only K_I, we can calculate that the concentration of H^+ in 0.10 M H_2S is approximately 1×10^{-4} M and the HS^- concentration is 1×10^{-4} M.

Because of the second step of the dissociation of H_2S, there is a small trace of sulfide ion, S^{--}, in the solution. Its numerical magnitude can be calculated by using K_{II}.

$$K_{II} = \frac{[H^+][S^{--}]}{[HS^-]} = 1 \times 10^{-14}$$

If, as is the case in 0.10 M H_2S, the concentrations of H^+ and HS^- are 1×10^{-4} M, they cancel each other out of the expression, and $[S^{--}] = 1 \times 10^{-14}$ M.

In any solution of H_2S, both K_I and K_{II} must be simultaneously satisfied and give rise to the two simultaneous equations

$$\frac{[H^+][HS^-]}{[H_2S]} = 1.1 \times 10^{-7} \tag{1}$$

$$\frac{[H^+][S^{--}]}{[HS^-]} = 1 \times 10^{-14} \tag{2}$$

Solving equations (1) and (2) for $[HS^-]$, we get

$$[HS^-] = 1.1 \times 10^{-7} \frac{[H_2S]}{[H^+]} \tag{3}$$

$$[HS^-] = \frac{[H^+][S^{--}]}{1 \times 10^{-14}} \tag{4}$$

and equating (3) and (4) gives

$$\frac{1.1 \times 10^{-7}[H_2S]}{[H^+]} = \frac{[H^+][S^{--}]}{1 \times 10^{-14}} \tag{5}$$

Rearranging the terms in Equation (5), we get the condition for any H_2S solution that

$$(1.1 \times 10^{-7})(1 \times 10^{-14}) = \frac{[H^+]^2[S^{--}]}{[H_2S]}$$

For a saturated solution of H_2S at atmospheric pressure and room temperature, the concentration of H_2S in solution is constant at 0.10 M. This means that, for a saturated solution of H_2S,

$$[H^+]^2[S^{--}] = (1.1 \times 10^{-7})(1 \times 10^{-14})(0.10)$$

$$[H^+]^2[S^{--}] = 1 \times 10^{-22} \tag{6}$$

Equation (6) is useful because it states that the sulfide-ion concentration of a saturated H_2S solution can be changed by changing the concentration of H^+. For example, if enough HCl is added to a saturated H_2S solution to make the H^+ concentration 1 M, the S^{--} concentration becomes 1×10^{-22} M. This possibility of changing the S^{--} concentration by juggling the concentration of H^+ is the basis of the classic method of ion separation, in qualitative analysis, by sulfide precipitation.

EXAMPLE 12

A solution contains Zn^{++} and Cu^{++}, each at 0.02 M. The K_{sp} of ZnS is 1×10^{-22}; that of CuS, 8×10^{-37}. If the solution is made 1 M in H^+ and H_2S gas is bubbled in until the solution is saturated, should a precipitate form?

In a saturated H_2S solution $[H^+]^2[S^{--}] = 1 \times 10^{-22}$

If $[H^+] = 1\ M$, $[S^{--}] = 1 \times 10^{-22}\ M$

For ZnS, the ion product is

$$[Zn^{++}][S^{--}] = (0.02)(1 \times 10^{-22}),\ \text{or}\ 2 \times 10^{-24}$$

For CuS, the ion product is

$$[Cu^{++}][S^{--}] = (0.02)(1 \times 10^{-22}),\ \text{or}\ 2 \times 10^{-24}$$

Since the ion product of ZnS does not exceed 1×10^{-22}, the K_{sp} of ZnS, ZnS does not precipitate. Since the ion product of CuS does exceed 8×10^{-37}, the K_{sp} of CuS, CuS does precipitate.

The principles of simultaneous equilibrium can also be applied to dissolving solids by introducing appropriate secondary equilibria. For example, although ZnS is essentially insoluble in water, it can be made to dissolve by the addition of acid. The qualitative argument is as follows: If solid ZnS is added to pure water, the equilibrium is

$$ZnS(s) \rightleftharpoons Zn^{++} + S^{--} \tag{7}$$

When acid is added, the additional equilibria

$$H^+ + S^{--} \rightleftharpoons HS^- \tag{8}$$

$$H^+ + HS^- \rightleftharpoons H_2S \tag{9}$$

become important. The added H^+ ties up S^{--} in the form of HS^- and H_2S. As the concentration of S^{--} is reduced, more ZnS can dissolve. The net reaction for the dissolving is the sum of Equations (7), (8), and (9), or

$$ZnS(s) + 2H^+ \rightleftharpoons Zn^{++} + H_2S$$

Similarly, although AgCl is insoluble in water, it can be dissolved by addition of sodium thiosulfate, $Na_2S_2O_3$. In water the equilibrium is

$$AgCl(s) \rightleftharpoons Ag^+ + Cl^-$$

Added thiosulfate ion, $S_2O_3^{--}$, combines with Ag^+ to form the complex ion $Ag(S_2O_3)_2^{-3}$ by the equation

$$Ag^+ + 2S_2O_3^{--} \rightleftharpoons Ag(S_2O_3)_2^{-3}$$

Since the concentration of Ag^+ is thereby reduced, more AgCl can dissolve. The net reaction for the dissolving is

$$AgCl(s) + 2S_2O_3^{--} \rightleftharpoons Ag(S_2O_3)_2^{-3} + Cl^-$$

The last reaction is of practical value in photographic developing. An insoluble silver salt such as AgCl is the active ingredient in photographic emulsions and must be removed in order to fix the picture. Dissolution is accomplished through the use of *hypo,* a solution of $Na_2S_2O_3$.

12.10 HYDROLYSIS

One of the most important applications of simultaneous equilibria is the quantitative description of hydrolysis. The subject was discussed qualitatively in Section 9.4, where it was pointed out that what is important is the relative proton affinity of a solute species compared to that of water. Specifically, for the case of sodium acetate, $NaC_2H_3O_2$, the solution is slightly basic owing to a reaction between $C_2H_3O_2^-$ and H_2O:

$$C_2H_3O_2^- + H_2O \rightleftharpoons HC_2H_3O_2 + OH^-$$

In the forward reaction a proton is transferred from a water molecule to an acetate ion; in the reverse reaction a proton is transferred from an acetic acid molecule to a hydroxide ion. Clearly, what is involved is the relative proton affinity of $C_2H_3O_2^-$ and OH^-. The former can be described by K_{diss} of $HC_2H_3O_2$; the latter, by K_w. This can be seen explicitly by writing the equilibrium condition for the net hydrolysis reaction as given above.

$$\frac{[HC_2H_3O_2][OH^-]}{[C_2H_3O_2^-]} = K$$

Multiplying the numerator and denominator by $[H^+]$ gives

$$\frac{[HC_2H_3O_2][OH^-][H^+]}{[C_2H_3O_2^-][H^+]} = K$$

or

$$\frac{[OH^-][H^+]}{[C_2H_3O_2^-][H^+]/[HC_2H_3O_2]} = K$$

In the last step the terms have been rearranged to emphasize that the numerator is K_w and the denominator is K_{diss}.

$$\frac{K_w}{K_{diss}} = K$$

In other words, the hydrolysis constant K is just the ratio of the water dissociation constant to the weak-acid dissociation constant.

The quantitative treatment of hydrolysis can also be approached as follows. For the hydrolysis of X^- ion the equilibria are

$$H_2O \rightleftharpoons H^+ + OH^- \qquad [H^+][OH^-] = K_w$$

$$X^- + H^+ \rightleftharpoons HX \qquad \frac{[HX]}{[H^+][X^-]} = \frac{1}{K_{diss}}$$

These two equilibrium conditions must be satisfied simultaneously and so can be combined into one. This is done by solving for $[H^+]$ and equating to eliminate $[H^+]$.

$$[H^+] = \frac{K_w}{[OH^-]} = \frac{[HX]}{[X^-]} K_{diss}$$

$$\frac{[HX][OH^-]}{[X^-]} = \frac{K_w}{K_{diss}}$$

This final expression represents a condition that must be satisfied by the hydrolysis. The net reaction for hydrolysis can be written

$$X^- + H_2O \rightleftharpoons HX + OH^-$$

The equilibrium condition is

$$\frac{[HX][OH^-]}{[X^-]} = K$$

where H_2O is omitted because it is constant.

Once the numerical value of K has been obtained, it can be used for equilibrium calculations in the usual way. The following problems illustrate specific cases.

EXAMPLE 13

Calculate the pH of 0.10 M $NaC_2H_3O_2$ and the percent hydrolysis.

The net hydrolysis reaction is

$$C_2H_3O_2^- + H_2O \rightleftharpoons HC_2H_3O_2 + OH^-$$

for which

$$\frac{[HC_2H_3O_2][OH^-]}{[C_2H_3O_2^-]} = \frac{K_w}{K_{diss}} = \frac{1.0 \times 10^{-14}}{1.8 \times 10^{-5}} = 5.6 \times 10^{-10}$$

Let x = moles of $C_2H_3O_2^-$ that hydrolyze per liter. This forms x moles of $HC_2H_3O_2$ and x moles of OH^- and leaves $(0.10 - x)$ moles of $C_2H_3O_2^-$. At equilibrium

$$[HC_2H_3O_2] = x \text{ moles liter}^{-1}$$

$$[OH^-] = x \text{ moles liter}^{-1}$$

$$[C_2H_3O_2^-] = (0.10 - x) \text{ moles liter}^{-1}$$

Substituting in the mass-action expression gives

$$\frac{(x)(x)}{(0.10 - x)} = 5.6 \times 10^{-10}$$

Assuming that x is small compared to 0.10

$$\frac{x^2}{0.10} \cong 5.6 \times 10^{-10}$$

$$x = 7.5 \times 10^{-6} M$$

Since x represents the concentration of OH^-,

$$[H^+] = \frac{K_w}{[OH^-]} = \frac{1.0 \times 10^{-14}}{x} = \frac{1.0 \times 10^{-14}}{7.5 \times 10^{-6}} = 1.3 \times 10^{-9} M$$

$$pH = -\log [H^+] = -\log 1.3 \times 10^{-9} = 8.89$$

The percent hydrolysis of acetate ion in this solution is given as follows:

$$\frac{\text{Moles } C_2H_3O_2^- \text{ hydrolyzed} \times 100}{\text{Moles } C_2H_3O_2^- \text{ available}} = \frac{7.5 \times 10^{-6} \times 100}{0.10}$$

$$= 0.0075\%$$

EXAMPLE 14

What is the concentration of H^+ in 0.10 M $AlCl_3$? The hydrolysis constant of Al^{+3} is 1.4×10^{-5}.

$$Al^{+3} + H_2O \rightleftharpoons AlOH^{++} + H^+$$

$$\frac{[AlOH^{++}][H^+]}{[Al^{+3}]} = 1.4 \times 10^{-5}$$

Let x = moles of Al^{+3} that hydrolyze. At equilibrium

$[Al^{+3}] = (0.10 - x)$ moles liter^{-1}

$[AlOH^{++}] = x$ moles liter^{-1}

$[H^+] = x$ moles liter^{-1}

$$\frac{(x)(x)}{(0.10 - x)} = 1.4 \times 10^{-5}$$

$$x = 1.2 \times 10^{-3} M$$

The concentration of H^+ in 0.10 M $AlCl_3$ should be $1.2 \times 10^{-3} M$, according to this calculation. (For comparison, the concentration of H^+ in 0.10 M $HC_2H_3O_2$ is $1.3 \times 10^{-3} M$.)

QUESTIONS

12.1 *Dissociation*   How does the percent dissociation change when 0.25 M HCN solution is diluted tenfold? $K_{diss} = 4 \times 10^{-10}$ for HCN.

12.2 *Dissociation*   The hydrogen-ion concentration of a 0.0202 M HNO_2 solution is $2.8 \times 10^{-3} M$. Calculate the K_{diss} for HNO_2.

12.3 *pH and K_{diss}*   The pH of 0.10 M HCN solution is 5.2. Calculate the K_{diss}.

12.4 *K_{diss}*   Calculate the concentration of hydrogen ion in 0.15 M HOCl. The K_{diss} for HOCl $\rightleftharpoons H^+ + OCl^-$ is 3.2×10^{-8}.

12.5 *pH*   Calculate the pH of a solution that is 0.12 M HOBr. The K_{diss} for HOBr $\rightleftharpoons H^+ + OBr^-$ is 2.1×10^{-9}.

12.6 *Solubility product*   The solubility product of AgBr is 5.0×10^{-13}. Calculate how many moles of AgBr can dissolve in 0.100 liter of each of the following: (a) water, (b) 0.10 M NaBr, (c) 0.010 M Ag_2SO_4.

12.7 *Hydrolysis*   How does the percent hydrolysis change when 0.25 M NaCN solution is diluted tenfold? $K_{diss} = 4 \times 10^{-10}$ for HCN.

12.8 *Buffer*   How many moles of NH_4Cl must be dissolved in a liter of 0.10 M NH_3 solution to buffer it at a pH of 9.00? Use $K = 1.8 \times 10^{-5}$ for $NH_3 + H_2O \rightleftharpoons NH_4^+ + OH^-$.

12.9 Complex ions   Given a solution in which there is established the equilibrium $Ag(NH_3)_2{}^+ \rightleftharpoons Ag^+ + 2NH_3$. How would the equilibrium concentration of Ag^+ be affected by each of the following? (a) Add NH_3. (b) Add H_2O. (c) Add HNO_3. (d) Add $NaCl$. (e) Add $Na_2S_2O_3$.

12.10 Complex ions   Given the constant 1.8×10^{-19} for the equilibrium $Ag(CN)_2{}^- \rightleftharpoons Ag^+ + 2CN^-$, calculate the concentration of each species in the final solution made by mixing 0.0010 mole of NaCN with 1.0×10^{-5} mole of $AgNO_3$ in a liter of water.

12.11 pH   Given the equilibrium constants as follows:

$$CO_2 + H_2O \rightleftharpoons H^+ + HCO_3{}^- \qquad K = 4.2 \times 10^{-7}$$
$$HCO_3{}^- \rightleftharpoons H^+ + CO_3{}^{--} \qquad K = 4.8 \times 10^{-11}$$
$$Pu^{+3} + H_2O \rightleftharpoons PuOH^{++} + H^+ \qquad K = 1 \times 10^{-7}$$
$$HSO_4{}^- \rightleftharpoons H^+ + SO_4{}^{--} \qquad K = 1.3 \times 10^{-2}$$
$$NH_3 + H_2O \rightleftharpoons NH_4{}^+ + OH^- \qquad K = 1.8 \times 10^{-5}$$
$$Zn^{++} + H_2O \rightleftharpoons ZnOH^+ + H^+ \qquad K = 2 \times 10^{-10}$$
$$Cr^{+3} + H_2O \rightleftharpoons CrOH^{++} + H^+ \qquad K = 2 \times 10^{-4}$$

Arrange in order of increasing pH equimolar solutions of each species at the extreme left of each of the above equilibria.

12.12 Hydrolysis   Given that $K = 4.8 \times 10^{-11}$ for $HCO_3{}^- \rightleftharpoons H^+ + CO_3{}^{--}$, calculate the pH of $0.10\ M\ Na_2CO_3$ solution.

12.13 Hydrolysis   Given that K_{diss} for HOCl is 3.2×10^{-8}, calculate the hydrolysis constant and the percent hydrolysis of OCl^- in $0.010\ M$ NaOCl.

12.14 Diprotic acids   Show that, for solutions containing only the diprotic acid H_2X, the concentration of X^{--} is equal to K_{II} no matter what the concentration of the solution so long as K_{II} is small compared to K_I.

12.15 Dissociation   Calculate the hydrogen-ion concentration in each of the following solutions: (a) 0.50 mole $HC_2H_3O_2$ ($K_{diss} = 1.8 \times 10^{-5}$) added to enough water to make a liter of solution. (b) 0.25 mole $NaC_2H_3O_2$ added (assume no volume change) to the solution from (a). (c) 0.50 mole $HC_2H_3O_2$ added (assume no volume change) to the solution from (b).

12.16 pH titration   Calculate the pH of each of the following solutions, assuming volumes are additive: (a) 20.0 ml of $0.050\ M$ HCl, (b) 20.0 ml of $0.050\ M$ HCl plus 10.0 ml of $0.050\ M$ NaOH, (c) 20.0 ml of $0.050\ M$ HCl plus 19.0 ml of $0.050\ M$ NaOH, (d) 20.0 ml of $0.050\ M$ HCl plus 21.0 ml of $0.050\ M$ NaOH, (e) 20.0 ml of $0.050\ M$ HCl plus 30.0 ml of $0.050\ M$ NaOH.

12.17 Buffer   Calculate the pH before and after the addition of 0.010 mole HCl to a liter of each of the following solutions: (a) water, (b) 0.10 $M\ NaC_2H_3O_2$, (c) $0.10\ M\ NaC_2H_3O_2$ and $0.10\ M\ HC_2H_3O_2$, (d) $0.10\ M$ $HC_2H_3O_2$. $K_{diss} = 1.8 \times 10^{-5}$ for $HC_2H_3O_2$.

12.18 Buffer   Calculate the pH change brought about by adding each of the following to 0.50 liter of a buffer solution that is $0.50\ M$

NH_3 and 0.50 M NH_4Cl. Use the constant $K = 1.8 \times 10^{-5}$ for $NH_3 + H_2O \rightleftharpoons NH_4^+ + OH^-$. (a) 0.010 mole HCl. (b) 0.010 mole NaOH. (c) 0.010 mole NH_3. (d) 0.010 mole NH_4Cl.

12.19 Complex ions Given 0.0010 mole each of Cu^{++}, Co^{++}, and Ag^+. By using the data of Figure 12.5, calculate the amount of NH_3 required to be added to a liter of solution of each in order to lower the concentration of uncomplexed metal ion to 1.0×10^{-4} M.

12.20 Solubility product The solubility product of $Mg(OH)_2$ is 8.9×10^{-12}. Calculate how many moles of $Mg(OH)_2$ can dissolve in 0.200 liter of each of the following: (a) water, (b) 0.020 M $MgCl_2$, (c) 0.020 M NaOH, (d) 0.020 M $Ba(OH)_2$, (e) solution buffered at pH = 9.00.

12.21 Precipitation The K_{sp} of $La(OH)_3$ is 1.0×10^{-19}; that of $BaSO_4$ is 1.5×10^{-9}. Show whether a precipitate would be expected on mixing 40.0 ml of 1.0×10^{-4} M $Ba(OH)_2$ with 60.0 ml of 2.0×10^{-5} M $La_2(SO_4)_3$.

12.22 Simultaneous equilibria By using the data of Section 12.9, calculate the highest pH possible for dissolving 0.010 mole ZnS per liter of solution saturated with respect to H_2S.

12.23 Simultaneous equilibria Given a solid mixture of 0.010 mole AgCl ($K_{sp} = 1.7 \times 10^{-10}$) and 0.010 mole AgBr ($K_{sp} = 5.0 \times 10^{-13}$) shaken up with a liter of 1.0 M NH_3. What will be the relative concentrations of Cl^- to Br^- in the equilibrium solution?

12.24 Hydrolysis Given that $K = 1 \times 10^{-12}$ for $HPO_4^{--} \rightleftharpoons H^+ + PO_4^{-3}$, calculate the hydrolysis constant and the percent hydrolysis of PO_4^{-3} in 0.010 M Na_3PO_4 solution.

12.25 Simultaneous equilibria Given a liter of 0.50 M NH_4NO_3 in contact with 0.010 mole AgCl ($K_{sp} = 1.7 \times 10^{-10}$). How much NaOH must be added so that all the AgCl dissolves as $Ag(NH_3)_2^+$, for which $K_{diss} = 6 \times 10^{-8}$?

12.26 Simultaneous equilibria Given a solution made by mixing 0.10 mole $NaHSO_4$ and 0.10 mole Na_3PO_4 in enough water to make a liter of solution. By using $K = 1.3 \times 10^{-2}$ for $HSO_4^- \rightleftharpoons H^+ + SO_4^{--}$ and $K = 1 \times 10^{-12}$ for $HPO_4^{--} \rightleftharpoons H^+ + PO_4^{-3}$, calculate the pH of the final solution.

12.27 Dissociation Calculate the percent dissociation of 0.10 mole of HNO_2 ($K_{diss} = 4.5 \times 10^{-4}$) when added to (a) 1.0 liter of water, (b) 1.0 liter of 0.10 M $NaNO_2$, (c) 1.0 liter of 0.10 M HNO_2, (d) the 2.0-liter mixture of (b) and (c).

12.28 pH Given a solution that is 0.50 M $HC_2H_3O_2$. To what volume must one liter of this solution be diluted in order to (a) double the pH, (b) double the hydroxide-ion concentration?

12.29 pH titration of weak acid Calculate the pH of each of the following solutions, assuming volumes are additive: (a) 20.0 ml of 0.050 M $HC_2H_3O_2$ ($K_{diss} = 1.8 \times 10^{-5}$), (b) 20.0 ml of 0.050 M $HC_2H_3O_2$ plus 10.0 ml of 0.050 M NaOH, (c) 20.0 ml of 0.050 M

$HC_2H_3O_2$ plus 19.0 ml of 0.050 M NaOH, (d) 20.0 ml of 0.050 M $HC_2H_3O_2$ plus 20.0 ml of 0.050 M NaOH, (e) 20.0 ml of 0.050 M $HC_2H_3O_2$ plus 21.0 ml of 0.050 M NaOH.

12.30 pH and dissociation Assuming the first dissociation step $H_2SO_4 \longrightarrow H^+ + HSO_4^-$ to be complete and taking $K_{II} = 1.3 \times 10^{-2}$ for the second dissociation step $HSO_4^- \rightleftharpoons H^+ + SO_4^{--}$, calculate the pH of each of the following solutions: (a) 0.25 M H_2SO_4, (b) 0.25 M $KHSO_4$ (100% dissociated to K^+ and HSO_4^-), (c) 0.25 M K_2SO_4 (100% dissociated to $2K^+$ and SO_4^{--}).

ANSWERS

12.1 $4 \times 10^{-3}\%$ to $1 \times 10^{-2}\%$ 12.3 4×10^{-10} 12.5 4.80
12.7 From 1% to 3%   12.10 $[Ag(CN)_2^-] = 1.0 \times 10^{-5}$ M; $[Ag^+] =$ 1.8×10^{-18} M; $[CN^-] = 1.0 \times 10^{-3}$ M 12.12 11.65   12.15 (a) $3.0 \times$ 10^{-3} M (b) 3.6×10^{-5} M (c) 7.2×10^{-5} M 12.17 (a) 7.00 and 2.00   (b) 8.87 and 5.70   (c) 4.74 and 4.66   (d) 2.87 and 1.99
12.19 For Cu^{++}, 5.3×10^{-3} mole; for Co^{++}, 0.27 mole; for Ag^+, 2.5×10^{-3} mole   12.22 1.0   12.24 1×10^{-2}; 62%   12.26 pH $= 7.0$
12.28 (a) 37000 liters   (b) 4.0 liters   12.30 (a) 0.58   (b) 1.29
(c) 7.65

13 electrochemistry

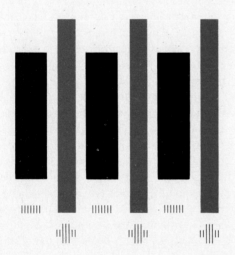

When a chemical reaction occurs, there is a net increase or decrease in potential energy. In most cases the change in potential energy appears as heat evolved to or absorbed from the surroundings. Occasionally, however, the change in potential energy may be made to appear as electric energy. In this chapter the relation between chemical energy and electric energy is explored. We consider the transport of electric energy through matter, the conversion of electric energy into chemical energy, and the conversion of chemical energy into electric energy. These topics belong to the field of *electrochemistry*.

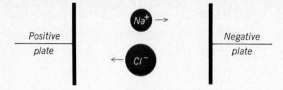

13.1 ELECTRICAL CONDUCTIVITY

Electric energy may be transported through matter by the conduction of electric charge from one point to another in the form of an *electric current* (see Appendix 3.5 to 3.7 for a discussion of electrical terms). In order that the electric current exist, there must be charge carriers in the matter and there must be a force that makes the carriers move. The charge carriers can be electrons, as in the case of metals, or they can be positive and negative ions, as in the case of electrolytic solutions and molten salts. In the former case, conduction is said to be *metallic;* in the latter, *electrolytic*. The electric force that makes charges move is usually supplied by a battery or some similar source of electric energy. Any region of space in which there is an electric force is called an *electric field*.

As pointed out in Section 6.5, solid metals consist of ordered arrays of positive ions immersed in a sea of electrons. For example, silver consists of Ag^+ ions arranged in a face-centered-cubic pattern with the entire lattice permeated by a cloud of electrons equal in number to the number of Ag^+ ions in the crystal. The Ag^+ ions are more or less fixed in positions from which they do not move except under great stress. The electrons of the cloud, on the contrary, are free to roam throughout the crystal. When an electric field is impressed on the metal, the electrons migrate and thereby carry negative electric charge through the metal. In principle, it should be possible for an electric field to force all the loose electrons toward one end of a metal sample. In practice, it is extraordinarily difficult to separate positive and negative charges from each other without the expenditure of relatively enormous amounts of energy. The only way it is possible to keep a sustained flow of charge in a wire is to add electrons to one end of the wire and drain off electrons from the other end as fast as they accumulate. The metal conductor thus remains everywhere electrically neutral, since just as many electrons move into a region per unit time as move out.

Most of the electrons that make up the electron cloud of a metal are of very high kinetic energy. Metallic conductivity would therefore be extremely high were it not for a *resistance* effect. Electrical resistance is believed to arise because lattice ions vibrate about their lattice points. By interfering with the migration of electrons, the ions keep the conductivity down. At higher temperatures the thermal vibrations of the lattice increase, and therefore it is not surprising to find that, as the temperature of a metal is raised, its conductivity diminishes.

In solutions the mechanism of conductivity is complicated by the fact that the positive carriers are also free to move. As pointed out in Section

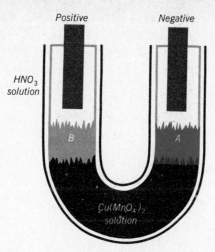

Positive   Negative

HNO_3
solution

B   A

$Cu(MnO_4)_2$
solution

13.2
Migration of ions in
electrolytic conductivity

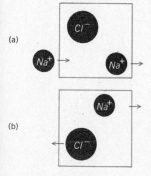

(a)

Cl^-

Na^+ Na^+

(b)

Na^+

Cl^-

13.3
Two ways that migrating
ions could maintain
electrical neutrality in a
region of solution

8.4, solutions of electrolytes contain positive and negative ions. There are no free electrons in aqueous solutions. The ions are not fixed in position but are free to roam throughout the body of the solution. When an electric field is applied to such a solution, as shown in Figure 13.1, the positive ions experience a force in one direction, while the negative ions experience a force in the opposite direction. The simultaneous motion of positive and negative ions in opposite directions constitutes the *electrolytic current*. The current would stop if positive ions accumulated at the negative electrode and negative ions at the positive electrode. In order that the electrolytic current can continue, appropriate chemical reactions must occur at the electrodes to maintain electrical neutrality.

That ions migrate when electrolytic solutions conduct electricity can be seen from the experiment diagramed in Figure 13.2. The U tube is initially half filled with a deep-purple aqueous solution of copper permanganate, $Cu(MnO_4)_2$. The solution contains blue hydrated Cu^{++} ions and purple MnO_4^- ions. A colorless aqueous solution of nitric acid, HNO_3, is floated on top of the $Cu(MnO_4)_2$ solution. An electric field is maintained across the solution by the two electrodes. After some time, it is observed that the blue color characteristic of hydrated Cu^{++} ions has moved into the region marked A, suggesting a migration toward the negative electrode. At the same time, the purple color characteristic of MnO_4^- has moved into the region marked B, indicating that negative ions move simultaneously toward the positive electrode.

As in the case of metallic conduction, electrical neutrality must be preserved in all regions of the solution at all times. Otherwise, the current soon ceases. Figure 13.3 shows two of the possible ways by which electrical neutrality can be preserved for a given region of a NaCl solution. In (a) one Na^+ ion enters the region defined by the dotted line to compensate for the charge of the departing Na^+ ion. In (b), as one Na^+ ion leaves the region, one Cl^- ion departs in the opposite direction; hence, the region shows no net change in charge. *Both* effects occur simultaneously, their relative importance depending on the relative mobilities of the positive and negative ions.

Unlike metallic conduction, electrolytic conduction is usually increased when the temperature of a solution is raised.* The difference arises from the fact that in metals the conducting electrons are already of such high energy that a rise in temperature does not appreciably affect their kinetic energy. In solutions, ions have average kinetic energies proportional to the absolute temperature, just as do the molecules of an ideal gas. When the temperature of a solution is raised, the average kinetic energy of the ions is increased, the ions migrate faster, and the solution becomes a better conductor of electricity.

13.2 ELECTROLYSIS

In order to maintain an electric current, it is necessary to have a complete circuit; i.e., there must be a closed loop whereby the electric charge can return to its starting point. If the complete circuit includes as one component an electrolytic conductor, chemical reaction must occur at the electrodes. Electric energy is thus used to produce chemical change, and the process is called *electrolysis*.

A typical electrolysis circuit is shown in Figure 13.4. The two vertical lines at the top of the diagram represent a battery with the long line the positive terminal and the short line the negative one. The curved lines represent strips of connecting wire, usually copper, that join the battery to the electrodes. The electrodes dip into the electrolytic conductor, which contains the ions M^+ and X^- that are free to move. When operating, the battery creates an electric field which pushes the electrons in the wires in the directions shown by the arrows. Electrons are crowded onto the left-hand electrode and drained away from the right-hand electrode. The circuit is not complete unless there is some way by which electrons can be used up at the left electrode and formed at the right electrode. Chemical changes must occur. At the left electrode a *reduction* process must occur; in the process some ion or molecule accepts electrons and is thereby reduced. The electrode at which reduction occurs is always called a *cathode*. At the right-hand electrode electrons must be released by an ion or molecule to the electrode. An *oxidation* process must occur. The electrode at which oxidation occurs is always called an *anode*. In order for the reduction process to continue at the cathode, ions must keep moving toward it. These ions are the positive ions and are called *cations*. Simultaneously, negative ions move toward the anode, and they are called *anions*.

As a specific example we consider first the electrolysis of *molten* NaCl. As in later examples, we shall assume here that the electrodes themselves are inert and do not react chemically. Of the two ions pres-

* There are exceptions to this generalization. For example, with some weak electrolytes, the percent dissociation (Section 8.5) may decrease with rising temperature. The decrease in the concentration of ions may be big enough to cause a decrease in conductivity.

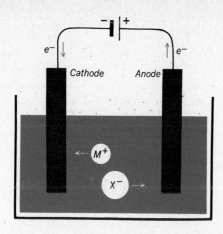

ent, Na$^+$ and Cl$^-$, only the Na$^+$ can be reduced. At the cathode, where reduction must occur, the following reaction takes place:

$$Na^+(l) + e^- \longrightarrow Na(l)$$

This is called the *cathode half-reaction*. At the anode, oxidation occurs. Of the two species in the cell, only the Cl$^-$ can be oxidized. Cl$^-$ releases an electron to the anode, and a neutral chlorine atom forms. Two such atoms combine to produce the molecule Cl$_2$, and the Cl$_2$ molecules bubble off as a gas. The net *anode half-reaction* can be written

$$2Cl^-(l) \longrightarrow Cl_2(g) + 2e^-$$

At the cathode, electric energy has been used to convert Na$^+$ into Na metal; at the anode, to convert Cl$^-$ into Cl$_2$. By addition, the two electrode half-reactions can be combined into a single overall *cell reaction*. In order to keep electrons from accumulating in the cell, as many electrons must disappear at the cathode as appear at the anode. To ensure electron balance, the half-reactions are multiplied by appropriate coefficients so that, when the half-reactions are added, the electrons cancel out of the final equation. Thus, for the electrolysis of molten NaCl:

Cathode reaction:

$$2Na^+(l) + 2e^- \longrightarrow 2Na(l)$$

Anode reaction:

$$2Cl^-(l) \longrightarrow Cl_2(g) + 2e^-$$

Overall reaction:

$$2Na^+(l) + 2Cl^-(l) \xrightarrow{\text{electrolysis}} 2Na(l) + Cl_2(g)$$

In order to emphasize that this reaction occurs by the consumption of electric energy, the word "electrolysis" is often written under the arrow.

As a second example of electrolysis we consider what happens when *aqueous* NaCl is electrolyzed. Under usual conditions, and again employing electrodes that do not react, it is observed that hydrogen gas is liberated at the cathode and chlorine gas is liberated at the anode. How can these observations be accounted for? The electrolysis cell contains, besides Na^+ and Cl^- ions, H_2O molecules and traces of H^+ and OH^- from the dissociation of water. Molecules of H_2O can be either oxidized to O_2 and H^+ by removal of electrons or reduced to H_2 and OH^- by the addition of electrons. The H_2O must thus be considered as a possible reactant at each electrode. At the cathode, reduction must occur. Three different reactions are possible:

$$Na^+ + e^- \longrightarrow Na(s) \tag{1}$$

$$2H_2O + 2e^- \longrightarrow H_2(g) + 2OH^- \tag{2}$$

$$2H^+ + 2e^- \longrightarrow H_2(g) \tag{3}$$

It is not easy to predict which of several possible reactions will occur at a cathode. It is necessary to consider which reactant is reduced most *rapidly*. The strongest oxidizing agent is not necessarily the fastest. Further complications appear when currents are very large and when concentrations of reactants are very small. The fact that hydrogen gas and not metallic sodium is observed in the electrolysis of aqueous NaCl indicates that reaction (2) or (3) occurs.* In NaCl solution, the concentration of H^+ is not large enough to make reaction (3) reasonable as a *net change*. Therefore, in the electrolysis of aqueous NaCl, reaction (2) is usually written for the cathode reaction. [However, in acidic solutions, the concentration of H^+ may be high enough for H^+ to appear in the net electrode reaction. For example, in the electrolysis of aqueous HCl, the cathode reaction is written as Equation (3).] In the electrolysis of NaCl solution OH^- accumulates in the region around the cathode and positive ions (Na^+) must move toward the cathode to preserve electrical neutrality. In addition, OH^- migrates away from the cathode. Both migrations are consistent with the requirement that cations migrate toward the cathode and anions toward the anode. At the anode, oxidation must occur. Two different reactions are possible:

$$2Cl^- \longrightarrow Cl_2(g) + 2e^- \tag{4}$$

$$2H_2O \longrightarrow O_2(g) + 4H^+ + 4e^- \tag{5}$$

Experiment shows that reaction (4) predominates. As the chloride-ion concentration around the anode is depleted, fresh Cl^- moves into the region and Na^+ moves out. In summary, the equations for the electrolysis of aqueous NaCl are:

Cathode reaction:

$$2e^- + 2H_2O \longrightarrow H_2(g) + 2OH^-$$

* Years ago it was thought that the metal Na was first formed by reaction (1) and that it subsequently reacted with water to liberate H_2. However, there is no evidence that any intermediate Na is ever formed in this electrolysis.

Anode reaction:

$$2Cl^- \longrightarrow Cl_2(g) + 2e^-$$

Overall reaction:

$$2Cl^- + 2H_2O \xrightarrow[\text{electrolysis}]{} H_2(g) + Cl_2(g) + 2OH^-$$

As expressed by the overall reaction, during the electrolysis, the concentration of Cl^- diminishes and the concentration of OH^- increases. Since there is always Na^+ in the solution, the solution is gradually converted from aqueous NaCl to aqueous NaOH. In fact, in the commercial production of chlorine by the electrolysis of aqueous NaCl, solid NaOH is obtained as a by-product by evaporating H_2O from the residual solution left after electrolysis.

As a final example of electrolysis, we consider aqueous Na_2SO_4. With inert electrodes it is observed that H_2 gas is formed at the cathode and O_2 is formed at the anode. At the same time, the solution near the cathode becomes basic; that near the anode, acidic. Consistent with these observations are the following electrode reactions:

Cathode:

$$2e^- + 2H_2O \longrightarrow H_2(g) + 2OH^-$$

Anode:

$$2H_2O \longrightarrow O_2(g) + 4H^+ + 4e^-$$

The overall cell reaction is obtained by doubling the cathode reaction and adding to the anode reaction. The four electrons cancel, and the result is

$$6H_2O \xrightarrow[\text{electrolysis}]{} 2H_2(g) + O_2(g) + 4H^+ + 4OH^-$$

In this equation, both H^+ and OH^- appear as products. If H^+ from the anode and OH^- from the cathode are allowed to mix, then neutralization occurs and the net reaction becomes

$$2H_2O \xrightarrow[\text{electrolysis}]{} 2H_2(g) + O_2(g)$$

In this electrolysis only water disappears. The Na^+ and SO_4^{--} initially present are also present at the conclusion of the electrolysis. Is the Na_2SO_4 necessary? Because of the requirements of electrical neutrality, some kind of electrolytic solute must be present. Positive ions must be available to move into the cathode region to counterbalance the charge of the OH^- produced. Negative ions must be available to move to the anode to counterbalance the H^+ produced.

In some cases the electrodes themselves may take part in the electrode reactions. In each of the above cells the electrodes were assumed to be inert. This would almost always be the case if the electrodes were made of the inert metal platinum. If, however, the electrode material is reactive, it must be considered as a possible reactant. For example, copper anodes are frequently themselves oxidized during electrolysis when no other species present is more readily oxidized.

13.3 QUANTITATIVE ASPECTS OF ELECTROLYSIS

By experimentation, Michael Faraday, the great English chemist and physicist, established early in the nineteenth century the laws of electrolysis that bear his name. These laws state that the mass of substance produced at an electrode is proportional to the amount of electricity transferred at the electrode and to the gram-equivalent mass of the substance. Faraday's laws can be accounted for by considering the electrode reactions. For example, in the electrolysis of molten NaCl, the cathode reaction

$$Na^+(l) + e^- \longrightarrow Na(l)$$

tells that one sodium atom is produced at the electrode when one sodium ion disappears and one electron is transferred. When the Avogadro number of electrons is transferred, one mole of Na^+ disappears and one gram-atom of Na is formed. For this reaction, one gram-equivalent of Na is 22.99 g; hence, transfer of the Avogadro number of electrons liberates 22.99 g of Na. Doubling the amount of electricity transferred doubles the mass of sodium produced.

The Avogadro number of electrons is such a convenient measure of the amount of electricity that it is designated by a special name, the *faraday*. In electrical units one faraday is equal to 96500 coulombs of charge. As described in Appendix 3.7, a *coulomb* of charge is the amount of electricity that is transferred when a current of one ampere flows for one second. It is useful to remember that the current, in amperes, multiplied by the time, in seconds, is equal to the number of coulombs. The electric charge, in coulombs, divided by 96500 is equal to the number of faradays.

Electrode half-reactions expressed in ions, electrons, and atoms can be read in terms of moles and gram-atoms if the electricity is measured in faradays. Thus,

$$Na^+(l) + e^- \longrightarrow Na(l)$$

can be read either "one sodium ion reacts with one electron to form one sodium atom" or "one mole of sodium ions reacts with one faraday of electricity to form one gram-atom of sodium."

EXAMPLE 1

How many grams of chlorine can be produced by the electrolysis of molten NaCl at a current of 1.00 amp for 5.00 min?

$$1.00 \text{ amp} = 1.00 \text{ coulomb sec}^{-1}$$

$$\left(1.00 \frac{\text{coulomb}}{\text{sec}}\right)(5.00 \text{ min})\left(60 \frac{\text{sec}}{\text{min}}\right) = 300 \text{ coulombs}$$

$$\frac{300 \text{ coulombs}}{96500 \text{ coulombs faraday}^{-1}} = 0.00311 \text{ faraday}$$

Since $2Cl^-(l) \longrightarrow Cl_2(g) + 2e^-$, 0.00311 faraday produces

$$(0.00311 \text{ faraday})\left(\frac{1 \text{ mole } Cl_2}{2 \text{ faradays}}\right)\left(\frac{70.9 \text{ g } Cl_2}{\text{mole } Cl_2}\right) = 0.111 \text{ g } Cl_2$$

EXAMPLE 2

A current of 0.0965 amp is passed for 1000 sec through 50.0 ml of 0.100 M NaCl. If the only reactions are reduction of H_2O to H_2 at the cathode and oxidation of Cl^- to Cl_2 at the anode, what will be the average concentration of OH^- in the final solution?

$$\frac{(0.0965 \text{ coulomb sec}^{-1})(1000 \text{ sec})}{96500 \text{ coulombs faraday}^{-1}} = 0.00100 \text{ faraday}$$

The cathode reaction is $2e^- + 2H_2O \longrightarrow H_2(g) + 2OH^-$. Two faradays liberate two moles OH^-; 0.00100 faraday liberates 0.00100 mole OH^-. Assuming the final volume of solution is still 50.0 ml, concentration of OH^- is

$$\frac{0.00100 \text{ mole}}{0.0500 \text{ liter}} = 0.0200 \text{ } M$$

13.4 GALVANIC CELLS

In the cells discussed in the preceding section, electric energy in the form of a current was used to bring about oxidation-reduction reactions. It is also possible to do the reverse, i.e., use an oxidation-reduction reaction to produce electric current. The main requirement is that the oxidizing and reducing agents be kept separate from each other so that electron transfer must occur through a wire. Any device which accomplishes this is called a *galvanic,* or *voltaic,* cell after Luigi Galvani (1780) and Alessandro Volta (1800), who made the basic discoveries.

When a bar of zinc is dipped into a solution of copper sulfate, $CuSO_4$, copper plating is obtained. The net reaction is

$$Zn(s) + Cu^{++} \longrightarrow Zn^{++} + Cu(s)$$

In this change, Zn is oxidized and Cu^{++} is reduced, presumably by the direct transfer of electrons from zinc atoms to copper ions. To emphasize this transfer of electrons, the net reaction can be split into two half-reactions:

$$Zn(s) \longrightarrow Zn^{++} + 2e^-$$

$$Cu^{++} + 2e^- \longrightarrow Cu(s)$$

The galvanic cell operates on the principle that two separated half-reactions can be made to take place simultaneously, with the electron transfer occurring through a wire. The galvanic cell shown in Figure 13.5 uses the reaction

$$Zn(s) + Cu^{++} \longrightarrow Zn^{++} + Cu(s)$$

The dotted line represents a porous partition which separates the container into two compartments but still permits diffusion of ions between them. In the left-hand compartment is a solution of zinc sulfate, into

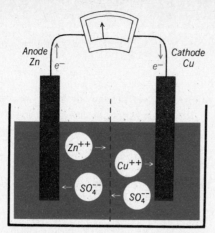

13.5
Example of a galvanic cell

which a zinc bar is dipped; in the right-hand compartment is a copper bar dipping into a solution of copper sulfate. When the two electrodes are connected by a wire, electric current flows, as shown by a meter in the circuit. As time progresses, the zinc bar is eaten away and copper plates out on the copper bar.

The cell operates as follows: At the zinc bar, oxidation occurs, making Zn the anode. The half-reaction

$$Zn(s) \longrightarrow Zn^{++} + 2e^-$$

produces Zn^{++} ions and electrons. The zinc ions migrate away from the anode into the solution, and the electrons move through the wire, as indicated in the figure. At the copper bar, reduction occurs, making Cu the cathode. The electrons come through the wire and move onto the cathode, where they are picked up and used in the reaction

$$Cu^{++} + 2e^- \longrightarrow Cu(s)$$

Copper ions in the solution are depleted, and new copper ions move into the vicinity of the cathode. The circuit is complete. Consistent with previous notation, cations (Zn^{++} and Cu^{++}) in the solution move toward the cathode (the copper bar) and anions (SO_4^{--}) move toward the anode (the zinc bar). Electrons flow through the wire, and a current is obtained from an oxidation-reduction reaction. The cell runs until either the Zn or Cu^{++} is depleted.

In describing the operation of a galvanic cell it is not necessary to specify the relative charges of the electrodes. In fact, a simple assignment of charges to the electrodes will not account for the direction of both electron and ion currents. To account for the *electron current* (from anode to cathode in the wire), the anode must be labeled *negative* with respect to the cathode. To account for the *ion current* (negative ions to the anode and positive ions to the cathode), the anode must be labeled *positive* with respect to the cathode. How can the anode be positive and negative at the same time? The discrepancy is resolved by considering the electrode in detail. For example, at the

13.4 Galvanic cells

296

anode of the above cell Zn^{++} is produced. The Zn^{++} ions form a layer which makes the anode appear positive as viewed from the solution. The electrons released in forming Zn^{++} make the anode appear negative as viewed from the wire.

Actually, to get a current from the cell, the Zn^{++} ions and the Cu bar need not be initially present. Any metal support for the plating of Cu will do in place of the Cu bar. Any positive ion that does not react with Zn metal will do in place of Zn^{++}. However, as the cell reaction proceeds, Zn^{++} is necessarily produced at the anode. Furthermore, the porous partition is necessary only to keep Cu^{++} from easily getting over to the Zn metal, where direct electron transfer would short-circuit the cell. The partition must be porous in order to allow the diffusion of positive and negative ions from one compartment to the other. Otherwise, the solution would soon become positively charged in the anode compartment (owing to accumulation of Zn^{++}) and negatively charged in the cathode compartment (owing to depletion of Cu^{++}), causing the current to cease.

In principle, any oxidation-reduction reaction is separable into two half-reactions and can be made a source of electric current as a galvanic cell. Probably the most famous example is the *lead storage battery*, or *accumulator*. The basic features are electrodes of lead, Pb, and lead dioxide, PbO_2, dipping into aqueous H_2SO_4. When the cell operates, the reactions are:

Anode:

$$Pb(s) + HSO_4^- \longrightarrow PbSO_4(s) + 2e^- + H^+$$

Cathode:

$$PbO_2(s) + HSO_4^- + 3H^+ + 2e^- \longrightarrow PbSO_4(s) + 2H_2O$$

Overall cell reaction:

$$Pb(s) + 2HSO_4^- + 2H^+ + PbO_2(s) \longrightarrow 2PbSO_4(s) + 2H_2O$$

The insoluble lead sulfate, $PbSO_4$, that is formed at each electrode adheres to the electrode. During the *charging* of a battery, the electrode reactions are reversed so as to restore the cell to its original condition. In *discharge,* as shown by the overall cell reaction, Pb and PbO_2 are depleted, and the concentration of H_2SO_4 is diminished. Since the density of the aqueous solution is chiefly dependent on the concentration of H_2SO_4, measurement of the density tells how far the cell is discharged.*

Another common galvanic cell is the Leclanché dry cell used in flashlights. The cell consists of a zinc can containing a centered graphite rod surrounded by a moist paste of manganese dioxide, MnO_2, zinc chloride, $ZnCl_2$, and ammonium chloride, NH_4Cl. The zinc can is the

* It would seem natural to say that, when the battery is discharging, the anion HSO_4^- moves to the anode. However, as is obvious from the cathode half-reaction, some of the HSO_4^- must also move to the cathode in order to form $PbSO_4$. Thus we have the unusual but not unique situation that the anion moves toward both electrodes.

anode, and the graphite rod is the cathode. At the anode, Zn is oxidized; at the cathode, MnO_2 is reduced. The electrode reactions are extremely complex and seem to vary, depending on how much current is drawn from the cell. For the delivery of very small currents, the following reactions are probable:

Anode:

$$Zn(s) \longrightarrow Zn^{++} + 2e^-$$

Cathode:

$$2MnO_2(s) + Zn^{++} + 2e^- \longrightarrow ZnMn_2O_4(s)$$

Overall cell reaction:

$$Zn(s) + 2MnO_2(s) \longrightarrow ZnMn_2O_4(s)$$

Other technologically important galvanic cells are the Edison cell, using the oxidation of Fe by Ni_2O_3 in basic medium, for which the overall reaction can be written

$$Fe(s) + Ni_2O_3(s) + 3H_2O \longrightarrow Fe(OH)_2(s) + 2Ni(OH)_2(s)$$

and the so-called "mercury battery," using the oxidation of Zn by HgO in basic medium, for which we can write

$$Zn(s) + HgO(s) \longrightarrow ZnO(s) + Hg(amalgam)$$

13.5 FUEL CELLS

In principle, any oxidation-reduction reaction can be separated into half-reactions and used to drive a galvanic cell. In particular, the reaction for the oxidation of a fuel gas such as CH_4 should be so separable. Major interest has been attracted to this possibility because the *direct* conversion of chemical energy to electric energy can be made considerably more efficient (i.e., up to 75%) than the 40% maximum now obtainable through burning the fuel and using the heat to form steam for driving turbines. For the oxidation of natural gas, we can write

$$CH_4(g) + 2O_2(g) \longrightarrow CO_2(g) + 2H_2O$$

By the methods outlined in Section 4.8, this reaction can be separated into two halves, which, for acidic solution, are

Anode:

$$CH_4(g) + 2H_2O \longrightarrow CO_2(g) + 8H^+ + 8e^-$$

Cathode:

$$O_2(g) + 4H^+ + 4e^- \longrightarrow 2H_2O$$

In practice, the reaction is better utilized in basic medium where the product CO_2 exists as carbonate ion, CO_3^{--}. For basic media, the corresponding half-reactions are:

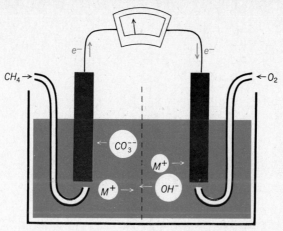

13.6
Schematic representation
of a fuel cell

Anode:

$$CH_4(g) + 10\ OH^- \longrightarrow CO_3^{--} + 7H_2O + 8e^-$$

Cathode:

$$O_2(g) + 2H_2O + 4e^- \longrightarrow 4OH^-$$

The detailed construction of a workable cell has proved to be a challenging engineering task involving such tricks as using molten K_2CO_3
as a high-temperature electrolyte medium. However, the basic design
principles must be the same for this as for any galvanic cell, viz., two
electrode compartments each containing all reactants called for by the
respective half-reaction. In the present case two of the reactants are
gases and must be bubbled in as shown schematically in Figure 13.6.
In order to make electrical contact with the reactant gases, conducting
but otherwise inert electrodes are suspended in the cell in the bubble
streams. The porous partition indicates that ion migration between
compartments must be permitted but the reactant gases must be kept
separated.

The first really workable fuel cell made use of the reaction

$$2H_2(g) + O_2(g) \longrightarrow 2H_2O$$

for which the half-reactions in basic solution are:

Anode:

$$H_2(g) + 2OH^- \longrightarrow 2H_2O + 2e^-$$

Cathode:

$$O_2(g) + 2H_2O + 4e^- \longrightarrow 4OH^-$$

Figure 13.7 shows one design which has been used successfully. Two
chambers constructed of porous carbon dip into an aqueous solution of
KOH. Hydrogen gas is flowed into one chamber while oxygen gas is simultaneously introduced in the other. Because H_2 and O_2 each react

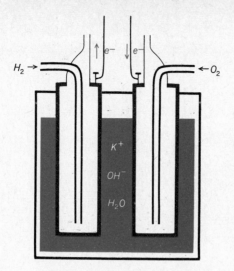

very slowly at room temperature, suitable catalysts must be used to accelerate the electrode reactions. These catalysts are mixed in and pressed with the carbon. At the anode, suitable catalysts are finely divided platinum or palladium; at the cathode, cobaltous oxide (CoO), platinum, or silver.

13.6 OXIDATION POTENTIALS

A voltmeter connected between the two electrodes of a galvanic cell shows a characteristic voltage which depends in magnitude on what reactants take part in the electrode reactions and on what their concentrations are. For example, in the Zn-Cu cell, if Zn^{++} and Cu^{++} are at 1 m concentrations and the temperature is 25°C, the voltage measured between the Zn electrode and the Cu electrode is 1.10 volts, no matter how big the cell or how big the electrodes. This voltage is characteristic of the reaction

$$Zn(s) + Cu^{++} \longrightarrow Zn^{++} + Cu(s)$$

The voltage measures the force with which electrons are moved around the circuit and therefore measures the tendency of this reaction to take place. Thus, galvanic cells give a quantitative measure of the relative tendency of various oxidation-reduction reactions to occur.

Figure 13.8 shows on the left a galvanic cell set up to study the reaction

$$Zn(s) + 2H^+ \longrightarrow H_2(g) + Zn^{++}$$

In the anode compartment a zinc bar dips into a solution of a zinc salt. In the cathode compartment H_2 gas is led in through a tube so as to bubble over an inert electrode, made, for example, of Pt, dipped into an acidic solution. The anode reaction is

$$Zn(s) \longrightarrow Zn^{++} + 2e^-$$

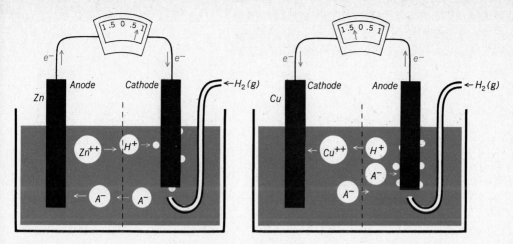

13.8
Comparison of zinc and
copper electrodes vs. the
hydrogen electrode

The cathode reaction is

$$2H^+ + 2e^- \longrightarrow H_2(g)$$

When the concentrations of H^+ and of Zn^{++} are 1 m and when
the pressure of the H_2 gas is 1 atm, the voltmeter reads 0.76 volt (at
25°C) and the deflection is in such direction as to indicate that Zn has
a greater tendency to give off electrons than H_2 has. In other words,
the half-reaction $Zn(s) \longrightarrow Zn^{++} + 2e^-$ has a greater tendency to occur than $H_2(g) \longrightarrow 2H^+ + 2e^-$ by 0.76 volt.

The galvanic cell on the right in Figure 13.8 makes use of the
reaction

$$H_2(g) + Cu^{++} \longrightarrow 2H^+ + Cu(s)$$

The anode reaction is

$$H_2(g) \longrightarrow 2H^+ + 2e^-$$

and the cathode reaction is

$$Cu^{++} + 2e^- \longrightarrow Cu(s)$$

When the concentrations of H^+ and Cu^{++} are 1 m and when the pressure of H_2 is 1 atm, the voltmeter reads 0.34 volt (at 25°C) and the deflection direction indicates that H_2 has a greater tendency to give off
electrons than Cu has. In other words, the half-reaction $H_2(g) \longrightarrow$
$2H^+ + 2e^-$ has a greater tendency to occur than $Cu(s) \longrightarrow Cu^{++} +$
$2e^-$ by 0.34 volt.

In all cells the voltage observed arises from two sources: a voltage at
the anode and a voltage at the cathode. If either of these voltages were
known, the other could be obtained by subtraction. However, it is impossible to measure the voltage of an individual electrode, since any
complete circuit necessarily contains two electrodes. We are forced to
assign a completely arbitrary voltage to one electrode. The voltage of
the other electrode is thereby fixed. For convenience, the voltage of
the standard hydrogen electrode (at 25°C, 1 atm H_2 pressure, and 1 m

Electrochemistry

301

Half-reaction	Oxidation potential, volts
$Li(s) \longrightarrow Li^+ + e^-$	$+3.05$
$Na(s) \longrightarrow Na^+ + e^-$	$+2.71$
$Mg(s) \longrightarrow Mg^{++} + 2e^-$	$+2.37$
$Al(s) \longrightarrow Al^{+3} + 3e^-$	$+1.66$
$Zn(s) \longrightarrow Zn^{++} + 2e^-$	$+0.76$
$Fe(s) \longrightarrow Fe^{++} + 2e^-$	$+0.44$
$H_2(g) \longrightarrow 2H^+ + 2e^-$	0
$Cu(s) \longrightarrow Cu^{++} + 2e^-$	-0.34
$2I^- \longrightarrow I_2 + 2e^-$	-0.54
$Ag(s) \longrightarrow Ag^+ + e^-$	-0.80
$2Br^- \longrightarrow Br_2 + 2e^-$	-1.09
$2H_2O \longrightarrow O_2(g) + 4H^+ + 4e^-$	-1.23
$2Cl^- \longrightarrow Cl_2(g) + 2e^-$	-1.36
$2F^- \longrightarrow F_2(g) + 2e^-$	-2.87

13.9
Some half-reactions and
their oxidation potentials

H^+ concentration) is given the value zero. Consequently, in any cell which contains the hydrogen electrode, the entire measured voltage is attributed to the half-reaction at the other electrode. Voltages thus assigned are called *oxidation potentials*.

Figure 13.9 lists various half-reactions with their oxidation potentials. A more extensive listing is given in Appendix 6. The value given applies for the half-reaction in the forward direction. For the reverse direction, the sign must be changed.

The forward reaction is an oxidation in which the reducing agent, shown on the left, is oxidized. The table is so arranged that the reducing agents are listed in order of decreasing strength. In other words, there is decreasing tendency of the forward half-reaction to occur from the top of the table to the bottom. For example, of the list given, lithium, Li, is the best reducing agent, since it has the highest tendency to give off electrons. Fluoride ion, F^-, is the worst reducing agent and has the least tendency to give off electrons. Such a list of reducing agents arranged in decreasing order is sometimes called the *electromotive force* or *emf series*.

The numerical values of the oxidation potentials given in Figure 13.9 apply to aqueous solutions at 25°C in which the concentration or, more exactly, the activity of dissolved species is 1 m. A positive value of the oxidation potential indicates that the reducing agent is stronger than H_2; a negative value indicates that the reducing agent is weaker than H_2.* The magnitude of the potential is a quantitative measure of the relative tendency of the half-reaction to occur from left to right. (It should be noted that nothing is implied about whether the reaction is *fast* enough to be observed.)

13.6 Oxidation potentials

* This assignment of "positive" and "negative" is arbitrary and could perhaps be better chosen in the opposite sense. In fact, most of the world outside America does use the opposite convention. *Gustibus fructibus.*

Each reducing agent in Figure 13.9 is coupled in its half-reaction with its oxidized form. For example, Cu is coupled with Cu^{++}. The oxidized form is capable of acting as an oxidizing agent when the half-reaction is reversed by some means. Thus, the oxidation potentials in Figure 13.9 also give information about the relative tendency of oxidizing agents to pick up electrons. If a half-reaction, such as the one at the top of the table, has great tendency to go to the right, it is hard to reverse, and the oxidizing agent is a poor one. Of the oxidizing agents listed, Li^+ is the poorest and fluorine, F_2, is the best. The half-reaction

$$e^- + Li^+ \longrightarrow Li(s) \qquad -3.05 \text{ volts}$$

has smaller tendency to occur than

$$2e^- + F_2(g) \longrightarrow 2F^- \qquad +2.87 \text{ volts}$$

Figure 13.9 lists oxidizing agents (on the right) in order of increasing strength.

The potential of a half-reaction is a measure of the tendency of the half-reaction to occur. This potential is independent of the other half of the complete reaction. The potential of any complete reaction can be obtained by addition of the potentials of its two half-reactions. The potential so obtained gives the tendency of the complete reaction to occur and gives the voltage measured for a galvanic cell which uses the reaction. For example, in the Zn-Cu cell:

Anode:

$$Zn(s) \longrightarrow Zn^{++} + 2e^- \qquad\qquad +0.76 \text{ volt}$$

Cathode:

$$2e^- + Cu^{++} \longrightarrow Cu(s) \qquad\qquad + 0.34 \text{ volt}$$

Complete cell: _____

$$Zn(s) + Cu^{++} \longrightarrow Zn^{++} + Cu(s) \qquad +1.10 \text{ volts}$$

The voltage, $+1.10$, so calculated is that observed for the cell. It is positive, which indicates that the reaction tends to go spontaneously as written. It should be noted that the value 1.10 volts applies when the concentrations of the ions are $1\ m$, since oxidation potentials are defined for concentrations of $1\ m$.

Any oxidation-reduction reaction for which the potential is positive has the tendency to take place as written. Whether a given reaction should take place spontaneously can be determined from the relative positions of its two half-reactions in a table of oxidation potentials; e.g., in Figure 13.9, any reducing agent reacts with any oxidizing agent below it. Zn reduces Fe^{++}, H^+, Cu^{++}, etc., but does not reduce Al^{+3}, Mg^{++}, Na^+, etc. Similarly, any oxidizing agent reacts with any reducing agent above it. I_2 oxidizes Cu, H_2, Fe, etc., but does not oxidize Br^-, H_2O, Cl^-, etc.

EXAMPLE 3

I_2 and Br_2 are added to a solution containing I^- and Br^-. What reaction would occur if the concentration of each species were 1 m?

The half-reactions to be considered are

$$2I^- \longrightarrow I_2 + 2e^- \qquad -0.54 \text{ volt}$$

$$2Br^- \longrightarrow Br_2 + 2e^- \qquad -1.09 \text{ volts}$$

Method a:

From the positions in Figure 13.9, I^- can reduce Br_2, whereas Br^- cannot reduce I_2. Therefore, the reaction is predicted to be

$$2I^- + Br_2 \longrightarrow I_2 + 2Br^-$$

Method b:

$$
\begin{array}{ll}
2I^- \longrightarrow I_2 + 2e^- & -0.54 \text{ volt} \\
2e^- + Br_2 \longrightarrow 2Br^- & +1.09 \text{ volts} \\
\hline
2I + Br_2 \longrightarrow I_2 + 2Br^- & +0.55 \text{ volt}
\end{array}
$$

Reaction should occur as written, since its voltage is positive.

$$
\begin{array}{ll}
2Br^- \longrightarrow Br_2 + 2e^- & -1.09 \text{ volts} \\
2e^- + I_2 \longrightarrow 2I^- & +0.54 \text{ volt} \\
\hline
2Br^- + I_2 \longrightarrow Br_2 + 2I^- & -0.55 \text{ volt}
\end{array}
$$

Therefore, this reaction should not occur spontaneously as written.

Further consideration of oxidation potentials and how to combine them is given in Section 18.1

13.7 NERNST EQUATION

The inherent tendency for a chemical reaction or half-reaction to occur depends not only on the chemical nature of the reactants but also upon their concentrations. The oxidation potentials just discussed are *standard emf's* and as such describe the chemical nature of reactants at fixed unit concentration (more precisely, unit activity). What happens to reaction tendencies when concentrations are changed? Qualitatively, the principle of Le Chatelier predicts that increasing a reactant concentration favors its tendency to react and decreasing a reactant concentration diminishes its tendency to react. Similarly, decreasing the concentration of a product favors the tendency toward formation of that product and increasing the concentration of a product decreases the tendency to form that product.

Quantitatively, the change of reaction tendency is given by the Nernst equation as worked out by the German thermodynamicist, Walter Nernst. The equation relates E, the emf for a reaction or half-reaction, to $E°$, the standard emf for that reaction or half-reaction at unit activities. The Nernst equation for 25°C is

$$E = E° - \frac{0.0591}{n} \log Q$$

where n is the number of electrons transferred in the reaction and Q is the mass-action expression for the reaction. In writing Q, concentrations of gases are given in atmospheres of pressure, and, for half-reactions, electrons are omitted from the expression. As a specific example, we consider the half-reaction

$$H_2(g) \longrightarrow 2H^+ + 2e^-$$

for which the Nernst equation is

$$E = E° - \frac{0.0591}{2} \log \frac{[H^+]^2}{p_{H_2}}$$

For this half-reaction the standard emf $E°$ is zero, and therefore

$$E = 0.00 - 0.0296 \log \frac{[H^+]^2}{p_{H_2}}$$

Under standard conditions (hydrogen pressure equal to one atmosphere and hydrogen-ion activity at unity), the mass-action term $[H^+]^2/p_{H_2}$ is unity, the log of it is zero, and $E = 0.00$ volt. As a further illustration, in pure water the hydrogen-ion concentration is 1.0×10^{-7} M. In such a dilute solution the molarity equals the molality, and for dilute solutions this is a good measure of activity. Substituting $p_{H_2} = 1$ and $[H^+] = 1.0 \times 10^{-7}$, we get for the emf of the hydrogen electrode in pure water

$$E = 0.00 - 0.0296 \log \frac{(1.0 \times 10^{-7})^2}{1.0} = 0.41 \text{ volt}$$

As a more complex example, we consider the complete reaction:

$$2I^- + H_3AsO_4 + 2H^+ \longrightarrow I_2(s) + H_3AsO_3 + H_2O$$

For this reaction the Nernst equation is

$$E = E° - \frac{0.0591}{n} \log \frac{[I_2(s)][H_3AsO_3][H_2O]}{[I^-]^2[H_3AsO_4][H^+]^2}$$

$E°$ has the value $+0.02$ volt (as can be calculated by taking the difference between $E° = -0.54$ volt for $2I^- \longrightarrow I_2(s) + 2e^-$ and $E° = -0.56$ volt for $H_3AsO_3 + H_2O \longrightarrow H_3AsO_4 + 2H^+ + 2e^-$ from Appendix 6). For the overall reaction, two electrons are transferred from $2I^-$ to H_3AsO_4, so $n = 2$. In general, the activity of pure substances is unity, so that both $I_2(s)$ and H_2O can be omitted from the expression, which now becomes

$$E = 0.02 - 0.0296 \log \frac{[H_3AsO_3]}{[I^-]^2[H_3AsO_4][H^+]^2}$$

Under standard conditions of concentration, the mass-action fraction is unity. Its log is zero, and the emf is slightly positive, thus being favorable for the reaction in the direction written. However, if the pH of the solution is raised, as by addition of base, the lowered value of $[H^+]$ can make the E change sign. For example, in neutral solution with $[H^+] = 1.0 \times 10^{-7}$ and assuming all other species at unit activity, we get

$$E = 0.02 - 0.0296 \log \frac{1}{(1.0 \times 10^{-7})^2} = -0.39 \text{ volt}$$

The negative value for E indicates the reaction as written should not occur, but instead the reverse reaction should take place.

QUESTIONS

13.1 Conductivity   Aqueous salt solutions conduct alternating current with no apparent chemical change at the electrodes. Explain.

13.2 Electrolysis   In the electrolysis of aqueous NaOH, O_2 is produced at one electrode and H_2 at the other. Diagram a cell for this electrolysis, showing clearly the directions of migration of electrons, cations, and anions. Write the electrode reactions.

13.3 Galvanic cell   Design a cell that makes use of the reaction $Zn(s) + Br_2 \longrightarrow Zn^{++} + 2Br^-$. Label the anode and cathode and indicate direction of electron and ion flow.

13.4 Electrolysis   Quite often, the amount of charge passed is determined by measuring the mass of $Ag(s)$ deposited by electrolysis of Ag^+ solution. If such a cathode increases in mass by 0.287 g, how many coulombs have been transferred?

13.5 Electrolysis   Under suitable conditions electrolysis of an aqueous $CuSO_4$ solution will convert it into a solution of H_2SO_4. Write electrode reactions to show how this comes about.

13.6 Fuel cell   Write electrode reactions for fuel cells using the oxidation of propane, C_3H_8, by air in (*a*) acidic medium (to give CO_2) and (*b*) basic medium (to give CO_3^{--}).

13.7 Nernst equation   What pressure of H_2 would be required to make the emf of the hydrogen electrode be zero in pure water?

13.8 Electrolysis   In a given electrolysis of aqueous $CuSO_4$, the cathode shows in 10 min a mass increase of 0.287 g due to deposition of copper. What is the average current through the solution?

13.9 Electrolysis   Lake Cayuga has a volume of water estimated to be 8.2×10^{12} liters. A power station not so far above Cayuga's waters produces electricity at the rate of 1.5×10^6 coulomb sec^{-1} at an appropriate voltage. How long would it take to electrolyze Lake Cayuga?

13.10 Electrolysis   Aluminum is generally produced by the electrolysis of melts containing Al_2O_3 in various fluorides. Taking 6.4×10^6 tons as the average annual world production of Al, calculate the average current required, assuming round-the-clock operation.

13.11 Conductivity   Compare the effect of increasing temperature on the electrical resistance (i.e., reciprocal of the conductivity) of a metal, a semiconductor (Section 6.7), and an electrolytic solution. Account for the difference.

13.12 Electrolysis In the electrolysis of aqueous Na_2SO_4 it is found by careful measurement that the ratio of $H_2(g)$ to $O_2(g)$ formed is slightly greater than 2, probably owing to some formation of H_2O_2. Yet when the solution is thoroughly mixed, the pH is found to be the same as at the start of the electrolysis. Show by writing electrode reactions that these observations are not inconsistent.

13.13 Electrolysis Chrome-plating can be accomplished by electrolyzing an acidic aqueous solution of $Na_2Cr_2O_7$. Assuming O_2 formation at the anode, diagram a suitable cell, write appropriate electrode reactions, and indicate direction of migration of each ion. What will be the overall reaction?

13.14 Galvanic cell Suppose you have an Edison cell that contains 248 g of Fe and 604 g of Ni_2O_3. How long could this cell deliver a current of 1.00 amp?

13.15 Nernst equation At what relative concentrations of Zn^{++} and Fe^{++} will $Zn(s)$ and $Fe(s)$ have equal oxidation potentials?

13.16 Oxidation potentials Given for acid solutions that UO_2^{++} going to UO_2^+ will oxidize V^{++} to V^{+3} but will not oxidize Sn^{++} to Sn^{+4}, that Sn^{+4} going to Sn^{++} will not oxidize $S_4O_6^{--}$ to H_2SO_3, and that V^{+3} going to VO^{++} will reduce H_2SO_3 to $S_4O_6^{--}$ but will not reduce Sn^{+4} to Sn^{++}. Write five balanced half-reactions and arrange them in order of decreasing oxidation potential.

13.17 Oxidation potentials (a) Write half-reactions in acid solution for the conversion of Mn^{++} to Mn^{+3} and for Mn^{+3} to $MnO_2(s)$. The $E°$ values are -1.51 volts and -0.95 volt, respectively. (b) Show that Mn^{+3} should disproportionate, i.e., oxidize and reduce itself. (c) Write half-reactions in acid solution for the conversion of $MnO_2(s)$ to MnO_4^- and for Mn^{++} to $MnO_2(s)$. The $E°$ values are -1.70 and -1.23 volts respectively. Decide whether $MnO_2(s)$ should disproportionate.

13.18 Electrolysis Given 50.0 ml of 0.10 M NaCl. How long must a current of 0.500 amp be passed in order to make a solution of pH $=$ 12.00, assuming no volume change and reactions as given in Section 13.2?

13.19 Galvanic cells (a) Referring to Figure 13.9, design a galvanic cell that gives the maximum standard emf without the possibility of oxidizing or reducing water. (b) Show whether the emf of the cell should change as the pH is altered.

13.20 Galvanic cells Given a lead storage battery containing originally equal masses of Pb and PbO_2. If the cells are run down until completely discharged, what will be the ratio of the final masses of anode to cathode, assuming solid discharge products stick on the electrodes?

13.21 Conductivity In a dilute nitric acid solution 80% of the current would be carried by H^+ moving one way and 20% by NO_3^- moving the other way. For a particular experiment in which a 0.10 M HNO_3 solution in a tube of 1-cm² cross section is carrying 0.010 amp, what is the average velocity of the H⁺ ions?

13.22 Electrolysis   Given 50.0 ml of 0.100 M CuSO$_4$ which is electrolyzed for 12.0 min at a current of 0.0600 amp. If Cu is produced at one electrode and O$_2$ at the other, what will be the pH of the final solution? For HSO$_4^-$ $\rightleftharpoons$ H⁺ + SO$_4^{--}$, K_{diss} is 1.3×10^{-2}.

ANSWERS

13.4 257 coulombs   *13.7* 1×10^{-14} atm   *13.9* 1.9 million years
13.14 8.16 days   *13.18* 97 sec   *13.21* 8.3×10^{-4} cm sec⁻¹
13.22 2.95

14 chemical thermodynamics

At several points in preceding chapters we have found it necessary to introduce concepts of energy, enthalpy, entropy, etc. in order to gain some insight into the fundamental concepts underlying observed phenomena. Such discussions of energy, entropy, and related functions comprise the broad field of thermodynamics, which by its sweeping generalizations unifies all the sciences into a single magnificent structure. Unfortunately, the field of thermodynamics is necessarily abstract, and a reasonable appreciation of it can come only after the accumulation of considerable background information. In this chapter, we can at best only begin to lay a foundation for further study in this field.

14.1 SYSTEMS AND FUNCTIONS

In thermodynamics the term *system* is used to delineate that region of the physical world that is being considered. This might be, for example, one mole of CO_2 gas in a sealed container, a liter of 0.10 M $CuSO_4$ solution, or a particular crystal of sodium chloride containing calcium chloride impurity. In general, we shall need to be concerned with the relationship of the system to its surroundings. For example, there might be heat flow from the surroundings to the system, or vice versa, in order to keep the system at a fixed temperature. Such a system is referred to as an *isothermal* system. Another possibility would be to have complete insulation of the system from its surroundings; such an isolated system is called *adiabatic*.

To describe a system completely, we must specify values for a number of variables. In chemistry the most frequently used variables are temperature, pressure, volume, and chemical composition. The major concern of thermodynamics is with those properties of a system which depend only on the present state of the system and not on its past history. This means that a thermodynamic property, such as the internal energy, of a system is completely determined once the temperature, pressure, volume, and composition are specified. The internal energy does not depend on the path whereby the system reached its present condition. (As an example of a nonthermodynamic property—one that depends on past history—we might mention the mechanical strength of crystals, where strains may be introduced and persist to different extents depending on the treatment.)

Because a thermodynamic property depends only on the state of the system, changes in thermodynamic properties are independent of how the system is taken from state 1 to state 2. For example, suppose one mole of O_2 gas is taken from the state in which it occupies 100 liters at 273°K and 0.224 atm to the state in which it occupies 100 liters at 546°K and 0.448 atm. The thermodynamic properties, such as energy, entropy, heat content, and free energy, change from the initial state to the final state by amounts that do not depend on whether the gas is first heated and then expanded or first expanded and then heated. Thus, if the energy of the initial state is designated E_1 and the energy of the final state E_2, the increase in energy $E_2 - E_1$, designated by ΔE, is independent of the path. It might be noted that for any thermodynamic property X, ΔX means the X of the final state minus the X of the initial state—in other words, ΔX is always the increase in X in going from initial to final state. If in this process X should happen to decrease, ΔX will, of course, have a negative value.

14.2 FIRST LAW

14.2 First law

Two laws form the basis of thermodynamics. The first of these, and by far the simpler, is equivalent to the law of conservation of energy. It states that for any system considered the increase in energy, ΔE, is equal to the heat *absorbed by* the system, q, minus the work *performed by* the system, w:

$$\Delta E = q - w$$

Since ΔE is an energy change, both q (heat) and w (work) must be in energy units. The major difficulty students have in understanding the first law is in keeping straight the sign convention used for q and w. When q is positive, heat is absorbed by the system and the energy of the system increases; when w is positive, the system is doing work on its surroundings and the energy of the system decreases. In other words, q and w act in opposition so far as the ΔE of the system is concerned. We might also note that $\Delta E = 0$ for any system completely isolated from its surroundings (i.e., heat cannot flow into or out of the system, no work can be done by the system on its surroundings, and no work can be done by the surroundings on the system). $\Delta E = 0$ means the energy of the system is constant and does not change.

Examples of heat energy q are discussed in the following sections. Before considering them we might mention some examples of w. Suppose a gas sample trapped in a cylinder with a sliding piston expands from initial volume V_1 to final volume V_2 against a constant atmospheric pressure P. The work the gas sample does against the surrounding atmosphere is $P(V_2 - V_1) = P\Delta V$. As a second example, suppose a lead storage battery is so connected as to drive an electric motor. The work done by the battery is equal to its voltage times the total charge conducted, where the total charge is simply current multiplied by the elapsed time.

14.3 HEAT CONTENT AND HEAT CAPACITY

In chemistry most experiments are conducted at constant pressure (e.g., at atmospheric pressure). If there is a volume change ΔV of the system, then associated with this ΔV there will be work done by the system equal to $P\Delta V$. To take account simultaneously of energy change in the system and accompanying work done by the system on its surroundings, there is a thermodynamic property called the *enthalpy*, designated by H. In general, $H = E + PV$ and $\Delta H = \Delta E + \Delta(PV)$. The latter equation states that the increase in enthalpy of a system is equal to its increase in energy plus its increase in the PV product. At constant pressure, to which we shall henceforth restrict our attention, $\Delta(PV)$ is just $P\Delta V$, which is the amount of work done on constant-pressure surroundings by a volume change ΔV. Thus, at constant pressure

$$\Delta H = \Delta E + P\Delta V$$

or, rearranging,

$$\Delta E = \Delta H - P\Delta V$$

Comparison of this last relation with the first law, $\Delta E = q - w$, shows that if the only work done is $P\Delta V$ work, then, *at constant pressure*, $\Delta H = q$. In other words, the enthalpy increase ΔH is equal to the heat absorbed by the system at constant pressure. For this reason H is sometimes referred to as the *heat content* of the system. Another way to summarize the above relations is to say that if heat is added to a system at constant pressure, part of the heat is used to increase the internal energy of the system and the rest is used to do work on the surroundings.

EXAMPLE 1

For the decomposition $CaCO_3(s) \longrightarrow CaO(s) + CO_2(g)$ at 950°C and a carbon dioxide pressure of 1 atm, the ΔH is 42 kcal mole^{-1}. Assuming that the volume of the solid phase changes by an amount small compared to the volume of the gas, calculate the ΔE for the process at one atmosphere.

$$\Delta E = \Delta H - P\Delta V$$

$$\Delta V = V_{\text{products}} - V_{\text{reactants}} \cong V_{\text{gas}}$$

$$= \frac{n_{\text{gas}}RT}{P}$$

$$P\Delta V = n_{\text{gas}}RT = (1.00 \text{ mole})\left(1.99 \frac{\text{cal}}{\text{mole deg}}\right)(1223 \text{ deg})$$

$$= 2.4 \text{ kcal}$$

$$\Delta E = 42 \text{ kcal} - 2.4 \text{ kcal} = 40 \text{ kcal}$$

In words, the preceding example states that if to a mole of $CaCO_3(s)$ at 950°C and 1 atm of pressure 42 kcal of heat is added, then 40 kcal goes into the chemical energy of decomposition and 2.4 kcal is used to do expansion work against the atmosphere. In those reactions in which gases are not involved or in which the number of moles of gas does not change, the $P\Delta V$ work will be so small as to be negligible; consequently, in such reactions practically all the heat added goes to chemical energy. This last statement is equivalent to saying $\Delta E \cong \Delta H$, as was shown in Example 5 of Section 7.9.

Thus far we have considered what happens to the heat content (enthalpy) of a system if the system is kept at constant temperature and pressure while a chemical reaction occurs. What happens if the temperature is allowed to change? Obviously, added heat may then be used to "heat up" the system to a higher temperature. To describe this "heating up" process quantitatively, we use the concept of *heat capacity,* which is defined as the amount of heat required to raise the temperature of a mole of material by one degree. Throughout our discussion we shall restrict ourselves to the heat capacity at constant pressure, usually designated by C_p. The values of C_p are found to be dependent on the chemical identity of the material, its state (whether gaseous, liquid, or solid), and its temperature. Typical values are listed in Figure 14.1. For most substances, the liquid state has the highest heat capacity, then the solid, then the gas. Finally, we should note that the

$H_2O(s)$ at $-34°C$	7.96	$SO_2(s)$ at $-75°C$	16.5
$H_2O(s)$ at $-2.2°C$	9.03	$Zn(s)$ at $420°C$	7.1
$H_2O(l)$ at $0°C$	18.13	$Zn(l)$ at $727°C$	7.5
$H_2O(l)$ at $25°C$	17.98	$SO_2(l)$ at $-3°C$	20.7
$H_2O(l)$ at $100°C$	18.14	$Hg(l)$ at $227°C$	6.6
$H_2O(g)$ at $110°C$	8.67	$Xe(g)$ at $-108°C$	5.0

14.1
Heat capacity at 1 atm,
cal mole^{-1} deg^{-1}

heat capacity can also be given per gram instead of per mole, in which case it is sometimes called *specific heat.**

For simplicity, we consider a mole of a single substance. What happens if its temperature increases from T_1 to T_2, where ΔT is small enough that the heat capacity C_p is the same at T_2 as at T_1? The amount of heat absorbed by the substance is equal to $C_p \Delta T$. This heat goes to raise the heat content H of the material by an amount ΔH. Hence, we can write

$$\Delta H = C_p \Delta T$$

For example, to take one mole of H_2O from 20 to 30°C requires that (18.0 cal mole^{-1} deg^{-1})(10 deg), or 180 cal, be added to the heat content of H_2O, that is, $\Delta H = 180$ cal. If C_p changes with temperature, then it is necessary to take this into account by the methods of integral calculus

$$\Delta H = \int_{T_1}^{T_2} C_p \, dT$$

For mixtures of substances the total ΔH is calculated as the sum of the individual components.

Finally, if a phase change occurs somewhere in the interval between T_1 and T_2, then it is necessary to take into account the change in heat content associated with the phase change as well as the difference in heat capacity between the two phases.

EXAMPLE 2

By using data from Figure 14.1, calculate the increase of enthalpy for 100 g of H_2O going from ice at $-10°C$ to liquid water at $+15°C$. The molar heat of fusion of ice is 1.44 kcal.

* There is a mild problem here for those who like to worry about such things. Some handbooks give specific heat in calories per gram; others give no units, arguing that specific heat was originally defined as a comparison with water, i.e., as a ratio of the heat capacity per gram of substance divided by the heat capacity per gram of H_2O. Because the heat capacity per gram of H_2O is very close to 1 cal deg^{-1}, dividing by this quantity does not change the numerical value but does get rid of the units. The problem is the same as that encountered in the distinction between density and specific gravity. Density is grams per cubic centimeter; specific gravity has no units, being a ratio of the density of the material to the density of water. Since the density of H_2O is very close to unity, dividing by 1 g cc^{-1} only gets rid of the units. In spite of all this, most practicing chemists use the term specific heat as if it had the units of calories per gram. *Facilis descensus Averno.*

$$\frac{100 \text{ g}}{18.0 \text{ g mole}^{-1}} = 5.55 \text{ mole } H_2O$$

To heat ice

$$(5.55 \text{ mole})\left(9.03 \frac{\text{cal}}{\text{mole deg}}\right)(10 \text{ deg}) = 500 \text{ cal}$$

To melt ice

$$(5.55 \text{ mole})\left(1440 \frac{\text{cal}}{\text{mole}}\right) = 7990 \text{ cal}$$

To heat liquid

$$(5.55 \text{ mole})\left(18.1 \frac{\text{cal}}{\text{mole deg}}\right)(15 \text{ deg}) = 1500 \text{ cal}$$

$$\Delta H = 500 \text{ cal} + 7990 \text{ cal} + 1500 \text{ cal} = 9990 \text{ cal}$$

14.4 HEAT OF REACTION

In general, when a chemical reaction occurs, heat is either evolved to or absorbed from the surroundings, so that the heat content of the system changes. As a specific example we consider the reaction between hydrogen and oxygen to form water. The initial state consists of one mole of $H_2(g)$ and half a mole of $O_2(g)$ at one atmosphere pressure and 25°C; the final state, one mole of $H_2O(l)$ at one atmosphere pressure and 25°C. The change can be written

$$H_2(g) + \frac{1}{2}O_2(g) \longrightarrow H_2O(l)$$

If the pressure is to remain constant at one atmosphere, then clearly the volume must be allowed to shrink. This can be accomplished experimentally through use of a reaction chamber consisting of a cylinder fitted with a sliding piston. If the temperature is to remain constant, despite the fact that heat is liberated in this reaction, then a thermostatted constant-temperature bath in which the reaction chamber is immersed must be provided. Both the pressure and the temperature need to be fixed, since the heat content of a material depends on its pressure and temperature. By convention, most data are quoted for one atmosphere and 25°C, these conditions being used to define the so-called *standard state*. When the above reaction so occurs that H_2 and O_2 in their standard states change to H_2O in its standard state, 68 kcal of heat is liberated to the surrounding bath per mole of H_2O formed. Clearly, the chemical system (initially H_2 and O_2, finally H_2O) has decreased in heat content by 68 kcal. Recalling that ΔH is the heat content of the final system minus the heat content of the initial system, we can write for this reaction

$$\Delta H = -68 \text{ kcal mole}^{-1}$$

In general, for all exothermic reactions (heat liberated), ΔH is negative; for all endothermic reactions (heat absorbed), ΔH is positive.

In the preceding example the -68 kcal mole^{-1} may be referred to

Compound	ΔH	Compound	ΔH	Compound	ΔH
$H_2O(l)$	-68.4	$LiF(s)$	-146.3	$H_2SO_4(aq)$	-216.9
$H_2O(g)$	-57.8	$NaF(s)$	-136.0	$HNO_3(l)$	-41.4
$H_2O_2(l)$	-44.8	$NaCl(s)$	-98.2	$HNO_3(aq)$	-49.4
$HF(g)$	-64.2	$NaBr(s)$	-86.0	$H_3PO_4(aq)$	-308.2
$HCl(g)$	-22.1	$NaI(s)$	-68.8	$H_3PO_3(aq)$	-232.2
$HBr(g)$	-8.7	$CaO(s)$	-151.9	$CaCO_3(s)$	-288.5
$HI(g)$	$+6.2$	$BaO(s)$	-133.4	$BaCO_3(s)$	-291.3
$H_2S(g)$	-4.8	$Al_2O_3(s)$	-399.1	$Na_2SO_4(s)$	-330.9
$NH_3(g)$	-11.0	$Cr_2O_3(s)$	-269.7	$NaHSO_4(s)$	-269.2
$CH_4(g)$	-17.9	$CO(g)$	-26.4	$NaOH(s)$	-102.0
$C_2H_6(g)$	-20.2	$CO_2(g)$	-94.1	$Ca(OH)_2(s)$	-235.8
$C_2H_4(g)$	$+12.5$	$SiO_2(s)$	-205.4	$CaSO_4(s)$	-342.4
$C_2H_2(g)$	$+54.2$	$SO_3(g)$	-94.5	$CaSO_4 \cdot 2H_2O(s)$	-483.1

14.2
Heats of formation,
kcal mole^{-1}, at
298°K, 1 atm

as the heat of formation of liquid H_2O from the elements in their standard states. Figure 14.2 gives representative values for the heats of formation of several common compounds. Italicized abbreviations in parentheses indicate the state of the substance. When the abbreviation is *aq*, the state is an extremely dilute aqueous solution.

Once the heats of formation from the elements are known, it is possible to calculate the heats of various reactions. For instance, at 298°K and 1 atm the heat of reaction for

$$CaO(s) + CO_2(g) \longrightarrow CaCO_3(s)$$

is found as follows:

$$\Delta H_{reaction} = \Delta H_{CaCO_3} - \Delta H_{CaO} - \Delta H_{CO_2} = -42.5 \text{ kcal mole}^{-1}$$

The justification for this procedure is that ΔH_{CaCO_3}, which represents the heat of formation of $CaCO_3(s)$, gives the heat content of $CaCO_3$ relative to the elements $Ca(s)$, $C(s)$, and $O_2(g)$. Similarly, ΔH_{CO_2} and ΔH_{CaO} give the heat contents of these compounds relative to the elements. The change in heat content between the elements as CaO plus CO_2 and as $CaCO_3$ is simply the heat of reaction. The procedure can also be justified through use of *Hess's law*, which states that *the heat of reaction is the same whether the reaction takes place in one or several steps*. The reaction above can be regarded as the sum of the following reactions:

$CaO(s) \longrightarrow Ca(s) + \frac{1}{2}O_2(g)$	$\Delta H =$	151.9 kcal
$CO_2(g) \longrightarrow C(s) + O_2(g)$	$\Delta H =$	94.1 kcal
$Ca(s) + C(s) + \frac{3}{2}O_2(g) \longrightarrow CaCO_3(s)$	$\Delta H =$	-288.5 kcal
$CaO(s) + CO_2(g) \longrightarrow CaCO_3(s)$	$\Delta H =$	-42.5 kcal

It should be noted that in the first two steps use was made of the fact that reversal of a chemical equation causes reversal of the sign of ΔH.

Chemical thermodynamics

EXAMPLE 3

Calculate the heat of combustion of a mole of $C_2H_4(g)$ to form $CO_2(g)$ and $H_2O(g)$ at 298°K and 1 atm.

$$C_2H_4(g) + 3O_2(g) \longrightarrow 2CO_2(g) + 2H_2O(g)$$

$$\Delta H_{\text{combustion}} = 2\,\Delta H_{CO_2} + 2\,\Delta H_{H_2O} - \Delta H_{C_2H_4} - 3\,\Delta H_{O_2}$$

$$= (2)(-94.1) + (2)(-57.8) - (12.5) - (3)(0)$$

$$= -316.3 \text{ kcal}$$

Notice that the heat of formation of an element in its standard state (for example, O_2) is zero.

14.5 SECOND LAW

The first law of thermodynamics is concerned with the conservation of energy in an isolated system. It is possible that, within this limit of constant energy, changes may occur. So far as the first law is concerned, all such changes are equally possible. However, experience tells us that some changes do not occur, for example, H_2O does not freeze above its melting point, heat does not flow from low to high temperature, gases do not contract spontaneously. The second law of thermodynamics is concerned with the restrictions that are met by spontaneous changes. For our purposes we shall use the following formulation: *Any system when left to itself will tend to change to a condition of maximum probability.* As noted in Section 7.9, the condition of maximum probability is the one of maximum randomness, or disorder. Entropy S is the thermodynamic property that measures probability, or randomness. Thus, the second law of thermodynamics can be stated in another way: *for spontaneous change in an isolated system, the entropy must increase,* that is, ΔS must be greater than zero. From this it follows that for a system not isolated from its surroundings a decrease in the total entropy of system plus surroundings will not spontaneously occur.

$$\Delta S_{\text{total}} = \Delta S_{\text{system}} + \Delta S_{\text{surroundings}} > 0 \tag{1}$$

The $\Delta S_{\text{surroundings}}$ corresponds to the amount of heat transferred to the surroundings divided by the temperature at which the transfer occurs. That both heat and temperature should be involved can be appreciated by noting that heat added to the surroundings can increase thermal motion and hence increase random disorder; however, the higher the temperature, the more disordered are the surroundings already, so the less significant is the added contribution. For the situations most usually encountered, where temperature and pressure are kept constant, we can write

$$\Delta S_{\text{surroundings}} = \frac{\Delta H_{\text{surroundings}}}{T} = -\frac{\Delta H_{\text{system}}}{T}$$

where $\Delta H_{\text{surroundings}}$ is the increase in the heat content of the surroundings due to the heat transfer from the system to the surroundings. In the process the heat content of the system diminishes by the same amount. Substituting in Equation (1), we get

$$\Delta S_{\text{total}} = \Delta S_{\text{system}} - \frac{\Delta H_{\text{system}}}{T} > 0 \tag{2}$$

Usually, we consider only what happens to the system and not to its surroundings. For the system alone, then, the second law states that the quantity which must increase in a spontaneous change is $\Delta S - \Delta H/T$. As we shall see, this is related to the free-energy change.

The definition of free energy, as given in Section 7.9, is

$$G = H - TS$$

or, at constant temperature and pressure, the free-energy change is given by

$$\Delta G = \Delta H - T\Delta S$$

Dividing by T gives

$$\frac{\Delta G}{T} = \frac{\Delta H}{T} - \Delta S$$

or, by changing sign and rearranging,

$$-\frac{\Delta G}{T} = \Delta S - \frac{\Delta H}{T} \tag{3}$$

According to Equation (2), for a spontaneous change to occur in a system in contact with its surroundings, the right-hand side of equation (3) must be greater than zero, so the left-hand side must also be greater than zero.

$$-\frac{\Delta G}{T} > 0$$

The temperature T is always positive. Hence, the only way $-\Delta G/T$ can be greater than zero is to have ΔG be negative. In other words, *for a spontaneous change at constant temperature and pressure the free energy of a system must decrease.* If the free energy does not decrease, then a spontaneous change will not occur.

As an example of the foregoing principles, we consider the reaction between one mole of liquid bromine and one mole of gaseous chlorine to form BrCl(g).

$$Br_2(l) + Cl_2(g) \longrightarrow 2BrCl(g)$$

At 25°C and one atmosphere pressure, ΔH for the reaction as written is 7.0 kcal. This means that when one mole of liquid bromine combines with one mole of gaseous chlorine to form two moles of gaseous BrCl, 7.0 kcal of heat is absorbed from the surroundings. Thus the change is endothermic and, noting that most spontaneous reactions are exothermic, it might seem that this particular reaction would not occur spontaneously. However, the second law requires that we consider the ΔS for the change. The entropy of $Br_2(l)$ is 36.4 cal mole^{-1} deg^{-1} at 25°C; the entropy of $Cl_2(g)$, 53.3 cal mole^{-1} deg^{-1}; and the entropy of

BrCl(g), 57.3 cal mole^{-1} deg^{-1}. Consequently, $\Delta S = 2S_{\mathrm{BrCl}} - S_{\mathrm{Br_2}} - S_{\mathrm{Cl_2}} = (2)(57.3) - 36.4 - 53.3 = +24.9$ cal mole^{-1} deg^{-1}. At 25°C, or 298°K, the free-energy change is

$$\Delta G = \Delta H - T\Delta S$$

$$= 7.0 \text{ kcal} - (298 \text{ deg})(0.0249 \text{ kcal deg}^{-1})$$

$$= -0.4 \text{ kcal}$$

Because ΔG is negative, i.e., the free energy decreases on reaction—Br$_2$(l) plus Cl$_2$(g) tend to react to form BrCl(g). In other words, a chemical change should occur spontaneously. We hasten to add, however, that thermodynamics does not tell us how fast the change should occur, but merely tells us in what direction it should eventually go.

What about equilibrium? As equilibrium is approached, i.e., as one chemical species converts to another, the free energy of the system with all its species decreases progressively until a minimum free energy is achieved. This state, being at a minimum, has no tendency to change and therefore represents an equilibrium state. For the BrCl example above it might seem that the free-energy minimum would be reached when complete conversion from Br$_2$(l) and Cl$_2$(g) had occurred. However, such a conclusion would be incorrect, because it fails to take into account that the free energy of each component depends on its concentration. The dependence is such that a minimum total free energy for the components is achieved when the concentration of BrCl(g) is about 3.6 times that of Cl$_2$(g). When these equilibrium concentrations have been achieved, the conversion of a small amount of Br$_2$ plus Cl$_2$ to BrCl or vice versa is accompanied by no change in free energy; i.e., at equilibrium $\Delta G = 0$. We shall explore this problem further in the following sections.

14.6 STANDARD FREE-ENERGY CHANGES

The free energy of a substance (as well as its heat content and its entropy) depends on the state of the substance, i.e., whether it is solid, liquid, or gas. Furthermore, it depends on the temperature and the pressure and, in the case of solutions, on the concentration. Consequently, the change of free energy during a chemical reaction depends on the state, conditions, and concentrations of the reactants and products. For convenience, standard conditions have been chosen for reference. These correspond to one atmosphere pressure, 25°C, and if the substance is pure, the state (s, l, or g) in which the substance exists at one atmosphere and 25°C. For *gaseous* solutions the standard state is generally taken to correspond to a partial pressure of one atmosphere. For *liquid* solutions the standard state can be taken as unit mole fraction; or, more generally, solutes in dilute solution are referred to a standard state of one molal concentration corrected for nonideal solution behavior. For *solid* solutions the standard state corresponds to unit mole fraction.

As a specific example of the significance of standard states we can consider the reaction

$$Zn(s) + 2H^+(aq) \longrightarrow H_2(g) + Zn^{++}(aq)$$

For this reaction the standard free-energy change ΔG° is equal to -35.18 kcal, the standard enthalpy change ΔH° is -36.43 kcal, and the standard entropy change ΔS° is -4.19 cal mole^{-1} deg^{-1}. (Note the superscript zero, which indicates that the change involves substances in their standard states only.) $\Delta G^\circ = -35.18$ kcal means that the free energy of the system at 25°C and one atmosphere decreases by 35.18 kcal when one mole of solid zinc reacts completely with two moles of hydrogen ion, from an aqueous solution in which the concentration of H$^+$ is an ideal one molal, to produce one mole of gaseous H$_2$, at a pressure of one atmosphere, and one mole of zinc ion, in aqueous solution at a concentration that is ideal one molal. "Ideal one molal" means that the concentration is one mole per kilogram of solvent except that corrections have been applied for all nonideal behavior such as interionic attraction.

14.7 CHEMICAL ACTIVITIES AND CHEMICAL EQUILIBRIUM

Most chemical reactions involve mixtures of substances. In general, these substances are not in their standard states, so we need to know how to describe their tendency for chemical reaction under other than standard conditions. The relative tendency for chemical reaction is most often expressed in terms of *chemical activity,* which is defined as the ratio of the "effective" concentration to the concentration in the standard state. The concentration of gases can be measured by pressure, so the activity of an ideal gas can be set equal to its actual pressure divided by its pressure in the standard state. For gases that are nonideal it is still a good approximation to measure activity as the ratio of actual pressure to standard-state pressure. For liquid solutions the activity of a solute is generally given as the ideal molal concentration of the solute divided by its molality in the standard state. It might seem that dividing by the standard-state pressure or molality is unnecessary, since the numerical value in the standard state is unity. However, we must not forget units. By dividing as indicated, we arrive at activity as a *dimensionless quantity* embodying a comparison to a standard state.

To see better what is meant by activity, let us consider a mixture of gaseous hydrogen and gaseous iodine. The total free energy of the mixture, G_{total}, can be written as the sum of a contribution from the hydrogen $n_{H_2}\bar{G}_{H_2}$, plus a contribution from the iodine, $n_{I_2}\bar{G}_{I_2}$.

$$G_{\text{total}} = n_{H_2}\bar{G}_{H_2} + n_{I_2}\bar{G}_{I_2}$$

where n is the number of moles of each component and $\bar{G}$ is the free-energy contribution per mole ascribable to each component in this particular mixture. How, for example, does $\bar{G}_{H_2}$ in this mixture differ from what it would be in the standard state of H$_2$? In other words, how does $\bar{G}_{H_2}$ change with H$_2$ pressure (i.e., concentration)? If we represent the molar free-energy contribution in the standard state by $\bar{G}_{H_2}^{\circ}$, then it turns out that

$$\bar{G}_{H_2} = \bar{G}_{H_2}^{\circ} + RT \ln a_{H_2}$$

Thus, a_{H_2}, the activity of the hydrogen, gives a measure of the change in free-energy contribution in going away from the standard state. In the standard state of hydrogen, $a_{H_2} = 1$, and hence $\bar{G}_{H_2} = \bar{G}_{H_2}^{\circ}$. For activities less than unity (that is, H_2 pressure less than one atmosphere), $\bar{G}_{H_2}$ will be less than $\bar{G}_{H_2}^{\circ}$; for activities greater than unity (that is, H_2 pressure greater than one atmosphere), $\bar{G}_{H_2}$ will be greater than $\bar{G}_{H_2}^{\circ}$. Stated differently, as the hydrogen pressure is increased, its molar free-energy contribution increases.

A mixture consisting of H_2 and I_2 is not at equilibrium, since the free energy can decrease by conversion of some H_2 and I_2 into HI. Suppose we ask what is the free-energy change for the chemical reaction

$$H_2 + I_2 \longrightarrow 2HI$$

The change in free energy, ΔG, is the free energy of the product, $2\bar{G}_{HI}$, minus the sum of the free energies of the reactants, $\bar{G}_{H_2} + \bar{G}_{I_2}$.

$$\Delta G = 2\bar{G}_{HI} - \bar{G}_{H_2} - \bar{G}_{I_2}$$

By using activities (that is, $\bar{G} = \bar{G}^{\circ} + RT \ln a$), we can write

$$\Delta G = 2\bar{G}_{HI}^{\circ} + 2RT \ln a_{HI} - \bar{G}_{H_2}^{\circ} - RT \ln a_{H_2} - \bar{G}_{I_2}^{\circ} - RT \ln a_{I_2}$$

Noting that $\Delta G^{\circ} = 2\bar{G}_{HI}^{\circ} - \bar{G}_{H_2}^{\circ} - \bar{G}_{I_2}^{\circ}$ and that $2RT \ln a_{HI} = RT \ln a_{HI}^2$, we find that

$$\Delta G = \Delta G^{\circ} + RT \ln \frac{a_{HI}^2}{a_{H_2} a_{I_2}}$$

At equilibrium, the total free energy must reach a minimum. From the definition of a minimum, it follows that $\Delta G = 0$. Therefore, at equilibrium we can write

$$0 = \Delta G^{\circ} + RT \ln \frac{a_{HI}^2}{a_{H_2} a_{I_2}}$$

or

$$\Delta G^{\circ} = -RT \ln \frac{a_{HI}^2}{a_{H_2} a_{I_2}}$$

The last equation is most important. Because the activity ratio is just the mass-action expression and hence equal to the equilibrium constant, we can write

$$\frac{a_{HI}^2}{a_{H_2} a_{I_2}} = K$$

and

$$\Delta G^{\circ} = -RT \ln K$$

The final relation is noteworthy in that it states that the *final equilibrium state* as characterized by K is determined by the free-energy change from reactants to products *in the standard state*. Thus, we learn about the *equilibrium* state by considering free-energy properties in the *nonequilibrium* standard state. The reason for this is that the free-energy difference for reactants and products at their standard conditions gives a measure of how far away from final equilibrium the standard conditions are.

For chemical reactions in general, $\Delta G°$ may be zero, positive, or negative. If $\Delta G° = 0$, then $K = 1$, which means that the final equilibrium system has reactants and products contributing equally to the activity ratio. If $\Delta G° > 0$, than $K < 1$, which means that the products contribute much less to the activity ratio than the reactants; in other words, reaction does not proceed far from left to right. If $\Delta G° < 0$, then $K > 1$; the reaction is favorable and product activities predominate.

The actual numerical value for K is dependent on the choice of standard states for the reactants and products. When standard free-energy changes are computed from values given in compilations such as those of the National Bureau of Standards, gases will turn out to be measured in atmospheres. Hence, the equilibrium constants so calculated (that is, K deduced from $\Delta G° = -RT \ln K$) will not in general be the same as those for which concentrations are expressed in moles per liter (see Section 11.3). However, if the number of gas moles is the same on both sides of the chemical equation (as is true for Example 4 below, but not for Example 5), then the K useful for concentrations, usually designated K_c, is numerically equal to the K useful for pressures, usually designated K_p.

EXAMPLE 4

The standard free energy of formation of HI from H_2 and I_2 at 490°C is -2.90 kcal mole^{-1}. Calculate the equilibrium constant for $H_2 + I_2 \rightleftharpoons 2HI$.

$$\Delta G° = (2 \text{ moles HI})(-2.90 \text{ kcal mole}^{-1} \text{ HI}) = -5.80 \text{ kcal}$$

$$\Delta G° = -RT \ln K$$

$$\ln K = -\frac{\Delta G°}{RT} = \frac{-(-5800 \text{ cal})}{(1.99 \text{ cal deg}^{-1})(763 \text{ deg})} = 3.82$$

$$\log K = \frac{\ln K}{2.303} = \frac{3.82}{2.303} = 1.66$$

$$K = 46$$

EXAMPLE 5

For the reaction $2NO(g) + O_2(g) \rightleftharpoons 2NO_2(g)$ at 298°K, the equilibrium constant K equals 1.6×10^{12}. Given that the standard free energy of formation of $NO(g)$ is 20.7 kcal mole^{-1} at 298°K, calculate the standard free energy of formation of $NO_2(g)$ at 298°K.

For $2NO(g) + O_2(g) \rightleftharpoons 2NO_2(g)$

$$\Delta G^\circ = -RT \ln K$$

$$= -(1.99 \text{ cal deg}^{-1})(298^\circ)(2.303) \log (1.6 \times 10^{12})$$

$$= -16.7 \text{ kcal}$$

$$\Delta G^\circ = 2\Delta G^\circ_{NO_2} - 2\Delta G^\circ_{NO} - \Delta G^\circ_{O_2}$$

Note that the ΔG° of formation of an element in its standard state is taken to be zero, so $\Delta G^\circ_{O_2} = 0$.

$$\Delta G^\circ_{NO_2} = \frac{1}{2}(\Delta G^\circ + 2\Delta G^\circ_{NO})$$

$$= \frac{1}{2}(-16.7 + 2 \times 20.7) \text{ kcal mole}^{-1}$$

$$= 12.4 \text{ kcal mole}^{-1}$$

For oxidation-reduction reactions, the net free-energy change is directly related to the voltage that would be obtained if the reaction were set up as a galvanic cell (Section 13.6). The relationship between the overall free-energy change ΔG and the cell voltage E is

$$\Delta G = -n\mathscr{F}E$$

where n is the number of faradays of electricity transferred between the reducing and the oxidizing agent and $\mathscr{F}$ is the value of the faraday, which for conversion to kilocalories per mole is 23.06 kcal volt-equivalent^{-1}. As noted in Section 13.7, the Nernst equation indicates that the voltage of a cell depends on the concentrations, or better, activities, of the species involved. Hence, we can substitute the general form of the Nernst equation

$$E = E^\circ - \frac{RT}{n\mathscr{F}} \ln Q$$

in $\Delta G = -n\mathscr{F}E$ to get

$$\Delta G = -n\mathscr{F}\left(E^\circ - \frac{RT}{n\mathscr{F}} \ln Q\right)$$

$$= -n\mathscr{F}E^\circ + RT \ln Q$$

The term $-n\mathscr{F}E^\circ$ is just equal to ΔG°, the standard free-energy change for the reaction when all species are in their standard states, i.e., at unit activity.

$$\Delta G = \Delta G^\circ + RT \ln Q$$

At *equilibrium* (species *not* in standard states), ΔG equals zero. Therefore, we have

$$0 = \Delta G^\circ + RT \ln Q$$

The activity quotient Q at equilibrium is equal to K, the equilibrium constant.

$$0 = \Delta G^\circ + RT \ln K$$

Rearranging and then setting $\Delta G° = -n\mathcal{F}E°$, we get

$$\Delta G° = -RT \ln K = -n\mathcal{F}E°$$

Solving for log K gives

$$\log K = \frac{n\mathcal{F}E°}{2.303 \, RT}$$

At 25°C, this relation becomes

$$\log K = 16.9nE°$$

For the reaction

$$Zn(s) + Cu^{++} \rightleftharpoons Zn^{++} + Cu(s)$$

the standard voltage is 1.10. The number of faradays transferred is 2.

$$\log K = (16.9)(2)(1.10)$$

$$K = 1.5 \times 10^{37}$$

The mass-action expression for the reaction is

$$\frac{[Zn^{++}]}{[Cu^{++}]} = K = 1.5 \times 10^{37}$$

This means that, at equilibrium, the activity of Zn^{++} is 1.5×10^{37} times that of Cu^{++}. It is no wonder that the addition of zinc metal to a solution of copper ion results in essentially complete reduction of Cu^{++} to Cu.

For the reaction

$$Cr_2O_7^{--} + 6Fe^{++} + 14H^+ \rightleftharpoons 2Cr^{+3} + 6Fe^{+3} + 7H_2O$$

the voltage is 0.46 and n is 6. The equilibrium constant calculated as above has a value of 4.4×10^{46}.

EXAMPLE 6

Given the reaction

$$H_2(g) + 2AgCl(s) \longrightarrow 2Ag(s) + 2H^+(aq) + 2Cl^-(aq)$$

At 25°C the standard free energy of formation of AgCl(s) is -26.22 kcal mole^{-1} and that of $(H^+ + Cl^-)(aq)$ is -31.35 kcal mole^{-1}. Calculate what will be the cell voltage if this reaction is run at 25°C and one atmosphere in a cell in which the $H_2(g)$ activity is unity and the $H^+(aq)$ and $Cl^-(aq)$ activities are each at 0.0100.

$$\Delta G° = 2\,\Delta G°_{H^+,Cl^-} - 2\,\Delta G°_{AgCl}$$

$$= (2)(-31.35) - 2(-26.22) \text{ kcal}$$

$$= -10.26 \text{ kcal}$$

$$E° = \frac{\Delta G°}{-n\mathcal{F}} = \frac{-10.26 \text{ kcal}}{-(2)(23.06 \text{ kcal volt}^{-1})} = 0.222 \text{ volt}$$

$$E = E° - \frac{RT}{n\mathcal{F}} \ln \frac{a_{H^+}{}^2 a_{Cl^-}{}^2}{a_{H_2}}$$

Note that the activities of *solid* Ag and of *solid* AgCl are unity and, hence, can be omitted.

$$E = 0.222 - \frac{(1.99)(298)(2.303)}{(2)(23060)} \log \frac{(0.0100)^2(0.0100)^2}{(1.00)}$$

$$= 0.222 + 0.237 = 0.459 \text{ volt}$$

14.8 TEMPERATURE AND CHEMICAL EQUILIBRIUM

In preceding sections we have stressed the importance of the free-energy change for a reaction at constant temperature and pressure. Specifically, we have shown that the standard free-energy change—the free energy of the products minus the free energy of the reactants, all in their standard states—is directly related to the equilibrium constant for the reaction

$$\Delta G° = -RT \ln K$$

What happens when the temperature is changed? To find out, we first note that the definition of free energy leads to

$$\Delta G° = \Delta H° - T \Delta S°$$

which combines with the preceding equation to give

$$-RT \ln K = \Delta H° - T \Delta S°$$

Solving this for ln K, we get

$$\ln K = - \frac{\Delta H°}{RT} + \frac{\Delta S°}{R}$$

Now our question becomes: How does ln K change with temperature? Suppose we differentiate the last equation, i.e., examine infinitesimal changes for each of the variable quantities.

$$d(\ln K) = d\left(\frac{-\Delta H°}{R}\frac{1}{T}\right) + d\left(\frac{\Delta S°}{R}\right)$$

If the change of temperature is not very large, then $\Delta H°$ and $\Delta S°$ will be constant just as R is. The equation then becomes

$$d(\ln K) = \frac{-\Delta H°}{R} d\left(\frac{1}{T}\right)$$

where the last term has dropped out because there is no change in $\Delta S°/R$. The last equation states that the change in ln K is directly proportional to the change in $1/T$. In other words, if we plot ln K versus $1/T$, we should get a straight line with slope $-\Delta H°/R$, as is shown in Figure 14.3. For the temperature interval between T_1 and T_2, where the respective equilibrium constants are K_1 and K_2, we can write for the slope

$$\frac{\ln K_2 - \ln K_1}{1/T_2 - 1/T_1} = \frac{-\Delta H°}{R}$$

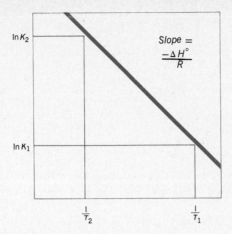

14.3
Change of equilibrium
constant with temperature

which can also be written

$$\ln \frac{K_2}{K_1} = \frac{\Delta H°}{R}\left(\frac{1}{T_1} - \frac{1}{T_2}\right)$$

This relation represents one form of the so-called *van't Hoff equation*. It is important not only because it provides a method for calculating K at one temperature when $\Delta H°$ and K at another temperature are known but also because it allows determination of the standard heat of a reaction, $\Delta H°$, from measurements of equilibrium constants at different temperatures. It must be emphasized that the above form of the equation rests on the assumption that $\Delta H°$ and $\Delta S°$ are constant and do not change with temperature. This assumption will, in general, be valid only for small temperature intervals.

When computing with logs to the base 10, the above equation becomes

$$\log \frac{K_2}{K_1} = \frac{\Delta H°}{2.303\,R}\left(\frac{1}{T_1} - \frac{1}{T_2}\right) = \frac{\Delta H°}{4.58}\left(\frac{1}{T_1} - \frac{1}{T_2}\right)$$

where $\Delta H°$ is in calories.

EXAMPLE 7

For the reaction

$$2NO(g) + O_2(g) \rightleftharpoons 2NO_2(g)$$

the standard heat of reaction is -27.0 kcal and the equilibrium constant is 1.6×10^{12} at $298°K$. Calculate K for this reaction at $373°K$, assuming $\Delta H°$ stays constant.

$$\log \frac{K_2}{K_1} = \frac{\Delta H°}{4.58}\left(\frac{1}{T_1} - \frac{1}{T_2}\right)$$

Let $K_1 = 1.6 \times 10^{12}$ at $T_1 = 298°K$

$$\log \frac{K_2}{1.6 \times 10^{12}} = \frac{-27000}{4.58}\left(\frac{1}{298} - \frac{1}{373}\right)$$

$$K_2 = 1.7 \times 10^8$$

EXAMPLE 8

The molecule NO_2 can dimerize to form N_2O_4. Calculate $\Delta H°$ for the reaction

$$2NO_2(g) \rightleftharpoons N_2O_4(g)$$

given that $K = 8.85$ at $298°K$ and $K = 0.0792$ at $373°K$.

$$\log \frac{K_2}{K_1} = \frac{\Delta H°}{4.58}\left(\frac{1}{T_1} - \frac{1}{T_2}\right)$$

$$\log \frac{0.0792}{8.85} = \frac{\Delta H°}{4.58}\left(\frac{1}{298} - \frac{1}{373}\right)$$

$$\Delta H° = -13900 \text{ cal}$$

QUESTIONS

14.1 Terms   Tell how you might do an experiment with the reaction

$$2NO(g) + O_2(g) \longrightarrow 2NO_2(g)$$

ensuring that (a) pressure stays constant, (b) the system remains isothermal, (c) the system is adiabatic instead of isothermal.

14.2 Thermodynamic properties   (a) Tell what is meant by a thermodynamic property. (b) Which of the following is a thermodynamic property: energy, work done, heat absorbed, entropy, temperature?

14.3 First law   Tell whether each of the following will increase or decrease the total energy content of a system: (a) work done by the system, (b) heat transferred to the surroundings, (c) work done on the system, (d) system expands against an external pressure, (e) an external battery is used to produce electrolytic decomposition within the system.

14.4 Heat content   Compare the heat contents of the following: 1 g of $H_2O(s)$ at $0°C$, 10 g of $H_2O(l)$ at $100°C$, 1 g of H_2O (l) at $0°C$, 10 g of $H_2O(g)$ at $100°C$, 1 g of $H_2O(l)$ at $100°C$.

14.5 Heat capacity   On the basis of Figure 14.1, how many calories are needed to bring about each of the following changes? (a) Raising the temperature of 100 g of $H_2O(l)$ from 20 to $30°C$. (b) Raising the temperature of 100 g of $Zn(s)$ from 410 to $420°C$. (c) Lowering the temperature of 100 g of $SO_2(l)$ from -3 to $-18°C$.

14.6 Heat of formation   By using Figure 14.2, tell whether heat is absorbed from or liberated to the surroundings when hydrogen reacts at standard conditions with the appropriate elements to form each of the following: $H_2O_2(l)$, $HI(g)$, $NH_3(g)$, $C_2H_6(g)$, $C_2H_4(g)$, $HNO_3(l)$.

14.7 Heat of reaction   By using Figure 14.2, calculate the standard heat of reaction for each of the following changes:

(a) $2Al(s) + Cr_2O_3(s) \longrightarrow Al_2O_3(s) + 2Cr(s)$
(b) $CaO(s) + SO_3(g) \longrightarrow CaSO_4(s)$
(c) $2Ca(s) + 4H_2O(l) \longrightarrow 2Ca(OH)_2(s) + 2H_2(g)$

14.8 Chemical change Criticize each of the following: (a) "Energy is the driving force for chemical change." (b) "Free energy is the driving force for chemical change." (c) "For any spontaneous chemical change at constant pressure and temperature the entropy of the chemical system must increase."

14.9 Energy and enthalpy (a) When $NH_4NO_2(s)$ decomposes at 100°C, it forms $N_2(g)$ and $H_2O(g)$. The ΔH for the reaction at one atmosphere pressure and 100°C is -53.50 kcal mole^{-1} of $NH_4NO_2(s)$ decomposed. What is the ΔE for the reaction under these same conditions? (b) Account for the fact that ΔE is numerically bigger than ΔH.

14.10 Energy and enthalpy At 25°C and one atmosphere pressure the molar heat of formation of $NH_4NO_3(s)$ is -87.93 kcal, that of $N_2O(g)$ is $+19.49$ kcal, and that of $H_2O(l)$ is -68.37 kcal. Calculate ΔH and ΔE for the reaction

$$NH_4NO_3(s) \longrightarrow N_2O(g) + 2H_2O(l)$$

14.11 Heat capacity Suppose we mix 1.0 g of -10°C ice with 100 g of 40°C water in a completely insulated container. What will be the final temperature?

14.12 Heat of reaction By using data from Figure 14.2, calculate the standard heat of reaction for each of the following:

(a) $2C_2H_6(g) + 7O_2(g) \longrightarrow 4CO_2(g) + 6H_2O(g)$
(b) $2NaHSO_4(s) \longrightarrow Na_2SO_4(s) + H_2O(g) + SO_3(g)$
(c) $BaO(s) + CaCO_3(s) \longrightarrow BaCO_3(s) + CaO(s)$

14.13 Free-energy change and equilibrium For the reaction at 25°C

$$Br_2(l) + Cl_2(g) \longrightarrow 2BrCl(g)$$

the standard free-energy change $\Delta G°$ is -0.4 kcal. $\Delta H°$ for the reaction is 7.0 kcal. Calculate (a) the equilibrium constant at 25°C, (b) the equilibrium constant at 50°C, (c) the free-energy change at 50°C associated with the transfer of one mole of liquid bromine and one mole of $Cl_2(g)$ at one atmosphere pressure to two moles of $BrCl(g)$ at one atmosphere pressure, and (d) the free-energy change at 50°C associated with the transfer of one mole of liquid bromine and one mole of $Cl_2(g)$ at its equilibrium pressure to two moles of $BrCl(g)$ at its equilibrium pressure.

14.14 Equilibrium constant For the reaction at 25°C

$$COCl_2(g) \rightleftharpoons CO(g) + Cl_2(g)$$

the standard free-energy change is 17.50 kcal. Calculate the value of K, at 25°C, (a) useful for describing gas concentrations, in atmospheres, (b) useful for describing gas concentrations, in moles per liter.

14.15 Equilibrium An equilibrium mixture at 1000°K contains $NH_3(g)$ at 8.37 atm, $N_2(g)$ at 84.5 atm, and $H_2(g)$ at 133 atm. Calculate the free-energy change for the formation of one mole of $NH_3(g)$ at one atmosphere from the elements at one atmosphere and 1000°K.

14.16 Activities   Given a galvanic cell using the reaction

$$H_2(g) + 2AgCl(s) \longrightarrow 2Ag(s) + 2H^+(aq) + 2Cl^-(aq)$$

At 25°C the $E°$ of this reaction is +0.222 volt. In a particular cell having unit-atmosphere hydrogen and unit-activity $H^+(aq)$, it is observed that the cell voltage is +0.234 volt. What is the activity of the $Cl^-(aq)$?

14.17 Temperature and equilibrium   For the reaction

$$PCl_5(g) \rightleftharpoons PCl_3(g) + Cl_2(g)$$

at 25°C the $\Delta G°$ is +9.15 kcal and the $\Delta H°$ is +22.1 kcal. Calculate K at 25°C and at 50°C, assuming $\Delta H°$ does not change.

14.18 Temperature and equilibrium   For the equilibrium

$$COCl_2(g) \rightleftharpoons CO(g) + Cl_2(g)$$

the equilibrium constant K (in terms of atmospheres) is 27.0 at 1000°K and 6.06 at 900°K. Calculate the ΔH and ΔS for this reaction, assuming they stay constant for this temperature range.

14.19 Activities   The values of $E°$ are −0.536 and −0.559 volt, respectively, for the half-reactions $2I^- \longrightarrow I_2 + 2e^-$ and $HAsO_2 + 2H_2O \longrightarrow H_3AsO_4 + 2H^+ + 2e^-$. Given solutions containing I^-, I_2, $HAsO_2$, and H_3AsO_4, tell whether more I_2 or less I_2 should be formed in each of the following cases: (*a*) all species present at unity activity, (*b*) same as (*a*) but pH = 5.00, (*c*) same as (*a*) and then diluted to reduce all activities to 0.01 of original.

14.20 Enthalpy and Entropy   Tell whether the enthalpy and the entropy each increase, decrease, or stay constant for each of the following: (*a*) expansion of an ideal gas into an evacuated container, (*b*) melting of ice, (*c*) diffusion of one ideal gas into another.

14.21 Free-energy change   Assume that ΔH and ΔS for the process $H_2O(s) \longrightarrow H_2O(l)$ do not change with temperature in the range from −5 to +5°C. Plot quantitatively the ΔG for the process as a function of temperature from −5 to +5°C. $\Delta H = 1.44$ kcal mole^{-1}.

14.22 Activities   For the reaction at 25°C

$$H_2(g) + 2AgCl(s) \longrightarrow 2Ag(s) + 2H^+(aq) + 2Cl^-(aq)$$

the $\Delta G°$ equals −10.26 kcal. Given a cell using this reaction, where the activities of $H^+(aq)$ and $Cl^-(aq)$ are each at 0.100, calculate the hydrogen pressure (activity) needed to make the cell voltage zero.

14.23 Equilibrium constant   Given the oxidation potentials

$$2Hg(l) \longrightarrow Hg_2^{++} + 2e^- \qquad E° = -0.789 \text{ volt}$$
$$Hg_2^{++} \longrightarrow 2Hg^{++} + 2e^- \qquad E° = -0.920 \text{ volt}$$

Calculate K at 25°C for the disproportionation reaction

$$Hg_2^{++} \rightleftharpoons Hg^{++} + Hg(l)$$

14.24 Free-energy change and equilibrium   For the reaction

$$2SO_2(g) + O_2(g) \rightleftharpoons 2SO_3(g)$$

at 1000°K the standard free-energy change, referred to standard states in terms of atmospheres of pressure at 1000°K, equals -2.29 kcal. Calculate the free-energy change for each of the following at 1000°K: (a) two moles of SO_2 at one atmosphere plus one mole of O_2 at one atmosphere converting to two moles of SO_3 at one atmosphere, (b) two moles of SO_2 at 0.90 atm plus one mole O_2 at 0.95 atm converting to two moles SO_3 at 1.10 atm, (c) two moles of SO_2 at 0.80 atm plus one mole O_2 at 0.90 atm converting to two moles SO_3 at 1.20 atm, (d) two moles of SO_2 at 0.75 atm plus one mole O_2 at 0.875 atm converting to two moles SO_3 at 1.25 atm. What is the value of K for this reaction?

14.25 Entropy   Take a rubber band. Sense its temperature by touching it to your lips. Stretch it and quickly touch it to your lips again. Now let it contract. Quickly touch it to your lips again. (a) Is heat evolved or absorbed on stretching? (b) Is heat evolved or absorbed on contraction? (c) Tell whether the enthalpy change is favorable for the spontaneous contraction. (d) Noting that rubber is a high-polymer material consisting of tangles of coiled, giant molecules which are pulled into more orderly alignment when rubber is stretched, suggest why it is that a stretched rubber band tends to contract spontaneously.

ANSWERS

14.5 (a) 998 cal   (b) 110 cal   (c) -484 cal   14.9 -55.77 kcal 14.11 38.7°C   14.13 (a) 2   (b) 5   (c) -1.0 (d) zero   14.15 14.8 kcal   14.17 2.0×10^{-7}; 3.6×10^{-6} 14.22 3.1×10^{-12} atm 14.24 (a) -2.29 kcal   (b) -1.40 kcal   (c) -0.48 kcal   (d) zero: $K = 3.18$

15 hydrogen

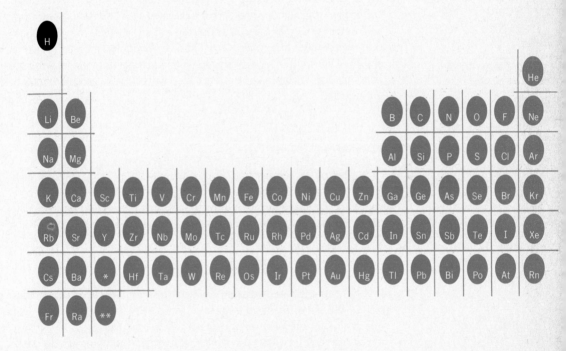

The first element of the periodic table, hydrogen, has but one proton in its nucleus and one orbital electron. In its lowest energy state the H atom has the electron in a K shell, or $1s$ energy level. Because the $1s$ level can contain but one more electron, H atoms can normally attain a lower energy state by pairing up to form H_2 molecules. H_2 molecules react with many other elements to form a large variety of compounds containing H atoms.

15.1 OCCURRENCE

In the universe, hydrogen is apparently the most abundant element. Analysis of light emitted by stars indicates that most stars are predominantly hydrogen. For example, of the sun's mass, approximately 90% is hydrogen. On the earth, hydrogen is much less abundant. The earth's gravitational attraction, being much less than that of stars and larger planets, is too small to hold very light molecules. Considering only the earth's crust (atmosphere, oceans, and 10 miles of solid material), hydrogen is third in abundance on an atom basis. Of each 1000 atoms of crust, 530 are oxygen, 160 are silicon, and 150 are hydrogen. On a mass basis, hydrogen is ninth in order and contributes only 0.88% of the mass of the earth's crust.

On the earth, free, or uncombined, hydrogen is rare. It is found occasionally in volcanic gases. Also, as shown by study of the aurora borealis, it is found in traces in the upper atmosphere. On the other hand, combined hydrogen is quite common. In water, hydrogen is combined with oxygen and makes up 11.2% of the total mass. The human body, two-thirds of which is water, is approximately 10% H by mass. In coal and petroleum, hydrogen is combined with carbon as hydrocarbons. Clay and a few other minerals contain appreciable amounts of hydrogen, usually combined with oxygen. Finally, all plant and animal matter is composed of compounds of hydrogen with oxygen, carbon, nitrogen, sulfur, etc.

15.2 PREPARATION

In producing an element for commercial use the primary consideration is usually cost. For laboratory use the important consideration is convenience. For *commercial* hydrogen, sources are water and hydrocarbons. Hydrogen can be made inexpensively by passing steam over hot carbon.

$$C(s) + H_2O(g) \xrightarrow[1000°C]{} CO(g) + H_2(g)$$

It is hard to get pure hydrogen from this source, because carbon monoxide, CO, is difficult to separate completely from hydrogen. The mixture of H_2 and CO is an industrial fuel, *water gas*.

Purer and still relatively inexpensive hydrogen can be made by passing steam over hot iron:

$$3Fe(s) + 4H_2O(g) \longrightarrow Fe_3O_4(s) + 4H_2(g)$$

The iron can be recovered by reducing Fe_3O_4 with water gas.

The purest (99.9%) but most expensive hydrogen available commercially is *electrolytic hydrogen,* made from the electrolysis of water.

$$2H_2O \xrightarrow[electrolysis]{} 2H_2(g) + O_2(g) - 135 \text{ kcal}$$

The reaction is endothermic and requires energy, which must be supplied by the electric current. It is the power consumption, not the raw material, that makes electrolytic hydrogen expensive. In practice, alkaline (basic) solutions are electrolyzed with cells designed to keep anode and cathode products separate. The electrode reactions are

Anode:

$$4OH^- \longrightarrow O_2(g) + 2H_2O + 4e^-$$

Cathode:

$$2e^- + 2H_2O \longrightarrow H_2(g) + 2OH^-$$

Net:

$$2H_2O \longrightarrow 2H_2(g) + O_2(g)$$

Considerable hydrogen is also formed as a by-product of the commercial preparation of Cl_2 and NaOH by the electrolysis of aqueous NaCl (Section 13.2).

In petroleum refineries, where gasoline is made by the catalytic cracking of hydrocarbons, hydrogen is a by-product. When gaseous hydrocarbons are passed over hot catalyst, decomposition occurs to form hydrogen and other hydrocarbons. In fact, this is now the principal source of commercial hydrogen.

In the *laboratory,* pure hydrogen is usually made by the reaction of zinc metal with acid:

$$Zn(s) + 2H^+ \longrightarrow Zn^{++} + H_2(g)$$

In principle, reaction should occur with any metal having a positive oxidation potential (Section 13.6). For some metals, such as iron, the reaction is quite slow, even though the voltage is favorable. In water, where the concentration of H^+ is only 1.0×10^{-7} M, the reduction by metals is more difficult. The voltage for the half-reaction

$$H_2(g) \longrightarrow 2H^+(1.0 \times 10^{-7} M) + 2e^-$$

is $+0.41$ volt. In order to liberate H_2 from water, a metal must have an oxidation potential of $+0.41$ volt or higher. Thus, the element sodium reacts with water to liberate H_2 by the reaction

$$2Na(s) + 2H_2O \longrightarrow H_2(g) + 2Na^+ + 2OH^-$$

In principle, zinc should liberate H_2 from H_2O by a similar reaction, but the reaction is too slow to be useful at room temperature.

Laboratory hydrogen can also be made conveniently from the reaction of aluminum metal with base (Section 23.3) or from the reaction of CaH_2 with water (Section 15.4).

15.3 PROPERTIES AND USES

Hydrogen at room temperature is a colorless, odorless, tasteless gas. The quantitative properties are summarized in Figure 15.1. The gas is diatomic and consists of nonpolar molecules containing two hydrogen atoms held together by a covalent bond. In order to rupture the bonds in one mole of H_2 to form H atoms, 103 kcal of heat must be supplied. Because the dissociation is endothermic, it increases with temperature. At $4000°K$ and 1 atm pressure, H_2 is about 60% disso-

Molecular mass	2.016 amu
Bond length	0.749 Å
Bond energy	103 kcal mole^{-1}
Approx. molecular diameter	2 Å
Normal melting point	14.1°K
Normal boiling point	20.4°K
Critical temperature	33.2°K
Density at STP	0.0899 g liter^{-1}
Density of liquid (20°K)	0.07 g ml^{-1}

ciated. When H$_2$ reacts, one of the steps is usually the breaking of the H—H bond. Because of the high energy required for this step, the activation energy is high, and H$_2$ reactions are slow. Most hydrogen compounds contain H covalently bound, since neither H$^+$ nor H$^-$ is readily formed. The ionization potential (Section 2.7) is 13.60 ev, which is about 2½ times the ionization potential of sodium. The electron affinity (Section 2.8) is 0.72 ev, which is about one-fifth that of chlorine.

Molecular hydrogen is the lightest of all gases. It is one-fourteenth as heavy as air. A balloon filled with hydrogen rises in accord with Archimedes' principle that the buoyant force on an object immersed in a fluid (such as air) is equal to the weight of fluid displaced by the object. Until recently, H$_2$ was used extensively to lift dirigibles, but because of its combustibility it is no longer in demand for this purpose. However, meteorologists still frequently send aloft weather balloons inflated with hydrogen.

The very low melting and boiling points of hydrogen indicate that the intermolecular attractions are quite small (Section 5.12). Because of the low boiling point, liquid hydrogen is used in the laboratory to produce low temperatures, but it can be kept for only a few hours, even in a Dewar flask immersed in liquid air. When the pressure above liquid H$_2$ in an insulated container is reduced below 54 torr (the triple-point pressure), the temperature drops and hydrogen solidifies. The critical temperature of H$_2$ (above which it can exist only as a gas) is 33.2°K.

Chemically, H$_2$ is able, under appropriate conditions, to combine directly with most elements. With oxygen, H$_2$ reacts to release large amounts of energy by the change

$$2H_2(g) + O_2(g) \longrightarrow 2H_2O(g) + 116 \text{ kcal}$$

which occurs at an appreciable rate only at high temperatures or in the presence of catalyst. In the oxyhydrogen torch the above reaction occurs to produce temperatures of about 2800°C, and the reaction is self-sustaining. Mixtures of H$_2$ and O$_2$ are explosive, and especially violently so when the ratio of H$_2$ to O$_2$ is approximately 2:1. With F$_2$, the reaction

$$H_2(g) + F_2(g) \longrightarrow 2HF(g) + 130 \text{ kcal}$$

is explosive even at liquid-hydrogen temperatures.

With metals the reaction of H_2 is not nearly so violent and often requires elevated temperatures. For example, sodium hydride, NaH, is formed by bubbling H_2 through molten sodium at about 360°C. Hydrides of group II elements are just as difficult to form.

Hydrogen also reacts with certain compounds. In some cases it simply adds on to the other molecule as, for instance, in forming methyl alcohol, CH_3OH, from CO:

$$CO(g) + 2H_2(g) \xrightarrow{\text{catalyst}} CH_3OH(g)$$

Such addition reactions, called *hydrogenation* reactions, account for much of the industrial consumption of hydrogen. In other cases hydrogen removes atoms from other molecules, as in the reduction of tungsten trioxide, WO_3, to W.

15.4 COMPOUNDS

In its compounds hydrogen is found in the three oxidation states $+1$, -1, and 0. In the first two cases, H forms compounds by losing a share of its lone electron or gaining a share of another electron. According to the rules for assigning oxidation numbers (Section 4.6), the relative electronegativity of H and the atom to which it is joined must be considered. In the general compound H_nX, the oxidation number of H is $+1$ if X is the more electronegative atom and -1 if X is the less electronegative atom. The oxidation state 0 for hydrogen in compounds represents a rather special case.

Oxidation state $+1$. This is the most important oxidation state of hydrogen, since it includes most of the hydrogen compounds. In these compounds, H is combined with a more electronegative element such as any element taken from the right-hand side of the periodic table. In period 2, for example, the elements more electronegative than H are C, N, O, and F. With these elements H forms compounds such as methane, CH_4; ammonia, NH_3; water, H_2O; and hydrogen fluoride, HF.

It might be noted that, even though H is thought to be the more positive in these compounds, there is no uniformity in writing H first in the formula as expected. It should be emphasized that in all these compounds the binding of hydrogen is covalent and that none of these compounds contains simple H^+ ion. These compounds can be formed by direct union of the elements. The reactions are often slow, sometimes requiring a large amount of activation energy, and so catalysts and high temperatures may be required. For example, the reaction between N_2 and H_2 to form NH_3 is usually carried out under pressure at about 500°C in the presence of a suitable catalyst.

In compounds containing more than two elements, the H is usually considered to be in a positive oxidation state. In most such compounds (for example, $NaHSO_4$) the H is bonded to an atom more electronegative than itself.

Oxidation state -1. When hydrogen is combined with an atom less electronegative than itself, the compound is said to be a *hydride*.

Hydrides may be predominantly ionic, as with the elements of groups I and II, or covalent, as with the lighter elements of group III.

In the hydrides of elements of groups I and II, the H occurs as the negative hydride ion, H^-. The compounds at room temperature are ionic solids forming cubic or hexagonal crystals. When melted, they conduct electric current and on electrolysis form H_2 *at the anode* by the reaction

$$2H^- \longrightarrow H_2(g) + 2e^-$$

The hydride ion is unstable in water solution and is oxidized to H_2. Thus, for example, calcium hydride, CaH_2, in H_2O reacts as follows:

$$CaH_2(s) + 2H_2O \longrightarrow Ca^{++} + 2OH^- + 2H_2(g)$$

The covalent hydrides such as silane, SiH_4, and arsine, AsH_3, are generally volatile liquids or gases. They are nonconductors and apparently contain no H^- ion. They are relatively mild reducing agents.

The term "hydride" is also applied to compounds in which H is joined to a less electronegative atom in a complex ion. Thus, for example, in the compound lithium aluminum hydride, $LiAlH_4$, the cation is Li^+ and the anion is the complex AlH_4^-. These complex hydrides are generally solids, react with water to liberate H_2, and are of great use as reducing agents.

Oxidation state 0. Hydrogen reacts with some metals such as uranium, copper, and palladium to form hard, brittle substances that conduct electricity and have typical metallic luster. In some cases, as uranium hydride, UH_3, the number of H atoms per metal atom is fixed and is a whole number. In other cases, as palladium hydride, PdH_n, the number of H atoms per metal atom is variable and can even be less than one. It is believed that, in these metallic hydrides, the hydrogen is dissolved as elementary hydrogen. Consequently, H is assigned a zero oxidation state. It may be that in these substances hydrogen exists as H atoms, which might even be dissociated into protons and electrons.

The dissolution of hydrogen in metals is important, because metals which dissolve hydrogen are catalysts for hydrogenation reactions. The catalyst is thought to act by dissolving the hydrogen as H atoms, which react more rapidly than H_2 molecules. The catalysis, by finely divided nickel, of the hydrogenation of oils to give fats is explainable in this way.

When hydrogen dissolves in a metal, the H atom may go into the lattice as a lattice defect (Section 6.7) and simply expand the lattice of the metal, or it may completely alter the type of lattice. In either case the change may be significant enough to make the metal lose some of its desirable properties. This phenomenon, called "hydrogen embrittlement," occurs even with small amounts of dissolved hydrogen, amounts that may be unavoidable in the preparation of pure metals. Thus, the large-scale industrial use of the very valuable metal titanium was possible only after preparation methods that avoided hydrogen entrapment were developed.

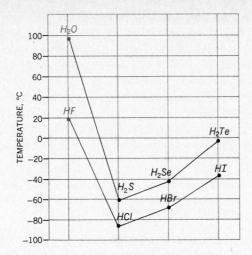

15.5 HYDROGEN BOND

In some compounds a hydrogen atom is apparently bonded simultaneously to two other atoms. For example, in the compound potassium hydrogen fluoride, KHF_2, the anion HF_2^- is believed to have the structure $(FHF)^-$, in which the hydrogen acts as a bridge between the two fluorine atoms. The hydrogen bridge consists of a proton shared between two atoms and is called a *hydrogen bond*. Hydrogen bonds seem to be formed only between small electronegative atoms like F, O, and N.

Evidence in support of the existence of hydrogen bonds comes from comparing properties of hydrogen-containing substances. For example, in Figure 15.2 are shown the normal boiling points for the hydrogen halides (lower curve) and for the hydrogen compounds of group VI elements (upper curve). It is evident that the boiling points of HF and H_2O are abnormally high compared with other members of each series. In the series HF, HCl, HBr, and HI there is an increasing number of electrons per molecule, and, therefore, rising boiling points would be expected because of increased van der Waals attractions (Section 5.12). The unexpectedly high boiling point of HF is attributed to hydrogen bonds between fluorine atoms. The hydrogen bonding makes it more difficult to detach HF from the liquid. Independent evidence for hydrogen bonding in HF comes from studies of the vapor phase, which is found to contain aggregates such as $(HF)_6$, presumed to be held together by hydrogen bonds. The unexpectedly high boiling point of H_2O in the series H_2O, H_2S, H_2Se, and H_2Te is similarly attributed to hydrogen bonding. In Section 16.5 the importance of hydrogen bonding in the structure of water is discussed.

What is responsible for the hydrogen bond? The simplest view is that the positively charged proton is attracted by the negative electrons of two different atoms. When a hydrogen atom is bound to a very electronegative atom, the hydrogen has such a small share of the electron pair that it is almost like a bare proton. As such, it can be attracted to another electronegative atom. Because of its very tiny size, a given proton has room for only two atoms around it. This picture is consistent with the observations that hydrogen bonds are limited to compounds containing hydrogen that is bonded to very electronegative atoms and that one H can bridge between only two atoms.

Hydrogen bonds are important in biological systems. Proteins, for example, contain both $>$ CO and $>$ NH groups, and hydrogen bonds can be formed to bridge the space between the N and the O. The structure and hence the properties of proteins depend on the existence of hydrogen bonds.

15.6 ISOTOPES OF HYDROGEN

Natural hydrogen consists of three isotopes: protium ($_1H^1$), deuterium, or heavy hydrogen ($_1H^2$, or D), and tritium ($_1H^3$, or T). The protium nucleus consists of a lone proton; the deuterium nucleus, of a proton and a neutron; and the tritium nucleus, of a proton and two neutrons. The protium nucleus is by far the most abundant of the three. In nature, there are 7000 times as many protium atoms as deuterium atoms and only 1×10^{-17} times as many tritium atoms. The scarcity of tritium atoms in nature is due to the instability and consequent radioactivity of its nucleus.

In general, the properties of isotopes are *qualitatively* very similar. However, there may be *quantitative* differences, especially when the percentage difference in mass is appreciable. Figure 15.3 shows some of the properties of protium and deuterium.

In chemical reaction, protium and deuterium show a quantitative difference both in their equilibrium and in their rate properties. Property differences arising from differences in mass are called *isotope effects*. For example, the dissociation constant of ordinary water in the equilibrium

$$H_2O \rightleftharpoons H^+ + OH^-$$

is 1.0×10^{-14} at room temperature. For the corresponding dissociation of heavy water

$$D_2O \rightleftharpoons D^+ + OD^-$$

the constant is 0.2×10^{-14}, which is significantly smaller. The isotope effect on the rates of reactions is even more marked. Thus, a bond to a protium atom can be broken as much as 18 times faster than the bond to a deuterium atom. As an example, H_2 reacts with Cl_2 13.4 times as fast as D_2 does.

For elements heavier than hydrogen the isotope effect is much smaller. For example, $_{53}I^{127}$ reacts at most only 1.02 times faster than $_{53}I^{129}$, and the equilibrium properties are even more similar. The isotope effect becomes negligible for the heavier elements, where the percentage difference in mass between the isotopes is small.

Property	Protium	Deuterium
Mass of atom (H), amu	1.0078	2.0141
Freezing point (H_2), °K	14.0	18.7
Boiling point (H_2), °K	20.4	23.5
Freezing point (H_2O), °C	0	3.8
Boiling point (H_2O), °C	100	101.4
Density at 20°C (H_2O), g ml^{-1}	0.998	1.106

15.3
Properties of isotopes

The isotope effect in hydrogen is used as a basis for the separation of protium and deuterium. Since protium bonds are broken faster than deuterium bonds, electrolysis of water releases the light isotope faster than the heavy isotope. There is an enrichment of the heavy hydrogen in the residual water. By continuing the electrolysis until the residual volume is very small, practically pure deuterium oxide can be obtained. In a typical experiment, 2400 liters of ordinary water produces 83 ml of D_2O that is 99% pure.

15.7 PROTON MAGNETIC RESONANCE

Just as the electron behaves like a tiny magnet (assignable to electron "spin"), so a proton has associated with it a small magnetic moment (assignable to nuclear "spin"). Because the proton is some 2000 times as massive as the electron, proton magnetism is only about 1/2000 as great as electron magnetism. Small as it is, however, the proton magnetic moment is utilized in certain experiments to give important structural information about molecules which contain H atoms. In these experiments energy is absorbed in the hydrogen-containing sample, where it is used to change the alignment of nuclear magnetic moments from less favorable to more favorable orientations relative to an externally applied magnetic field. The energy transfer is somewhat similar to that involved in exciting sympathetic resonance as, for example, in a violin. The absorption of energy by nuclei in a magnetic field is called *nuclear magnetic resonance** or NMR. Many nuclei other than hydrogen also exhibit NMR, but we shall limit our discussion to proton magnetic resonance.

Figure 15.4 is a schematic representation of one type of NMR experiment. The sample under investigation is placed in a coil between the pole pieces of an electromagnet. A radio-frequency signal is fed into the coil from the external oscillator. As the magnetic field produced by the electromagnet is gradually varied, the loss of radio-frequency power in the sample coil is measured and recorded. At a particular value of the

Hydrogen

339

* This is a more appropriate use of the word "resonance" than that employed for certain chemical bond descriptions (Section 3.7). Whereas valence-bond resonance has compounded its difficulties through analogies with irreproducible hybrid mermaids and jackasses, magnetic resonance remains a physical phenomenon capable of being reproduced.

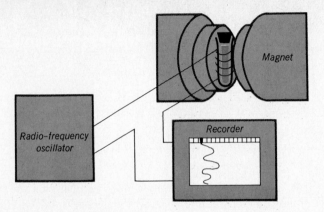

Magnet

Radio-frequency
oscillator

Recorder

magnetic field strength, nuclear magnetic resonance will occur and be detected as a sharp increase in power absorption by the sample.

The magnetic field strength at which absorption occurs depends on a number of factors: the identity of the nucleus being observed (e.g., whether it is H^1 or F^{19}), the frequency of the radio-frequency signal (e.g., 60 megacycles, as commonly used), and the chemical environment of the nucleus being studied—the so-called "chemical shift." This last point is what makes NMR of such great interest to chemists, since it makes possible the identification of structurally distinct H atoms in molecules. Figure 15.5 shows a representation of the NMR absorption signal for protons in ethyl alcohol, CH_3CH_2OH. The three absorption peaks correspond to the three kinds of environment for the hydrogen nucleus in this molecule. The peak on the left is attributed to the hydrogen in OH, the middle peak to the hydrogens in CH_2, and the peak on the right to the hydrogens in CH_3. It turns out that the integrated areas under the three peaks are in the ratio $1:2:3$ corresponding to the relative numbers of the H atoms of the three structural types.

Why does resonance absorption occur at different magnetic field strengths for structurally different H atoms? The answer lies in the relative shielding of the nucleus from the external magnetic field by the surrounding electrons. For example, in CH_3CH_2OH the H bound to the oxygen is the least shielded because the very electronegative oxygen tends to pull the bonding electrons to itself. The H of OH is thus more exposed to the external magnetic field than the other H atoms of the molecule are. The general effect of imposing a magnetic field on any molecule is to create or induce an electron current that tends to oppose the applied field. Part of the applied field is thus nullified in its effect on the nucleus. In the CH_3CH_2OH molecule the electron density is such that the effective magnetic field is greatest at the OH proton and smallest at the CH_3 protons. As the external field is increased, resonance is observed to occur first for the OH proton. In order to produce the same effective magnetic field at the other H nuclei, the external magnetic field must be increased. When this is done, the protons of CH_2 next come into resonance and then finally the most shielded ones, those of CH_3.

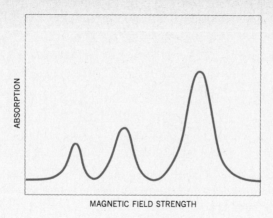

ABSORPTION

MAGNETIC FIELD STRENGTH

15.5
Plot of NMR absorption
for protons in ethyl
alcohol, CH_3CH_2OH

QUESTIONS

15.1 Equations Write balanced equations for each of the following:
(*a*) electrolysis of 1 *M* NaOH to give $H_2(g)$ and $O_2(g)$, (*b*) preparation of
a compound containing hydrogen in a -1 oxidation state, (*c*) reduction
of WO_3 to W by H_2, (*d*) burning of silane to form $SiO_2(s)$, (*e*) reaction of
$LiAlH_4(s)$ with water to form $Al(OH)_3$ and LiOH.

15.2 Electronic configuration In terms of electron configuration account for each of the following: (*a*) H forms compounds in both $+1$
and -1 states. (*b*) There are no simple compounds known to contain
H^+ ions. (*c*) H_2 has the lowest boiling point of any diatomic molecule.

15.3 Deuterium Calculate the chemical atomic mass of a hydrogen
sample enriched in deuterium so the relative ratio of protium to
deuterium abundance is 100.0/1.000.

15.4 Hydrogen bond Predict the relative strength of intermolecular
hydrogen bonding in liquid HF, H_2O, NH_3. Explain.

15.5 Abundance By using the numerical atomic abundance and the
mass abundance for hydrogen in the earth's crust, calculate the
average atomic mass for all the atoms other than H in the earth's
crust.

15.6 Proton resonance How many magnetic resonance peaks would
you expect to see for $CH_3CH_2-O-CH_2CH_3$, and what would you predict for their relative intensities?

15.7 Proton resonance Predict the order in which resonance peaks
would be observed with increasing field strength in the following series
of compounds: HF, H_2O, NH_3.

15.8 Free energy From the dissociation constants of H_2O and D_2O, calculate the difference in standard free energies for the dissociations.

15.9 Bond energies Calculate the apparent bond energy for F—H, O—H, and N—H from the following data:

$$H_2(g) \longrightarrow 2H(g) \qquad \Delta H = 103 \text{ kcal}$$
$$F_2(g) \longrightarrow 2F(g) \qquad \Delta H = 36 \text{ kcal}$$
$$O_2(g) \longrightarrow 2O(g) \qquad \Delta H = 118 \text{ kcal}$$
$$N_2(g) \longrightarrow 2N(g) \qquad \Delta H = 225 \text{ kcal}$$
$$H_2(g) + F_2(g) \longrightarrow 2HF(g) \qquad \Delta H = -130 \text{ kcal}$$
$$2H_2(g) + O_2(g) \longrightarrow 2H_2O(g) \qquad \Delta H = -116 \text{ kcal}$$
$$3H_2(g) + N_2(g) \longrightarrow 2NH_3(g) \qquad \Delta H = -22 \text{ kcal}$$

15.10 Hydrogen bond In the gas phase, acetic acid forms a dimer of the formula $(CH_3COOH)_2$ which is held together by two hydrogen bonds. Draw a probable structure.

15.11 Clausius-Clapeyron By using the Clausius-Clapeyron equation, calculate what should be the temperature of boiling hydrogen being pumped on to maintain a vapor pressure of 100 torr. The heat of vaporization of H_2 is 108 cal g^{-1}; the normal boiling point, $20.4°K$.

15.12 Bonding Give a description of the H_2 molecule from both the valence-bond and the molecular-orbital viewpoints.

15.13 Nernst equation Assuming ideal behavior, calculate the oxidation potential for $H_2(g) \longrightarrow 2H^+(aq) + 2e^-$ under each of the following conditions: (*a*) in 0.1 M H^+, (*b*) in neutral solution, (*c*) in 0.1 M OH^-.

15.14 Stoichiometry The current cost of CaH_2 is \$80.00 kg^{-1}. What would be the cost of hydrogen for inflating a completely collapsed balloon in order to lift a radiosonde to 90000 ft under the following conditions? To reach 90000 ft with a 1700-g payload, the balloon needs to be able to stretch to a diameter of 25 ft from its initial diameter at inflation of 6.5 ft. Assume the initial inflation is to a pressure of 1.01 atm at 27°C.

15.15 Thermodynamics of the moon The lunar surface is constantly bombarded by H^+ and e^- from the sun. We assume the surface is mostly SiO_2. From the free energies of formation (given below) appropriate to the average lunar-surface temperature decide which of the following reactions is the most favorable per H^+, e^- pair.

$$SiO_2(s) + 8H^+(g) + 8e^-(g) \longrightarrow SiH_4(g) + 2H_2O(g)$$
$$SiO_2(s) + 2H^+(g) + 2e^-(g) \longrightarrow SiO(g) + H_2O(g)$$
$$SiO_2(s) + 4H^+(g) + 4e^-(g) \longrightarrow Si(s) + 2H_2O(g)$$

Free energies of formation are $SiO_2(s)$, -192.4 kcal; $SiO(g)$, -32.1 kcal; $SiH_4(g)$, -9.4 kcal; $H^+(g) + e^-(g)$, $+360$ kcal; $H_2O(g)$, -54.6 kcal.

15.16 Free energy of H At 25°C the free energy of formation of one mole of H atoms from H_2 is 48.6 kcal. (*a*) Calculate the equilibrium constant for the reaction $H_2(g) \longrightarrow 2H(g)$. (*b*) Assuming ΔH of the reaction in (*a*) to remain constant at 104.2 kcal, calculate K at 1000°C.

15.17 *Protonic acids*   Calculate the pH of each of the following solutions: (*a*) 0.50 M H_2SO_4, (*b*) 0.50 M $NaHSO_4$, (*c*) a solution made by mixing equal volumes of (*a*) and (*b*).

15.18 *Hydrogen bond*   Many protein crystals contain spiral molecules held in shape by hydrogen bonding between peptide links $\left(\begin{smallmatrix} H & O \\ | & \| \\ -N & -C- \end{smallmatrix}\right)$ in successive turns of the spiral. By representing a protein as

$$\left(\begin{matrix} R & H & O \\ | & | & \| \\ -C-N-C- \\ | \\ H \end{matrix}\right)_n$$

and assuming hydrogen bonds between a nitrogen in one turn and an oxygen four peptide links ahead in the next turn, draw a possible configuration for the protein.

ANSWERS

15.3 1.018   15.8 Difference is one kilocalorie   15.11 14.8°K
15.16 (*a*) 5×10^{-72} (*b*) 2×10^{-13} 15.17 (*a*) 0.29   (*b*) 1.13
(*c*) 0.56

16 oxygen

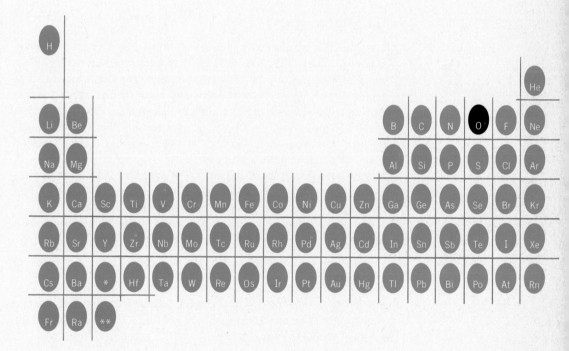

The element oxygen, atomic number 8, has two 1s, two 2s, and four 2p electrons. Except for fluorine, it is more electronegative than any other element and forms compounds with all elements except some noble gases. The study of oxygen compounds has been important in unraveling the chemistry of other elements. One of these compounds, water, is the most important reaction medium in chemistry.

16.1 OCCURRENCE

Oxygen is by far the most abundant element in the earth's crust on the basis of both mass and number of atoms. Of the mass of the earth's crust, 49.5% is due to oxygen atoms. Silicon, the next most abundant element, is only half as plentiful. On a number basis, oxygen atoms are more numerous than all other kinds of atoms combined.

In the free state, oxygen occurs in the atmosphere as O_2 molecules. Air is 20% oxygen by volume; i.e., for every 100 molecules in air, approximately 20 are oxygen. On a mass basis, air is 21% oxygen; of every 100 g of air approximately 21 g is oxygen.

In the combined state, oxygen occurs naturally in many minerals, plants and animals, and water. Of the oxygen-containing minerals, the most abundant are ones which contain silicon. The simplest of these is silica, SiO_2, the main constituent of sand. The most abundant mineral that does not contain silicon is limestone, $CaCO_3$. In plant and animal material, oxygen is combined with carbon, sulfur, nitrogen, or hydrogen.

16.2 PREPARATION

The industrial sources of oxygen are air and water. From air, oxygen is made by liquefaction and fractional distillation. Air, consisting of 21 mole percent oxygen, 78 mole percent nitrogen, and 1 mole percent total of argon, neon, carbon dioxide, and water, is first freed of carbon dioxide and water, compressed, cooled, and expanded until liquefaction results to give liquid air. On partial evaporation, the N_2, being lower boiling, boils away first, leaving the residue richer in O_2. Repeated cycles of this kind give oxygen that is 99.5% pure.

From water, very pure oxygen can be made by electrolysis as a by-product of hydrogen manufacture. Power consumption makes electrolytic oxygen more expensive than oxygen obtained from air.

In the laboratory, oxygen is usually made by the thermal decomposition of potassium chlorate, $KClO_3$. The reaction

$$2KClO_3(s) \longrightarrow 2KCl(s) + 3O_2(g)$$

is catalyzed by the presence of various solids such as manganese dioxide, MnO_2, ferric oxide, Fe_2O_3, fine sand, or powdered glass. It is thought that the function of the catalyst is to provide a surface on which the evolution of oxygen gas can occur.

16.3 PROPERTIES AND USES

At room temperature, oxygen is a colorless, odorless gas. The molecule is diatomic and, both as a liquid and gas, paramagnetic to the extent consistent with two unpaired electrons per molecule. The bond energy of O_2, 118 kcal, lies between that of the triply bonded N_2 (225 kcal) and the singly bonded F_2 (36 kcal), and it is thus in accord with a bond order of two. The electron structure of the O_2 molecule can be rationalized, as was done in Section 3.9, by the molecular-orbital approach. The electronic configuration for the orbitals principally involved in the bonding can be written as $\sigma_{p_x}^2 \pi_{p_y}^2 \pi_{p_z}^2 \pi_{p_y}^* \pi_{p_z}^*$, where the superscripts 2 indicate pairs of electrons in the three bonding orbitals (σ derived from the p_x atomic orbitals, π derived from the p_y orbitals, and π derived from the

p_z orbitals). In addition, there is one electron in each of the two π^* antibonding orbitals. The bond order, defined as half the excess of bonding over antibonding electrons, equals $\frac{1}{2}(6 - 2) = 2$. It is difficult to describe the O_2 molecule adequately from the valence-bond approach, since $:\overset{..}{O}:\overset{..}{O}:$ clearly violates the octet rule. However, as noted in the footnote on page 72, a paramagnetic, doubly bonded configuration can be arrived at from the double-quartet approach.

When cooled to $-183°C$, oxygen condenses to a pale blue liquid. At $-219°C$, it solidifies to form a bluish-white solid. There is some formation of O_4 in the liquid and solid states.

Oxygen exhibits *allotropy;* i.e., it can exist as the element in more than one form. When energy is added to diatomic oxygen, the triatomic molecule ozone, O_3, is formed by the reaction

$$3O_2(g) + 68 \text{ kcal} \longrightarrow 2O_3(g)$$

At room temperature the equilibrium constant for this reaction is calculated to be 10^{-54}. Even though it increases with temperature, the equilibrium concentration of O_3 is not appreciable at any temperature. Thus, not much O_2 can be converted to O_3 by the simple addition of heat. However, when energy is added in other forms such as electric energy or high-energy radiation, significant amounts of O_3 result. Once O_3 is obtained, it only slowly reverts to O_2. In the laboratory, ozone is easily made by passing air or oxygen between tin-foil conductors that are connected to the terminals of an electric-induction coil. Under the influence of the silent electric discharge in this *ozonizer,* about 5% of the oxygen is converted to ozone. Ozone is also formed in appreciable amounts by lightning bolts, ultraviolet light, and by sparking electric motors. Trace amounts found in air are apparently formed in the stratosphere by the absorption of ultraviolet sunlight. In industrial centers the atmosphere contains reducing agents which destroy the ozone. However, minute amounts of ozone occur in unpolluted areas such as the mountains and the seashore. The ozone layer in the stratosphere makes difficult the astrophysical observations of light emitted by stars, because ozone absorbs some of the light, especially those wavelengths needed to identify nonmetallic elements.

The ozone molecule is not magnetic, so all its electrons must be paired. The three oxygen atoms are arranged in the form of an isosceles triangle in which two of the atoms are not directly bound to each other. If the octet rule is followed, it is necessary to write two contributing resonance forms for the structure:

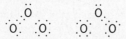

Ozone gas has a sharp, penetrating odor. Its solubility in water, in moles per liter, is about 50% higher than that of oxygen, probably because O_3 is a polar molecule, whereas O_2 is not. When cooled to $-111.5°C$, ozone forms a deep blue liquid that is explosive because of

Property	O_2	O_3
Molecular mass, amu	31.999	47.998
Bond length, Å	1.20	1.26
Normal melting point, °K	54.3	23.6
Normal boiling point, °K	90.2	161.7
Critical temperature, °K	154	268
Density of liquid (90°K), g ml^{-1}	1.14	1.71

16.1
Properties of allotropic
forms of oxygen

the tendency of O_3 to decompose to O_2. The decomposition is normally slow but increases rapidly as the temperature is increased or a catalyst is added.

Some of the properties of oxygen and ozone are given in Figure 16.1. Both O_2 and O_3 are good oxidizing agents, as shown by their oxidation potentials

$$2H_2O \longrightarrow O_2(g) + 4H^+ + 4e^- \qquad -1.23 \text{ volts}$$

$$H_2O + O_2(g) \longrightarrow O_3(g) + 2H^+ + 2e^- \qquad -2.07 \text{ volts}$$

(As pointed out in Section 13.6, a large negative oxidation potential indicates that the species to the right of the arrow is a strong oxidizing agent.) Of the common oxidizing agents, ozone is second only to fluorine in oxidizing strength. In most reactions, at least at room temperature, O_2 is a slow oxidizing agent, whereas O_3 is more rapid.

Because of its cheapness and ready availability, oxygen is one of the most widely used industrial oxidizing agents. For example, in the manufacture of steel it is used to burn off impurities such as carbon, phosphorus, and sulfur, which may give undesirable properties to steels. In the oxyacetylene torch, used for cutting and welding metals, temperatures in excess of 3000°C can be obtained by the reaction

$$2C_2H_2(g) + 5O_2(g) \longrightarrow 4CO_2(g) + 2H_2O(g) + 600 \text{ kcal}$$

Liquid oxygen is mixed with alcohol, charcoal, gasoline, powdered aluminum, etc., to give powerful explosives.

The use of oxygen in respiration of plants and animals is well known. In man, oxygen, inhaled from the atmosphere, is picked up in the lungs by the hemoglobin in the blood and distributed to the various cells, which use it for tissue respiration. In tissue respiration, carbohydrates are oxidized to provide energy required for cellular activities. Since oxygen is a slow oxidizing agent, catalysts (enzymes) must be present in order that reaction may proceed at body temperature. In the treatment of heart trouble, pneumonia, and shock, air oxygen is supplemented with additional oxygen.

The uses of ozone depend on its strong oxidizing properties. For example, its germicidal use depends on its oxidation of bacteria. Inasmuch as oxidation of colored compounds often results in colorless ones, ozone is a bleaching agent for wax, starch, fats, and varnishes. When added to the air in small amounts, ozone destroys odors; but it

16.3 Properties and uses

348

can be used safely only in low concentration, because it irritates the lungs. In the laboratory, ozone aids in certain structure studies. Since it has a specific action on carbon-carbon double bonds, it can be used to determine their position in molecules.

16.4 COMPOUNDS

Except for the oxygen fluorides, O_2F_2 and OF_2, the oxidation state of oxygen in compounds is negative. The oxidation numbers $-\frac{1}{2}$, -1, and -2 are observed.

Oxidation state $-\frac{1}{2}$. The heavier elements of group I (K, Rb, and Cs) react with oxygen to form compounds of the type MO_2, called superoxides. These are ionic solids containing the cation M^+ and the anion O_2^-. The solids are colored and paramagnetic; therefore, they must contain unpaired electrons.* The superoxide ion exists only in the solid state. When superoxides are placed in water, O_2 and H_2O_2 are formed by the reaction

$$2MO_2(s) + 2H_2O \longrightarrow O_2(g) + H_2O_2 + 2M^+ + 2OH^-$$

Oxidation state -1. Compounds which contain oxygen with oxidation number -1 are called peroxides. They are characterized by a direct oxygen-oxygen bond, which usually breaks at high temperatures. Metals such as Na, Sr, and Ba form solid peroxides which contain the peroxide ion, O_2^{--}. This ion contains no unpaired electrons. Barium peroxide, BaO_2, is formed by heating solid barium with oxygen gas at a pressure of 3 atm. On further heating under reduced oxygen pressure, BaO_2 decomposes to give barium oxide, BaO.

$$2BaO_2(s) \longrightarrow 2BaO(s) + O_2(g) - 39 \text{ kcal}$$

Since this reaction is endothermic, it reverses at lower temperature; then BaO picks up O_2. This reversible process has been used to extract O_2 from the air.

When solid peroxides are added to acidic solutions, hydrogen peroxide, H_2O_2, is formed. For example,

$$BaO_2(s) + 2H^+ \longrightarrow Ba^{++} + H_2O_2$$

If sulfuric acid is used, the barium ion precipitates as insoluble barium sulfate, $BaSO_4$, leaving a dilute solution of pure H_2O_2. Commercially, most H_2O_2 is prepared by the electrolysis of cold H_2SO_4 or NH_4HSO_4 solutions followed by distillation under reduced pressure. Because H_2O_2 is unstable, owing to the reaction

$$2H_2O_2 \longrightarrow 2H_2O + O_2(g)$$

---

* The anion O_2^- has 13 valence electrons. If we assume that these electrons are divided equally, as they most certainly are, then we must assign each atom an oxidation number of $-\frac{1}{2}$. Frequently, a fractional oxidation number is explained away by assuming that the compound contains atoms of the same element in different oxidation states. In this case, such an explanation is unlikely. The odd electron belongs to the whole O_2^- ion. The molecular-orbital description of the bonding electrons would show one electron pair and one unpaired electron in the two antibonding orbitals $\pi_{p_y}^*$ and $\pi_{p_z}^*$.

it is difficult to keep. The decomposition is slow but is catalyzed by impurities such as dust and dissolved compounds. It is also accelerated in the presence of light. For these reasons, solutions of H_2O_2 are stored in dark bottles with various chemicals added which destroy catalysts.

Pure anhydrous H_2O_2, obtained by distillation under reduced pressure, is a colorless liquid having a freezing point of $-0.9°C$ and an estimated boiling point of $151.4°C$. The structure corresponds to the electronic formula $:\ddot{O}:\ddot{O}:$, where the bond angle H—O—O is $103°$.

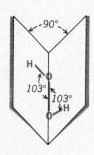

16.2
Structure of H_2O_2 molecule

All four atoms do not lie in the same plane, but, as shown in Figure 16.2, one H sticks out from the plane of the other three atoms at an angle of $90°$.

In aqueous solution H_2O_2 is a weak acid dissociating

$$H_2O_2 \rightleftharpoons H^+ + HO_2^-$$

with a dissociation constant of the order of 10^{-12}. Because oxygen also shows oxidation states of 0 and -2, compounds containing peroxide oxygen (-1) can gain or lose electrons; hence, they can act both as oxidizing agents and as reducing agents. In fact, in the decomposition

$$2H_2O_2 \longrightarrow 2H_2O + O_2(g)$$

hydrogen peroxide oxidizes and reduces itself. In the reaction

$$5H_2O_2 + 2MnO_4^- + 6H^+ \longrightarrow 5O_2(g) + 2Mn^{++} + 8H_2O$$

hydrogen peroxide is a reducing agent (goes to O_2). In the reaction

$$H_2O_2 + 2I^- + 2H^+ \longrightarrow I_2 + 2H_2O$$

H_2O_2 is an oxidizing agent (goes to H_2O).

Oxidation state -2. Minus two is the most common oxidation state of oxygen in compounds. These compounds include the *oxides,* such as BaO, and the *oxy compounds,* such as $BaSO_4$. In none of these is there an oxygen-oxygen bond. Instead, the oxygen atoms have completed their octets by gaining a major share of two electrons from atoms other than oxygen.

All the elements except some noble gases form oxides. Some of these oxides are ionic; others are covalent. In general, the more ionic ones are formed with the elements on the left of the periodic table. Thus, BaO contains Ba^{++} and O^{--} ions and, like all ionic substances, is a solid at room temperature. It can be heated to $2000°C$ without decomposition. When placed in water, the O^{--} ion reacts to give basic solutions:

$$O^{--} + H_2O \longrightarrow 2OH^-$$

The ionic oxides are therefore called *basic oxides,* or *basic anhydrides,* or, most simply, *bases.* They have the ability to neutralize acids. Thus, for example, when CaO is placed in acidic solution, neutralization occurs according to the equation

16.4 Compounds

$$CaO(s) + 2H^+ \longrightarrow Ca^{++} + H_2O$$

Elements on the right of the periodic table do not form simple ionic oxides but instead share electrons with oxygen atoms. Many of these molecular oxides, such as sulfur dioxide, SO_2, are gases at room temperature. They dissolve in water to give acidic solutions. For example,

$$SO_2 + H_2O \rightleftharpoons H_2SO_3 \rightleftharpoons H^+ + HSO_3^-$$

The molecular oxides are therefore called *acidic oxides*, or *acidic anhydrides*, or, most simply, *acids*. They have the ability to neutralize bases. As an example, when CO_2 is bubbled through a basic solution, neutralization occurs as follows:

$$CO_2(g) + OH^- \longrightarrow HCO_3^-$$

It is not possible to classify all oxides sharply as either acidic or basic. Some oxides, especially those formed by elements toward the center of the periodic table, are able to *neutralize both acids and bases*. Such oxides are called *amphoteric* (Section 9.5). An example of an amphoteric oxide is ZnO, which undergoes both the following reactions:

$$ZnO(s) + 2H^+ \longrightarrow Zn^{++} + H_2O$$

$$ZnO(s) + 2OH^- + H_2O \longrightarrow Zn(OH)_4^{--}$$

When any oxide reacts with water, the resulting compound contains OH, or *hydroxyl,* groups. If the hydroxyl group exists in the compound as the OH^- ion, the compound is called a *hydroxide*. Hydroxides are formed by the reaction of ionic oxides with water; e.g.,

$$BaO(s) + H_2O \longrightarrow Ba(OH)_2(s)$$

Barium hydroxide, $Ba(OH)_2$, is a solid which contains Ba^{++} and OH^- ions in its lattice. It, like all hydroxides except those of group I elements, reverts to the oxide when heated. Many hydroxides, e.g., aluminum hydroxide, $Al(OH)_3$, are insoluble in water. The soluble ones give basic solutions.

Some compounds contain the OH group, not as an ion, but covalently bound to another atom. For example, in H_2SO_3 there are two OH groups and one O joined to a central S atom. When placed in water, such compounds give acid solutions by rupture of the O—H bond. For this reason, they are called *oxyacids*. Most oxyacids can be dehydrated by heat to give oxides. They can also be neutralized to give *oxysalts* such as sodium sulfite, Na_2SO_3.

16.5 WATER

The most important of all oxides, possibly the most important of all compounds, is H_2O. The water molecule is nonlinear, with the H—O—H angle equal to $104.5°$. Because each bond is polar covalent, with the H end of the bond positive with respect to the O end, the molecule has a net dipole moment (Section 3.4). The attraction between the H atom of one molecule and the O atom of another leads to the association of water molecules in both the liquid and solid states. A two-dimensional representation of the association is given in Figure 16.3. The cluster of water molecules is held together by hydrogen bonds (Sec-

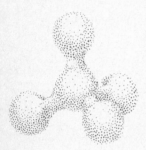

tion 15.5). The H atom, placed between two O atoms, may be considered bonded equally to both.* The result of hydrogen bonding is to form a giant molecule in which each O atom is surrounded by four H atoms. (The simplest formula is still H_2O, because, of the four H atoms about a given O atom, only half of each H belongs to that O.) That there are four H atoms about each O is known from X-ray studies of ice. These studies do not detect the H atoms, but they do show that there are four oxygen atoms symmetrically placed about each oxygen. If the O atoms are joined to each other by H bonds, there must be four H atoms about each oxygen. This can be seen by considering the central atom in Figure 16.3.

The X-ray studies indicate also that the O atoms (of neighboring H_2O molecules) about a given O are located at the corners of a regular tetrahedron, as shown in Figure 16.4. Because of the tetrahedral arrangement, the ice structure extends in three dimensions and is not the flat, two-dimensional representation of Figure 16.3. Figure 16.5 is a better picture of the ice structure. It shows part of the crystal lattice, which extends in three dimensions. The large circles represent oxygen atoms, each of which is tetrahedrally surrounded by four H atoms, represented by the small circles. Every other oxygen atom has its fourth H hidden beneath it. This hidden H joins to another oxygen below, and so the structure continues in three dimensions. A notable feature of the structure is that it is honeycombed with hexagonal channels. Because of these holes, ice has a relatively small density.

When ice melts, the structure becomes less orderly but is not completely destroyed. In liquid water near the melting point it is thought that the O atoms are still tetrahedrally surrounded by four H atoms as in ice. However, the overall arrangement of tetrahedra is more random and is constantly changing. An instantaneous view might be like that shown in Figure 16.6, where some of the hexagonal channels have collapsed to give a more dense structure. Liquid water is more dense than ice, as the data in Figure 16.7 indicate.

The data in Figure 16.7 also show that water has a maximum density

---

* In Figure 16.3 the H atoms are shown midway between adjacent O atoms. Actually, a given H atom can jump back and forth from a position nearer one O atom to a position nearer the other. Thus, it is only the "average" position that is shown.

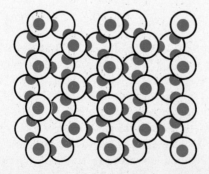

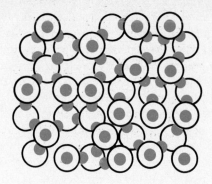

16.6
Water structure

at 3.98°C. The maximum in the density of H_2O can be interpreted as follows: When ice is melted, the collapse of the structure leads to an increase in density. As the temperature of the liquid is raised, the collapse should continue further. However, there is an opposing effect. The higher the temperature, the greater the kinetic motion of the molecules. Hydrogen bonds are broken, and the H_2O molecules move farther apart on the average. This effect becomes dominant at temperatures above 3.98°C. Below this temperature, collapse of structure is the more important.

Temperature, °C	State	Density, g ml^{-1}
0	Solid	0.917
0	Liquid	0.9998
3.98	Liquid	1.0000
10	Liquid	0.9997
25	Liquid	0.9971
100	Liquid	0.9584

16.7
Density of water at
various temperatures

16.6 WATER AS A SOLVENT

Water is the most common solvent both in nature and in the laboratory. However, it is far from being a universal solvent, since many substances are essentially insoluble in water. The factors influencing solubility are many (Section 8.7), and therefore predictions concerning solubility are difficult. The situation for water is especially complex, because there is strong association of H_2O molecules. For solution to occur, considerable energy is required to tear water molecules from their neighbors in order to make room for solute particles.

In general, water is a rather poor solvent for substances which exist in solution as molecules. Thus, gasoline, oxygen, and methane are practically insoluble in water. In these cases water interacts so weakly with the molecular solute that not nearly enough energy is liberated to

Oxygen

353

break down the water structure. There are, however, some molecular solutes which are highly soluble in water. Examples are ammonia, NH_3, and ethyl alcohol, C_2H_5OH. These substances apparently interact sufficiently strongly with the water to break its structure. In the case of NH_3, hydrogen bonds are established between the N of NH_3 and the O of H_2O. These hydrogen bonds have been used to justify the occasional practice of writing NH_4OH as the formula of dissolved NH_3. In aqueous solutions of ethyl alcohol, hydrogen bonds are formed between the O of C_2H_5OH and the O of H_2O. Sucrose, $C_{12}H_{22}O_{11}$, owes its appreciable solubility in large measure to hydrogen bonding, since it, like C_2H_5OH, has OH groups.

Although water is the best solvent known for substances which exist in solution as ions, many ionic solutes are practically insoluble in water. In general, the attractions between ions and polar H_2O molecules (hydration energies) are great enough to break the water structure. However, there are strong attractions between the oppositely charged ions in the solid (lattice energies), which must be overcome in order that solution may occur. Both of these attractions must be considered in explaining solubility. In sodium chloride, ion-water attractions are great enough, and NaCl is quite soluble. In $BaSO_4$, ion-water attractions are not great enough, and $BaSO_4$ is quite insoluble, despite the fact that the ion-water attraction involved is greater than that for NaCl.

When we compare NaCl with $BaSO_4$ an important factor that needs to be considered is that in NaCl the ions are singly charged, whereas in $BaSO_4$ they are doubly charged. The higher the charge of an ion, the more strongly it will attract one end of a polar H_2O molecule. But the higher charge also causes a greater attraction between the ions in the solid. Thus increase of ionic charge seems to favor both solubility and insolubility. The problem is obviously complex, and a simple, satisfactory theory has not yet been developed. It seems to be generally true that, if the charge on both anion and cation is increased, insolubility is favored. Thus, for example, $BaSO_4$ (both ions doubly charged) and $AlPO_4$ (both ions triply charged) are much less soluble than NaCl (both ions singly charged). On the other hand, if the charge of only one ion is increased, the solubility is not much changed. As an example, NaCl, $BaCl_2$, and $AlCl_3$ are all appreciably soluble. Similarly, NaCl, Na_2SO_4, and Na_3PO_4 are also soluble.

In addition to charge, there are other factors which affect solubility. One of these is size. In general, the smaller an ion, the more strongly it attracts other ions and water molecules. Another factor we have ignored is that there may be specific interactions either in the solid or in the solution. An example of specific interactions occurs in solid silver chloride, AgCl, where there are stronger van der Waals attractions between Ag^+ and Cl^- than between the ions of NaCl, thus favoring lower solubility for AgCl than for NaCl. In barium sulfide, BaS, reaction of the sulfide ion, S^{--}, with water occurs, to help make BaS more soluble than $BaSO_4$. Thus, predictions as to solubility must be made with caution, since solubility depends on a number of factors.

16.7 HYDRATES

Analysis shows that many solids contain water molecules. These solids, called *hydrates,* are represented by formulas like that for nickel sulfate heptahydrate, $NiSO_4 \cdot 7H_2O$. The formula states that there are seven water molecules per formula-unit but does not specify how the H_2O is bound in the crystal. For example, in $NiSO_4 \cdot 7H_2O$ all seven H_2O molecules are not equivalent. Six are bound to the Ni^{++} ion to give $Ni(H_2O)_6^{++}$, and the seventh is shared between $Ni(H_2O)_6^{++}$ and SO_4^{--}. The solid is better represented by the formula $Ni(H_2O)_6SO_4 \cdot H_2O$. In other hydrates, such as sodium carbonate decahydrate, $Na_2CO_3 \cdot 10H_2O$, water molecules are not bound directly to the ions, but their principal function seems to be to improve the packing of the ions in the crystal. Water of hydration can be driven off by heating to give *anhydrous* material. The loss of water is usually accompanied by a change in crystal structure. However, some substances, such as certain silicate minerals, called zeolites, and proteins, lose water on heating without much change in crystal structure. On reexposure to water they, like sponges, take up water and swell. Apparently, water taken up this way occupies semirigid tunnels within the solid.

Actually, water of hydration is more common than not in the usual salts of the chemistry laboratory. Blue copper sulfate, for example, is $CuSO_4 \cdot 5H_2O$ or, better, $Cu(H_2O)_4SO_4 \cdot H_2O$. Even acids and bases can exist as hydrates in the solid form. Examples are barium hydroxide, $Ba(OH)_2 \cdot 8H_2O$, and oxalic acid, $H_2C_2O_4 \cdot 2H_2O$.

Frequently, hydrous compounds whose composition may be known but whose structure is in doubt are encountered. Such a substance is obtained, for example, from the reaction of a base with a solution of aluminum salt. Under certain conditions, the product might have the composition AlO_3H_3. The most obvious conclusion is that the compound is the hydroxide, $Al(OH)_3$. However, it could just as well be the hydrated oxide, $Al_2O_3 \cdot 3H_2O$, for which the simplest formula also is AlO_3H_3. In order to distinguish the two possibilities, structure studies are needed, but in many cases they have not been made.

QUESTIONS

16.1 Gas stochiometry   A mixture is made of equal volumes of $CO(g)$ and air. A spark is passed through so that all the O_2 is converted to CO_2 by the reaction

$$2CO(g) + O_2(g) \longrightarrow 2CO_2(g)$$

What will be the fractional decrease in the total volume of the system, assuming pressure and temperature stay constant?

16.2 Preparation   How much H_2O needs to be electrolyzed to produce sufficient O_2 to fill a 50-liter tank at a pressure of 150 atm and a temperature of 25°C?

16.3 Nernst equation   Calculate the oxidation potential for

$$2H_2O \longrightarrow O_2(g) + 4H^+ + 4e^-$$

in neutral solution and in basic solution where the OH^- activity is unity.

16.4 Occurrence   What volume of air (20% O_2 by volume) at STP contains the same number of oxygen atoms as a drop of water (0.050 cc)?

16.5 Hess's law   From the equations given in Section 16.3 calculate the heat of reaction for the oxidation of $C_2H_2(g)$ by $O_3(g)$ to form $CO_2(g)$ and $H_2O(g)$.

16.6 Equations   Write balanced equations for each of the following: (a) laboratory preparation of O_2, (b) complete oxidation of acetylene by ozone to CO_2 and H_2O, (c) oxidation of H_2O_2 in acid by $H_4IO_6^-$ going to I^-, (d) $Zn(OH)_2$ reacting with a strong acid, (e) $Zn(OH)_2$ reacting with a strong base.

16.7 Peroxide   What sort of experiment might you perform to show that a given white solid is a peroxide and not an oxide?

16.8 Molecular orbitals   (a) Using the same molecular orbitals for all species, tell what the bond order is in each of the following: O_2, O_2^+, O_2^-, O_2^{++}, O_2^{--}. (b) How many unpaired electrons in each of these species?

16.9 Stoichiometry   Given an aqueous H_2O_2 solution, the concentration of which is to be determined by titration with acidic $KMnO_4$ to form Mn^{++} and O_2. If 25.0 ml of the H_2O_2 solution requires 43.6 ml of 0.1024 M $KMnO_4$ solution, what is the molarity of the H_2O_2 solution?

16.10 Hydrate stoichiometry   How many grams of $NiSO_4 \cdot 7H_2O$ must be dissolved in 100.0 g of H_2O to make a solution that is 0.500 m in Ni^{++}?

16.11 Occurrence   Account quantitatively for the fact that air is 20% oxygen by volume but 21% oxygen by mass.

16.12 pH   What is the pH of the solution made by dissolving each of the following in enough water to make a liter of solution? (a) 1.0×10^{-4} mole CaO. (b) 2.0×10^{-2} mole $Ba(OH)_2$. (c) 3.0×10^{-3} mole CO_2 ($K = 4.2 \times 10^{-7}$).

16.13 Equilibrium constant   Calculate K for the equilibrium

$$CO_2 + OH^- \rightleftharpoons HCO_3^-$$

given that $K = 4.2 \times 10^{-7}$ for

$$CO_2 + H_2O \rightleftharpoons H^+ + HCO_3^-$$

16.14 Thermodynamics   Referred to $O_2(g)$ at one atmosphere pressure and 25°C, for $O_3(g)$ the standard free energy of formation is $+39.1$ kcal mole^{-1} and the standard enthalpy of formation is $+34.0$ kcal mole^{-1}. Calculate $\Delta S°$ for $3O_2(g) \longrightarrow 2O_3(g)$ under standard conditions.

16.15 Bond energy   Account for the fact that bond energy is increased when an electron is removed from an O_2 molecule or an F_2 molecule but decreased when an electron is removed from an N_2 molecule.

16.16 Water structure   (a) Considering the H_2O molecule as a sphere of radius 1.45 Å, calculate the density of water if it were a close-packed liquid in which 76% of the volume is occupied. (b) Comparing this to the observed maximum density, what would be the apparent percent empty space in water?

16.17 Free energy   For $BaO(s)$ and $BaO_2(s)$, the free energies of formation at 25°C are −126.3 and −135.8 kcal mole^{-1}, respectively, and the standard heats of formation are −133.4 and −150.5 kcal mole^{-1}, respectively. Assuming that $\Delta H°$ and $\Delta S°$ do not change with temperature, calculate the temperature at which the reaction

$$2BaO(s) + O_2(g) \longrightarrow 2BaO_2(s)$$

reverses, i.e., the temperature above which the O_2 pressure exceeds that in air (0.20 atm) and below which the O_2 pressure is less than that in air.

16.18 Structure   (a) Given the H_2O_2 structure shown in Figure 16.2, calculate the internuclear H-to-H distance. The O-to-O distance is 1.49 Å and the O-to-H, 0.97 Å. (b) In H_2O the O-to-H distance is 0.96 Å and the bond angle is 104.5°. Compare the H-to-H distance in H_2O with that in H_2O_2.

ANSWERS

16.1 0.10   *16.3* −0.82 volt; −0.41 volt   *16.5* 357 kcal evolved per mole   *16.10* 15.0 g   *16.12* (a) 10.30   (b) 12.60   (c) 4.45 *16.14* −34.2 cal mole^{-1} deg^{-1} *16.17* 630°K   *16.18* (a) 2.35 Å (b) 1.52 Å

17 the alkali metals

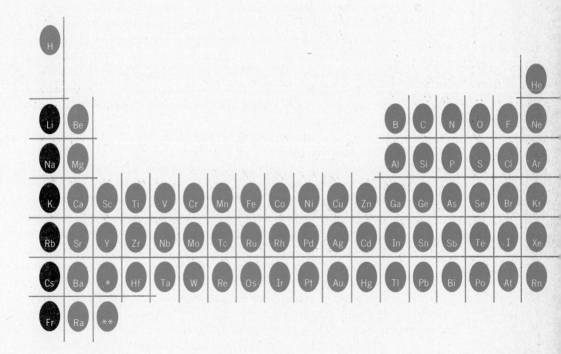

Having discussed the characteristic behavior of hydrogen and oxygen, we can now consider the detailed descriptive chemistry of the other elements. We shall begin with group I and proceed from left to right across the periodic table. The chemistry of group I elements is relatively simple, since but one valence electron is involved.

The elements of group I are lithium ($Z = 3$), sodium ($Z = 11$), potassium ($Z = 19$), rubidium ($Z = 37$), cesium ($Z = 55$), and francium ($Z = 87$). They are usually referred to as the alkali metals, after the Arabic word *al-qili,* meaning plant ashes, since the ashes of plants are particularly rich in sodium and potassium carbonate. The term "alkali" is also applied to any substance with marked basic properties. In addition to forming hydroxides which are strongly basic, the elements of group I show metallic behavior to a high degree and are very good reducing agents.

17.1 METALLIC PROPERTIES

The term "metal" is applied to any substance which has a silvery luster and good conductivity of electricity and heat. Some metals, of which the alkali metals are examples, also are relatively soft, malleable (can be beaten into sheets), and ductile (can be drawn into wires). All of these properties can be accounted for in terms of the metallic structure mentioned in Section 6.5.

The alkali elements crystallize with a body-centered-cubic lattice in which the lattice points are occupied by $+1$ ions. The valence electrons (one from each atom) make up a sea of negative charges, which permeates the whole lattice. Since they are not fixed in position, these electrons can wander at will throughout the metal and thus produce high electrical conductivity (see Section 13.1). Furthermore, it is almost invariably observed that high conductivity of electricity is accompanied by high conductivity of heat. This is not surprising, because thermal energy is transported rapidly from one part of a metal to another by the conduction electrons.

The high luster observed in the alkali metals is also explained by the highly mobile electrons of the metallic lattice. When a light beam strikes the surface of a metal, electric fields associated with the light wave set the electrons in the metal surface into back-and-forth oscillation. This is easy to do, because the valence electrons are not bound to specific atoms. However, like any moving electric charge, oscillating electrons give off electromagnetic energy as light. The net effect is that the beam of light is "reflected." In this respect the electrons in metals act like tiny radio stations which receive a radio signal and send it out again. Actually, nonmetals, even paper, also show high reflectivity, but only when looked at from very low angles. For nonmetals there is a critical angle beyond which the reflectivity disappears. The unusual thing about metals is that they show high reflectivity of light at all angles.

The softness, malleability, and ductility that also characterize the alkali metals are accounted for by the nature of the forces holding the lattice together. For example, in metallic sodium the principal force holding the lattice together is the attraction between Na^+ ions and the valence-electron cloud. Since this attraction is uniform in all directions, there are no strongly preferred positions for the Na^+ ions. The result is that Na^+ ions can easily be moved from one lattice site to another. Under pounding, the crystal can be flattened out like a pancake with but little expenditure of energy. Also, it can be cut with a knife like soft processed cheese. All this behavior is in contrast to the case of iron, in which there are strong, directed forces between adjacent positive ions which are due to covalent binding (Section 19.2).

The above discussion interprets metallic properties in terms of the metallic lattice, but a more fundamental question is, Why do the alkali

Element	Atomic number	Electronic configuration (core e^-'s in parentheses)	Ionization potential, ev		Ionic radius, Å (M^+)
			First	Second	
Lithium	3	(2) $2s^1$	5.39	75.6	0.68
Sodium	11	(10) $3s^1$	5.14	47.3	0.97
Potassium	19	(18) $4s^1$	4.34	31.8	1.33
Rubidium	37	(36) $5s^1$	4.18	27.5	1.47
Cesium	55	(54) $6s^1$	3.89	25.1	1.67
Francium	87	(86) $7s^1$	—	—	(1.75)

17.1
Properties of alkali atoms

elements prefer to form a crystal consisting of +1 ions and electrons? The question is complex, but it can be at least partly answered by considering the properties of the individual atoms. Figure 17.1 shows some of these properties. The column headed Electronic configuration indicates the population according to the principal quantum number in the undisturbed neutral atom. As indicated, each of the atoms has one electron in the outermost energy level. The energy required to pull off this valence electron is given in the column headed First ionization potential. As ionization potentials go, these are relatively small values, indicating that it is relatively easy to pull this one electron off a neutral alkali atom. However, the second ionization potential, the energy required to pull off a second electron, is many times higher than the first ionization potential. This means that, although it is relatively easy to form the M^+ ion, it is practically impossible under ordinary conditions to form the M^{++} ion of the alkali metals. All of this is consistent with the notion that the closed shell of electrons is difficult to break up. The result is that, when alkali atoms come together to form liquid or solid, M^+ ions are formed. The valence electrons are so weakly held that they can move throughout the lattice.

The properties of the alkali-metal atoms shown in Figure 17.1 are well illustrative of the general changes expected in going through a group of the periodic table. For example, the radius of the +1 cation* increases progressively from lithium down. This is expected because of the increasing number of electronic shells populated. Similarly, the ionization potential shows progressive decrease in going down the group. This is consistent with increased size and resulting smaller attraction for the valence electron, as discussed in Section 2.7. Actually, the change in properties in group I is so regular as to give a false sense of confidence about how well periodic-table trends can be predicted. There are traps for the unwary in later groups.

* From X-ray studies of ionic solids it is possible to determine the radius of an ion. There is a problem, however, in that X-ray investigations give only the distance between centers of adjacent atoms. How should this distance be apportioned? The usual procedure is to adopt one ion as a standard and to assume that it has a definite radius in all its compounds. Other radii are then assigned so that the sum of radii equals the observed spacing. A standard may be obtained from a salt like LiI, where Li^+ is so small that the spacing can be assumed to be due to large I^- ions in contact.

The alkali metals

361

Element	Oxidation potential, volts	Density, g cc^{-1}	Melting point, °C	Boiling point, °C
Lithium	+3.05	0.53	186	1336
Sodium	+2.71	0.97	97.5	880
Potassium	+2.93	0.86	62.3	760
Rubidium	+2.93	1.53	38.5	700
Cesium	+2.92	1.87	28.5	670

17.2
Properties of alkali metals

17.2 REDUCING PROPERTIES

The alkali metals are the most reactive metals known. Practically any oxidizing agent, no matter how weak, can be reduced by the alkali metals. Quantitatively, reducing strength (at least for aqueous solutions) is measured by the oxidation potential. Figure 17.2 lists the oxidation potentials of the alkali metals, along with other properties that characterize the behavior of these elements. As mentioned in Section 13.6, the oxidation potential measures the tendency of a substance, compared to that of hydrogen, to act as a reducing agent. For the alkali metals, the oxidation potential is characteristic of the reaction

$$M(s) \longrightarrow M^+ + e^-$$

in which the solid metal gives off electrons and forms ions in aqueous solution. The high values indicate that all these elements are excellent reducing agents and that lithium is the best of the lot.

At first sight there seems to be a discrepancy between the implications of Figures 17.1 and 17.2. The ionization potentials of Figure 17.1 indicate that lithium holds its electron most tightly. The oxidation potentials of Figure 17.2 indicate that lithium gives off its electron most readily. The apparent discrepancy is resolved by noting that the ionization potential is a property of the *isolated atom,* whereas the oxidation potential describes the *metal* as it goes into *solution.* The difference between ionization potential and oxidation potential may be clarified by the following consideration: The process

$$M(s) \longrightarrow M^+ + e^-$$

can be thought of as consisting of three consecutive steps:

$$M(s) \longrightarrow M(g) \tag{1}$$

$$M(g) \longrightarrow M^+(g) + e^- \tag{2}$$

$$M^+(g) + H_2O \longrightarrow M^+(aq) \tag{3}$$

In step (1) the metal is evaporated; i.e., the atoms are converted to the gaseous state, in which they are independent of each other. The energy required to do this (called the *sublimation energy*) is approximately the same for all the metals of group I. In step (2) an electron is pulled off the neutral atom to give a gaseous ion. The energy required (the

Step°	Li	Na	K	Rb	Cs
1) Sublimation	+1.62	+1.07	+0.88	+0.79	+0.75
2) Ionization	+5.39	+5.14	+4.34	+4.18	+3.89
3) Hydration	−4.90	−3.86	−3.08	−2.86	−2.52
$e^- + H^+(aq) \longrightarrow \frac{1}{2}H_2(g)$	−5.0	−5.0	−5.0	−5.0	−5.0
Calculated $E°$	2.9	2.7	2.9	2.9	2.9

17.3
Oxidation potential data, ev

ionization potential) is largest for lithium. In step (3) the gaseous ion is placed in water, i.e., hydrated. Energy (hydration energy) is liberated. The tendency of the overall change to occur (the oxidation potential) depends on the net effect of all three of these steps. The fact that for lithium the tendency of the overall change to occur is greatest suggests that the relative difficulty of step (2) has been more than compensated for by step (3). Apparently, the hydration energy of the tiny Li⁺ ion is so great that it makes up for the higher energy required to pull the electron off. In other words, the stabilizing effect of water on lithium ion makes the reaction

$$Li(s) \longrightarrow Li^+ + e^-$$

have a greater tendency to occur than the corresponding reaction for the other alkali elements.

The quantitative comparison of the above steps for the different alkali metals is shown in Figure 17.3. The numbers given represent free energies, in electron volts. (To convert to kilocalories per mole, multiply by 23.06.) A positive sign indicates energy must be added; a negative sign indicates energy is evolved. The values given for step 2, ionization, are taken to be equal to the ionization potentials—not quite true, but close enough to match the accuracy of the other data. In addition to totaling the three steps (sublimation, ionization, and hydration), we must include a term which places these values on the scale of oxidation potentials. Since $E°$'s are referred to the hydrogen electrode, this amounts to subtracting 5.0 ev (or 115 kcal) for the reference half-reaction. The final values turn out to be negative; but with the convention we are using, $\Delta G° = -n\mathcal{F}E°$, there is a change of sign in going from $\Delta G°$ to $E°$. Note that here $n = 1$ and $\mathcal{F}$ need not be included, since the data are already expressed in electron volts.

The great reactivity of the alkali metals poses a special problem in their handling. For example, water, although a relatively poor oxidizing agent, has great tendency to attack them. The tarnishing of freshly cut sodium is partially due to this oxidation by moisture in the air. To avoid such problems, alkali metals are usually stored under kerosene or other inert hydrocarbon compounds.

The alkali metals

363

As shown in Figure 17.2, the melting points of the alkali metals are quite low, in which respect they are unlike many other metals such as iron. The explanation for the low melting points lies in the ease of moving the positive ions, the feature that also accounts for malleability and ductility. However, the boiling points are fairly high, showing that it is hard to remove atoms from the metal. This indicates that metallic forces are appreciable.

17.3 OCCURRENCE

The alkali metals occur in nature only as $+1$ ions. Sodium and potassium are most abundant, ranking sixth and seventh of all the elements in the earth's crust. Lithium is moderately rare but is found in small amounts in practically all rocks. Rubidium and cesium are rare. Francium is essentially nonexistent, since it has an unstable nucleus and is radioactive. Trace amounts of it have been prepared by nuclear reactions.

Since most of the compounds of the alkali metals are soluble in water, they are generally found in seawater and in brine wells. However, there are many clays which are insoluble complex compounds of the alkali metals combined with Si, O, and Al. Presumably as the result of evaporation of ancient seas, there are also large salt deposits which serve as convenient sources of the alkali metals and their compounds.

Sodium ion and potassium ion are among the indispensable constituents of animal and plant tissue. Na^+ is the principal cation of the fluids outside the cells, whereas K^+ is the principal cation inside the cells. Besides filling general physiological roles, such as aiding water retention, these ions have specific functions. For example, Na^+ depresses the activity of muscle enzymes and is required for contraction of all animal muscle. In plants, K^+, but not Na^+, is a primary requirement. As a result, more than 90% of the alkali content of ashes is due to potassium. Plants have such a high demand for potassium that, even in soils in which the sodium content predominates manyfold, the potassium is taken up preferentially. Since an average crop extracts from the soil about 50 lb of potassium per acre, the necessity for potassium fertilizers is obvious.

17.4 PREPARATION

To prepare the alkali elements, it is necessary to reduce the $+1$ ion. This can be done chemically or electrolytically. Purely chemical methods would seem impossible, since they require a reducing agent stronger than the alkali metals. However, chemical reduction can be carried out in special cases, as in the reaction of rubidium chloride with calcium at high temperature.

$$Ca(s) + 2RbCl(s) \longrightarrow CaCl_2(s) + 2Rb(g)$$

The reaction occurs in the direction indicated only because the rubidium escapes as a gas out of the reacting mixture, thus preventing the attainment of equilibrium. In the equilibrium state the concentration of rubidium would be very small.

In practice, the alkali metals are generally prepared by electrolysis of molten alkali compounds. For example, sodium is made commercially in ton quantities by the electrolysis of a fused mixture of NaCl and $CaCl_2$ at about 600°C. ($CaCl_2$ is added to reduce the melting point of the bath.) Sodium metal is formed at the iron or copper cathodes, and chlorine at the carbon anodes. To prevent oxidation of the Na by the chlorine, the electrode compartments are separated by a wire-gauze partition.

17.5 PROPERTIES AND USES

As mentioned, the alkali metals exhibit, to a high degree, typically metallic properties. Although too expensive and too chemically reactive to be used for their metallic properties, they do find special application. For example, liquid alkali metal is used to solve the difficult engineering problem of conducting heat energy from the center of a nuclear reactor to the exterior, where it can be converted into useful work (Chapter 29). The expense and difficulty involved in working with alkali metal are partially compensated for by its excellence as a heat conductor.

Cesium has the distinction of being the metal from which electrons are ejected most easily by light; such light-induced emission is termed the *photoelectric effect*. For this reason, cesium finds use in the *photocell,* a device for converting a light signal to an electric signal. An evacuated tube contains two electrodes with a voltage difference between them. The negative electrode is coated with cesium metal, cesium oxide, or an alloy of cesium, antimony, and silver. In the absence of light the tube does not conduct electricity, since there is nothing to carry the charge from one electrode to the other. When struck by light, the cesium-coated electrode emits electrons, which are attracted to the positive electrode, and thus the circuit is completed. Television pickup devices such as the iconoscope and the image orthicon use the photocell principle. Color effects are made possible because the cesium metal has a high response to red light and a low response to blue light, whereas cesium oxide is most sensitive to the blue.

Though all the alkali metals are very good reducing agents, only sodium finds extensive use for this purpose. It is used to make other metals by reducing their chlorides, and it is also used in the production of various compounds of carbon. For this latter purpose, sodium is frequently used in the form of its solution in liquid ammonia. It is a remarkable fact that sodium and the other alkali metals dissolve in the waterlike solvent NH_3 to give colored solutions which can be evaporated to give the alkali metal unchanged. In the blue solutions it is assumed that the alkali metal is dissociated into $+1$ ions and electrons. The electrons are associated with NH_3 molecules; therefore, the anions in these solutions can be considered as solvated electrons. More concentrated solutions have a metallic, bronzelike appearance and have very high electrical conductivity, indicating that the electrons are extremely mobile. Reducing properties are somewhat toned down in all these solutions compared with the pure alkali metals.

17.6 COMPOUNDS

The alkali metals readily form compounds by reacting with other substances. For example, sodium metal on standing in air becomes covered with sodium peroxide, Na_2O_2. Furthermore, water vigorously attacks any of the alkali metals to liberate hydrogen

$$2M(s) + 2H_2O \longrightarrow 2M^+ + 2OH^- + H_2(g)$$

Thus, the problem with the alkali metals is not to get them to form compounds but to keep them from doing so.

All the compounds of the alkali metals are ionic, even the hydrides, and all contain the alkali metal as a $+1$ ion. Most of the compounds are quite soluble in water; hence, a convenient way to get a desired anion in solution is to use its sodium salt. The alkali-metal ions do not hydrolyze appreciably and do not form complex ions to any appreciable extent. Since the alkali-metal ions are colorless, any color of alkali-metal compounds must be due to the anion.

The hydrides (Section 15.4) of the alkali metals are white solids prepared by heating alkali metal in hydrogen. The simple oxides, M_2O, are not so easily formed. Of the alkali metals, only lithium reacts directly with oxygen to form Li_2O. When sodium reacts with oxygen, the peroxide Na_2O_2 is formed instead. Potassium, rubidium, and cesium under similar conditions form superoxides of the type MO_2. In order to get the simple oxides, it is necessary to reduce some alkali-metal compound such as the nitrate. For example,

$$2KNO_3(s) + 10K(s) \longrightarrow 6K_2O(s) + N_2(g)$$

All the oxides are basic oxides and react with water to form hydroxides. Commercially, however, the hydroxides of the alkali metals are made by electrolysis of aqueous alkali-chloride solutions. For example, as discussed in Section 13.2, sodium hydroxide, or *caustic soda,* as it is often called, is made by electrolysis of aqueous NaCl.

Other important compounds of the alkali metals, such as *washing soda,* Na_2CO_3, and *baking soda,* $NaHCO_3$, are discussed in later chapters in connection with the corresponding anions.

17.7 SPECTRA

As described in Sections 1.5 and 1.6, an electron which changes from a higher energy level of an atom to a lower energy level must give up the excess energy to the surroundings. If the energy is emitted as light, as is often the case, the light will be made up of one or more energies, each of which corresponds to a definite energy jump in the atom. This distribution of energies, or spectrum of the atom, is characteristic of the atom in question.

For the alkali metals, it is particularly easy to excite electrons to higher energy states and thus produce their spectra. Even a bunsen burner flame can do it. For this reason, alkali-metal compounds impart characteristic colors to flames. Lithium salts produce red flames;

sodium, yellow; potassium, violet; rubidium, reddish violet; and cesium, reddish violet. These colors serve as the basis of the well-known flame tests for these elements.

17.8 QUALITATIVE ANALYSIS

Because the alkali metals do not form many insoluble compounds and because the alkali ions are colorless, it is difficult to detect the presence of these elements by chemical methods. Instead, their presence is usually shown by running flame tests on the sample in question. The simplest way to run a flame test is to shape a piece of fine platinum wire into a loop, dip the loop in HCl solution and heat to remove volatile impurities, and then use the loop to heat the sample in a burner flame. The sodium yellow is extremely intense, so that even traces of it can mask other flame colors. The main reason for cleaning the platinum loop by the HCl treatment is to help expel sodium as the relatively volatile chloride. (In general, chlorides are more volatile than most other solids.) The potassium flame is colored a delicate violet and can be observed in many cases only through cobalt glass, which filters out interfering colors such as sodium yellow. The flames of K, Rb, and Cs look so similar that definite identification requires examination of the line spectrum with a spectroscope. The strongest lines are Li, 6708 Å; Na, 5890 and 5896 Å; K, 7665 and 7699 Å; Rb, 4202 and 4215 Å; Cs, 4556 and 4593 Å.

QUESTIONS

17.1 Periodic behavior   How does each of the following change in going down group I: (*a*) ionic radius, (*b*) density of the solid, (*c*) melting point, (*d*) number of valence electrons, (*e*) sublimation free energy?

17.2 Equations   Write a complete balanced equation for each of the following changes: (*a*) oxidation of lithium hydride by water to give $H_2(g)$, (*b*) reaction of lithium peroxide with $CO_2(g)$ to form lithium carbonate plus $O_2(g)$, (*c*) reaction of potassium superoxide with water to form oxygen and HO_2^-, (*d*) production of elemental sodium by electrolysis of molten NaOH.

17.3 Seawater   The principal species in seawater are H_2O, Cl^-, Na^+, SO_4^{--}, Mg^{++}, Ca^{++}, and K^+. The average concentrations are 55.0, 0.535, 0.454, 0.0276, 0.0523, 0.0102, and 0.0096 mole liter^{-1}, respectively. Calculate the average density of seawater.

17.4 Structure   Sodium metal crystallizes in the body-centered-cubic structure. The unit-cell edge length is 4.24 Å. Assuming sodium metal consists of definite Na^+ ions and free electrons, what fraction of solid sodium crystal is actually filled by the ions? The ionic radius of Na^+ is usually given as 0.97 Å.

17.5 Stoichiometry   (*a*) Suppose you want to make up a solution of sodium hydroxide that is precisely 0.1000 *M* NaOH. You think you can do this by dissolving a piece of pure sodium in water. How much Na will you need to weigh out to make 100.0 ml of 0.1000 M NaOH? (*b*) What error, if any, would there be in the final OH^- concentration if, after the weighing, 10.0 mg of the Na were oxidized by the atmosphere to Na_2O_2? Assume that when Na_2O_2 is added to H_2O the reaction is

$$Na_2O_2(s) + H_2O \longrightarrow 2Na^+ + OH^- + HO_2^-$$

17.6 Reaction prediction By referring to the data of Figure 17.3, tell whether under standard conditions each of the following should occur as written:

(*a*) $Na(g) + Li^+(g) \longrightarrow Na^+(g) + Li(g)$
(*b*) $Na(g) + Rb^+(g) \longrightarrow Na^+(g) + Rb(g)$
(*c*) $Na(g) + K^+(g) \longrightarrow Na^+(g) + K(s)$

17.7 Free energy By using the data of Figure 17.3, calculate the standard free energy in kilocalories for the reaction

$$Na(s) + Rb^+(aq) \longrightarrow Na^+(aq) + Rb(g)$$

17.8 Liquid-ammonia solutions When sodium is dissolved in liquid NH_3, there is considerable expansion in total volume. From the following data at $-34°C$ calculate the change in the apparent volume per mole of Na, assuming the volume contributed by the NH_3 does not change.

Density of pure Na = 0.97 g cc^{-1}
Density of pure NH_3 = 0.677 g cc^{-1}
Density of Na-NH_3 solution having Na mole fraction 0.0500 = 0.641 g cc^{-1}

17.9 Alkali halide structure (*a*) LiI has the same structure as NaCl. In LiI the unit-cell length is 6.00 Å. Assuming that the Li^+ ion is so small in this structure that I^- ions are in contact, calculate the apparent radius of iodide ion in crystalline LiI. (*b*) Assuming the same I^- radius as in (*a*), calculate the apparent radius of Rb^+ in RbI, where the structure is the same as in NaCl and the unit-cell length is 7.33 Å.

17.10 Stoichiometry In making the NaOH solution of Problem 17.5, you worry about the error discussed in part (*b*) so much that you give up that method as a poor risk. Instead you decide to make your 100.0 ml of 0.1000 M NaOH by weighing out "pure" NaOH. Unfortunately, no one has told you that "pure" NaOH is usually 5% converted to Na_2CO_3 because of reaction with the atmosphere. How big an error, if any, would this make in the final OH^- concentration? Assume 5.0% by weight Na_2CO_3 reacts according to

$$CO_3^{--} + H_2O \rightleftharpoons HCO_3^- + OH^-$$

with equilibrium constant for the net reaction of 2.1×10^{-4}.

17.11 Oxidation potential of francium By extrapolating the data of Figure 17.3, predict whether the $E°$ for $Fr(s) \longrightarrow Fr^+(aq) + e^-$ is greater or less than that for cesium.

17.12 Thermodynamics It has been reported that the apparent molecular mass of sodium vapor is 26.0 at 570.5°C and a total pressure

of 13.5 torr. It is known that sodium vapor contains appreciable concentrations of Na_2 from the reaction

$$2Na(g) \longrightarrow Na_2(g)$$

for which ΔH is -18 kcal under these conditions. (a) Calculate the
equilibrium constant at 570.5°C for the above reaction in terms of
pressure, in torr. (b) Assuming a constant ΔH and ideal-gas behavior,
calculate the apparent molecular mass of sodium vapor at its boiling
point of 880°C at one atmosphere.

ANSWERS

17.3 1.025 g cc^{-1} *17.5* 0.2299 g; 2.17% low   *17.8* From 24 cc
to 63 cc   *17.9* (a) 2.12 Å   (b) 1.55 Å   *17.12* (a) 0.0129   (b) 29.5

18 the alkaline-earth metals

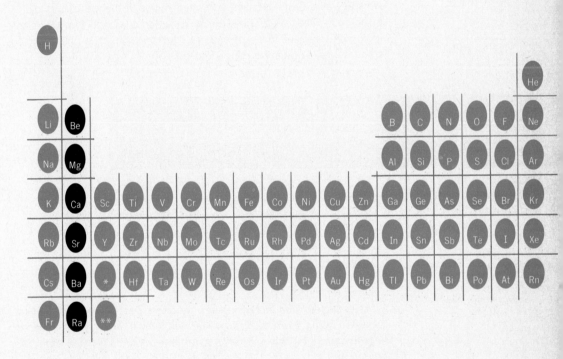

Group II of the periodic table contains the elements beryllium ($Z = 4$), magnesium ($Z = 12$), calcium ($Z = 20$), strontium ($Z = 38$), barium ($Z = 56$), and radium ($Z = 88$). They are called the *alkaline-earth metals*, because the alchemists referred to any nonmetallic substance insoluble in water and unchanged by fire as an "earth" and because the "earths" of this group, e.g., lime (CaO) and magnesia (MgO), give decidedly alkaline reactions.

Probably the most characteristic features of the group II elements are their good metallic properties, their strength as reducing agents, and their formation of compounds in which they show oxidation state

+2. Many of these compounds are of low solubility. Compared with group I elements, the alkaline-earth elements are both less metallic and poorer reducing agents.

18.1 PROPERTIES

Electronic configurations and some related properties of the alkaline-earth-metal atoms are shown in Figure 18.1. It should also be noted that radium atoms are radioactive and undergo spontaneous nuclear disintegration. In each of the alkaline-earth-metal atoms there are two electrons in the outer-most energy level. With the exception of beryllium, the next lower principal quantum level contains eight electrons. The chief difference in going down the group is the stepwise inclusion of sets of 8, 18, and 32 electrons. As expected, there is a corresponding increase in size from Be to Ra. This is illustrated in the last column, which gives experimentally determined values of the M^{++} cation radius in crystals. The values need to be considered as approximate, since ionic sizes depend on environment, but they do show the expected trend as more levels are populated.

Element	Atomic number	Electronic configuration (core e^-'s in parentheses)	Ionization potential, ev			Ionic radius, Å (M^{++})
			First	Second	Third	
Beryllium	4	(2) $2s^2$	9.32	18.2	153.8	0.35
Magnesium	12	(10) $3s^2$	7.64	15.0	80.1	0.66
Calcium	20	(18) $4s^2$	6.11	11.9	51.2	0.99
Strontium	38	(36) $5s^2$	5.69	11.0	(43)	1.12
Barium	56	(54) $6s^2$	5.21	10.0	(36)	1.34
Radium	88	(86) $7s^2$	5.28	10.1	—	1.43

18.1
Properties of alkaline-earth atoms

As expected, with increasing size we find a decreasing ionization potential in going down the group. The first ionization potential is the energy required to pull one electron off the neutral, isolated atom. As mentioned in Section 2.7, the larger atoms hold their outer electrons less tightly than do the smaller atoms, hence the decreasing ionization potential from Be to Ba. The anomaly for radium is not explained. The second ionization potential measures the energy required to pull one electron off the +1 ion to form a +2 ion. Because the electron is pulled off a positively charged ion rather than a neutral atom, the second ionization potential of an atom is always greater than the first. The third ionization potential indicates the energy to pull one electron off a +2 ion to form a +3 ion and, for a given element, is greater than the second ionization potential.

Inspection of the ionization potentials in Figure 18.1 shows that removal of the third electron from alkaline-earth elements requires very high energies. Such high energies are usually not available in chemical reactions, and therefore +3 ions of the alkaline-earth elements are not encountered except in some hot stars. In practice, only the +2 ions of these elements are observed. How can this be justified in the light of the fact that the second ionization potentials are almost twice as great as the first? It would seem that these elements, like group I elements, should prefer to form +1 ions rather than +2. If only the ionization potentials were involved, such would indeed be the case. For example, 6.11 ev is required to pull off the first electron from calcium and 11.9 ev to pull off the second. This means that return of one electron to Ca^{++} liberates 11.9 ev of energy. As a consequence, calcium gas and doubly charged calcium ions are unstable with respect to conversion to singly charged calcium ions.

$$Ca(g) \longrightarrow Ca^+(g) + e^- \qquad\qquad \text{Requires 6.11 ev}$$

$$e^- + Ca^{++}(g) \longrightarrow Ca^+(g) \qquad\qquad \text{Liberates 11.9 ev}$$

Net:

$$Ca(g) + Ca^{++}(g) \longrightarrow 2Ca^+(g) \qquad \text{Liberates 5.8 ev}$$

The net energy release is enormous (5.8 ev, or 134 kcal); hence, Ca^+ should be formed in the gas phase. It has, in fact, been detected at high temperatures.

In aqueous solutions the situation is more complicated, since we must also consider the effect of hydration on stabilizing the ionic products. Following a procedure similar to that used in Section 17.2, we consider the steps leading up to a calculated oxidation potential. For example, for calcium, to calculate the $E°$ for the reaction

$$Ca(s) + H^+(aq) \longrightarrow Ca^+(aq) + \tfrac{1}{2}H_2(g)$$

the steps are

$$Ca(s) \longrightarrow Ca(g) \tag{1}$$

$$Ca(g) \longrightarrow Ca^+(g) + e^- \tag{2}$$

$$Ca^+(g) \longrightarrow Ca^+(aq) \tag{3}$$

$$e^- + H^+(aq) \longrightarrow \tfrac{1}{2}H_2(g) \tag{4}$$

The free-energy change associated with step (1), sublimation, is 38.0 kcal, or 1.65 ev; the free-energy change associated with step (2), ionization, is about 141 kcal, or 6.11 ev. Thus, for the first two steps, the free-energy increase is 179 kcal, or 7.76 ev. Step (3) liberates energy which can be estimated by comparison with data for known +1 ions; for step (3) we guess ΔG to be about −70 kcal, or −3.0 ev. For the last step, as we have previously noted, the free-energy change is favorable, that is, −115 kcal, or −5.0 ev. Adding the four steps, we get for the overall process a net free-energy change of −6 kcal, or −0.2 ev. This means that the net reaction is favorable as written, and, using $\Delta G° = -n\mathfrak{F}E°$ with $n = 1$, the oxidation potential $E°$ for $Ca(s)$ to $Ca^+(aq)$ is +0.2 volt.

The fact that $E°$ for a reaction is positive does not necessarily mean that the final products will be those formed by this reaction, since there may be other possible reactions. For the present case we need to consider the possibility of subsequent oxidation of $Ca^+(aq)$ to $Ca^{++}(aq)$. Referred to hydrogen, this reaction would be written

$$Ca^+(aq) + H^+(aq) \longrightarrow Ca^{++}(aq) + \tfrac{1}{2}H_2(g)$$

Component steps could be the following:

$$Ca^+(aq) \longrightarrow Ca^+(g) \tag{5}$$

$$Ca^+(g) \longrightarrow Ca^{++}(g) + e^- \tag{6}$$

$$Ca^{++}(g) \longrightarrow Ca^{++}(aq) \tag{7}$$

$$e^- + H^+(aq) \longrightarrow \tfrac{1}{2}H_2(g) \tag{8}$$

Step (5) is the reverse of step (3) and has a free-energy change of about $+70$ kcal, or $+3.0$ ev. Step (6) is the second ionization of Ca; its free-energy change is about $+274$ kcal, or $+11.9$ ev. Step (7) has a free-energy change of -362 kcal, or -15.7 ev. Step (8) has ΔG equal to -115 kcal, or -5.0 ev. The sum of steps (5) to (8) gives for the net free-energy change -133 kcal, or -5.8 ev. This large, negative free-energy change means that the reaction

$$Ca^+(aq) + H^+(aq) \longrightarrow Ca^{++}(aq) + \tfrac{1}{2}H_2(g)$$

has a tendency to go as written; in fact, more so than the oxidation of $Ca(s)$ to $Ca^+(aq)$. Taking out the hydrogen half-reaction with its $E° = 0$, we get the following:

$$Ca^+(aq) \longrightarrow Ca^{++}(aq) + e^- \qquad E° = +5.8 \text{ volts}$$

$$Ca(s) \longrightarrow Ca^+(aq) + e^- \qquad E° = +0.2 \text{ volt}$$

Since $Ca^+(aq)$ is a stronger reducing agent than $Ca(s)$, it will reverse the lower half-reaction to give the net reaction

$$2Ca^+(aq) \longrightarrow Ca(s) + Ca^{++}(aq) \qquad E° = +5.6 \text{ volts}$$

The high positive value of $E°$ for this net reaction indicates a great tendency for $Ca^+(aq)$ to *oxidize and reduce itself*, i.e., to *disproportionate*. For all of the other alkaline-earth elements the corresponding disproportionation reactions are also favored, so that in no case is the $+1$ aqueous ion stable. Even in the solid state, where lattice energy plays the role that hydration energy plays in solution, the $+1$ alkaline-earth ions are not generally stable.

Once we have given the $E°$ for the conversion of $Ca(s)$ to $Ca^+(aq)$ and the $E°$ for the conversion of $Ca^+(aq)$ to $Ca^{++}(aq)$, we can easily calculate the $E°$ for the conversion of $Ca(s)$ to $Ca^{++}(aq)$. The important thing to remember when adding half-reactions is that the voltage $E°$ gives the free-energy change *per* electron. Hence, to add half-reactions, we must first convert to free-energy change (i.e., multiply voltage by the number of electrons) and then add. The sum half-reaction now contains several electrons, so its free-energy change must be divided by

Element	Oxidation potential, volts	Density, g cc^{-1}	Melting point, °C	Boiling point, °C
Beryllium	+1.85	1.86	1280	1500(?)
Magnesium	+2.37	1.74	650	1100
Calcium	+2.87	1.55	810	1300(?)
Strontium	+2.89	2.6	800	1300(?)
Barium	+2.90	3.6	850	1500(?)
Radium	+2.92	5(?)	960(?)	1100(?)

18.2
Properties of alkaline-earth metals

the number of electrons to give $E°$. Following this procedure for calcium, we get

	$E°$, volts	$\Delta G° = -n\mathfrak{F}E°$
$Ca(s) \longrightarrow Ca^+(aq) + e^-$	0.2	$-(1)(\mathfrak{F})(0.2)$
$Ca^+(aq) \longrightarrow Ca^{++}(aq) + e^-$	5.8	$-(1)(\mathfrak{F})(5.8)$
$Ca(s) \longrightarrow Ca^{++}(aq) + 2e^-$	3.0	$-(2)(\mathfrak{F})(3.0)$

Note that $E°$ for the last half-reaction, 3.0 volts, is calculated as the sum of the first two free-energy changes divided by $-n\mathfrak{F}$, where $n = 2$. Stated another way, the $E°$ for a sum half-reaction is the weighted average of the component $E°$ values.

Figure 18.2 shows some of the properties of the group II elements in the solid state, as distinguished from the properties of the isolated atoms. In the solid state the elements have typically metallic properties: high luster and good conductivity. They are harder than the group I elements but still can be cut with a hard steel knife. The fairly high melting points are in line with this greater hardness. The boiling points (many of which have not been accurately determined) are higher than those of the alkali metals and suggest that the forces of attraction between the electron cloud and M^{++} ions are greater than those between the electron cloud and M^+ ions.

The oxidation potentials, shown in the second column, are relatively high. They correspond to the reaction

$$M(s) \longrightarrow M^{++} + 2e^-$$

and indicate that in aqueous solutions these elements are good reducing agents. For example, all the alkaline-earth metals have the ability to react with water to release hydrogen by the reaction

$$M(s) + 2H_2O \longrightarrow M^{++} + H_2(g) + 2OH^-$$

18.2 COMPARISON WITH ALKALI METALS

The alkaline-earth metals

375

It is interesting to compare the properties of group I and group II elements and attempt to account for any differences. We first consider size, which is fundamental for many properties. Examination of Figures 17.1 and 18.1 shows that the ionic radius of any group II element is smaller than that of the group I element of the same period. For example, Mg^{++} has an ionic radius of 0.66 Å compared to 0.97 Å for Na^+. Both these elements fall in the third period of the periodic table. Why the difference in size? Sodium ion has a nuclear charge of $+11$ and has two electrons in the K shell and eight electrons in the L shell ($1s^2 2s^2 2p^6$); magnesium ion has a nuclear charge of $+12$ and also has two electrons in the K shell and eight electrons in the L shell ($1s^2 2s^2 2p^6$). These two ions are *isoelectronic;* i.e., they have identical electronic configurations. The difference between Na^+ and Mg^{++} is that the latter has a higher nuclear charge. Increased nuclear charge means increased attraction for electrons, which in turn means a smaller K shell and a smaller L shell. In any isoelectronic sequence, ionic size decreases with increased nuclear charge.

Just as the ionic size decreases in going from group I to group II, the apparent atomic size (Section 2.6) also decreases. This smaller atomic size of the group II neutral atoms accounts for the difference between the first ionization potentials of groups I and II. Figures 17.1 and 18.1 show that, in going from group I to group II, there is a rather large increase in the energy required to pull off one electron (for example, 5.14 ev for Na and 7.64 ev for Mg). This, of course, is in line with the smaller size of group II atoms and their consequent tighter hold on electrons.

The most puzzling comparison between groups I and II is in the oxidation potentials. For the lighter elements at the top of the group there is a distinct difference, and it is in the direction that group I elements have higher oxidation potentials and are, therefore, better reducing agents. For example, the oxidation potential of beryllium is $+1.85$ volts compared to that of lithium, $+3.05$ volts. However, for the heavier elements at the bottom of the group, there is little difference between groups I and II. Barium, for instance, has an oxidation potential of $+2.90$, whereas cesium, of the same period, has $+2.92$ volts.

Actually, it is not surprising that group I elements are stronger reducing agents than corresponding group II elements. After all, the ionization potentials of group I elements are much lower. The surprising thing is that group II elements are as good reducing agents as they are. The key to the explanation apparently lies in the hydration energy. Although it takes a fair amount of energy to pull two electrons off a group II atom, the net process $M(s) \longrightarrow M^{++}(aq) + 2e^-$ nevertheless has a great tendency to occur, because the doubly charged ion interacts strongly with water in forming the hydrated ion.

18.3 OCCURRENCE

In nature, the alkaline-earth elements are found only in compounds as $+2$ ions. As discussed in Section 16.6, $+2$ ions combine with -2 ions to form compounds less soluble than those of $+1$ ions. Consequently, many alkaline-earth compounds are insoluble and, unlike alkali-metal compounds, are found as insoluble deposits in the earth's crust. Most important of these deposits are the silicates, carbonates, sulfates, and phosphates.

Beryllium on a weight basis makes up only 0.0006% of the earth's crust. It is very widespread, but only in trace amounts. The only important beryllium mineral found in any quantity is a silicate, beryl, or $Be_3Al_2Si_6O_{18}$. Enormous single crystals of beryl weighing many tons have been found. The gem stone emerald is beryl, colored deep green by trace amounts of chromium.

Magnesium is the eighth most abundant element in the earth's crust, making up about 2% of its mass. It is widely distributed, principally as the silicate minerals such as asbestos ($CaMg_3Si_4O_{12}$) and the carbonate, oxide, and chloride. Magnesite ($MgCO_3$) and dolomite ($MgCO_3 \cdot CaCO_3$) are the principal sources of magnesium in addition to seawater and deep salt wells.

Calcium is the most abundant of the group I and group II elements on a mass basis (3.6% of the earth's crust), but it is outnumbered 6 to 5 on an atom basis by sodium. The principal minerals of calcium are the silicates, carbonate, sulfate, phosphate, and fluoride. Calcium carbonate ($CaCO_3$) appears in such diverse minerals as limestone, marble, and chalk. Most of these appear to be derived from the skeletons of marine animals which have been laid down on seabeds and consolidated. The mineral gypsum ($CaSO_4 \cdot 2H_2O$) is also very common. It apparently owes its origin in many cases to limestone beds which have been acted on by sulfuric acid produced from the oxidation of sulfide minerals. Phosphate rock is essentially $Ca_3(PO_4)_2$, an important ingredient of bones, teeth, and seashells.

Strontium is relatively rare and ranks twentieth in order of abundance; barium, which makes up 0.05% of the earth's crust, is about 2.5 times as abundant. The principal mineral of strontium is strontianite ($SrCO_3$); of barium, barite ($BaSO_4$).

Radium is very rare, but its presence is easily detected by its radioactivity. Because its nucleus spontaneously disintegrates, all the radium found is due to the nuclear breakdown of heavier elements, particularly uranium. For this reason, uranium ores such as pitchblende (impure U_3O_8) are principal sources of radium. It has been estimated that the average abundance of radium in the earth's crust is less than 1 part per million million. This makes a uranium mineral which contains ¼ g of radium per ton of ore a relatively rich source of radium.

18.4 PREPARATION

Since the alkaline-earth elements occur only as the $+2$ ions, preparation of the metals requires a reduction process. Reduction can be accomplished by electrolysis of the molten halides or hydroxides or by chemical reduction with appropriate reducing agents. Beryllium, for example, is made by heating beryllium fluoride, BeF_2, with Mg and also by electrolyzing a mixture of beryllium chloride, $BeCl_2$, and NaCl.

The extraction of magnesium from seawater accounts for the bulk of

United States production. In the process the magnesium ion in sea-water (about 0.13%) is precipitated as $Mg(OH)_2$ by the addition of lime, CaO. The hydroxide is filtered off and converted to $MgCl_2$ by reaction with HCl. The dried $MgCl_2$ is mixed with other salts to lower the melting point and then electrolyzed at about 700°C to give metal of 99.9% purity.

Magnesium can also be prepared by a chemical reduction process in which magnesium oxide, obtained by heating dolomite, is reduced at high temperatures by iron and silicon. Since the reaction is carried out above 1100°C, the boiling point of magnesium, the process produces gaseous magnesium, which escapes from the reaction mixture to condense as a very high purity product.

18.5 PROPERTIES AND USES

All the alkaline-earth metals are good conductors of heat and electricity, but of them only magnesium finds any considerable use. Surprisingly, this use is based on the structural qualities of magnesium rather than on its electrical properties. Lightest of all the commercially important structural metals, magnesium has relatively low structural strength, but this can be increased by alloying with other elements. The principal elements added are aluminum, zinc, and manganese. The aluminum helps increase the tensile strength; the zinc improves the working properties (machining); and the manganese reduces corrosion. The use of magnesium alloys is ever increasing because of modern emphasis on weight reduction in such things as aircraft, railroad equipment, and household goods.

Too rare and costly for most large-scale uses, beryllium is important as a trace addition for hardening other metals such as copper. In the finely powdered form, beryllium (and its compounds) must be handled carefully, since it is extremely toxic.

Calcium, strontium, and barium are more reactive than beryllium and magnesium. The situation is complicated further by the fact that, when exposed to air, they form oxides which flake off to expose fresh surface. Their great affinity for oxygen makes these elements useful as deoxidizers in steel production and as getters in the production of low-cost electron tubes. Most radio tubes, for example, have a thin deposit of barium metal on the inner wall of the glass or metal envelope. The purpose is to pick up any gases such as oxygen in the tube.

Finely divided magnesium burns rather vigorously to emit very intense light which is particularly rich in the higher energies. For this reason, magnesium is used as one of the important light sources for photography. Flash bulbs contain wire or foil of magnesium (or aluminum) packed in an oxygen atmosphere. When the bulb is fired, an electric current heats the metal and initiates the oxidation reaction.

The flame spectra of strontium salts are characteristically red, and those of barium are yellowish green. Strontium and barium salts are frequently used for color effect in pyrotechnics.

18.6 COMPOUNDS

At ordinary temperatures the alkaline-earth elements form compounds only in the $+2$ oxidation state. With the exception of beryllium, all such compounds are essentially ionic. The alkaline-earth ions are colorless and, except for Be^{++}, do not hydrolyze appreciably in aqueous solution. Beryllium salts hydrolyze to give acid solutions. Unlike the compounds of group I, many group II compounds are not soluble in water.

1. *Hydrides.* When heated in hydrogen gas, Ca, Sr, and Ba form hydrides. These are white powders which react with H_2O to liberate H_2. Calcium hydride, CaH_2, is used as a convenient, portable hydrogen supply.

$$CaH_2(s) + 2H_2O \longrightarrow Ca^{++} + 2OH^- + 2H_2(g)$$

2. *Oxides.* The oxides of these elements are characteristically very high melting (*refractory*). They can be made by heating the metals in oxygen or thermally decomposing the carbonates or hydroxides. For example, lime (CaO) is made from limestone ($CaCO_3$) by the reaction

$$CaCO_3(s) \longrightarrow CaO(s) + CO_2(g)$$

Except for beryllium oxide, BeO, which is amphoteric, the oxides of group II are basic. Both lime and magnesia (MgO) are used as linings in furnaces, sometimes specifically to counteract acidic impurities, as in steel production.

3. *Hydroxides.* The hydroxides of group II are made by adding water to the oxides in a process called *slaking*. For example, the slaking of lime produces calcium hydroxide, $Ca(OH)_2$, sometimes called slaked lime. The reaction

$$CaO(s) + H_2O \longrightarrow Ca(OH)_2(s) + 16 \text{ kcal}$$

is accompanied by a threefold expansion in volume, sometimes to the consternation of building contractors whose lime supplies accidentally get wet. Lime is an important constituent of cement and is also used as an important industrial base, since it is cheaper than NaOH.

The hydroxides of the alkaline-earth elements are only slightly soluble in water; however, the solubility increases with increasing ionic size. The solubility products are given in Figure 18.3. With the exception of $Be(OH)_2$, which is amphoteric, the other hydroxides are dissociated in water to give basic solutions.

4. *Sulfates.* The sulfates of group II range from the very soluble beryllium sulfate to the practically insoluble radium sulfate. Going down the group, the solubilities decrease in regular order; for $BeSO_4$, K_{sp} is

18.3
K_{sp} for alkaline-earth hydroxides

$Be(OH)_2$	Less than 10^{-19}
$Mg(OH)_2$	8.9×10^{-12}
$Ca(OH)_2$	1.3×10^{-6}
$Sr(OH)_2$	3.2×10^{-4}
$Ba(OH)_2$	5.0×10^{-3}

very large; $MgSO_4$, about 10; $CaSO_4$, 2.4×10^{-5}; $SrSO_4$, 7.6×10^{-7}; $BaSO_4$, 1.5×10^{-9}; and $RaSO_4$, 4×10^{-11}. This decreasing order is opposite to that observed for the hydroxides. To account for the alteration of trend, two factors need to be considered: As discussed in Section 16.6, solubility depends on lattice energy and on hydration energy. For the alkaline-earth sulfates the lattice energies are all about the same, apparently because the sulfate ion is so large (about 3 Å radius) that changing the size of the much smaller cation makes little difference. The difference in solubility must therefore be due to differences in hydration energy. From Be^{++} to Ba^{++}, size increases, hydration energy decreases, and the sulfates become less soluble. For the alkaline-earth hydroxides the lattice energies are not the same but decrease with increasing cation size. Apparently for these hydroxides this is a larger effect than the change in hydration energy. Thus, the hydroxides increase in solubility down the group.

Magnesium sulfate is well known as the heptahydrate, $MgSO_4 \cdot 7H_2O$, or epsom salt. In medicine it is useful as a purgative, apparently because magnesium ions in the alimentary canal favor passage of water from other body fluids into the bowel to dilute the salt.

Calcium sulfate has already been mentioned as the mineral gypsum, $CaSO_4 \cdot 2H_2O$. When gypsum is partially dehydrated

$$CaSO_4 \cdot 2H_2O(s) \rightleftharpoons CaSO_4 \cdot \frac{1}{2}H_2O(s) + \frac{3}{2}H_2O(g)$$

it forms plaster of paris, sometimes written $2CaSO_4 \cdot H_2O$. The use of plaster of paris in making casts and molds arises from the reversibility of the above reaction. On water uptake, plaster of paris sets to gypsum, and the expansion of volume results in remarkably faithful reproductions.

Barium sulfate and its insolubility have been repeatedly mentioned. Although Ba^{++}, like most heavy metals, is poisonous, the solubility of $BaSO_4$ is so low that $BaSO_4$ can safely be ingested into the stomach. The use of $BaSO_4$ in taking X-ray pictures of the digestive tract depends on the great scattering of X rays by the Ba^{++} ion.* Actually, $BaSO_4$ is more important as a white pigment.

5. *Chlorides and fluorides.* Beryllium chloride and fluoride, $BeCl_2$ and BeF_2, are unusual in that they do not conduct electricity in the molten state. For this reason, they are usually considered to be molecular rather than ionic salts. All the chlorides and fluorides of the other group II elements are typical ionic solids. Calcium fluoride, CaF_2, occurring in nature as the mineral fluorspar, is quite insoluble in water. The chloride, $CaCl_2$, is very soluble in water and, in fact, has such great affinity for water that it is used as a dehydrating agent.

6. *Carbonates.* All the carbonates of group II are quite insoluble and therefore are found as solid minerals in nature. Calcium carbonate, $CaCO_3$, or limestone, is the most common nonsilicate mineral. The existence of large natural beds of $CaCO_3$ poses a special problem for

18.6 Compounds

380

---

* The scattering of X rays by atoms is proportional to the electron density of the atom. Ba^{++} contains 54 electrons in a relatively small volume and hence scatters X rays more efficiently than do ions of lighter elements. *Mole ruit sua.*

water supplies, because $CaCO_3$, though essentially insoluble in water, is soluble in water containing carbon dioxide. Since our atmosphere contains an average of 0.04% CO_2 at all times, essentially all ground waters are solutions of CO_2 in H_2O. These ground waters dissolve limestone by the reaction

$$CaCO_3(s) + CO_2 + H_2O \rightleftharpoons Ca^{++} + 2HCO_3^-$$

which produces a weathering action on limestone deposits and results in contamination of most ground waters with calcium ion and bicarbonate ion, HCO_3^-. The dissolving action of CO_2-containing water explains the many caves found in limestone regions. These caves abound in weird formations produced partly by the dissolving action and partly by reprecipitation of $CaCO_3$. The optimum conditions for $CaCO_3$ deposition are slow seepage of ground water, steady evaporation, and no disturbing air currents. In limestone caves these conditions are ideally met. Ground water containing Ca^{++} and HCO_3^- may seep through a fissure in the roof and hang as a drop from the ceiling. As the water evaporates along with the carbon dioxide, the above reaction reverses to deposit a bit of limestone. Later, another drop of ground water seeps onto the limestone speck, and the process repeats. In time, a long shaft reaching down from the roof may be built up in the form of a limestone stalactite. Occasionally, drops of ground water may drip off the stalactite to the cave floor, where they evaporate to form a spire, or stalagmite, of $CaCO_3$. The whole process of dissolving and reprecipitation of limestone is very slow and may take hundreds of years.

18.7 HARD WATER

Because limestone is such a widespread mineral, most ground water contains small but appreciable concentrations of calcium ion. The presence of this Ca^{++} (or of Mg^{++} or Fe^{++}) is objectionable because of the formation of insoluble precipitates when such water is boiled or when soap is added. Water that behaves in this way is called "hard" water. It represents an industrial and household problem of the first magnitude.

Hardness in water is always due to the presence of calcium, magnesium, or ferrous (Fe^{++}) ion. The hardness may be of two types: (a) *temporary*, or *carbonate, hardness*, in which HCO_3^- ions are present in the water in addition to the aforementioned metal ions; (b) *permanent*, or *noncarbonate, hardness*, in which the dipositive ions but no HCO_3^- ions are in the water. In either case the hardness manifests itself by a reaction with soap (but not with detergents) to produce a scum. Soap, as discussed in Section 24.4, is a sodium salt of a complicated hydrocarbon acid. The usual soap is sodium stearate, $NaC_{18}H_{35}O_2$, and consists of Na^+ ions and negative stearate ions. When stearate ions are added to water containing Ca^{++}, insoluble calcium stearate forms:

$$Ca^{++} + 2C_{18}H_{35}O_2^- \longrightarrow Ca(C_{18}H_{35}O_2)_2(s)$$

This insoluble calcium stearate is the familiar scum or bathtub ring.

Hardness in water is also objectionable because boiling a solution

The alkaline-earth metals

381

containing Ca^{++} and HCO_3^- results in the deposition of $CaCO_3$, as in cave formation. In industrial boilers the deposition of $CaCO_3$ is an economic headache, since, like most salts, $CaCO_3$ is a poor heat conductor. Fuel efficiency is drastically cut, and boilers have been put completely out of action by local overheating due to boiler scale.

The major question, then, is how to soften hard water effectively and economically. The most direct way to soften water (as is done in many households) is simply to add huge quantities of soap. Eventually, enough stearate ion can be added to precipitate all the objectionable Ca^{++} as scum, leaving the excess soap to carry on the cleansing action.

Another way to soften water (this works only for temporary hardness) is to boil the water. The reaction

$$Ca^{++} + 2HCO_3^- \rightleftharpoons CaCO_3(s) + H_2O + CO_2(g)$$

is reversible, but the forward reaction can be made dominant by boiling off the CO_2. Boiling is not practical for large-scale softening.

The third way to soften water is to precipitate the Ca^{++} out of solution. This can be done by adding washing soda, Na_2CO_3. The added carbonate ion, CO_3^{--}, reacts with Ca^{++} to give insoluble $CaCO_3$. If bicarbonate ion is present, the water may be softened by adding a base such as ammonia. The base deprotonates HCO_3^- to produce CO_3^{--}, which then precipitates the Ca^{++}. On a large scale, temporary hardness is removed by adding limewater. The added OH^- reacts with HCO_3^- and precipitates $CaCO_3$ by the process

$$Ca^{++} + HCO_3^- + OH^- \longrightarrow CaCO_3(s) + H_2O$$

It might seem odd that limewater, which itself contains Ca^{++}, can be added to hard water to remove Ca^{++}. Yet it should be noted that, when $Ca(OH)_2$ is added, there are two moles of OH^- per mole of Ca^{++}. Two moles of OH^- neutralize two moles of HCO_3^- and liberate two moles of CO_3^{--}, thus precipitating two moles of Ca^{++}—one that was added and one that was originally in the hard water.

A fourth way to soften water is to tie up the Ca^{++} so that it becomes harmless. One way to do this is to form a complex containing Ca^{++}. Certain phosphates, such as $(NaPO_3)_n$, sodium polyphosphate, presumably form such complexes in which the Ca^{++} is trapped by the phosphate.

The fifth and most clever way to soften water is to replace the offending calcium ion by a harmless one such as Na^+. This is done by the process called *ion exchange*.

18.8 ION EXCHANGE

An *ion exchanger* is a special type of giant molecule consisting of a three-dimensional, cross-linked network containing covalently bound atoms which carry an excess of negative charge. The molecule is thus a negatively charged network with a very porous structure. The pores are filled with water molecules and enough positive ions to give an electrically neutral structure. The identity of the positive ions is not very important, since their only function is to preserve electrical neutrality. Consequently, one type of cation such as Ca^{++} can take the place of another type such as Na^+ without much change in structure. It is this kind of ion exchange which is used in water softening. Hard water containing Ca^{++} is placed in contact with an ion exchanger whose mobile ion is Na^+. Exchange occurs which can be represented by the equilibrium

$$Ca^{++} + 2Na^+\ominus \rightleftharpoons 2Na^+ + \ominus Ca^{++}\ominus$$

where the negative circle represents a negative site on the exchanger. The equilibrium constant for this reaction is usually of the order of 10 or less, and therefore, in order to remove all the Ca^{++}, it is necessary to run the hard water through a large amount of ion exchanger. This is most conveniently done by pouring the water through a tube, a foot or more high, filled with ion exchanger. Once the exchanger has given up its supply of Na^+, it cannot soften water further. However, it can be regenerated by exposure to a concentrated solution of NaCl, which reverses the above reaction.

The ion exchangers originally used for softening water were naturally occurring silicate minerals called *zeolites*. The giant network of a zeolite is negatively charged and is composed of covalently bound silicon, oxygen, and aluminum atoms. Mobile Na^+ ions in the pores can be readily exchanged for Ca^{++} ions. Zeolites are very closely related in structure to the clays, which also show ion exchange. Such ion exchange is important for plant nutrition, since many plants receive nourishment from the soil in this fashion.

With the advent of high-polymer techniques, chemists have been able to synthesize ion exchangers superior to the zeolites. The most common synthetic exchanger consists of a giant hydrocarbon framework having a negative charge due to covalently bound SO_3^- groups. It has also been possible to prepare ion exchangers in which the giant network is positively charged, the charge being due to covalently bound groups of the type $N(CH_3)_3^+$. Such positively charged networks can function as *anion* exchangers; i.e., they have mobile negative ions which can be displaced by other anions.

Combination of synthetic anion exchangers with cation exchangers has made possible the removal of all ions from a salt solution. If a salt solution containing M^+ and A^- is first run through a cation exchanger whose exchangeable ions are H^+, the salt solution is completely converted to a solution of an acid containing H^+ and A^-. If now the acid solution is run through an anion exchanger whose exchangeable ions are OH^-, the anions A^- in the solution are replaced by OH^-. Since in the original solution the number of negative charges is exactly equal to the number of positive charges, equal amounts of H^+ and OH^- are exchanged into the solution. Neutralization occurs, and pure water results. Water thus "deionized" contains fewer ions than the most carefully distilled water.

18.9 QUALITATIVE ANALYSIS

As a group, the alkaline-earth cations (excluding beryllium) can be distinguished from other common cations by taking advantage of the fact that, like group I elements, they form soluble sulfides but, unlike group I elements, they form insoluble carbonates.

Given a solution containing alkaline-earth cations, the barium can be precipitated as yellow $BaCrO_4$ by addition of K_2CrO_4 in the presence of an acetic acid buffer. From the residual solution (containing Sr^{++}, Ca^{++}, Mg^{++}), light-yellow $SrCrO_4$ can be precipitated by subsequent addition of NH_3 and alcohol. The $BaCrO_4$ precipitates in the first step and $SrCrO_4$ in the second, because $BaCrO_4$ ($K_{sp} = 8.5 \times 10^{-11}$) is less soluble than $SrCrO_4$ ($K_{sp} = 3.6 \times 10^{-5}$). The point of using an acetic acid buffer (Section 12.5) is to keep the H^+ concentration around 10^{-5}, where the chromate concentration, governed by the equilibrium

$$2CrO_4^{--} + 2H^+ \rightleftharpoons Cr_2O_7^{--} + H_2O$$

is too low to precipitate Sr^{++} but high enough to precipitate Ba^{++}. Subsequent addition of NH_3 reduces the H^+ concentration, thereby increasing the CrO_4^{--} concentration sufficiently to precipitate $SrCrO_4$, especially in the presence of alcohol, which lowers its solubility.

Calcium ion can be separated from magnesium ion by addition of ammonium oxalate to form white, insoluble calcium oxalate, CaC_2O_4. (The K_{sp} of CaC_2O_4 is 1.3×10^{-9}, compared to 8.6×10^{-5} for MgC_2O_4.) Finally, the presence of Mg^{++} can be shown by adding more NH_3 and Na_2HPO_4, which precipitates white magnesium ammonium phosphate, $MgNH_4PO_4$.

QUESTIONS

18.1 Chemical equations   Write balanced equations for each of the following: (*a*) oxidation of $Ba(s)$ by H_2O to give H_2, (*b*) dissolving of $Sr(s)$ in H_2O, (*c*) electrolysis of molten CaH_2, (*d*) dissolving of $MgCO_3(s)$ in acid, (*e*) burning of $Mg(s)$ in pure $N_2(g)$, (*f*) "deionization" of $MgSO_4$ solution via ion exchange, (*g*) chemical preparation of beryllium.

18.2 Structure   CaO has the NaCl structure with a unit-cell length of 4.797 Å. Calculate the density of an ideal crystal of CaO. The observed value of the density is 3.37 g cc^{-1}.

18.3 Hess's law   Given the following:

$$CaO(s) + H_2O(l) \longrightarrow Ca(OH)_2(s) \qquad \Delta H^\circ = -15.6 \text{ kcal}$$
$$CaCO_3(s) \longrightarrow CaO(s) + CO_2(g) \qquad \Delta H^\circ = +42.5 \text{ kcal}$$

calculate the ΔH° for

$$Ca(OH)_2(s) + CO_2(g) \longrightarrow CaCO_3(s) + H_2O(l)$$

18.4 Oxidation potential calculations   Given three metals X, Y, Z. On the basis of the following free-energy data, predict for each element which ion ($+1$, $+2$, or $+3$) will be most stable in aqueous solution and calculate its E° for formation from the metal.

Process	X	Y	Z
Sublimation, kcal	66	82	31
First ionization, ev	6.00	7.72	9.39
Second ionization, ev	20.43	20.34	17.89
Third ionization, ev	30.6	29.5	40.0
Hydration of M^+, kcal	-105	-95	-110
Hydration of M^{++}, kcal	-520	-501	-487
Hydration of M^{+3}, kcal	-1015	-1085	-1145

18.5 Solution stoichiometry (a) Assuming complete reaction, calculate the pH for each of the following solutions: (1) 40.0 mg of CaH_2 in enough water to make 100.0 ml of solution, (2) 40.0 mg of Ba in enough water to make 100.0 ml of solution. (b) How much 0.100 M H_2SO_4 would you need to add to neutralize each of the above solutions?

18.6 Solubility product Neglecting hydrolysis, calculate the number of moles of CaF_2 ($K_{sp} = 1.7 \times 10^{-10}$) that can dissolve in one liter of each of the following: (a) water, (b) 0.10 M $Ca(NO_3)_2$, (c) 0.10 M NaF.

18.7 Solubility product A mixture is made of 10.0 ml of 0.10 M $Mg(NO_3)_2$, 20.0 ml of 0.20 M $Ca(NO_3)_2$, 30.0 ml of 0.30 M $Sr(NO_3)_2$, and 40.0 ml of 1.00 M NaF. All the nitrates are soluble, but the fluorides have the following K_{sp} values: MgF_2, 8×10^{-8}; CaF_2, 1.7×10^{-10}; SrF_2, 7.9×10^{-10}. Assuming the final total volume of the solution to be 0.100 liter, calculate the concentration of each cation and anion in the final mix. Neglect hydrolysis.

18.8 Quantitative analysis You are given a white solid of formula $Na_2SO_4 \cdot xH_2O$. A sample weighing 0.2456 g is dissolved in water and treated with $BaCl_2$ solution to precipitate $BaSO_4$, and the $BaSO_4$ is dried and weighed. If the final weight of $BaSO_4$ is 0.2138 g, what is the value of x in the hydrate formula?

18.9 Qualitative analysis A given aqueous solution may contain one or more of the following: Na^+, K^+, Mg^{++}, Ca^{++}, Sr^{++}, Ba^{++}. Addition of aqueous NH_3 plus $(NH_4)_2CO_3$ produces a white precipitate that is completely soluble in equimolar $HC_2H_3O_2$ plus $NH_4C_2H_3O_2$. If aqueous K_2CrO_4 is added to the buffered solution, no precipitate is formed until NH_3 and ethyl alcohol are added, at which point gentle warming produces a fine yellow precipitate. Subsequent addition of aqueous $(NH_4)_2C_2O_4$ produces no precipitate. The addition of $(NH_4)_2HPO_4$ to the filtrate from the initial NH_3 plus $(NH_4)_2CO_3$ treatment gives a white precipitate. A flame test on the final filtrate gives a brief violet coloration. Tell which of the original ions are present and which are absent.

The alkaline-earth metals

385

18.10 Thermodynamics Given, at 25°C, $\Delta H° = +42.5$ kcal and $\Delta S° = 38.4$ cal mole^{-1} deg^{-1} for the reaction

$$CaCO_3(s) \longrightarrow CaO(s) + CO_2(g)$$

(a) Calculate the equilibrium pressure of CO_2 at 25°C. (b) Assuming

$\Delta H°$ and $\Delta S°$ remain constant, at what temperature will the equilibrium pressure of CO_2 become equal to one atmosphere?

18.11 Qualitative analysis A given white solid may contain one or more of the following: Na_2SO_4, $BaSO_4$, $NaCl$, KCl, MgF_2, CaF_2, K_2CO_3, $BaCO_3$. The sample is partly soluble in water and gives a strong yellow flame that obscures any other colors. When the aqueous-solution part is acidified with dilute HNO_3, a gas evolves. When the insoluble part is treated with dilute HNO_3, it dissolves with evolution of a gas. Addition of NaOH to either acid solution does not produce a precipitate. Indicate with $+$, $-$, or ? the presence, absence, or indeterminacy of each compound in the original unknown sample.

18.12 Limestone cave When limestone dissolves in CO_2-containing water, the net reaction can be written

$$CaCO_3(s) + H_2O + CO_2 \rightleftharpoons Ca^{++} + 2HCO_3^-$$

for which the equilibrium constant is 4.3×10^{-5}. For saturated solution, the CO_2 concentration is 1.7×10^{-5} M. How long will it take a stream flowing at a rate of 560 liters sec^{-1} to deliver enough water to dissolve out of a limestone bed a cave as big as a lecture hall 1.0×10^4 meters^3 in size? Assume density of limestone is 2.7 g cc^{-1}.

18.13 Qualitative analysis equilibrium In lab you can separate the alkaline-earth ions by addition of a solution that is 0.50 M $(NH_4)_2CO_3$ and 1.0 M NH_3 in order to precipitate insoluble carbonates. One reason you do not use 0.50 M Na_2CO_3 is that it would give too high a concentration of CO_3^{--}. Calculate the ratio of the CO_3^{--} concentration in 0.50 M Na_2CO_3 as compared to that in 0.50 M $(NH_4)_2CO_3$ with 1.0 M NH_3. Note that CO_3^{--} hydrolyzes $CO_3^{--} + H_2O \rightleftharpoons HCO_3^- + OH^-$ but that NH_4^+/NH_3 in the same solution acts as a buffer to control OH^-. Constants are:

$$HCO_3^- \rightleftharpoons H^+ + CO_3^{--} \qquad K = 4.8 \times 10^{-11}$$
$$NH_3 + H_2O \rightleftharpoons NH_4^+ + OH^- \qquad K = 1.8 \times 10^{-5}$$

18.14 Solubility product Calculate the solubility of SrF_2 ($K_{sp} = 7.9 \times 10^{-10}$) in each of the following: (a) a solution buffered at pH $= 3.00$ ($K_{diss} = 6.71 \times 10^{-4}$ for HF), (b) a solution saturated with respect to BaF_2($K_{sp} = 2.4 \times 10^{-5}$), (c) a solution saturated with respect to CaF_2 ($K_{sp} = 1.7 \times 10^{-10}$).

ANSWERS

18.2 3.374 g cc^{-1} 18.4 1.63, 0.30, 1.21 volts 18.6 (a) 3.5×10^{-4} (b) 2.1×10^{-5} (c) 1.7×10^{-8} 18.8 7 18.10 1.6×10^{-23} atm; 834°C 18.12 27 years 18.14 (a) 1.1×10^{-3} M (b) 6.0×10^{-7} M (c) 5.1×10^{-4} M

19 transition elements I: general aspects

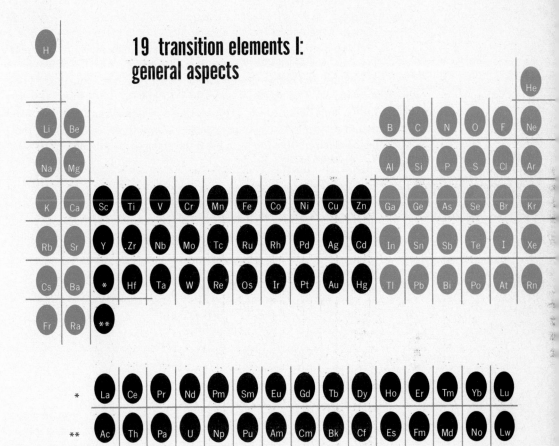

Intervening between groups II and III in the periodic table are subgroups of elements collectively referred to as the transition elements. The precise definition of "transition element" is a matter of taste, and frequently there is ambiguity on the question whether a given element is included in the classification or not. Using the form of the periodic table shown in Figure 2.2, we shall find it is most convenient to include all 10 of the intervening subgroups. Thus, in the fourth period the transition elements are scandium ($Z = 21$), titanium (22), vanadium (23), chromium (24), manganese (25), iron (26), cobalt (27), nickel (28), copper (29), and zinc (30). Each of these elements heads a subgroup named after itself. Thus, the titanium subgroup, for instance, includes the elements titanium ($Z = 22$), zirconium (40), and hafnium

(72). In this and the three succeeding chapters, we consider the properties characteristic of the transition elements.

19.1 ELECTRONIC CONFIGURATION

Transition elements owe their separate classification to belated filling of the next-to-outermost energy level of the atoms (Section 2.2). In Figure 19.1 are given the detailed electronic configurations of the first-row transition elements. The significant difference in these configurations is that the third principal quantum level is gradually built up to 18 electrons by progressive addition to the $3d$ subshell. With the exception of chromium and copper, there are two electrons in the fourth shell (the $4s$ subshell). The apparent anomaly of Cr and Cu is due to the fact that the $3d$ and $4s$ subshells are very close in energy and that half-filled and filled subshells have extra stability. Thus, Cr gains stability by moving an electron from the $4s$ to the $3d$ level to give a half-filled $3d$ subshell

Element	Symbol	Z	Electron configuration
Scandium	Sc	21	$1s^2 2s^2 2p^6 3s^2 3p^6 3d^1 4s^2$
Titanium	Ti	22	—— (18) —— $3d^2 4s^2$
Vanadium	V	23	—— (18) —— $3d^3 4s^2$
Chromium	Cr	24	—— (18) —— $3d^5 4s^1$
Manganese	Mn	25	—— (18) —— $3d^5 4s^2$
Iron	Fe	26	—— (18) —— $3d^6 4s^2$
Cobalt	Co	27	—— (18) —— $3d^7 4s^2$
Nickel	Ni	28	—— (18) —— $3d^8 4s^2$
Copper	Cu	29	—— (18) —— $3d^{10} 4s^1$
Zinc	Zn	30	—— (18) —— $3d^{10} 4s^2$

19.1
First-row transition
elements

(five out of ten maximum) and a half-filled $4s$ subshell (one out of two maximum). In Cu the dropping of a $4s$ electron to the $3d$ subshell gives a filled $3d$ subshell and a half-filled $4s$ subshell. Actually, these minor deviations in electron configuration are of little more than academic interest, since the configurations have been determined for the gaseous atoms and do not necessarily hold for other states.

When electrons are removed from transition-metal atoms, it is not clear from the electronic configuration of the atom which electronic levels will be depleted. On the basis of the order of orbital filling in the buildup of the periodic table, it might seem that, since the $3d$ electrons are added after the $4s$, they should on ionization be removed before the $4s$. However, this prediction is unwarranted, because the two processes are different in a major way. In the buildup of the periodic table, the number of electrons is being increased at the same time that the nuclear charge is being increased. On the other hand, in the ionization process the number of electrons is being decreased while the nuclear charge stays constant. The problem is actually a very complicated one, since interelectron repulsion is an important factor. The experimental fact is that $4s$ electrons are removed before $3d$ electrons in the ionization of transition-element atoms. The electronic configurations of the transition-element ions will be considered again later.

For the second-row transition elements, yttrium ($Z = 39$) through cadmium ($Z = 48$), the electronic expansion involves the $4d$ and $5s$ subshells as shown in Figure 2.9 on page 28. For the third-row transition elements, lanthanum ($Z = 57$) through mercury ($Z = 80$), a new problem arises. As shown on page 29, not only are the $5d$ and $6s$ subshells involved in the expansion but also the $4f$ subshell is being filled to 14 electrons. The elements involved in the $4f$ expansion are called the lanthanide elements; they are discussed in Section 20.2. A similar problem, involving the $5f$ expansion, occurs in the last row of the periodic table, giving rise to the actinide elements. The actinides are discussed in Section 20.3; their electronic configurations are given on page 409.

19.2 METALLIC PROPERTIES

The most characteristic property of the transition elements is that they are all metals. This is not surprising, since the outermost shell contains so few electrons. However, unlike the metals of groups I and II, the transition metals are likely to be hard, brittle, and fairly high melting (see Figure 19.2). The difference is partly due to the relatively small size of the atoms (Figure 2.19 shows that the atomic radii are consistently small) and partly to the existence of some covalent binding between the ions. There are exceptions to this general hardness, as in the case of mercury ($Z = 80$), which is a liquid and is about as soft as a metal can be.

Figure 19.2 lists some of the characteristic properties of the transition metals. In the structure column, standard abbreviations are used, *viz.*, fcc, face-centered cubic; hcp, hexagonal close-packed; bcc, body-centered cubic. These structures are described in Section 6.4. The close-packed arrays, fcc and hcp, have a coordination number of 12, that is, 12 near-neighbors for each atom; bcc has 8 for the number of near-neighbors. Thus in most cases the transition metals are rather densely packed and have the high coordination numbers characteristic of good conductors. The conductivity values listed in the last column of Figure 19.2 are given in units of reciprocal ohm-centimeters. An ohm-centimeter is the electrical resistance of a one-centimeter-long wire that is one square centimeter in cross section. For comparison, it might be noted that the specific conductivity of sodium metal at 0°C is 23×10^4 $(ohm \cdot cm)^{-1}$. In summary, the transition metals are generally good conductors, and silver, copper, and gold are outstandingly good.

The high electrical conductivity of the transition metals can be attributed to a delocalization (i.e., spreading out over many atoms) of the s electrons similar to what occurs in the alkali and alkaline-earth metals. The differences in other physical properties (e.g., hardness, brittleness, melting point) can be ascribed to covalent binding involving overlapping of partly filled d subshells of the transition-metal atoms.

19.3 OXIDATION STATES

One of the most frequently remarked characteristics of a typical transition element is the great variety of oxidation states it may show in its compounds. Figure 19.3 lists the more common states found for the transition elements. Included also (in parentheses) are less common states, such as those which are unstable to disproportionation in aqueous solution or which have been prepared in only a few solid-state compounds. It should be noted that there is considerable research activity at present in attempting to prepare unusual oxidation states of the transition elements. Therefore, the listing in the table should not be considered as the complete answer.

In addition to showing the large number of oxidation states for the transition elements, Figure 19.3 shows several marked features. In each row there is a peaking of the maximum state near the middle of the row, after which the maximum state gets smaller in magnitude

19.2
Properties of the
transition metals

Metal	Structure	Density, g cc^{-1}	Melting point, °C	Conductivity, 0°C (ohm-cm)$^{-1}$
Sc	fcc	3	1200	—
Ti	hcp	4.5	1660	1.2×10^4
V	bcc	6.0	1710	1.7×10^4
Cr	bcc	6.9	1600	6.5×10^4
Mn	bcc	7.4	1260	1.1×10^4
Fe	bcc;fcc	7.9	1535	11.2×10^4
Co	fcc;hcp	8.7	1490	16×10^4
Ni	fcc	8.9	1450	16×10^4
Cu	fcc	8.9	1083	64.5×10^4
Zn	hcp	7.1	419	18.1×10^4
Y	hcp	5.5	1490	—
Zr	hcp;bcc	6.4	1860	2.4×10^4
Nb	bcc	8.6	1950	4.4×10^4
Mo	bcc	10.2	2620	23×10^4
Tc	hcp	11.5	(2100)	—
Ru	hcp	12.4	2450	8.5×10^4
Rh	fcc	12.4	1970	22×10^4
Pd	fcc	12.0	1550	10×10^4
Ag	fcc	10.5	961	66.7×10^4
Cd	hcp	8.7	321	15×10^4
La	hcp;fcc	6.2	890	1.7×10^4
Hf	hcp	13.3	2200	3.4×10^4
Ta	bcc	16.6	>3000	7.2×10^4
W	bcc	19.3	3370	20×10^4
Re	hcp	20.5	3200	5.3×10^4
Os	hcp	22.7	2700	11×10^4
Ir	fcc	22.6	2450	20×10^4
Pt	fcc	21.5	1774	10.2×10^4
Au	fcc	19.3	1063	49×10^4
Hg	rhombic	14.2	−39	4.4×10^4

Sc	Ti	V	Cr	Mn	Fe	Co	Ni	Cu	Zn
+3	(+2) +3 +4	+2 +3 +4 +5	+2 +3 (+4) +6	+2 (+3) +4 (+6) +7	+2 +3 (+4) (+6)	+2 +3 (+4)	+2 (+3)	+1 +2	+2

Y	Zr	Nb	Mo	Tc	Ru	Rh	Pd	Ag	Cd
+3	+4	+3 +5	+3 +4 +5 +6	+4 (+6) +7	+2 +3 +4 (+5) +6 (+7) (+8)	+3 +4 (+6)	+2 (+3) +4	+1 (+2) (+3)	+2

La	Hf	Ta	W	Re	Os	Ir	Pt	Au	Hg
+3	+4	(+4) +5	(+2) (+3) +4 +5 +6	(+3) +4 (+5) +6 +7	(+2) (+3) +4 +6 +8	(+2) +3 +4 (+6)	+2 (+3) +4	+1 +3	+1 +2

19.3
Oxidation states of
transition elements
(less common states
in parentheses)

toward the end of the row. Thus, for the first row the maximum oxidation state formed increases regularly from $+3$ for Sc to $+7$ for Mn, after which there is a falloff to $+2$ for Zn. Connected with this trend is the fact that elements toward the center of the row generally show more oxidation states than those toward the ends. A careful look at the table discloses one other feature. In going down a subgroup of three elements, there is generally a favoring of higher oxidation states. For example, in the iron subgroup the $+2$ and $+3$ states, which predominate for iron, give way to $+4$, $+6$, and $+8$, which predominate for osmium.

Before making too much fuss over the reasons for trends in oxidation state, we should remind ourselves of the artificiality of the concept of oxidation state and how it rests on the arbitrary assignment of shared electrons to more electronegative atoms. Nevertheless, it is helpful to connect the increasing maximum oxidation state with the increasing number of s and d electrons available for binding. The falloff after the peak in the center of the row can be related to the lowering of the d-subshell energy relative to the s, and hence to the decreasing availability of d electrons for binding. Similarly, it is helpful to connect the increasing preference for higher states down a subgroup with increasing availability of d electrons relative to s as size increases.

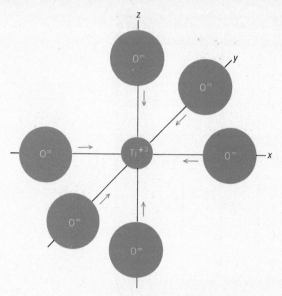

19.4 LIGAND-FIELD THEORY

Another frequently remarked feature of the transition elements is their relatively great tendency to form complex ions. In such complexes the transition-metal atoms or ions are surrounded by a definite number of bound groups whose charge clouds exert a marked influence on the electronic makeup of the transition element. These bound groups, whether ions such as F$^-$ or CN$^-$ or molecules such as H$_2$O or NH$_3$, are referred to as *ligands,* and their interaction with the central atom is the subject of *ligand-field theory.* Historically, the theory developed from a consideration of how atomic energy levels of ions in crystals are affected by the ionic surroundings. The treatment so developed, called *crystal-field theory,* forms the basis for the broader *ligand-field theory.* The latter may be visualized as crystal-field theory with superimposed molecular-orbital concepts.

Let us consider the problem of a Ti^{+3} ion in an oxide lattice (e.g., in Ti$_2$O$_3$, where the Ti^{+3} occupies octahedral holes in a close-packed array of oxide ions). The electron configuration of Ti^{+3} is $1s^22s^22p^63s^23p^63d^1$. Except for $3d^1$, the electron subshells are each filled and hence spherically symmetric. So far as $3d^1$ is concerned, the electron can be considered as occupying one of the five d orbitals, d_{xy}, d_{yz}, d_{zx}, d_{z^2}, or $d_{x^2-y^2}$ (Section 2.3). Which of these orbitals is likely to be the one occupied? For an isolated ion, it makes no difference, since all five of these orbitals are of equal energy. However, in a crystal in which there are interacting neighbors the answer depends on the disposition of these neighbors. Imagine the Ti^{+3} ion to be located at the origin of a set of axes, as shown in Figure 19.4. For octahedral coordination there will be one ligand equally distant from the origin on each of the six axial directions. If the set of six ligands is imagined to be drawn in uniformly toward the metal ion, what effect will there be on the $3d$ electron?

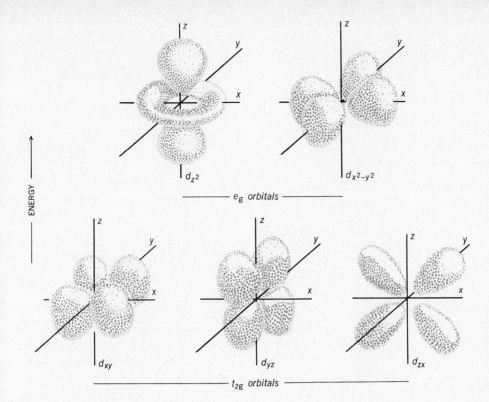

ENERGY

e_g orbitals

d_{z^2} $d_{x^2-y^2}$

d_{xy} d_{yz} d_{zx}

t_{2g} orbitals

19.5
Energy separation of $3d$ orbitals by octahedral ligands

Specifically, which of the five $3d$ orbitals will most likely be occupied? Of the five orbitals, two (d_{z^2} and $d_{x^2-y^2}$, see Figure 19.5) correspond to high electron density along the axes and the other three (d_{xy}, d_{yz}, d_{zx}) to high electron density along the 45° lines between axes.

Clearly, there will be strong repulsion between the negative-charge cloud of the ligand and the negative electron when it is in one of the d orbitals that are directed along the axes (d_{z^2} or $d_{x^2-y^2}$). On the other hand, the repulsion will be less if the electron is in one of the d orbitals that are directed away from the ligands with minimum charge density on the axes (d_{xy}, d_{yz}, d_{zx}). The result is that, as shown in Figure 19.5, the set of d orbitals separates into two subsets, a higher-energy one (called e_g) having high electron density on the axes and a lower-energy one (called t_{2g}) having high electron density away from the axes. Hence, the lowest-energy configuration for a Ti^{+3} ion is to have the $3d$ electron in one of the t_{2g} orbitals.

The problem of calculating the energy difference between the two subsets of d orbitals in an octahedral environment is a most difficult one. A calculation based on the assumption of only electrical repulsions between charge clouds, as in the ionic model described above, is not satisfactory. The energy-level difference so calculated is usually much smaller than that observed by spectroscopic techniques (Section 19.6). The principal reason for the quantitative discrepancy between experiment and prediction from crystal-field theory lies in the basic assump-

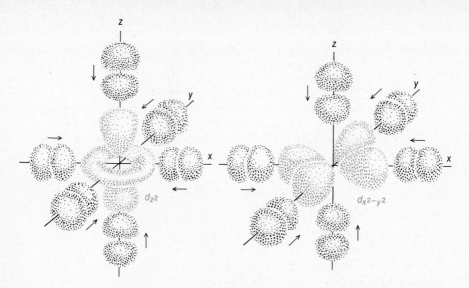

19.6
Molecular-orbital formation
from d orbitals of central
atom and p orbitals of
ligands

tion of a completely ionic model. In other words, it is not correct to assume that, when a transition-element ion is surrounded by ligands, the
only change is within the ion. There must be considerable mixing of the
charge clouds of the ligands and the central atom—covalent bonding
exists. Ligand-field theory, unlike crystal-field theory, allows for such
electron delocalization.

In its most elegant form, ligand-field theory sets up molecular orbitals which are derived from the central atom and its surrounding
ligands. For example, in the case of titanium surrounded by oxygens we
can get an idea of the molecular orbitals by considering the overlap of
those d orbitals that point toward the ligands (d_{z^2} and $d_{x^2-y^2}$) with p orbitals of the oxygens. A schematic representation of setting up the overlap is shown in Figure 19.6. As the ligands are brought up to their final
positions, the atomic orbitals merge to give molecular orbitals. Because
the electron density of the molecular orbitals is concentrated along
bonding directions, these orbitals are of the σ type (Section 3.9). Besides the orbitals shown in Figure 19.6, there are other overlaps, especially with the $4s$ and the three $4p$ orbitals of the titanium. All told,
from the two $3d$, one $4s$, and three $4p$ orbitals of Ti and one $2p$ orbital
from each of the six O neighbors, there will be twelve molecular orbitals, six of which are bonding and six of which are antibonding. Because oxygen is more electronegative than titanium, electrons shared
in the bonding orbitals tend to be concentrated more toward O than Ti.

In summary, when ligands are brought up to a transition-element
ion, the d orbitals are affected differently. Those which point away from
the ligands (d_{xy}, d_{yz}, d_{zx}) will be but slightly affected. Those which point
toward the ligands (d_{z^2} and $d_{x^2-y^2}$) merge with ligand orbitals to form
molecular orbitals that bind the complex. Electron pairs from the
ligands fill these bonding orbitals (effectively reducing the negative
charge of the ligands and reducing the positive charge of the central

ion). For the case of Ti^{+3} surrounded by six ligands, the single $3d$ electron will be accommodated in one of the d orbitals not involved in the bonding. Whether it is d_{xy}, d_{yz}, or d_{zx} is immaterial since, in an octahedral environment, all three are equivalent.

Finally, it must be noted that for transition-element ions having more than one d electron (for example, d^2, d^3) the situation is somewhat more complicated because of interelectron repulsions between the d electrons. Also, if the symmetry of the environment is not octahedral, the splitting of the d orbitals into subsets is different from that discussed above.

19.5 MAGNETIC PROPERTIES

Because of electron spin, unpaired electrons give rise to paramagnetism, i.e., attraction into a magnetic field (Section 2.4). For the transition elements, where there is usually partial filling of the d subshell, paramagnetism is a likely possibility. Both in the metallic state and in compounds, transition elements may show paramagnetism resulting from presence of one or more unpaired electron spins. In a few cases (for example, Fe, Co, Ni, Fe_3O_4, some Mn alloys) there is a reinforcement of paramagnetism owing to extensive electron-spin alignment within solids leading to ferromagnetism (Section 21.1).

There are two properties of electrons in atoms that give rise to magnetism: one is the intrinsic electron spin, and the other is the moment associated with the spatial or orbital orientation of the electron. In the lanthanides and actinides (in which f electrons are involved) both effects contribute to the measured magnetism. However, in most of the other transition elements the orbital moment contributes negligibly to the measured magnetism, largely because interaction of d electrons with surrounding atoms prevents orientation of the orbital moment with an externally applied magnetic field. For our purposes, the orbital moment of d electrons can be considered to be quenched and we shall deal with the magnetic moment from the electron spin only. It turns out that the magnetic moment due to electron spin can be calculated from the formula

$$\text{Spin magnetic moment} = \sqrt{n(n + 2)}$$

where n is the number of unpaired electrons and the units are Bohr magnetons. In these units, a single $1s$ electron has a magnetic moment of 1.73 Bohr magnetons.

Figure 19.7 summarizes both the magnetic moments calculated from the spin-only formula and those derived from experimental data for some ions of the first-row transition elements. The experimental data are mainly for hydrated ions in solution and in the solid state. In certain cases the data differ depending on the environment of the ion. Hence, there is a range of values given. As predicted by the spin-only calculation, as the number of unpaired electrons goes through a maximum at Mn^{++} (d^5), so the magnetic moment peaks there too. In the first half of the series the agreement between calculated and experimental mo-

Ion	e^- configuration	Unpaired e^-	Magnetic moment	
			Calc.	Expt.
Sc^{+3}	$3d^0$	0	0	0
Ti^{+3}	$3d^1$	1	1.73	1.75
Ti^{++}	$3d^2$	2	2.84	2.76
V^{++}	$3d^3$	3	3.87	3.86
Cr^{++}	$3d^4$	4	4.90	4.80
Mn^{++}	$3d^5$	5	5.92	5.96
Fe^{++}	$3d^6$	4	4.90	5.0–5.5
Co^{++}	$3d^7$	3	3.87	4.4–5.2
Ni^{++}	$3d^8$	2	2.84	2.9–3.4
Cu^{++}	$3d^9$	1	1.73	1.8–2.2
Zn^{++}	$3d^{10}$	0	0	0

19.7
Calculated and observed
paramagnetic moments

ments is quite good; in the second half of the series the experimental values turn out to exceed those predicted on the basis of spin only. These small discrepancies are probably due to incomplete quenching of the orbital magnetic moment.

For some compounds of the transition elements the observed magnetic moments turn out to be surprisingly small. For example, $K_4Fe(CN)_6$ does not show the paramagnetic moment of about 5 Bohr magnetons as predicted for Fe^{++} (d^6—four unpaired electrons). In fact, $K_4Fe(CN)_6$ is diamagnetic and so apparently contains no unpaired electrons. How can this and similar surprises be accounted for? The preceding section gives a basis for understanding the phenomenon by considering how the d orbitals are affected on interaction with the environment.

For the specific case of $K_4Fe(CN)_6$ the solid consists of potassium cations, K^+, and ferrocyanide anions, $Fe(CN)_6^{-4}$. We can consider the $Fe(CN)_6^{-4}$ anion as being assembled from Fe^{++} (d^6) and six ligand CN^- ions. If the six CN^- ions are brought up to surround the Fe^{++} octahedrally, as in the process illustrated in Figure 19.4, the various d orbitals of the iron atom are perturbed differently. With the introduction of ligand electrons along the axes, the six electrons of the iron are excluded from the d orbitals that lie along the axes. In other words, electrons are repelled out of the e_g set (d_{z^2} and $d_{x^2-y^2}$, refer to Figure 19.5) into the t_{2g} set (d_{xy}, d_{yz}, d_{zx}). The only way six electrons can be accommodated in this lower-energy set of three orbitals is for an electron pair to occupy each orbital. Actually, there is considerable electrical repulsion between members of an electron pair occupying the same orbital. However, if the ligand-field effect is strong enough—i.e., if the ligand electrons repel the d electrons out of the e_g orbitals strongly enough—then electron pairing in the t_{2g} orbitals may have to occur. In most cyanide complexes the ligand-field effect of CN is strong enough to cause electron pairing; in most hydrated ions the ligand-field effect of H_2O is *not* strong enough to cause electron pairing. However, a notable exception is $Co(H_2O)_6^{+3}$, in which electron pairing does occur.

19.5 Magnetic properties

396

For the second- and third-row transition elements, where the $4d$ and $5d$ orbitals come into use, the magnetic situation is more complicated. In general, ligand-field effects are greater than with the $3d$ elements partly because of increased nuclear charge and partly because of greater relative extension from the nucleus of the higher d orbitals. Such increased ligand-field effects favor electron pairing and hence lower paramagnetic moments.

19.6 SPECTRAL PROPERTIES

When white light interacts with a substance giving rise to color, there is absorption of part of the spectrum. For example, if the blue portion of white light is absorbed, then the remainder appears red; conversely, if red frequencies are absorbed, the substance appears blue. Since most transition-element compounds are colored, there must be energy transitions which can use up some of the energy of visible light. Figure 19.8 lists some characteristic colors of first-row transition-element ions

on	Configuration	Observed color	Absorption maxima, Å
i(H_2O)$_6^{+3}$	d^1	Violet	4930
(H$_2$O)$_6^{+3}$	d^2	Green	3890, 5620
(H$_2$O)$_6^{++}$	d^3	Violet	3580, 5410, 9100
r(H$_2$O)$_6^{+3}$	d^3	Violet	2640, 4070, 5800
e(H$_2$O)$_6^{+3}$	d^5	Colorless	—
e(H$_2$O)$_6^{++}$	d^6	Pale green	9620
Co(H$_2$O)$_6^{++}$	d^7	Pink	5150, 6250, 12200
i(H$_2$O)$_6^{++}$	d^8	Green	3950, 7410, 11760
u(H$_2$O)$_6^{++}$	d^9	Blue	7940

9.8
Colors and absorption
wavelengths

(dilute aqueous solution, no complexing, no hydrolysis) and indicates approximate wavelengths for maximum light absorption. Because the eye is not equally sensitive to all wavelengths, it is difficult to go from absorption maxima to the perceived color. Furthermore, the absorption does not occur sharply at a single wavelength, but instead spreads out over a band of the spectrum. Since the visible region of the light spectrum extends approximately from 4000 to 7000 Å, some of the maxima noted in the figure occur in the ultraviolet (below 4000 Å) and some in the infrared (above 7000 Å). In addition to the absorption bands noted in the figure, there is for any ion a strong absorption band in the ultraviolet that corresponds to transfer of electrons between ion and solvent.

The characteristic absorption bands of transition-element ions are attributed to electronic transitions in the d subshell. Because of ligand-field effects (Section 19.4), the d orbitals will be separated into different levels of energy. For example, in the ion Ti^{+3} surrounded by an octahedron of H_2O molecules there are two subsets of d-orbital energies, a lower set of three (d_{xy}, d_{yz}, d_{zx}) and an upper set of two (d_{z^2},

$d_{x^2-y^2}$). The minimum-energy state of $Ti^{+3}(aq)$ corresponds to having the $3d^1$ unpaired electron in one of the lower three orbitals (Figure 19.5). As light is absorbed by the sample, the electron of a Ti^{+3} ion is raised from the lower set of orbitals to the upper set. This absorption gives rise to the color. Subsequently, the stored energy must be dissipated, apparently as heat through vibrations of the environment.

In cases involving more than one d electron the cause of absorption bands is qualitatively similar to the d^1 case. However, the situation is considerably more complicated. More than one electron can be simultaneously excited, and interelectron repulsions can produce additional excited states. Hence, several absorption bands, as noted in Figure 19.8, may be observed.

In the case of Fe^{+3} in aqueous solution no major absorption band is observed except for the electron-transfer band in the ultraviolet (which on hydrolysis shifts into the visible region so as to make the solution appear reddish brown). The reason why $Fe(H_2O)_6^{+3}$ lacks color is its $3d^5$ configuration. In spite of the ligand-field effect of the H_2O, the energy-level splitting is small enough that there is no pairing of the d electrons; hence, there is one electron in each of the d orbitals. The only way energy can be absorbed is for an electron from a t_{2g} orbital to be raised to an e_g orbital, where it would have to pair up. Such electron-spin change during an optical transition rarely occurs, and the transition is said to be "spin-forbidden."

19.7 COMPLEX IONS

The availability of d orbitals for participating in the chemical bonding of ligands leads to a large variety of structures for complex ions of the transition elements. For certain transition elements (especially cobalt, chromium, and platinum-like elements) the complexes formed may be extremely slow to undergo structural changes. Hence the species may be persistent enough, even in aqueous solution, to allow separation and characterization of the various complex species. The study of such complex species is a large and growing area of research in inorganic chemistry, sometimes called coordination chemistry. In this area, primary emphasis is on the determination of structure and its relation to properties.

Most complex ions have structures that are basically octahedral arrangements of ligands about a central atom. As noted in Section 19.4, an octahedral arrangement of ligands will cause electron overlap between the ligand and two d, one s, and three p orbitals of the central atom. This set of orbitals is the same as the one from which the set of six d^2sp^3 hybrid orbitals is derived (Section 3.8, Figure 3.15). In most complex ions these orbitals are the ones used in bonding, and the complexes turn out to be octahedral. Figure 19.9 shows examples of several complex ions based on octahedral coordination of near-neighbor atoms to the central atom. In CrF_6^{-3} the octahedral corners are occupied by fluorine atoms; in $Cr(H_2O)_6^{+3}$ the octahedral corners are occupied by oxygen atoms, to each of which are joined the two H atoms; in

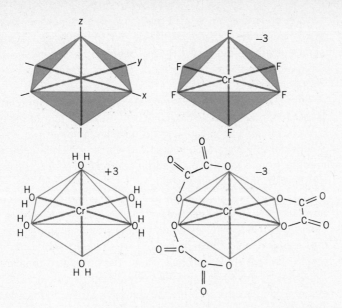

$Cr(C_2O_4)_3^{-3}$ the octahedral corners are again occupied by oxygen atoms, with adjacent oxygens bridged via carbon atoms of the oxalate ions.

Any group that bridges two or more coordination positions is called a *chelating agent,* and the resulting complex is a *chelate.* If the group binds at two points, as does oxalate, then it may also be called *bidentate.* Some chelating agents bind at more than two positions, in which case they are tridentate, tetradentate, pentadentate, or even hexadentate. An example of the last of these is ethylenediaminetetraacetate (generally abbreviated EDTA)

$$\begin{array}{cc} {}^-\text{OOCCH}_2 & \text{H}_2\text{CCOO}^- \\ & \text{N--CH}_2\text{--CH}_2\text{--N} \\ {}_-\text{OOCCH}_2 & \text{H}_2\text{CCOO}_- \end{array}$$

which can wrap itself around a central atom so that binding can occur at the four negative oxygens and also at the two nitrogens.

Other geometries arise if other sets of orbitals are used for binding on ligands. For example, if only one of the d orbitals is used (for example, $d_{x^2-y^2}$) and combined with an s and two of the p orbitals (for example, p_x and p_y), then we have a square-planar arrangement of ligands about the central atom. Figure 19.10 shows some typical examples drawn from platinum chemistry. In $PtCl_4^{--}$ the four chlorine atoms

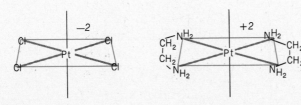

form a square about a central Pt; in Pt$en_2$$^{++}$ (where en stands for ethylenediamine, $NH_2CH_2CH_2NH_2$), the four nitrogen atoms form a square, with bridges of CH_2CH_2 between the members of a pair. Square-planar geometry is most likely to occur for ions having d^8 configurations.

Some complexes are intermediate between octahedral and square-planar. Such is the case for $Cu(H_2O)_6$$^{++}$, in which four of the H_2O molecules, arranged in a square, are nearer than the other two. The result is a considerably distorted octahedron, which can be imagined as being created from a regular octahedron (as in Figure 19.9) by pulling outward a pair of opposite corners.

If no d orbitals are used in binding the complex, then it is likely to have tetrahedral arrangement of ligands about the central atom. In such cases it is usually one s and three p orbitals that are used for bonding, giving rise to the familiar sp^3 tetrahedral hybrids. Zn^{++}, for example, has all its $3d$ orbitals filled. In forming a complex such as $Zn(NH_3)_4$$^{++}$, the $4s$ and three $4p$ orbitals of the zinc are used. The result is a complex in which the four nitrogen atoms define a tetrahedron about the zinc.

In each of the above-considered cases all of the near-neighbor atoms about a given central atom were identical. Let us now ask, What if this were not the case? If only one near-neighbor is made different from all the others, then only one species still results. For example, if one of the six F^- ions in $CrF_6$$^{-3}$ is replaced by an H_2O molecule to give $CrF_5(H_2O)^{-2}$, there is no difference in the product no matter which of the six fluorides is replaced. All the corners of a regular octahedron are equivalent. What if a second ligand is substituted? This time it matters, since two distinctly different geometries will result depending on whether the second substituted ligand goes on a corner adjacent to the first substituent or on the opposite corner.

19.11
Isomers of $CrF_4(H_2O)_2$$^-$

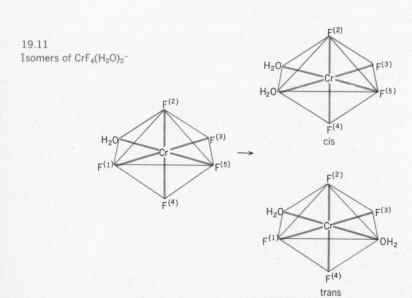

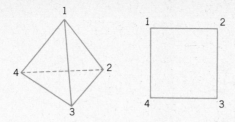

19.12
Isomerism in tetrahedral
and square-planar
configurations

Figure 19.11 shows the two possible configurations that result when a fluoride of $CrF_5(H_2O)^{--}$ is substituted by another H_2O to give $CrF_4(H_2O)_2^-$. The product at the top has the two H_2O molecules adjacent to each other (note that the product would be the same whether substitution was at position 1, 2, 3, or 4); the product at the bottom has the two H_2O molecules at opposite corners of the octahedron. The product at the top and the product at the bottom are chemically different. They are said to be *isomers*—two species of the same composition differing in structure and hence in properties. The isomer with adjacent positions substituted is called *cis*, and that with opposite positions substituted, *trans*. Substitution of a third H_2O for F^- on *cis*-$CrF_4(H_2O)_2^-$ gives rise to two possible products: one if the third H_2O goes into a position adjacent to both the other two H_2O (into position 2 or 4 of the cis form in Figure 19.11) and the other if the third H_2O goes into a position not adjacent to both the other two H_2O (into position 3 or 5 of the cis form in Figure 19.11). On the contrary, substitution of a third H_2O for F^- in *trans*-$CrF_4(H_2O)_2^-$ gives rise to only one possible product, which is identical with the second of the two noted above for cis.

Cis and trans substitution products are also possible in square-planar configurations, since two substituents on a square can be on either adjacent or opposite corners of the square. However, such is not the case in tetrahedral configurations. As shown in Figure 19.12, any corner on a tetrahedron is adjacent to the other three. In other words, if there is a substituent at position 1 of the tetrahedron, it makes no difference whether the second substitution occurs at position 2, 3, or 4. In the square, in contrast, with a substituent at position 1, different products result if the substitution occurs at 3 (giving rise to a trans product) as opposed to substitution at either 2 or 4 (cis product).

In addition to geometrical isomerism as discussed above, complex ions sometimes show a complication arising from what is called *optical isomerism*. Optical isomers occur when two species differ only in that one is the mirror image of the other. The two species have most properties identical, but they differ in that one turns the plane of polarized light clockwise and the other turns it counterclockwise. Figure 19.13 shows the relation between the two optical isomers of $Coen_3^{+3}$ (tris-ethylenediamine cobalt III). Although in both cases cobalt is bound only to six nitrogen atoms of three *en* molecules, there are two different ways in which this is done. As with more familiar mirror-image pairs (e.g., right and left hands), no amount of turning can superimpose one of these ions on its mirror image. The pair of optical isomers are called

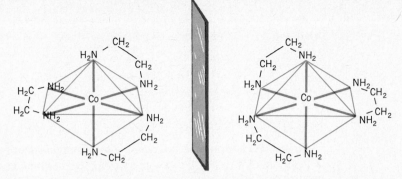

enantiomers or *enantiomorphs*. They may be individually designated d (for dextro) or l (for laevo) depending on whether the plane of polarized light is rotated clockwise or counterclockwise as viewed looking into the beam.

The general rules for naming complex ions are summarized in Appendix 1.

QUESTIONS

19.1 Nomenclature   Name the following complexes:

(a) CrF_6^{-3} (d) $Cr(C_2O_4)_3^{-3}$
(b) $CrF_5(H_2O)^{--}$ (e) $Pt(NH_2CH_2CH_2NH_2)_2^{++}$
(c) $Cr(H_2O)_6^{+3}$

19.2 Variable oxidation state   Give the apparent electron configuration for the common oxidation states of each of the following elements: Mn, Fe, W, Pt, Nb.

19.3 Magnetism   Calculate, in Bohr magnetons, the magnetic moment expected from spin-only for the following ions: Cr^{+3}, V^{+4}, Fe^{+3}, Ni^{+3}, Cu^+.

19.4 Nomenclature   Write the formulas for the following complexes: (a) hexacyanoferrate(II), (b) pentaammineaquocobalt(III), (c) trichloroethylenepalladiate(II), (d) dichlorobisethylenediamineplatinum(IV), (e) trioxomonohydroxosulfurate(VI).

19.5 Isomers   Which of the following can represent isomeric pairs: (a) $Co(NH_3)_5Cl^{++}$, (b) $Co(NH_3)_4Cl_2^+$, (c) $Co(NH_3)_3Cl_3$, (d) $Co(NH_3)_2Cl_4^-$, (e) $Co(NH_3)Cl_5^{--}$, (f) $Pt(NH_3)_2Cl_2$ (square-planar), (g) $Zn(NH_3)_2Cl_2$ (tetrahedral)?

19.6 Electron configuration   Without reference to a periodic table tell how many d electrons there are in the lowest energy state of neutral atoms of the following elements: (a) $Z = 23$, (b) $Z = 40$, (c) $Z = 57$, (d) $Z = 29$, (e) $Z = 86$.

19.7 Electron configuration   Give the electron configuration of outer d and s subshells of each of the following: (a) Ti, (b) Ti^{++}, (c) Cu^{++}, (d) Ru^{+3}, (e) Re^{+4}.

19.8 Density   Figure 19.2 shows that in each row of transition elements the density goes through a maximum. Correlate this with the changes in structure and atomic radii.

19.9 Oxidation states   (*a*) By reference to Figure 19.3, find all the subgroups that fully illustrate in their lowest common oxidation states the rule that in going down a subgroup higher states are favored. (*b*) Do the same thing for the highest common oxidation states.

19.10 Spectra   Which of the following ions, if hydrated, would you expect to be practically colorless: Ti^{++}, V^{+4}, Mn^{++}, Sc^{+3}, Cu^{+}, Hf^{+4}?

19.11 Optical isomers   Which of the following can represent a pair of enantiomers: (*a*) $Co(NH_3)_4en^{+3}$, (*b*) *trans*-$Co(NH_3)_2en_2^{+3}$, (*c*) *cis*-$Co(NH_3)_2en_2^{+3}$, (*d*) *cis*-$CoCl_2(C_2O_4)en^{-1}$, (*e*) *cis*-$CO(NH_3)_2Cl_2en^{+}$?

19.12 Conductivity   (*a*) The electrical resistance of a piece of wire is equal to its length divided by the product of its conductivity and its cross-sectional area. Given wires of equal length, calculate the diameter of an iron wire whose resistance is equal to that of a copper wire 1.00 mm in diameter. (*b*) Typical costs per kilogram of pure iron and pure copper are \$4.00 and \$15.00. Calculate the relative costs of an iron wire and a copper wire having equal electrical resistance per unit length.

19.13 Conductivity   Assuming one conduction electron per atom, calculate the number of conduction electrons per cubic centimeter in Na, Cu, Ag, and Au and compare with the conductivities as given in Section 19.2. Which element seems out of line?

19.14 Ligand-field theory   (*a*) What is the principal distinction between crystal-field theory and ligand-field theory? (*b*) What experimental reason is there for preferring one over the other?

19.15 Ligand-field theory   Assuming the following ions are placed in an octahedral environment (not strong enough to force electron pairing), tell what population would be expected for the t_{2g} and e_g orbitals: V^{++}, Co^{++}, Mn^{++}, Cu^{++}, Pt^{++}.

19.16 Magnetism   From spin-only calculate the magnetic moment expected for each of the following (*a*) in weak octahedral field and (*b*) in strong octahedral field: Ru^{+3}, Pd^{+4}, Rh^{+3}.

19.17 Magnetism   What do you predict for the magnetic moment of ferricyanide, $Fe(CN)_6^{-3}$, compared with ferrocyanide, $Fe(CN)_6^{-4}$?

19.18 Complex ions   Draw probable structures for each of the following: (*a*) tetraaminezinc(II), (*b*) *trans*-dichlorobisethylenediaminecobalt(III), (*c*) ethylenediaminetetraacetatecobaltate(III), (*d*) *cis*-dibromodiamminepalladium(II).

19.19 Spectra   Assuming it to be in an octahedral environment, why would a d^9 ion show a single absorption band just as does a d^1 ion?

19.20 Isomers   Given two substances both with the molecular formula $Pd(NH_3)_2Br_2$. Substance *A* has a dipole moment; substance *B* has no dipole moment. List the possible structures for *A* and for *B*.

19.21 Ionization potentials   Account, as best you can, for the following facts: (*a*) In going down the zinc subgroup of elements, the first ionization potentials pass through a minimum at Cd. (*b*) The third ionization potential of Hg is less than that for Cd.

19.22 Ligand-field theory   Show that ligands in square-planar array may separate d orbitals so that they order by increasing energy as d_{yz} and d_{zx}, d_{z^2}, d_{xy}, and $d_{x^2-y^2}$.

19.23 Spectra   What change in color might you expect in going from $Ti(H_2O)_6^{+3}$ to $Ti(CN)_6^{-3}$?

19.24 Ligand-field theory   Suppose you wish to predict the energy separation of d orbitals by a tetrahedral environment. You can proceed as follows: Locate the metal ion at the center of a cube with the x, y, z axes going through the face centers. Place the four ligands so as to occupy alternate corners of the cube. By examining the geometry of each d orbital relative to the cube surface, show that two of the orbitals are expected to be of lower energy than the other three.

ANSWERS

  19.3 3.87; 1.73; 5.92; 3.87; 0   *19.6* (*a*) 3   (*b*) 12   (*c*) 21   (*d*) 10   (*e*) 30   *19.13* 2.5×10^{22}; 8.4×10^{22}; 5.9×10^{22}; 5.9×10^{22} *19.16* (*a*) 5.92; 4.90; 4.90   (*b*) 1.73; 0; 0

20 transition elements II:
Sc, Ti, V, Cr, and Mn subgroups

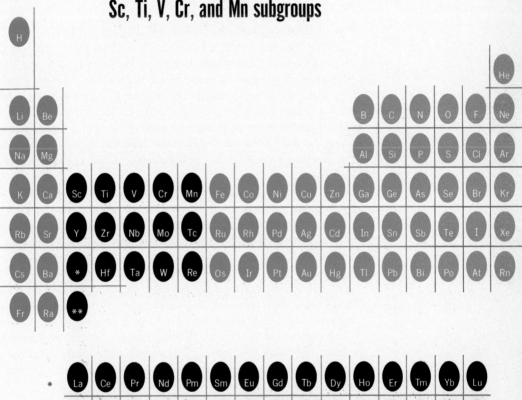

In the preceding chapter the general properties that characterize the transition elements have been discussed. In particular, the role of d orbitals in fixing observed properties has been considered. In this chapter we begin to take up the specific chemistry of individual elements. We shall do this by subgroups, starting from the left with the scandium subgroup and working toward the right. For each subgroup the emphasis will be on the top element, since in general it is both the most abundant and the most important technologically of the subgroup. The scandium subgroup is special in that it includes the lanthanides and actinides.

Element	Z	Electron population
Scandium	21	2, 8, 9, 2
Yttrium	39	2, 8, 18, 9, 2
La ⟶ Lu	57–71	2, 8, 18, 18 ⟶ 32, 9, 2
Ac ⟶ Lw	89–103	2, 8, 18, 32, 18 ⟶ 32, 9, 2

20.1
Electronic configurations
of scandium subgroup

20.1 SCANDIUM SUBGROUP

The scandium subgroup contains the elements scandium ($Z = 21$), yttrium ($Z = 39$), lanthanum through lutetium ($Z = 57$ through 71), and actinium through lawrencium ($Z = 89$ through 103). The 14 elements with lanthanum are called *the lanthanides* or *rare-earth elements*. The 14 elements with actinium are called the *actinides*. As usually displayed in the periodic table (Figure 2.2), all the lanthanides occupy the same position in the sixth period, below yttrium. The actinides occupy a corresponding position in the seventh period. Figure 20.1 indicates the electron configurations characteristic of the scandium-subgroup elements.

The lanthanide elements correspond to belated filling of the $4f$ subshell. Since in these elements the $4f$ subshell is third outermost, changes in its electronic population are well screened from neighboring atoms by the second-outermost and outermost shells. Consequently, all the lanthanides have properties that are remarkably alike. Similar belated filling of the $5f$ subshell occurs in the actinide series.

All the scandium-subgroup elements, including the lanthanides and actinides, are typically metallic with high luster and good conductivity. They are all quite reactive, with oxidation potentials of about 2 volts. Many of their compounds, such as hydroxides, carbonates, and phosphates, are of low solubility. There is some slight tendency for the +3 ions to hydrolyze in aqueous solution to give slightly acid solutions. All these elements are quite rare in nature.

1. Scandium. Scandium occurs in nature only in the combined form in minerals such as monazite (a complex phosphate) and gadolinite (a complex silicate). Not much is known about the element except that it reacts vigorously with water to liberate hydrogen, has a melting point of about 1200°C and a boiling point of about 2500°C, and forms compounds only in the +3 oxidation state. All of these compounds are colorless, and none is paramagnetic.

2. Yttrium. Like scandium, yttrium is quite rare. It occurs in the combined form in a few rare minerals, such as gadolinite. The metal is quite vigorously reactive but only to give compounds in which its oxidation state is +3. As expected, these compounds are colorless and are not paramagnetic. The oxide, Y_2O_3, or yttria, is a pure white powder. Yttrium compounds, when doped with europium, have proved to be remarkably efficient as red phosphors in color TV receivers.

Element	Symbol	Z	Probable electron configuration	Oxidation states
Lanthanum	La	57	2, 8, 18, 18, $5s^25p^65d^16s^2$	$+3$
Cerium	Ce	58	———————— $4f^26s^2$	$+3, +4$
Praseodymium	Pr	59	———————— $4f^36s^2$	$+3, +4$
Neodymium	Nd	60	———————— $4f^46s^2$	$+3$
Promethium	Pm	61	———————— $4f^56s^2$	$+3$
Samarium	Sm	62	———————— $4f^66s^2$	$+2, +3$
Europium	Eu	63	———————— $4f^76s^2$	$+2, +3$
Gadolinium	Gd	64	———————— $4f^75d^16s^2$	$+3$
Terbium	Tb	65	———————— $4f^96s^2$	$+3, +4$
Dysprosium	Dy	66	———————— $4f^{10}6s^2$	$+3$
Holmium	Ho	67	———————— $4f^{11}6s^2$	$+3$
Erbium	Er	68	———————— $4f^{12}6s^2$	$+3$
Thulium	Tm	69	———————— $4f^{13}6s^2$	$+3$
Ytterbium	Yb	70	———————— $4f^{14}6s^2$	$+3$
Lutetium	Lu	71	———————— $4f^{14}5d^16s^2$	$+3$

20.2
Lanthanide elements

20.2 LANTHANIDES

The 15 elements that constitute the lanthanide series are listed in Figure 20.2, which also gives the symbols and the most probable electron configurations. Because of the closeness of the $4f$ and $5d$ energy levels, there is considerable uncertainty in some of the electron-configuration assignments. It is not obvious in every case from the electron configurations of the neutral atoms, but all the lanthanides form $+3$ ions as their principal chemical species. It is generally assumed in forming these ions that the $6s^2$ electrons are lost along with the $5d^1$ (if present) or with one of the $4f$ (if no $5d^1$ is present).

Except for promethium, which has an unstable nucleus, all the lanthanides generally occur together. The richest source mineral is monazite, a complex phosphate. As a group the lanthanides are not very abundant—the most common lanthanide being cerium, which comprises but $3 \times 10^{-4}\%$ of the mass of the earth's crust. Because of the great similarity in chemical properties, it is difficult to separate one lanthanide from another. Separation has been made by careful repeated fractional crystallization and, more recently, by ion-exchange techniques. Both separations rely on slight differences of properties (e.g., solubility, complex-ion formation, hydration) arising from size differences in the $+3$ ions. In going through the sequence from La^{+3} to Lu^{+3} the ionic radius shrinks from 1.06 Å to 0.85 Å in steps averaging less than 0.02 Å. This shrinkage, which is called the *lanthanide contraction,* arises from the increase of nuclear charge during the progressive filling of an interior subshell. Although the lanthanide contraction is important in allowing separation of the lanthanide elements, it is more significant in its effect on the relative properties of elements before and after the lanthanide sequence. For example, zirconium ($Z = 40$) and hafnium

($Z = 72$) have almost identical chemical properties because the intervening lanthanide contraction has canceled the usual increase of radius down a group and made the two kinds of atoms nearly identical in size.

The lanthanide elements are soft, gray metals that conduct electricity fairly well; the conductivity of lanthanum, for example, is 1.7×10^4 $(ohm\text{-}cm)^{-1}$. They react vigorously with water and with oxygen of the air. The oxidation potentials decrease regularly from $E° = +2.52$ for $La(s) \longrightarrow La^{+3}(aq) + 3e^-$ to $E° = +2.25$ for $Lu(s) \longrightarrow Lu^{+3}(aq) + 3e^-$. The trihydroxides are relatively insoluble, with K_{sp} for $M(OH)_3(s) \rightleftharpoons M^{+3} + 3OH^-$ decreasing regularly from 1.0×10^{-19} for $La(OH)_3$ to 2.5×10^{-24} for $Lu(OH)_3$.

Because the lanthanide ions are generally characterized by an incomplete $4f$ subshell, paramagnetism due to unpaired electrons is observed for most lanthanide compounds. As noted in Section 19.5, unlike d electrons, f electrons contribute to paramagnetism through both spin moment and orbital moment. The calculation of the orbital contribution is complicated; it varies from zero for the case of Gd^{+3} ($4f^7$) to 5.7 Bohr magnetons for the case of Ho^{+3} ($4f^{10}$). In other words, the magnetic moments of the lanthanide ions *cannot* be calculated from the spin-only formula, which is found to work reasonably well for paramagnetism arising from d electrons. The reason for this difference is that, whereas d electrons are exposed to interaction with the ligands and so are prevented from orienting freely in an external magnetic field, f electrons are deep enough inside the ion to be shielded from the quenching effect of the environment.

The relatively good shielding of f electrons from interaction with the environment is important in determining the spectral characteristics of lanthanide ions. Instead of the broad absorption bands arising from d-electron transitions (Section 19.6), the lanthanide ions have spectra consisting generally of many sharp absorption bands. The sharpness—i.e., absorption over but a narrow range of wavelengths—is attributable to lack of interaction between the f levels and the environment. The large number (tens to hundreds) of bands is attributable to the large number of configurations possible within the partially filled f subshell.

Besides the $+3$ state, some of the lanthanides show other oxidation states. For example, cerium forms Ce^{+4} with an $E°$ of -1.61 volts for $Ce^{+3}(aq) \longrightarrow Ce^{+4}(aq) + e^-$. In other words, Ce^{+4} is as good an oxidizing agent as MnO_4^-. Other $+4$ lanthanides (Pr^{+4}, Tb^{+4}) are even more powerful oxidizing agents. Dipositive states (Eu^{++}, Sm^{++}, Yb^{++}) also occur; of them, only Eu^{++} is stable with respect to oxidation by water.

20.3 ACTINIDES

The 15 actinide elements together with probable electron configurations are listed in Figure 20.3. The electron configurations are even less certain than those given for the lanthanide elements. Not only are the energy levels close together but, because the nuclei are unstable to

Element	Symbol	Z	Probable electron configuration	Oxidation states
Actinium	Ac	89	2, 8, 18, 32, 18, $6s^26p^66d^17s^2$	+3
Thorium	Th	90	————————$6d^27s^2$	(+2), (+3), +4
Protactinium	Pa	91	————————$5f^26d^17s^2$	(+3), (+4), +5
Uranium	U	92	————————$5f^36d^17s^2$	+3, +4, +5, +6
Neptunium	Np	93	————————$5f^46d^17s^2$	+3, +4, +5, +6
Plutonium	Pu	94	————————$5f^67s^2$	(+2), +3, +4, +5, +6
Americium	Am	95	————————$5f^77s^2$	(+2), +3, +4, +5, +6
Curium	Cm	96	————————$5f^76d^17s^2$	+3
Berkelium	Bk	97	————————$5f^86d^17s^2$	+3, +4
Californium	Cf	98	————————$5f^{10}7s^2$	+3
Einsteinium	Es	99	————————$5f^{11}7s^2$	+3
Fermium	Fm	100	————————$5f^{12}7s^2$	+3
Mendelevium	Md	101	————————$5f^{13}7s^2$	+3
Nobelium	No	102	————————$5f^{14}7s^2$	+3
Lawrencium	Lw	103	————————$5f^{14}6d^17s^2$	+3

20.3
Actinide elements

radioactive decay, in some cases only minute amounts of the elements have been obtained for investigation. As will be discussed in Chapter 29, all of these nuclei are unstable with respect to alpha emission. In addition, the later members of the series tend to undergo spontaneous fission—a fact of nature that seems certain to limit the number of elements possible. Thorium and uranium, although radioactive, have sufficiently long half-lives (1.39×10^{10} years for Th^{232} and 4.50×10^9 years for U^{238}) that they occur in nature. The half-lives of all the others are short compared to the age of the earth (*ca.* 5×10^9 years), so that these elements do not occur naturally but have to be prepared by synthetic methods using particle accelerators or nuclear reactors (Section 29.3).

As elements the actinides are metallic. Like the lanthanides, they generally have relatively high oxidation potentials (*ca.* 2 volts) for going from the metal to the first stable state. Unlike the lanthanides, the actinides (at least the early ones which have been extensively studied) show a variety of oxidation states. Uranium, for example, forms many compounds in each of the states +3, +4, +5, and +6. In aqueous solution U^{+3} reduces water to liberate H_2 and form U^{+4}, which is slowly oxidized by air to UO_2^{++} (so-called uranyl ion). The uranyl ion is stable, but it can be reduced to form UO_2^+, which, however, is unstable to disproportionation into U^{+4} and UO_2^{++}. Like most ions of the actinides, these species are colored. For example, $U^{+3}(aq)$ is red, $U^{+4}(aq)$ is green, and $UO_2^{++}(aq)$ is yellow. As would be expected from the shielded nature of f electrons, the absorption spectra of the actinides generally consist of a large number of sharp absorption peaks. These peaks, however, are not so sharp as those arising from $4f$ transitions, primarily because $5f$ levels are not so well buried as $4f$ are.

Transition elements II:
Sc, Ti, V, Cr, and
Mn subgroups

409

Symbol	Z	Electronic configuration	Melting point, °C	Boiling point, °C	Ionization potential, ev	Oxidation potential, volts
Ti	22	(18) $3d^24s^2$	1660	>3000	6.83	+0.9 (to TiO^{++})
Zr	40	(36) $4d^25s^2$	1860	>3000	6.95	+1.5 (to ZrO^{++})
Hf	72	(68) $5d^26s^2$	2200	>3000	5.5	+1.7 (to HfO^{++})

20.4
Elements of titanium
subgroup

20.4 TITANIUM SUBGROUP

The elements of the titanium subgroup are titanium ($Z = 22$), zirconium ($Z = 40$), and hafnium ($Z = 72$). They are more common than the elements of the scandium subgroup, and their chemistry is more complicated than that of scandium because of the additional oxidation state, +4. As Figure 20.4 indicates, each of these elements has two s electrons in the outermost shell and two d electrons in the second-outermost shell. Removal of the s electrons would give the +2 oxidation state; further removal of one or two d electrons would give the +3 and the +4 states. Only in the case of Ti are all three of these states observed. There are some +3 compounds of Zr, but the +4 state is the more common. Hafnium forms compounds only in the +4 state. This trend of favoring the higher oxidation states in going down the group is typical of the transition subgroups.

Other characteristic properties of the titanium subgroup elements are that the elements are metallic, have very high melting and boiling points, and are quite reactive to most oxidizing agents. Although it does not show up in the physical properties, there is an extraordinary similarity in the chemical properties of Zr and Hf. This similarity is attributed to the lanthanide contraction (Section 20.2), which intervenes between these two elements and makes their atoms identical in size.

1. *Titanium.* In the earth's crust, titanium is tenth most abundant (0.58% by mass) and ranks ahead of such familiar elements as chlorine, carbon, and sulfur. However, it is distributed very widely, and commercially useful deposits are scarce. The principal sources are rutile (TiO_2), ilmenite ($FeTiO_3$), and iron ores. It is very difficult to prepare the pure metal, because it has great affinity for carbon, nitrogen, oxygen, and hydrogen. The usual method for getting Ti is to convert the oxides with chlorine to $TiCl_4$, which is then reduced with Mg.

Pure titanium which has low carbon impurity and is free from hydrogen embrittlement (Section 15.4) is extremely strong (stronger than iron). Because it also has a high melting point and is resistant to corrosion (because of surface coatings of oxide and nitride), the metal is in great demand as a structural material, for example, in rocket engines and supersonic planes. Until recently, the principal use of titanium had been for hardening and toughening steel.

In its compounds, titanium exhibits oxidation states of +2, +3, and +4. Compounds of the first two are colored and paramagnetic because

20.4 Titanium subgroup

of the presence of unpaired d electrons. They are also good reducing agents. For the half-reaction $Ti^{++} \longrightarrow Ti^{+3} + e^-$, the oxidation potential is about 2 volts, indicating that Ti^{++} is a much better reducing agent than H_2 and that Ti^{++} compounds added to H^+ solutions liberate H_2.

Titanous ion, Ti^{+3}, is a violet ion which also is a convenient reducing agent. When oxidized in aqueous solution, it does not form titanic ion, Ti^{+4}, as expected, but appears in a hydrolyzed form usually written TiO^{++} and called titanyl ion. From this are derived ionic salts such as $TiOSO_4$, titanyl sulfate. Like most of the $+3$ ions of the transition elements, Ti^{+3} forms an insoluble trihydroxide when base is added to its solutions. This black $Ti(OH)_3$ turns white and evolves H_2 when allowed to stand, indicating decomposition:

$$2Ti(OH)_3(s) \longrightarrow 2TiO_2(s) + 2H_2O + H_2(g)$$

The most important oxidation state of titanium is the $+4$, and probably the most important compound is TiO_2, titanium dioxide, or titania. This compound is quite inert and has good covering power; it is used extensively as a pigment in both the paint industry and the cosmetic industry. In crystalline form, it is used as a semiprecious, artificial gem. With a higher refractive index than diamond (Section 24.2), it has more sparkle than diamond, but, unfortunately, it is not very hard and becomes scratched. When TiO_2 is heated with carbon in a stream of chlorine, titanium tetrachloride ($TiCl_4$) is formed. This is a colorless, fuming liquid which is used for making smoke screens. The smoke is probably an oxychloride of the type $TiOCl_2$.

2. Zirconium and hafnium. These two elements are remarkable because they have essentially identical chemical properties. The atomic radii of Zr and Hf are 1.454 and 1.442 Å, respectively. Since their outer-electron configurations are the same, it is not surprising that the two elements resemble each other chemically. The resemblance is so marked that hafnium atoms replace zirconium atoms in crystals with ease. For this reason, all naturally occurring zirconium minerals are contaminated with hafnium. Zirconium is about 50 times as abundant as hafnium, which makes up only $4.5 \times 10^{-4}\%$ of the earth's crust. The principal minerals of Zr are baddeleyite (ZrO_2) and zircon ($ZrSiO_4$). In its transparent form, especially when colored, zircon finds use as a gem stone.

Zr and Hf metals are extremely difficult to prepare in the pure state, because, like Ti, they have such great affinity for hydrogen, carbon, oxygen, and nitrogen. One method for getting the pure metals is the thermal decomposition of the tetraiodide (ZrI_4) on a hot tungsten wire.

Practically all the known compounds of Zr and Hf correspond to the $+4$ oxidation state. Of these, the oxides zirconia (ZrO_2) and hafnia (HfO_2) are refractory and are used for high-temperature insulation. In the Nernst glow lamp, used in scientific work as a concentrated light source, the incandescent body is chiefly ZrO_2. The other $+4$ compounds readily hydrolyze to form the zirconyl (ZrO^{++}) or hafnyl (HfO^{++}) ions, which can also be written as $M(OH)_2^{++}$.

Like titanium, both zirconium and hafnium form complex ions, especially with fluorine. Examples of these are ZrF_6^{--} and ZrF_7^{-3}. The latter is a rather rare illustration of seven neighbors about a central atom. The complex salts K_2ZrF_6 and K_2HfF_6 differ in solubility, and this is the basis of the separation of Zr from Hf by fractional crystallization.

20.5 VANADIUM SUBGROUP

The elements of the vanadium subgroup are vanadium ($Z = 23$), niobium ($Z = 41$), and tantalum ($Z = 73$). The name "columbium" has also been used instead of niobium. These elements are considerably less abundant than those of the titanium subgroup, and their chemistry is more complicated because of the formation of a $+5$ oxidation state. Properties are summarized in Figure 20.5. Of these elements, vanadium shows compounds corresponding to oxidation states $+2$, $+3$, $+4$, and $+5$. Niobium shows $+5$ and some $+3$; tantalum shows $+4$ but mainly $+5$. Again because of the intervening lanthanide contraction, the last two elements of the subgroup are very similar in chemical properties.

Symbol	Z	Electronic configuration	Melting point, °C	Boiling point, °C	Ionization potential, ev	Oxidation potential, volts
V	23	(18) $3d^3 4s^2$	1710	3000(?)	6.74	$+1.2$ (to V^{++})
Nb	41	(36) $4d^4 5s^1$	1950	3000(?)	6.77	$+0.65$ (to Nb_2O_5)
Ta	73	(68) $5d^3 6s^2$	>3000	>4100	6	$+0.81$ (to Ta_2O_5)

20.5
Elements of vanadium
subgroup

1. *Vanadium.* The principal minerals of vanadium are patronite (V_2S_5) and vanadinite ($Pb_5V_3O_{12}Cl$), but the element is also obtained as a valuable by-product from the uranium mineral carnotite ($KUVO_6$). The name vanadium comes from Vanadis, the Scandinavian goddess of beauty, and recalls the beautiful colors of the various vanadium compounds. The pure metal is very hard to prepare, and since its main use is as an additive to steel alloys, V is usually made as ferrovanadium (solid solution of Fe and V). When added to steel, the V combines with the oxygen and nitrogen, and it also dissolves in the molten iron to increase the tensile strength, toughness, and elasticity of the resulting steel.

In its compounds, vanadium shows oxidation states of $+2$, $+3$, $+4$, and $+5$. These correspond to at least partial removal of the two $4s$ electrons plus none, one, two, or all three of the $3d$ electrons. Many of the compounds are characteristically colored. Those in the lower oxidation states are good reducing agents.

Probably the most important compound of vanadium is the pent-oxide, V_2O_5. This is a red or orange solid made by thermal decomposition of ammonium vanadate (NH_4VO_3). It is used as a catalyst in various oxidation reactions in which O_2 is the oxidizing agent, e.g., in the conversion of SO_2 to SO_3 for making sulfuric acid. Vanadium pentoxide is amphoteric. It dissolves in highly acid solutions to give an ion variously described as VO^{+3}, $V(OH)_2^{+3}$, VO_2^{+}, or $V(OH)_4^{+}$; in basic solution, V_2O_5 dissolves to give vanadate anions such as VO_4^{-3}. When acid is gradually added to these vanadate solutions, anions which contain more than one V atom per ion (such as $V_2O_7^{-4}$) are formed. Eventually V_2O_5 precipitates.

Acid solutions containing vanadium in the $+5$ oxidation state go through a series of color changes when a reducing agent such as zinc is added. The solutions first turn blue, then green, and then violet, corresponding to stepwise reduction to the $+4$, $+3$, and $+2$ states. The characteristic ions are $V(OH)_2^{++}$, V^{+3} (vanadic), and V^{++} (vanadous). The oxidation potentials relating these species are

$$V(s) \longrightarrow V^{++} + 2e^- \qquad\qquad\qquad\qquad\qquad +1.2 \text{ volts}$$

$$V^{++} \longrightarrow V^{+3} + e^- \qquad\qquad\qquad\qquad\qquad +0.25 \text{ volt}$$

$$2H_2O + V^{+3} \longrightarrow V(OH)_2^{++} + 2H^+ + e^- \qquad -0.36 \text{ volt}$$

$$2H_2O + V(OH)_2^{++} \longrightarrow V(OH)_4^{+} + 2H^+ + e^- \qquad -1.0 \text{ volt}$$

Since the oxidation potential of $Zn(s) \longrightarrow Zn^{++} + 2e^-$ is $+0.76$ volt, zinc can reverse each of the above half-reactions except the first.

2. *Niobium and tantalum.* Both niobium and tantalum are rather rare elements, and they are almost always found together in nature. The principal minerals are columbite and tantalite, which are mixed oxides of the two metals along with those of iron and manganese. Although Ta is rare in nature (0.00021%, an abundance about one-tenth that of Nb), its desirable properties have led to rather extensive use. The problem of preparation is a difficult one, and, in fact, the name tantalum reflects the frustrations in its first recovery. (In Greek mythology Tantalus was sent to Hell, where, plagued by hunger and thirst, he was placed near food and drink which always stayed out of reach. The close relationship of Nb to Ta is indicated by the name niobium, after Niobe, the tragic daughter of Tantalus.) In order to separate the two elements, the mixed oxides are converted by HF and KF to K_2TaF_7 [heptafluorotantalate(V)] and K_2NbOF_5 [oxopentafluoro-niobate(V)], which differ in solubility and can be concentrated by fractional crystallization.

Tantalum has very high ductility and preceded tungsten as filament material in electric light bulbs and electron tubes. It is also used in one kind of electrolytic *rectifier* for converting alternating current to direct current. This rectifier consists of an aqueous solution with two electrodes, one of which is Ta. When the Ta acts as an anode, it immediately forms an oxide coat, which cuts off the current. Ta can, however, act as a cathode and so permits flow of current in only one direction.

Since tantalum is very resistant to corrosion, it is used extensively for constructing apparatus in chemical plants, especially in apparatus designed for handling acids.

The most common compounds of Nb and Ta are the pentoxides, Nb_2O_5 and Ta_2O_5. These are rather inert, stable solids which can be formed by heating the finely divided metals in air or oxygen. They dissolve in concentrated bases to form niobate and tantalate anions. Little is known of these anions except that they are quite complex and can have varying numbers of metal atoms per ion. Tantalum carbide, TaC, made by heating the oxide with carbon, is extremely hard and finds use in making tools for high-speed machining of metals and wiredrawing dies.

20.6 CHROMIUM SUBGROUP

The chromium subgroup contains the elements chromium ($Z = 24$), molybdenum ($Z = 42$), and tungsten ($Z = 74$). They are all metals of small atomic volume, extremely high melting point, great hardness, and excellent resistance to corrosion. Their chemistry is complicated by the existence of several oxidation states ranging from $+2$ to $+6$ and by the formation of many complex ions, including oxyanions. Some properties are given in Figure 20.6. All of these elements form compounds

Symbol	Z	Electronic configuration	Melting point, °C	Boiling point, °C	Ionization potential, ev	Oxidation potential, volts
Cr	24	(18) $3d^54s^1$	1600	2500(?)	6.76	+0.91 (to Cr^{++})
Mo	42	(36) $4d^55s^1$	2620	>3700	7.18	+0.2 (to Mo^{+3})
W	74	(68) $5d^46s^2$	3370	5900	7.98	+0.12 (to WO$_2$)

20.6
Elements of chromium subgroup

in which they show the $+6$ oxidation state. In addition, chromium commonly shows $+2$ and $+3$ states, molybdenum $+3$, $+4$, and $+5$ states, and tungsten $+4$ and $+5$.

1. Chromium. Chromium is one of the less abundant metals (0.037% of the earth's crust), but still it is approximately 50 times as abundant as Mo and W. Its principal mineral is chromite ($FeCr_2O_4$), some of which is reduced directly by heating with carbon in order to provide ferrochromium (solid solution of Cr in Fe) for addition to alloy steels. Low-chrome steels (up to 1% Cr) are quite hard and strong; high-chrome steels (up to 30% Cr), or stainless steels, are very resistant to corrosion. Most of the remaining chromite is converted to sodium chromate (Na_2CrO_4) by heating it with Na_2CO_3 in air.

$$8Na_2CO_3(s) + 4FeCr_2O_4(s) + 7\,O_2(g) \longrightarrow$$

$$2Fe_2O_3(s) + 8Na_2CrO_4(s) + 8CO_2(g)$$

The sodium chromate is leached out with acid to form $Na_2Cr_2O_7$, an important oxidizing agent.

Chromium metal is very hard and, although quite reactive in the powdered form, in the massive form is quite resistant to corrosion. Furthermore, it takes a high polish, which lasts because of formation of an invisible, self-protective oxide coat. Consequently, chromium finds much use as a plating material, both for its decorative effect (0.00005 cm thick) and for its protective effect (0.0075 cm thick). The plate is usually put on by electrolyzing the object in a bath made by dissolving $Na_2Cr_2O_7$ and H_2SO_4 in water. Since plating will not occur unless the sulfate is present, the sulfate must be involved in some intermediate formed during the electrolysis.

All the compounds of chromium are colored, a fact which suggested the name chromium, from the Greek word for color, *chroma*. The characteristic oxidation states are $+2$, $+3$, and $+6$, represented in acid solution by Cr^{++} (chromous), Cr^{+3} (chromic), and $Cr_2O_7^{--}$ (dichromate) and in basic media by $Cr(OH)_2$, CrO_2^- (chromite), and CrO_4^{--} (chromate).

The chromous ion, Cr^{++}, is a beautiful blue ion obtained by reducing either Cr^{+3} or $Cr_2O_7^{--}$ with zinc metal. However, it is rapidly oxidized in aqueous solution by air. The oxidation potential for $Cr^{++} \longrightarrow Cr^{+3} + e^-$ is $+0.41$ volt, which means that Cr^{++} should also be oxidized by H^+, but the latter reaction is very slow. When base is added to solutions of chromous salts, chromous hydroxide precipitates. On exposure to air, $Cr(OH)_2$ is oxidized by O_2 to give $Cr(OH)_3$ (also written $Cr_2O_3 \cdot xH_2O$).

Many chromic salts, such as chromic nitrate, $Cr(NO_3)_3$, and chromic perchlorate, $Cr(ClO_4)_3$, dissolve in water to give violet solutions, in which the violet color is due to the hydrated chromic ion, $Cr(H_2O)_6^{+3}$. If high concentrations of chloride ion are added, some of the hydrate water is replaced, and the solution slowly turns green because of formation of a chloro complex. Solutions of chromic salts can be kept indefinitely, exposed to the air, without oxidation or reduction. In general, they are slightly acid because of hydrolysis of the chromic ion. This reaction can be written in either of the following ways:

$$Cr^{+3} + H_2O \rightleftharpoons CrOH^{++} + H^+$$

$$Cr(H_2O)_6^{+3} \rightleftharpoons Cr((H_2O)_5OH^{++} + H^+$$

When base is gradually added to chromic solutions, a green slimy precipitate, which is either $Cr(OH)_3 \cdot xH_2O$ or $Cr_2O_3 \cdot xH_2O$, first forms but then disappears as excess OH^- is added. A deep green color characteristic of chromite ion, written as CrO_2^- or $Cr(OH)_4^-$, is produced. The precipitation and redissolving associated with this amphoteric behavior can be described as follows:

$$Cr^{+3} + 3OH^- \longrightarrow Cr(OH)_3(s)$$

$$Cr(OH)_3(s) + OH^- \longrightarrow CrO_2^- + 2H_2O$$

The green species in the final solution is certainly more complicated than CrO_2^- and probably contains more than one Cr atom per ion.

When filtered off and heated, the insoluble hydroxide loses water to form Cr_2O_3, chromic oxide or chromium sesquioxide. This is an inert green powder much used as the pigment chrome green.

Chromic ion forms a great number of complex ions. In all of these the chromium atom is surrounded by six other atoms arranged at the corners of an octahedron. Typical octrahedral complexes are CrF_6^{-3}, $Cr(NH_3)_6^{+3}$, $Cr(H_2O)_6^{+3}$, $Cr(H_2O)_5Cl^{++}$, and $Cr(NH_3)_4Cl_2^+$. It is characteristic of chromic complexes that they form and dissociate very slowly. In potassium chrome alum, $KCr(SO_4)_2 \cdot 12H_2O$, the $Cr(H_2O)_6^{+3}$ complex occurs as a unit occupying some of the crystal lattice sites.

In the $+6$ oxidation state, chromium is known principally as the chromates and dichromates. The chromate ion, CrO_4^{--}, can be made quite easily by oxidizing chromite ion, CrO_2^-, in basic solution with a moderately good oxidizing agent such as hydrogen peroxide. The reaction is

$$2CrO_2^- + 3HO_2^- \longrightarrow 2CrO_4^{--} + H_2O + OH^-$$

where the peroxide is written as HO_2^- in basic solution. The chromate ion is yellow and has a tetrahedral structure with four oxygen atoms bound to a central chromium atom.

When solutions of chromate salts are acidified, the yellow color is replaced by a characteristic orange, the result of formation of $Cr_2O_7^{--}$, dichromate ion.

$$2CrO_4^{--} + 2H^+ \rightleftharpoons Cr_2O_7^{--} + H_2O$$

The change is reversed by adding base. The structure of the dichromate ion, shown in Figure 20.7, consists of two tetrahedra sharing an oxygen atom at a common corner. Each of the two chromium atoms at the centers of the tetrahedra is bound to four oxygen atoms at the corners. The dichromate ion is a very good oxidizing agent, especially in acid solution. The half-reaction

$$2Cr^{+3} + 7H_2O \longrightarrow Cr_2O_7^{--} + 14H^+ + 6e^-$$

has an oxidation potential of -1.33 volts; therefore, $Cr_2O_7^{--}$ is able to oxidize all but the very poorest reducing agents. It will, for example, oxidize hydrogen peroxide to form O_2:

$$Cr_2O_7^{--} + 3H_2O_2 + 8H^+ \longrightarrow 3O_2(g) + 2Cr^{+3} + 7H_2O$$

It might seem strange that in basic solution hydrogen peroxide oxidizes chromium, whereas in acid solution chromium oxidizes hydrogen peroxide. The reason for this is that, in going from the $+3$ to the $+6$ state of chromium (Cr^{+3} to $Cr_2O_7^{--}$), oxygen atoms have to be added, whereas, in going from the $+6$ to the $+3$ state ($Cr_2O_7^{--}$ to Cr^{+3}), oxygen is removed. In acid solution H^+ helps in removing oxygen by forming water; in basic solution the scarcity of H^+ allows addition of oxygen. In the general case of preparing compounds, the change to compounds of higher oxidation state is usually most easily done in

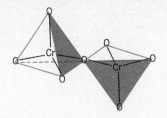

basic solution; to go to compounds of lower oxidation state, it is best to work in acid solution.

When solutions of dichromate ion are made very acid, especially in the presence of a dehydrating agent such as concentrated H_2SO_4, the uncharged species, CrO_3, is formed. This deep red solid is chromium trioxide, or, as it is sometimes called, chromic anhydride. It is a very powerful oxidizing agent and is used extensively in preparing organic compounds. Solutions of CrO_3 in concentrated H_2SO_4 are used as "cleaning solution" for glass equipment in laboratories. The cleaning action is due to the oxidation of grease.

2. Molybdenum. Molybdenum is found in nature as the mineral molybdenite, MoS_2, a beautiful blue-gray material of metallic luster, frequently confused with graphite. When heated in air, MoS_2 is oxidized to the trioxide, MoO_3, which is then reduced to the metal by heating with hydrogen. Because of its very high melting point (2620°C), Mo is obtained as a powder. This is pressed into bars and heated, so as to sinter the particles together to give sheet or wire for use as supports in X-ray tubes, electron tubes, electric furnaces, etc., where high temperatures may develop locally.

The major part of the Mo metal produced goes into iron alloys, where it acts as a toughening agent, favoring fine-grained structure. The molybdenum is added as ferromolybdenum (55 to 75% Mo in Fe), made by reducing mixed oxides of Mo and Fe.

The most important oxidation state of molybdenum is +6, as, for example, in molybdenum trioxide, MoO_3. This trioxide is acidic and dissolves in basic solutions to form a complicated series of oxyanions called the molybdates, the simplest of which is MoO_4^{--}. More complicated molybdates, having Mo-O-Mo bridges and containing up to 24 Mo atoms per ion, are known. These are called polymolybdates but are not well characterized. Neither MoO_3 nor the molybdates are particularly good oxidizing agents. When reduced, MoO_3 can form a deep blue oxide of variable composition, $MoO_{2.5-3.0}$, which is apparently some sort of defect structure (Section 6.7). Further reduction of MoO_3 or the molybdates usually forms the metal, but under appropriate conditions Mo^{+3} can be formed in aqueous solution. Its properties have not been well determined.

3. Tungsten. The element tungsten is frequently also called wolfram, whence the symbol W. It occurs in nature principally as the tungstates, e.g., as a calcium tungstate, $CaWO_4$, or scheelite, and as a mixture of iron and manganese tungstates, $(Fe,Mn)WO_4$, or wolframite. In order to get the metal, tungstates are treated with acid to precipitate insoluble tungstic acid, H_2WO_4, which is then dehydrated by ignition to tungstic oxide, WO_3. Hydrogen reduction of WO_3 produces W.

Since W has such a high melting point,[*] it, like Mo, is obtained as a fine powder, which is sintered into workable form. Fine tungsten wire for lamp filaments can be produced by heating the sintered powder in H_2 and subjecting the specimen to prolonged, vigorous pounding in a swaging machine (a machine for beating wire from large cross section down to small). Finally, an electric current through the wire heats it to a very high temperature, at which the microparticles coalesce.

The metal is rather inert to common oxidizing agents such as oxygen and nitric acid. However, it can be dissolved in a mixture of concentrated HNO_3 and HF. Most W goes into steel production, especially to make "high-speed steel" for cutting tools. Addition of W increases the ability to hold hardness at high temperatures and slows down the tearing off of small particles that causes the dulling of fast-finishing tools.

In its compounds tungsten usually occurs as the $+6$ oxidation state. The oxide WO_3 is acidic and dissolves in basic solutions or in molten basic oxides to form tungstates and polytungstates. Like the molybdates, the tungstates are not particularly good oxidizing agents. Unusual are the compounds called "tungsten bronzes," $M_xWO_3 (0 < x < 1)$, in which metal atoms such as Na fit interstitially into a WO_3 matrix.

20.7 MANGANESE SUBGROUP

The elements of the manganese subgroup are manganese ($Z = 25$), technetium ($Z = 43$), and rhenium ($Z = 75$). Manganese is by far the most important of the group; technetium is radioactive and does not occur in nature; rhenium is so rare as to constitute a chemical curiosity. Some of the properties of the subgroup are given in Figure 20.8.

1. Manganese. Manganese is not a very common element (abundance, 0.08%), but in the earth's crust it is as abundant as carbon and more so than sulfur. The most important minerals are the oxides: MnO_2 or pyrolusite, Mn_2O_3 or braunite (usually contaminated with iron oxide), and Mn_3O_4 or hausmannite. Probably the best way to prepare the metal is by reduction with powdered aluminum. However, since most metallic manganese goes into steel production, alloys of manganese are used instead. Two such alloys are ferromanganese (about 80% Mn in Fe) and spiegeleisen (about 20 to 30% Mn and about 5% C in Fe); they are made by reducing mixed oxides of iron and manganese in a blast furnace with carbon or carbon monoxide acting as reducing agent. When added to steel, Mn has two functions. In low amounts, it acts as a scavenger by combining with O and S in the molten iron to form easily removable substances. In high amounts (up to 14%) it imparts special hardness and toughness such as is needed for resistance to battering abrasion.

* At room temperature, tungsten has an extremely small vapor pressure. It has been calculated to correspond to one W atom per universe. *E pluribus unum.*

In its chemical compounds manganese shows oxidation states of $+2$, $+3$, $+4$, $+6$, and $+7$. Most of these compounds are colored and paramagnetic. In the $+2$ state, manganese exists as the manganous ion, Mn^{++}. Although Mn^{++} solutions are essentially colorless, many manganous salts, such as manganous sulfate, $MnSO_4$, and manganous chloride, $MnCl_2$, have pink coloration. Unlike Cr^{++}, Mn^{++} is a very poor reducing agent, and neutral or acid solutions of manganous salts can be kept indefinitely exposed to oxygen or other oxidizing agents. When base is added to Mn^{++}, a white precipitate of $Mn(OH)_2$ is formed. This solid, unlike manganous salts, is promptly oxidized by air to the $+3$ state.

In the $+3$ state, manganese can exist as the manganic ion, Mn^{+3}, but only in solids and complex ions. Unlike Cr^{+3}, Mn^{+3} is a very powerful oxidizing agent and can even oxidize H_2O to liberate oxygen. The oxidation potential of $Mn^{++} \longrightarrow Mn^{+3} + e^-$ is -1.51 volts, high enough that manganic ion can oxidize itself to the $+4$ state:

$$2Mn^{+3} + 2H_2O \longrightarrow Mn^{++} + MnO_2(s) + 4H^+$$

This disproportionation can be prevented and the $+3$ state stabilized by (1) complexing the manganese, e.g., with cyanide, CN^-, to give $Mn(CN)_6^{-3}$ or with oxalate, $C_2O_4^{--}$, to give $Mn(C_2O_4)_3^{-3}$, or by (2) forming an insoluble salt, such as $MnPO_4$, manganic phosphate, or the hydroxide, written as $Mn(OH)_3$ or $MnOOH$ or even Mn_2O_3.

Symbol	Z	Electronic configuration	Melting point, °C	Boiling point, °C	Ionization potential, ev	Oxidation potential, volts
Mn	25	(18) $3d^5 4s^2$	1260	1900	7.43	$+1.18$ (to Mn^{++})
Tc	43	(36) $4d^6 5s^1$?	—	—	—	-0.4(?) (to Tc^{++})
Re	75	(68) $5d^5 6s^2$	3200	—	7.87	-0.25 (to ReO_2)

20.8
Elements of manganese subgroup

In the $+4$ state the principal compound of manganese is manganese dioxide, MnO_2. It is not a simple compound, because no matter how careful the preparation, the product always contains fewer than two oxygen atoms per manganese atom. As mentioned in Section 13.4, MnO_2 is the oxidizing agent in the dry cell.

When MnO_2 is heated with basic substances in air, it is oxidized from its original black color to a deep green, the result of conversion to manganate ion, MnO_4^{--}. Though stable in alkaline solution, this ion (which represents Mn in the $+6$ state) disproportionates when the solution is acidified.

$$3MnO_4^{--} + 4H^+ \longrightarrow MnO_2(s) + 2MnO_4^- + 2H_2O$$

The MnO_4^- ion is the permanganate ion and shows manganese in its highest oxidation state. It is a very good oxidizing agent, especially in acid solution, where it is usually reduced all the way to manganous ion. For the half-reaction

$$Mn^{++} + 4H_2O \longrightarrow MnO_4^- + 8H^+ + 5e^-$$

the oxidation potential is -1.51 volts. This means that MnO_4^- is one of the strongest common oxidizing agents. Solutions of permanganate salts are frequently used in analytical chemistry to determine amounts of reducing agents by titration. Titration is simplified by using the disappearance of the deep violet color of MnO_4^- as the end-point indicator. The usual procedure is to make the solutions acid, so as to complete reduction to Mn^{++}. In neutral or alkaline solutions, MnO_2 is formed; in very basic solutions, MnO_4^{--}. When $KMnO_4$ is treated with concentrated H_2SO_4, a violently explosive oil, Mn_2O_7, or manganese heptoxide, is formed.

The chemistry of manganese illustrates well how the characteristics of compounds change in going from low oxidation state to high. In the low oxidation states manganese exists as a cation which forms basic oxides and hydroxides. In the higher oxidation states it exists as anions derived from acidic oxides.

2. Technetium. Since the technetium nucleus is very unstable and rapidly undergoes radioactive decay, it does not occur in nature. The name is derived from the Greek *technetos,* for artificial, and draws attention to the fact that technetium is made synthetically by bombardment of molybdenum with neutrons. Tc does not resemble manganese nearly so much as it resembles the following element rhenium.

3. Rhenium. Rhenium is a very rare element (abundance, 10^{-7}% by mass) occurring in trace amounts in molybdenite, columbite, and pyrolusite. The element is extracted by oxidizing to perrhenic acid, $HReO_4$, and precipitating as slightly soluble potassium perrhenate, $KReO_4$. In many of its properties, Re is much like tungsten. It has a high melting point (about $3200°C$) and a high density (21 g cc^{-1}), and it is not particularly reactive. When heated in air, it gives off clouds of pale-yellow rhenium heptoxide, a volatile solid which, unlike Mn_2O_7, is not explosive. Like WO_3, Re_2O_7 is an acidic oxide and not especially reactive. Rhenium is too scarce to be much used, but it does have remarkable catalytic properties for hydrogenation reactions.

20.8 QUALITATIVE ANALYSIS

Of the elements discussed in this chapter, only manganese and chromium are included in the common schemes of qualitative analysis. The confirming tests depend on the characteristic colors of compounds of these elements.

If the chromium and manganese are present in the original unknown mixture as chromate or dichromate and permanganate, they will be reduced by H_2S (as from thioacetamide) in acid solution to Cr^{+3} and Mn^{++}, forming finely divided sulfur in the process. When the solution, still containing sulfide, is made basic, $Cr(OH)_3$ and MnS precipitate. Treatment with acid and an oxidizing agent serves to remove the sulfide, and subsequent addition of excess NaOH precipitates manganese as a hydroxide and converts the chromium to soluble chromite ion. The appearance of a green color in the solution at this point is strong indication of the presence of chromium. It can be confirmed by treating the green, basic solution with H_2O_2 to oxidize chromite to yellow chromate, which can be precipitated as yellow $BaCrO_4$ by the addition of barium ion in an acetic acid buffer.

The hydroxide precipitate suspected of containing manganese, on treatment with acid and a very strong oxidizing agent such as sodium bismuthate, $NaBiO_3$, or sodium periodate, $NaIO_4$, produces the characteristic violet color of MnO_4^- if manganese is present.

QUESTIONS

20.1 Mn equations   Write balanced equations for the following changes: In acid medium:

(a) $Mn_2O_7 + SO_2 \longrightarrow Mn^{++} + HSO_4^-$

(b) $MnO_4^- + Cr^{++} \longrightarrow Cr(H_2O)_6^{+3} + Mn^{++}$

(c) $MnO_4^- + SCN^- \longrightarrow Mn^{++} + HSO_4^- + CO_2 + NO_3^-$

In basic medium:

(d) $HO_2^- + Mn(OH)_2(s) \longrightarrow MnO_4^{--}$

(e) $Mn(OH)_2(s) + MnO_4^{--} \longrightarrow MnO_2(s)$

(f) $Mn(OH)_2(s) + O_2(g) \longrightarrow Mn(OH)_3(s)$

20.2 Stoichiometry   Given 1.00 kg of $FeCr_2O_4$, how many grams of each of the following can you make: (a) K_2CrO_4, (b) $(NH_4)_2Cr_2O_7$, (c) $KCr(SO_4)_2 \cdot 12\ H_2O$?

20.3 Solution stoichiometry   Standard solutions of $KMnO_4$ cannot be kept very long because they tend to decompose, particularly when exposed to strong light or to dust particles. For this reason, solutions of $KMnO_4$ used in precise work need to be "standardized" at frequent intervals. One very good standard of reference is sodium oxalate, $Na_2C_2O_4$, which can be thoroughly dried by heating to 240°C with no decomposition. If it takes precisely 13.97 ml of an unknown solution of $KMnO_4$ to be just decolorized (all MnO_4^- converted to Mn^{++}) by 0.6700 g of $Na_2C_2O_4$ in presence of acid, what is the concentration of the $KMnO_4$ solution? Note that the oxalate is oxidized to CO_2.

20.4 Equations   Write balanced equations for each of the following changes in acid solution: (a) reduction of Eu^{+3} by Zn, (b) oxidation of H_2O_2 by Ce^{+4}, (c) disproportionation of UO_2^+, (d) oxidation of Ti^{+3} by $Cr_2O_7^{--}$ to give TiO^{++} and Cr^{+3}, (e) reduction of VO_2^+ by SO_2 to give V^{+3} and HSO_4^-.

20.5 Solution stoichiometry   How many grams of $K_2Cr_2O_7$ are needed to prepare a liter of solution, 20.0 ml of which just reacts with 28.63 ml of 0.123 M Sn^{++} in acidic conditions to form Cr^{+3} and Sn^{+4}?

20.6 Tungsten bronze   The structure of $Na_{0.78}WO_3$ consists of cubes, edge length 3.85 Å, containing W atoms at each cube corner, O atoms in the middle of each cube edge, and Na^+ ions distributed among cube centers. The electrons from the sodium atoms are free to migrate over the entire structure. Calculate (a) the density of the tungsten bronze, in g cc^{-1}, (b) the electron density of the bronze, in e^- cc^{-1}.

20.7 Hydrolysis   The uranyl ion, UO_2^{++}, hydrolyzes by a reaction that can be written

$$UO_2^{++} + H_2O \rightleftharpoons UO_2(OH)^+ + H^+$$

having $K = 6.3 \times 10^{-5}$. Calculate the pH expected for a solution that is 0.16 M $UO_2(NO_3)_2$.

20.8 Solubility product   For $La(OH)_3(s) \rightleftharpoons La^{+3}(aq) + 3\,OH^-$, the K_{sp} is 1.0×10^{-19}. Calculate the pH of a saturated solution of $La(OH)_3$ in water.

20.9 Qualitative analysis   An unknown solution which may contain Na^+, K^+, Mg^{++}, Ca^{++}, Sr^{++}, Ba^{++}, Mn^{++}, and Cr^{+3} is treated with thio-acetamide in the presence of NH_4Cl-NH_3 buffer. A light pink precipitate A forms and is separated from the solution B by centrifugation. The precipitate A is dissolved in $NaHSO_4$-Na_2SO_4 buffer, and H_2S is removed by adding H_2SO_4 and boiling. Addition of NaOH to this solution yields a white precipitate that turns brown on standing in air. The solution B is treated with NH_3 and $(NH_4)_2CO_3$, and a white precipitate C is obtained. The precipitate C is dissolved in acetic acid. Addition of ammonium acetate and then K_2CrO_4 to the resulting solution gives no precipitation, but upon addition of alcohol a yellow precipitate D forms. A flame test on the filtrate from D gives a fleeting violet color. Which ions are definitely present, which absent, and which may or may not be present?

20.10 MnO_2 A given sample, labeled "MnO_2," weighs 0.900 g. It reacts with 98.7 ml of 0.100 M $H_2C_2O_4$ to form CO_2 and Mn^{++} in acid solution. What is the actual formula of the original compound, written as MnO_x?

20.11 Solution stoichiometry   Calculate the concentration of each ion in the final solution made by mixing 40.0 ml of 1.0 M Na_2SO_3, 40.0 ml of 0.50 M NaOH, and 20.0 ml of 0.10 M $KMnO_4$. Assume the reduction product in basic solution is $MnO_2(s)$. K_{diss} for HSO_4^- is 1.3×10^{-2} and K_{diss} for HSO_3^- is 5.6×10^{-8}.

20.12 Thermodynamics   (a) Calculate the $E°$ (as done in Section 18.1) for the three half-reactions

$$Sc(s) \longrightarrow Sc^+(aq) + e^-$$
$$Sc^+(aq) \longrightarrow Sc^{++}(aq) + e^-$$
$$Sc^{++}(aq) \longrightarrow Sc^{+3}(aq) + e^-$$

by using the following standard free-energy data:

Sublimation of scandium, $+83$ kcal mole^{-1}
First ionization, $+152$ kcal mole^{-1}
Second ionization, $+298$ kcal mole^{-1}
Third ionization, $+570$ kcal mole^{-1}
Hydration of $Sc^+(g)$, *ca.* -80 kcal mole^{-1}

Hydration of $Sc^{++}(g)$, *ca.* -350 kcal mole^{-1}

Hydration of $Sc^{+3}(g)$, *ca.* -900 kcal mole^{-1}

(*b*) Decide which of these ions should disproportionate in aqueous solution and then calculate $E°$ for the conversion of $Sc(s)$ to the lowest stable state.

20.13 Radioactive elements   At the present time, Th^{232} atoms are 5.0 times as abundant as U^{238} atoms in the earth's crust. By using the data of Section 20.3, calculate the relative ratio "in the beginning."

ANSWERS

20.2 (*a*) 1.74 kg   (*b*) 1.13 kg   (*c*) 4.46 kg   20.5 17.2 g
20.6 7.27 g cc^{-1}; 1.37×10^{22} e^- cc^{-1} 20.8 9.36   20.10 $MnO_{1.94}$
20.12 (*a*) -1.7 volts; $+3.8$ volts; $+4.1$ volts   (*b*) $+2.1$ volts
20.13 3.0

21 transition elements III: iron triad and platinum metals

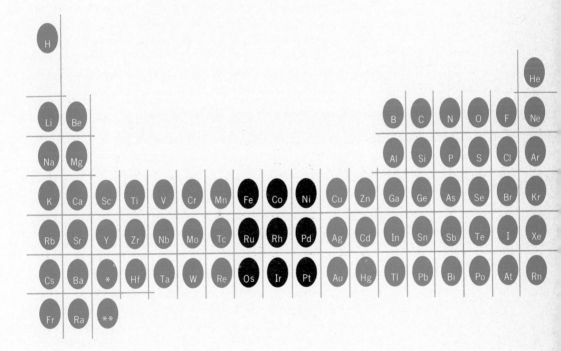

The first five subgroups of the transition elements were discussed as individual subgroups in Chapter 20. In the next three subgroups, the chemical resemblance along the horizontal sequence is more pronounced than the chemical resemblance down the subgroup. For this reason, it is convenient to consider the next three subgroups in terms of horizontal triads. In the top transition period, the elements iron ($Z = 26$), cobalt ($Z = 27$), and nickel ($Z = 28$) make up the *iron triad;* in the middle period, ruthenium ($Z = 44$), rhodium ($Z = 45$), and palladium ($Z = 46$) are the *light platinum triad;* in the bottom period, osmium ($Z = 76$), iridium ($Z = 77$), and platinum ($Z = 78$) are the *heavy platinum triad.* All of these elements are metals of low atomic volume with high melting points and high densities. The elements of the first triad are moderately reactive; those of the platinum triads are fairly inert. In the original Mendeleev periodic table all of these elements were lumped into what was called group VIII. The platinum elements (together with gold and silver) are sometimes referred to as the *noble metals*.

21.1 IRON TRIAD

In progressing from left to right in the first transition period, there is a progressive rise in the maximum oxidation state from $+3$ for Sc to $+7$ for Mn. The surprising thing about the following iron-triad elements is that their maximum oxidation states are less than those of the preceding elements. Furthermore, compounds containing these maximum oxidation states are such strong oxidizing agents that they are not usually encountered. Specifically, iron shows a maximum oxidation state of $+6$, but only the $+2$ and $+3$ states are common; cobalt shows only $+2$ and $+3$; nickel, usually only $+2$. Figure 21.1 indicates schematically the electron population of the neutral atoms. Removal of the two

Sublevel	Iron	Cobalt	Nickel
$1s$	2	2	2
$2s$ and $2p$	8	8	8
$3s$ and $3p$	8	8	8
$3d$	↑↓ ↑ ↑ ↑ ↑	↑↓ ↑↓ ↑ ↑ ↑	↑↓ ↑↓ ↑↓ ↑ ↑
$4s$	↑↓	↑↓	↑↓

21.1
Electron population of
iron triad

$4s$ electrons is relatively easy in each case; hence a $+2$ state is formed. Additional removal of a $3d$ electron would give a $+3$ state. In the case of iron this happens easily because a half-filled $3d$ level is left; in cobalt and nickel it does not happen so readily. The $+3$ state of cobalt must be stabilized as by the ligand field (Section 19.4) of a complex ion; the $+3$ state of nickel is very rare, and compounds of $+3$ nickel are powerful oxidizing agents.

The properties of the iron-triad elements are very similar, as shown in Figure 21.2. The melting points and boiling points are uniformly high; the energies required to pull an electron off the gas atom are nearly the same for the three elements; and all the oxidation potentials are moderately more positive than the oxidation potential of hydrogen. In addition to the properties listed, these elements are alike in that all are *ferromagnetic;* i.e., they are strongly attracted into a magnetic field and show permanent magnetization when removed from such a field. That these elements are magnetic is not surprising. The electronic configurations in Figure 21.1 would lead us to expect that there would be unpaired electrons in the $+2$ ions such as might exist in the metal lattice. However, it is surprising that the magnetization is so large and so

21.1 Iron triad

426

persistent. The explanation is that in these metals there are *domains* of magnetization, regions of a million or so ions, all of which cooperatively direct their individual magnetic effects the same way. In an unmagnetized piece of metal these domains point randomly in all directions in such a way that, in sum, the magnetic effect cancels. When placed in a magnetic field, the domains are turned so that all point in the same direction, giving rise to a large magnetic effect. If the metal is now removed from the field, it remains permanently magnetized unless the domain orientation is disorganized, as by heating or pounding. Of all the elements, only iron, cobalt, and nickel show this kind of magnetism at room temperature. Apparently they are the only ones that satisfy the conditions necessary for domain formation. These conditions are that the ions contain unpaired electrons and that the distance between ions be just exactly right in order that the interaction for lining up all the ions to form a domain may be effective. Manganese metal has most of the properties needed to be ferromagnetic, but the ions of the metal are too close; addition of copper to manganese increases this average spacing, and the resulting alloy is ferromagnetic.

Property	Fe	Co	Ni
Melting point, °C	1535	1490	1450
Boiling point, °C	2700	2900	2700
Ionization potential, ev	7.90	7.86	7.63
Oxidation potential (to M^{++}), volts	+0.44	+0.28	+0.25
Density, g cc^{-1}	7.9	8.7	8.9

21.2
Elements of the
iron triad

In their compounds the iron-triad elements behave like typical transition elements. Many of the compounds are colored and paramagnetic, and frequently they contain complex ions.

21.2 IRON

The element iron has an industrial importance which exceeds that of any other element. It is very abundant, ranking fourth in the earth's crust (after O, Si, and Al); it is very common, being an essential constituent of several hundred minerals; it is easy to make by simply heating some of its minerals with carbon; it has many desirable properties, especially when impure. For all these reasons, iron has become such a distinctive feature of civilization that it marks one of the ages in archaeological chronology.

About 5% of the earth's crust is iron. Some of this iron is meteoric in origin and occurs in the uncombined, metallic state. However, most of it is combined with oxygen, silicon, or sulfur. The important source minerals are hematite (Fe_2O_3), limonite ($Fe_2O_3 \cdot H_2O$), magnetite (Fe_3O_4), and siderite ($FeCO_3$), usually contaminated with complex iron silicates from which these minerals are produced by weathering. Iron sulfides, such as iron pyrites (FeS_2), or fool's gold, are also quite abundant, but they cannot be used as sources of iron because sulfur is an objectionable impurity in the final product.

In addition to abundant iron in the earth's crust, there is a possibility that the center of the earth may be iron. Indirect evidence based on the study of earthquake waves and tidal action indicates that the core of the earth is liquid and has a density corresponding to that of liquid iron at high pressure.

Iron is practically never produced in a pure state, since it is difficult to make and is too expensive for most purposes. Furthermore, impure iron (steel) has desirable properties, especially when the specific impurity is carbon in carefully controlled amounts. The industrial production of impure iron is carried out on a massive scale in the well-known blast furnace, in which occur complicated high-temperature reactions involving iron ore, limestone, and carbon. The iron ore, limestone, and coke are added at the top; preheated air or oxygen is blown in at the bottom. As the molten iron forms, it trickles down to a pit at the bottom, from which it is periodically drawn off. All told, it takes about 12 hr for material to pass through the furnace. The actual chemical processes which occur in such a furnace are still obscure. It is generally agreed, however, that the active reducing agent is not carbon, but carbon monoxide. As the charge settles through the furnace, the coke is oxidized by the incoming oxygen by the reaction

$$2C(s) + O_2(g) \longrightarrow 2CO(g) + 53 \text{ kcal}$$

thus forming the reducing agent CO and liberating large amounts of heat. As the carbon monoxide moves up the furnace, it encounters oxides of iron in various stages of reduction, depending on the temperature of the particular zone. At the top of the furnace, where the temperature is lowest (250°C), the iron ore (mostly Fe_2O_3) is reduced to Fe_3O_4 by the reaction

$$3Fe_2O_3(s) + CO(g) \longrightarrow 2Fe_3O_4(s) + CO_2(g)$$

As the Fe_3O_4 settles, it gets reduced further to FeO

$$Fe_3O_4(s) + CO(g) \longrightarrow 3FeO(s) + CO_2(g)$$

Finally, toward the bottom of the furnace, FeO is eventually reduced to iron

$$FeO(s) + CO(g) \longrightarrow Fe(s) + CO_2(g)$$

Since the temperature at the lowest part of the furnace (1500°C) is above the melting point of the impure iron, the solid melts and drips down into the hearth at the very bottom. The net equation for the reduction of Fe_2O_3 can be written as the sum of the last three equations.

$$Fe_2O_3(s) + 3CO(g) \longrightarrow 2Fe(l) + 3CO_2(g)$$

In addition to the foregoing reactions, there occurs the combination of CO_2 with hot carbon,

$$C(s) + CO_2(g) \longrightarrow 2CO(g)$$

and the thermal decomposition of limestone by the reaction

$$CaCO_3(s) \longrightarrow CaO(s) + CO_2(g)$$

Both of these reactions are helpful: the former raises the concentration of the reducing agent CO, and the latter facilitates the removal of silica-containing contaminants present in the original ore. Lime (CaO), being a basic oxide, reacts with the acidic oxide SiO_2 to form calcium silicate ($CaSiO_3$). In the form of a lava-like *slag,* calcium silicate collects at the bottom of the furnace, where it floats on the molten iron and protects it from oxidation by incoming oxygen.

Four times a day the liquid iron and molten slag are drawn off through tapholes in the bottom of the furnace. About 1000 tons of impure iron can be produced per day from one furnace. For each ton of iron, there is also produced approximately half a ton of slag. Since slag is essentially calcium aluminum silicate, some of it is put to good use in making cement (Section 24.5).

The crude product of the blast furnace (called pig iron) contains about 4% C, 2% Si, a trace of sulfur, up to 1% of phosphorus and manganese, and the rest iron. Sulfur is probably the worst impurity (making steel break when worked) and must be avoided, since it is hard to remove in refining operations. The refining operations are technical and of great variety. Only a few of the basic ideas will be discussed.

When pig iron is remelted with scrap iron and cast into molds, it forms *cast iron.* This can be either gray or white, depending on the rate of cooling. When cooled slowly (as in sand molds, where heat loss is slow), the carbon separates out almost completely in the form of tiny flakes of graphite (Section 24.2), giving gray cast iron that is relatively soft and tough. When cooled rapidly (as in water-cooled molds), the carbon does not have a chance to separate out but remains combined in the form of the compound iron carbide, Fe_3C. Such white cast iron is extremely hard and brittle.

Most pig iron is refined into steel by burning out the impurities to leave small controlled amounts of carbon. In the *open-hearth* process (which accounts for most of the United States production), carbon is removed by oxidation with air and iron oxide, the latter being added as hematite and rusted scrap iron. The process is usually carried out on a shallow hearth so arranged that a hot-air blast can play over the surface. In the *basic* open-hearth process, limestone is added to provide CaO for converting oxidation products, such as acidic P_2O_5, into slag. Since it takes about 8 hr to refine a batch of steel by this process, there is ample time for continuous testing to maintain quality control. The *Bessemer process* is much more rapid (10 to 15 min) but gives a less uniform product. In this process, molten pig iron taken directly from the blast furnace is poured into a large pot, and a blast of air is swept through the liquid mix to burn off most of the carbon and silicon. Frequently, the Bessemer and open-hearth processes are combined to take advantage of the good points of each. In the duplex process a preliminary blowing in the Bessemer converter gets rid of most of the C and Si, with a following burn-off in an open-hearth furnace to get rid of P. Elements such as Cr, V, or Mn can be added to produce steels with desired properties. In order to prevent the formation of blowholes (as in Swiss cheese) when the molten steel is poured into ingots, it is necessary for the finished steel to contain some Mn. The function of this Mn is apparently to combine with the oxygen and so keep it from bubbling out as the steel solidifies.

The properties of iron in the form of steel are very much dependent on the percentage composition of the impurities present, on the heat-treatment of the specimen, and even on the working to which the sample has been subjected. For these reasons, the following comments about iron properties do not necessarily apply to every given sample of iron. Compared with most metals, iron is a fairly good reducing agent, but it is not so good as the preceding transition elements. With non-oxidizing acids it reacts to liberate H_2 by the reaction $Fe(s) + 2H^+ \longrightarrow Fe^{++} + H_2(g)$. It also has the ability to replace less active metals in their solutions. For example, a bar of iron placed in a solution of $CuSO_4$ immediately is covered with a reddish deposit of copper formed by the reaction $Fe(s) + Cu^{++} \longrightarrow Fe^{++} + Cu(s)$. In concentrated nitric acid, iron, like many other metals (Cr, Mo, Co, Ni, etc.), becomes *passive;* i.e., it loses the ability to react with H^+ and Cu^{++} as above and appears to be inert. When scratched or subjected to shock, reactivity is restored. It may be that passivity is due to the formation of a thin surface coating of oxide which slows down the rates of oxidation below the limits of detectability. When the film is broken, reactivity is restored. Passivity is important in some methods of preventing corrosion of iron.

21.3 COMPOUNDS OF IRON

The two common oxidation states of iron are +2 (ferrous) and +3 (ferric). Under vigorous oxidizing conditions it is also possible to get compounds such as $BaFeO_4$, barium ferrate, but in general the +6 state is rare. Compounds in which the oxidation state is fractional, as in Fe_3O_4, can be thought of as mixtures of two oxidation states. Fe_3O_4 is a spinel (Section 6.4) in which Fe^{++} and Fe^{+3} ions occur in interstices of the close-packed oxide structure.

In the +2 state iron exists essentially as ferrous ion, Fe^{++}. This is a pale green, almost colorless ion which, except in acid solutions, is rather hard to keep, since it is easily oxidized to the +3 state by oxygen in the air. However, since the rate of oxidation by O_2 is inversely proportional to H^+ concentration, acid solutions of ferrous salts can be kept for long periods. When base is added to ferrous solutions, a nearly white precipitate of ferrous hydroxide, $Fe(OH)_2$, is formed. On exposure to air, $Fe(OH)_2$ turns brown, owing to oxidation to hydrated ferric oxide, $Fe_2O_3 \cdot xH_2O$. For convenience, the latter is often written as $Fe(OH)_3$, ferric hydroxide, and the oxidation can be written

$$4Fe(OH)_2(s) + O_2(g) + 2H_2O \longrightarrow 4Fe(OH)_3(s)$$

However, pure ferric hydroxide has never been prepared.

In the $+3$ state, iron exists as the colorless ferric ion, Fe^{+3}. Since solutions of ferric salts are acid, appreciable hydrolysis must take place. This can be written as

$$Fe^{+3} + H_2O \rightleftharpoons FeOH^{++} + H^+$$

Apparently, the yellow-brown color so characteristic of ferric solutions is mainly due to $FeOH^{++}$. By addition of an acid such as HNO_3, the color can be made to disappear.* On addition of base, a slimy, red-brown, gelatinous precipitate forms; it may be written as $Fe(OH)_3$. This can be dehydrated to form yellow or red Fe_2O_3.

In both the $+2$ and $+3$ states, iron shows a great tendency to form

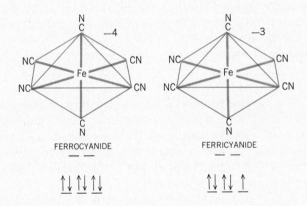

FERROCYANIDE

FERRICYANIDE

21.3
Octahedral complex ions
of iron and cyanide

complex ions. For example, ferric ion combines with thiocyanate ion, SCN^-, to form $FeNCS^{++}$, which has such a deep red color that it can be detected at concentrations of $10^{-5}\ M$. The formation of this complex is the basis of one of the most sensitive qualitative tests for the presence of Fe^{+3}. With cyanide ion, CN^-, both Fe^{++} and Fe^{+3} form complexes; these are so stable to dissociation that they can be thought of as single units like SO_4^{--} ion. As shown in Figure 21.3, both ferrocyanide, $Fe(CN)_6^{-4}$, and ferricyanide, $Fe(CN)_6^{-3}$, are octahedral with six CN groups joined through carbon to the central iron. Since, in assigning oxidation states, cyanide is usually given a -1 charge, Fe is assigned a $+2$ charge in ferrocyanide and a $+3$ charge in ferricyanide. Though simple in structure, these ions take part in some very complicated reactions, among which are the formation of prussian blue and Turnbull's blue.

* The color will not disappear on the addition of HCl because $FeCl^{++}$, which is yellow, forms.

Prussian blue is a deep blue precipitate obtained by mixing a solution of a ferric salt with a solution of potassium ferrocyanide, $K_4Fe(CN)_6$. It is used extensively as a dye for blueprint paper, for ink, and for bluing, in the last case because its color counteracts the yellow color of fabrics and makes them appear white. Turnbull's blue is a similar deep blue precipitate obtained by mixing a solution of a ferrous salt with a solution of potassium ferricyanide, $K_3Fe(CN)_6$. The surprising thing about prussian blue and Turnbull's blue is that apparently they have identical overall compositions, corresponding to $KFeFe(CN)_6$. However, no one has yet been able to carry out a definitive experiment to prove that they are the same or, for that matter, that they are different.

21.4 CORROSION OF IRON

"Corrosion" is a general term applied to the process in which uncombined metals change over to compounds. In the special case of iron the corrosion process is called *rusting*. Economically, rusting is a serious problem, and it has been estimated that one-seventh of the annual production of iron goes simply to replace that lost by rusting. Still, despite much study, corrosion is a mysterious process and its chemistry not well understood.

Rust appears to be a hydrated ferric oxide with a chemical composition corresponding approximately to $2Fe_2O_3 \cdot 3H_2O$, that is, three moles of water per two moles of ferric oxide. However, since the water content is not always the same, it is preferable to write $Fe_2O_3 \cdot xH_2O$. Because iron will not rust in dry air or in water that is completely free of air, it would seem that both O_2 and H_2O are required for rust formation. Furthermore, it is observed that rusting is speeded up by the presence of acids, strains in the metal, contact with less active metals, and the presence of rust itself (autocatalysis).

In order to account for the observed facts, the following steps have been proposed as the mechanism by which rusting occurs:

$$Fe(s) \longrightarrow Fe^{++} + 2e^- \tag{1}$$

$$e^- + H^+ \longrightarrow H \tag{2}$$

$$4H + O_2(g) \longrightarrow 2H_2O \tag{3}$$

$$4Fe^{++} + O_2(g) + (4 + 2x)H_2O \longrightarrow 2(Fe_2O_3 \cdot xH_2O)(s) + 8H^+ \tag{4}$$

In step (1) ferrous ions are produced by loss of electrons from neutral Fe atoms. However, this process cannot go very far unless there is some way to get rid of the electrons which accumulate on the residual iron. One way to do this is by step (2), in which H^+ ions, either from the water or from acid substances in the water, pick up the electrons to form neutral H atoms. (Normally, we would expect these H atoms to pair up to form H_2 molecules; however, H_2 gas is usually not observed in rust formation.) Since iron is a good catalyst for hydrogenation reactions, step (3) now occurs to use up the H atoms. In the meantime, the ferrous ion reacts with oxygen gas by step (4) to form the rust and restore H$^+$ required for step (2). The net reaction, obtained by adding these steps, is

$$4Fe(s) + 3O_2(g) + 2xH_2O \longrightarrow 2(Fe_2O_3 \cdot xH_2O)(s)$$

Since H$^+$ accelerates step (2) and is replenished in step (4), it is a true catalyst for the reaction and explains the observation that acids speed up the rate of rust formation. (A remarkable example of this is observed when iron pipes are so located as to be in contact with cinders. Such pipes corrode much more rapidly than they normally do, apparently because weathering of sulfur compounds in the cinders forms sulfuric acid.)

The above mechanism also accounts for many other observations and, in particular, for the process often called electrolytic corrosion. For example, when iron pipes are connected to copper pipes, the iron corrodes much faster than normally. The explanation lies in step (1). Residual electrons accumulating from the dissolution of Fe flow from the iron to the copper, where their energy is lower. This removes the excess negative charge from the iron and allows more Fe^{++} to leave the metal. A complicating feature which also accelerates the reaction is that H atoms, which now form on the negative copper surface instead of the iron, detach themselves more readily from copper than from iron, thus accelerating step (3).

One of the strongest supports for the stepwise rusting mechanism comes from the observation that the most serious pitting of a rusting iron bar occurs in that part of the bar where the oxygen supply is restricted. The reason for this is that, where the oxygen supply is unrestricted, step (4) promptly occurs to deposit rust before the Fe^{++} formed by step (1) can move away. This, of course, makes it more difficult for more Fe to dissolve, and the reaction is self-stopping. However, if the oxygen supply is restricted, Fe^{++} may have a chance to diffuse away before encountering enough oxygen to form rust. This means that the rust may deposit some distance away from the point where pitting occurs. Common examples of this are observed at the edges of overlapping plates or around rivet heads. In the latter case, the rivet shank, although protected from air, is eaten away, but the rust forms where the rivet head overlaps the plate. Apparently, moisture that seeps in allows Fe^{++} to diffuse out to the surface, where it can react with O$_2$. Another slightly different example is found in the well-known water-line deposition of rust on partially immersed steel posts. When a new post is placed in water, pitting usually starts where there are strains in the metal, but the rust forms near the water line, where oxygen is plentiful. This makes the situation go from bad to worse, since the water-line rust now acts as a screen to keep O$_2$ from reaching the iron. Self-protection is no longer possible, and severe pitting can now occur where the O$_2$ supply is restricted.

Although there are still many unanswered questions about rusting, it is clear what must be done to prevent it. The most direct approach is to shut off the reactants O$_2$ and H$_2$O. This can be done by smearing grease over the iron to be protected, painting it either with an ordinary paint or better with an oxidizing paint so as to make the iron passive, or plating the iron with some other metal. All these methods are used to some extent. Painting or greasing is probably the cheapest, but it must be done thoroughly; otherwise, rusting may only be accelerated by partial exclusion of oxygen. Plating with another metal is more common when appearance is a factor. Chrome plating, for example, is usually chosen because of its dressy look. Zinc plating, or galvanizing, is actually more permanent. Tin plating looks good and is extremely cheap, but it is not reliable.

The relative merits of metals used for plating depend on the activity of the metal relative to iron and the ability of the metal to form a self-protective coat. Zinc, for example, is a self-protecting metal which reacts with O_2 and CO_2 in the air to form an adherent coating which prevents further corrosion. Furthermore, it has a higher oxidation potential than iron, so that, if a hole is punched in a zinc plating so that both Zn and Fe are exposed to oxidation, it is the Zn that is preferentially oxidized. The Zn compound forms a plug to seal the hole. Tin also forms a self-protective coat, but tin has a smaller oxidation potential than iron, and iron is preferentially oxidized when a tin coating is punctured.

One of the most elegant ways to protect iron from corrosion is by "cathodic protection." In this method, iron is charged to a negative voltage compared to its surroundings. This forces the iron to act as a cathode instead of as the anode required for oxidation and effectively stops corrosion. Actually, zinc plating is a method of cathodic protection, since zinc has a higher oxidation potential than iron and forces electrons onto the iron. In practice, for pipelines and standpipes, cathodic protection is obtained by driving stakes of zinc or magnesium, for example, into the ground and connecting them to the object to be protected. In salt water, where rusting is unusually severe, the steel plates of ships have been protected by strapping blocks of magnesium to the hulls. These preferentially corrode (since they are acting as anodes) but can easily be replaced, while the iron is essentially untouched.

Cathodic protection also explains why tin plating (as in the ordinary tin can) is so unlasting. So long as the tin coating is unpunctured, there is no corrosion, since tin is a rather inert metal and can be exposed indefinitely to the atmosphere. Once the coating is punctured (and this happens very easily, because it is very thin), there is real trouble, and the iron is worse off than if the tin plating were not there. The reason for this is that iron, being more active than tin, acts as anode in setting up cathodic protection for the tin. This, of course, accelerates the dissolving of iron and the formation of rust; hence the rust spreads very rapidly.

21.5 COBALT AND NICKEL

The other elements of the iron triad, cobalt and nickel, although less important than iron, do have some interesting aspects. Both are much less abundant than iron (Co at 0.002% and Ni at 0.008%) and are harder to extract from their minerals. The name cobalt reflects this difficulty, since it comes from the German word *Kobold,* meaning goblin. Cobalt minerals look very much like copper minerals and were occasionally worked by mistake as sources of copper. Furthermore, since arsenic is usually present with cobalt, poisonous fumes were inevitably present, all obviously due to black magic. Similar troubles with nickel minerals led to their being named after "Old Nick" and his devilish assistants. Cobalt minerals and nickel minerals frequently occur together, associated with those of iron and copper. The principal compounds in these minerals are oxides, sulfides, and arsenides.

1. Cobalt. The more important minerals of cobalt are cobalt glance (CoAsS), linnaeite (Co_3S_4), and smaltite, or cobalt speiss ($CoAs_2$). The extraction is very complex and involves roasting in a blast furnace, dissolving with sulfuric acid, and precipitating by addition of sodium carbonate. The hydroxide so produced is dehydrated to the oxide, which can then be reduced with hydrogen.

The properties of the metal have been given in Figure 21.2. The oxidation potential of $+0.28$ volt for the reaction $Co(s) \longrightarrow Co^{++} + 2e^-$ indicates that cobalt should dissolve in acids with the liberation of hydrogen. The reaction is slow and does not occur at all in concentrated nitric acid, where Co becomes passive. The ferromagnetism of Co is actually higher than that of iron and accounts for its extensive use in magnets, especially in alloys such as the Alnico alloys (Co, Ni, Al, and Cu). Other alloys such as stellite (55% Co, 15% W, 25% Cr, 5% Mo) are important for their extreme hardness and resistance to corrosion. They are used, for example, in high-speed tools and surgical instruments.

In its compounds cobalt shows oxidation states of $+2$ (cobaltous) and $+3$ (cobaltic). Unlike ferrous ion, the cobaltous ion is quite stable to oxidation, and solutions of cobaltous salts can be kept indefinitely exposed to the air. Most cobaltous solutions are pink and presumably contain the hydrated ion $Co(H_2O)_6^{++}$. Addition of base precipitates dark blue insoluble hydroxide, which in the absence of oxygen can be dehydrated to give yellow-green cobaltous oxide, CoO. This is a basic oxide much used to produce blue color in pottery and enamel. When heated in the presence of air, cobaltous hydroxide dehydrates to give Co_3O_4, cobaltocobaltic oxide, reminiscent of Fe_3O_4. Cobaltous forms many complex ions, which, however, are easily oxidized.

In aqueous solution the cobaltic ion Co^{+3} is a very powerful oxidizing agent. The oxidation potential of $Co^{++} \longrightarrow Co^{+3} + e^-$ is -1.84 volts, which means that Co^{+3} is strong enough to oxidize water to form O_2. Only a few simple cobaltic salts such as CoF_3 and $Co_2(SO_4)_3 \cdot 18H_2O$ have been made, and these decompose in aqueous solution:

$$4Co^{+3} + 2H_2O \longrightarrow 4Co^{++} + O_2(g) + 4H^+$$

Unlike the simple ion, the complex ions of cobalt $+3$ are quite stable to reduction. There are a tremendous number of these, ranging from the simple $Co(CN)_6^{-3}$ and $Co(NH_3)_6^{+3}$ to complicated *polynuclear* complexes, in which several cobalt atoms are bridged together by shared complexing groups.

2. *Nickel.* The principal minerals of nickel are pentlandite and nickeliferous pyrrhotite (mixed sulfides of iron and nickel) and garnierite (a mixed silicate of magnesium and nickel). Since most ores are very poor in nickel content, they are concentrated before smelting, usually by *flotation.* In this process the ore is ground up and then agitated briskly with water to which oil and wetting agents have been added. Earthy particles (*gangue*) are wet by the water and hence sink, whereas the fine particles of mineral get carried off with the froth. The concentrate is then roasted in air to get rid of some of the sulfur as SO_2, burned in a furnace (smelted) to form oxide, and finally reduced with carbon. To get pure nickel, the final product must be refined, either electrolytically or by taking advantage of the instability of volatile nickel carbonyl. In the Mond process, carbon monoxide at 80°C is passed over impure nickel to form volatile $Ni(CO)_4$, nickel tetracarbonyl. This is then heated to about 200°C, where it decomposes into Ni and CO.

The properties of nickel metal are much like those of cobalt, except that Ni is less ferromagnetic and more inert to chemical oxidation. More than 65% of nickel production goes into iron alloys to increase their strength and corrosion resistance. The rest of it goes into nickel-copper alloys, e.g., into nickel coinage (from 10 to 100% Ni), or is used as the pure metal. In the latter case it is used for plating steel and as a catalyst for hydrogenation reactions.

The chemistry of nickel compounds is essentially that of the +2 state. In aqueous solution it exists either as the green nickelous ion, Ni^{++}, or as a complex ion. On treatment with base, nickelous ion precipitates as the light green nickelous hydroxide, $Ni(OH)_2$, which can be dehydrated thermally to black NiO. The complex ions of nickel are almost as numerous as those of cobalt. However, unlike cobaltous complexes, they are quite stable to air oxidation. Furthermore, not all of them are octahedral (as is the blue $Ni(NH_3)_6^{++}$) but may be planar ($Ni(CN)_4^{--}$).

In basic solution nickelous hydroxide can be oxidized by the powerful oxidizing agent hypochlorite, ClO^-. The product is a dark-colored oxide of indefinite composition variously described as NiO_2, Ni_2O_3, or Ni_3O_4. No matter what it is, it is a very good oxidizing agent and contains nickel in an oxidation state higher than +2. As such, it forms the cathode material in the Edison storage battery. On discharge, the cathode reaction can be written as

$$Ni_2O_3(s) + 2e^- + 3H_2O \longrightarrow 2Ni(OH)_2(s) + 2OH^-$$

Since $Ni(OH)_2$ sticks to the cathode and since the reaction is reversible, the discharged cell can be recharged by the application of an external voltage. The anode in the Edison cell is usually of iron, with NaOH as electrolyte. The anode reaction is probably

$$Fe(s) + 2OH^- \longrightarrow Fe(OH)_2(s) + 2e^-$$

The Edison cell has an advantage over the lead storage battery because the OH^- produced at the cathode is used up at the anode; hence, there is no concentration change in the electrolyte. Consequently, as the battery runs down, there is no change in its output voltage. Also, the materials are less dense and stronger than those of the lead storage battery, and hence the Edison battery is more easily portable and more rugged. Unfortunately, the chemical components are too expensive to make it of general usefulness.

21.6 LIGHT PLATINUM TRIAD

In the second transition period the three elements following technetium are ruthenium ($Z = 44$), rhodium ($Z = 45$), and palladium ($Z = 46$). Since these elements chemically resemble platinum but have only about half the density of platinum, they are called the light platinum elements. Their properties are summarized in Figure 21.4. As can be

Property	Ru	Rh	Pd
Atomic number	44	45	46
Electronic configuration	$4d^75s^1$	$4d^85s^1$	$4d^{10}$
Melting point, °C	2450	1970	1550
Boiling point, °C	>2700	>2500	2200(?)
Ionization potential, ev	7.5	7.7	8.3
Oxidation potential (to M^{++}), volts	−0.5	−0.6	−1.2
Density, g cc^{-1}	12.4	12.4	12.0

21.4
Light platinum elements

seen, these elements are high-melting and high-boiling with rather high densities. They are not very reactive, and their oxidation potentials indicate that, unlike the iron-triad elements, they are much poorer reducing agents than hydrogen. For this reason they are difficult to oxidize and, in fact, occur in nature as the uncombined elements. Because of great similarity in chemical properties, they usually occur together.

1. *Ruthenium.* Ruthenium occurs as a natural alloy of ruthenium, osmium, and iridium. To prepare the pure metal, the alloy is heated with alkaline oxidizing agents (e.g., a mixture of KOH and KNO_3) to form potassium ruthenate (K_2RuO_4). After being dissolved and acidified, the mixture is boiled to eliminate osmium as osmium tetroxide (OsO_4), and then, after the solution has been made basic, Ru is distilled off as ruthenium tetroxide, RuO_4. Reduction with hydrogen gives the metal. It is quite inert and thus far has found use only as a hardening agent for platinum and for making other hard, inert alloys required for fountain-pen tips and phonograph needles.

In its principal compounds, ruthenium shows oxidation states corresponding to +2, +3, +4, and +6. Some of these compounds are simple, like the volatile, toxic ruthenium tetroxide (RuO_4); others, like $K_3Ru(C_2O_4)_3$, are complex. In general, they are rarely encountered.

2. *Rhodium.* Rhodium is a rather rare element, amounting to only $10^{-7}\%$ of the earth's crust. It occurs principally with platinum, from which it can be separated by fusion with $KHSO_4$. Rhodium dissolves to give $KRh(SO_4)_2$, a rose-colored salt, which can be leached out and recrystallized from water. The metal is rather inert and finds use for plating scientific instruments. An alloy of rhodium and platinum is used to make high-temperature scientific apparatus such as crucibles and thermocouples. The principal oxidation state is $+3$ and is represented by many simple salts, such as $RhCl_3$, as well as by complex ones like K_3RhCl_6.

3. *Palladium.* Palladium is the most abundant ($10^{-6}\%$) of the platinum elements. Since it alone of the platinum elements forms an insoluble cyanide, it can be separated from the others by precipitation of $Pd(CN)_2$. On ignition, this decomposes to give pure metal. Like the other platinum elements, Pd is inert, but not so much so that it cannot dissolve in concentrated nitric acid. One of its most remarkable properties is that it has the ability to absorb hydrogen. At dull-red heat, a piece of palladium can absorb about 1000 times its own volume of hydrogen. When the temperature is raised further, the hydrogen is expelled. Apparently in this absorption process the H_2 molecule is ripped apart into H atoms, which can then fit into the Pd lattice. It may be that this dissociation $H_2 \longrightarrow 2H$ also explains the powerful catalytic effect of Pd on hydrogenation reactions. Because it is not corroded in air and is capable of taking a high polish, palladium finds use for making optical mirrors and for jewelry. The compounds, both simple and complex, are essentially those of the $+2$ oxidation state.

21.7 HEAVY PLATINUM TRIAD

The elements of the heavy platinum triad, osmium ($Z = 76$), iridium ($Z = 77$), and platinum ($Z = 78$), resemble very closely the elements just above them. Their properties are shown in Figure 21.5. They are all very high-melting, of extraordinarily high density, and generally quite unreactive.

1. *Osmium.* The chief source of osmium is naturally occurring osmiridium, an alloy of Os and Ir which is usually contaminated with ruthenium. As discussed in Section 21.6, this alloy can be dissolved by strong, alkaline oxidizing agents and osmium tetroxide can be driven off as a volatile material from the acidified product. Metallic osmium forms when OsO_4 is reduced with almost any reducing agent, since the half-reaction

$$Os(s) + 4H_2O \longrightarrow OsO_4(s) + 8H^+ + 8e^- \qquad -0.85 \text{ volt}$$

is easily reversed. In the massive state, the metal is quite inert, even to aqua regia. It is very hard, especially when alloyed with iridium, and is used as the alloy for the tips of fountain pens.

Property	Os	Ir	Pt
Atomic number	76	77	78
Electronic configuration	$5d^66s^2$	$5d^76s^2$	$5d^96s^1$
Melting point, °C	2700	2450	1774
Boiling point, °C	>5300	>4800	4100
Ionization potential, ev	8.7	9.2	8.96
Oxidation potential (to M^{++}), volts	−0.9	−1	−1.2
Density, g cc^{-1}	22.7	22.6	21.5

21.5
Heavy platinum elements

Compounds of osmium are known in the +2, +3, +4, +6, and +8 oxidation states. The most important of these is OsO_4, osmium tetroxide, sometimes called osmic acid. Though solid at room temperature (its melting point is 40°C, and its boiling point is 100°C), it is very volatile and hence very dangerous, since it is corrosive to animal tissue, especially the eyes. It is of importance in synthetic organic chemistry, since OsO_4 is a specific catalyst for the addition of OH to carbon-carbon double bonds by hydrogen peroxide.

2. Iridium. Iridium is obtained from natural osmiridium by driving off the osmium and ruthenium as mentioned above. The iridium is usually separated as the slightly soluble ammonium hexachloroiridiate(IV), $(NH_4)_2IrCl_6$. Thermal decomposition produces the metal, which in the massive state is quite inert. The chief use of iridium metal is for additive hardening of platinum. Compounds, corresponding principally to the +3 and +4 states, are known but are not commonly encountered.

3. Platinum. Of all the platinum elements, platinum is the most useful. Although not very abundant (5×10^{-7}%), it occurs in concentrated deposits, a fact which makes its separation feasible. In order to isolate it from the other platinum metals, the naturally occurring alloys are treated with aqua regia. Pt and Pd dissolve, and, from the resulting solution, Pt is precipitated as insoluble ammonium hexachloroplatinate(IV), $(NH_4)_2PtCl_6$. Thermal decomposition produces the metal.

The metal is quite inert to many kinds of chemical attack, and for this reason, especially when hardened with a few percent of iridium, it is used in making jewelry and laboratory equipment. In using platinum ware (e.g., crucibles), fused alkalis, such as NaOH, must be avoided, because Pt dissolves in molten bases to form platinates. Also to be avoided are phosphorus, silicon, arsenic, antimony, lead, etc., with which Pt forms alloys. Industrially, probably the most important use of platinum is as a catalyst. For example, it catalyzes the oxidation of ammonia in the manufacture of nitric acid (Section 25.2). It has been estimated that at present half the platinum in the United States is used as a catalyst in making gasoline.

Although rather inert, platinum occurs in many chemical combinations, principally in the +2 and +4 oxidation states. Many of these compounds contain complex ions, and practically all of them are unstable with respect to thermal decomposition.

21.8 QUALITATIVE ANALYSIS

All three iron-triad elements precipitate as black sulfides insoluble in basic solution. (If ferric ion were present, it would be reduced by H_2S in acid solution to ferrous ion.) FeS can be separated from CoS and NiS because it dissolves fairly quickly in Na_2SO_4-$NaHSO_4$ buffer, whereas CoS and NiS are slow to dissolve. Separation of iron from cobalt and nickel can also be achieved by making use of the fact that Fe^{++} plus an excess of NH_3 forms in air insoluble ferric hydroxide, whereas Co^{++} and Ni^{++} form soluble ammonia complexes. The presence of iron can be confirmed by adding thiocyanate after oxidation of Fe^{++} to Fe^{+3} with H_2O_2, if necessary. The deep red color of $FeNCS^{++}$ shows that iron is present.

To distinguish cobalt from nickel, the sulfides CoS and NiS can be dissolved in acid solution, boiled with bromine water to destroy H_2S, and treated with potassium nitrite. The appearance of insoluble, yellow potassium hexanitritocobaltate(III), $K_3Co(NO_2)_6$, shows the presence of cobalt. Nickel can be identified by adding a special reagent, dimethylglyoxime, which from basic solution precipitates the reddish-orange, voluminous solid, nickel dimethylglyoxime, $Ni[CH_3C(NO)C(NOH)CH_3]_2$.

QUESTIONS

21.1 Fe equations   Write balanced net equations for each of the following changes: (*a*) oxidation of FeO(*s*) by O_2(*g*) to Fe_3O_4(*s*), (*b*) formation of $BaFeO_4$ by oxidation of $Fe(OH)_3$(*s*) with OCl^-, (*c*) decolorization of a brown ferric nitrate solution by addition of nitric acid, (*d*) complete reduction of Fe_3O_4 in a blast furnace, (*e*) rusting of iron.

21.2 Preparations   How could you make each of the following conversions? Include balanced equations for each step. (*a*) Linnaeite (Co_3S_4) to pure Co. (*b*) $FeNiS_2$ to pure Ni. (*c*) NiS to $Ni(NH_3)_6^{++}$. (*d*) CoS to $K_3Co(NO_2)_6$. (*e*) Pt to $(NH_4)_2PtCl_6$. (*f*) $(NH_4)_2IrCl_6$ to Ir.

21.3 Qualitative analysis   A given solution may contain Fe^{++}, Co^{++}, Ni^{++}. Addition of NH_3 in excess produces a precipitate. The filtrate, when treated with dimethylglyoxime, gives no precipitate. Tell which of the three ions is present, which is absent, which is indeterminate.

21.4 Cast iron   Cast iron is mostly cementite, Fe_3C. Suppose you have a sample of cast iron that is 5.0% carbon by mass. Assuming the sample is cementite plus iron only, calculate the percent cementite.

21.5 Cathodic protection   In protecting an iron water tank from rusting, a magnesium stake used for cathodic protection is slowly consumed as it oxidizes. How long would a 1.00-kg stake of Mg last in protecting against corrosive attack by oxygen at a rate of 2.0 liter (STP) per day?

21.6 Corrosion kinetics   Assuming that step (2) in the given mechanism for iron corrosion is rate-determining, what will be the relative rates for iron rusting in neutral solution and in water exposed to the CO_2 in the atmosphere (assume pH = 5.0)?

21.7 Solution stoichiometry   A standard solution of Fe^{++} is prepared in the absence of air by dissolving 1.68 g of pure iron wire in sufficient dilute sulfuric acid to give 0.200 liter of solution. If 50.0 ml of this solution requires 46.9 ml of $KMnO_4$ solution for complete reaction in acid to form Fe^{+3} and Mn^{++}, what is the molarity of the $KMnO_4$ solution?

21.8 Cobalt half-reactions   It is observed that $Co(H_2O)_6^{+3}$ oxidizes water to form oxygen whereas $Co(CN)_6^{-4}$ reduces water to form hydrogen. Write the four appropriate half-reactions and tell what the minimum difference must be between the two $E°$'s involving cobalt.

21.9 Stoichiometry   Suppose you oxidize 1.00 g of each of the following to form Fe_2O_3. Calculate the weight change for each case. (*a*) Initially pure Fe. (*b*) Initially pure FeS_2. (*c*) Initially pure Fe_3O_4.

21.10 Heats of reaction   From the standard heats of formation (-26.4 kcal mole^{-1} for CO, -94.1 kcal mole^{-1} for CO_2, -63.7 kcal mole^{-1} for FeO, -267.9 kcal mole^{-1} for Fe_3O_4, and -196.5 kcal mole^{-1} for Fe_2O_3) calculate the ΔH for each of the three reduction steps of Fe_2O_3 by CO through Fe_3O_4 and FeO to Fe(*s*) and for the overall reduction from Fe_2O_3 to Fe(*s*).

21.11 Complex-ion equilibria   Given the following:

$$Fe^{+3} + SCN^- \longrightarrow FeNCS^{++} \qquad K = 800$$
$$Fe^{++} + SCN^- \longrightarrow FeNCS^+ \qquad K = 10$$

A solution is made by mixing equal volumes of 0.60 M Fe^{+3}, 0.60 M Fe^{++}, and 0.30 M SCN^-. Calculate the ratio of $FeNCS^{++}$ to $FeNCS^+$ in the final solution.

21.12 Solid-state structures   Write the formula for each of the following compounds: (*a*) Iron atoms in all the octahedral holes of a close-packed oxide structure. (*b*) A structure in which each iron atom is surrounded by an octahedral set of oxygen atoms and each oxygen atom is surrounded by a tetrahedral set of iron atoms. (*c*) A close-packed array of oxygen atoms in which iron atoms occupy one-eighth of the tetrahedral holes and one-half of the octahedral holes.

21.13 Hydrolysis   Given the following hydrolysis constants:

$$Fe^{++} + H_2O \rightleftharpoons FeOH^+ + H^+ \qquad K = 1 \times 10^{-7}$$
$$Ni^{++} + H_2O \rightleftharpoons NiOH^+ + H^+ \qquad K = 1 \times 10^{-9}$$

Calculate the pH of the following solutions: (*a*) 0.1 M Fe^{++}, (*b*) 0.1 M Ni^{++}, (*c*) equal-volume mixture of (*a*) and (*b*).

21.14 Magnetism   In going from $Co(H_2O)_6^{++}$ to $Co(H_2O)_6^{+3}$ the magnetic moment decreases by 3.8 Bohr magnetons; in going from $Co(CN)_6^{-4}$ to $Co(CN)_6^{-3}$, by 1.7 Bohr magnetons. Account for the difference in terms of ligand-field theory.

21.15 Nickel-complex structures   In terms of orbitals used, describe the bonding and predict the magnetic moment for each of the following: (*a*) $Ni(NH_3)_6^{++}$ (octahedral), (*b*) $Ni(CN)_4^{--}$ (square-planar), (*c*) $Ni(CO)_4$ (tetrahedral).

ANSWERS

21.4 75%   *21.6* 100 times faster for pH 5   *21.9* (*a*) $+0.430$ g (*b*) -0.334 g (*c*) $+0.0345$ g   *21.10* -14.0 kcal; $+9.1$ kcal; -4.0 kcal per mole of CO; -6.6 kcal per mole of Fe_2O_3 *21.11* 40   *21.13* (*a*) 4.0 (*b*) 5.0 (*c*) 4.2

22 transition elements IV: copper and zinc subgroups

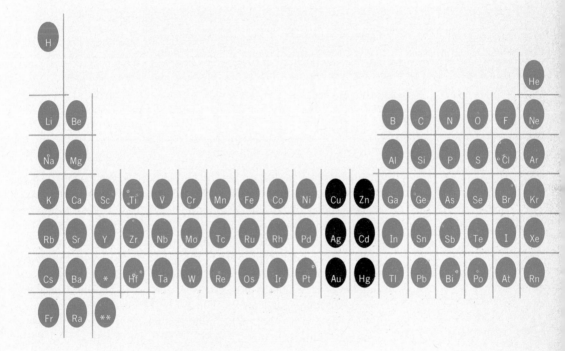

The chemical similarity between the members of the iron triad (Fe, Co, Ni) is more pronounced along the period than down the subgroup, as indicated in Chapter 21. With the elements of the next two subgroups the situation is reversed, and it is more convenient to compare them vertically than horizontally. The head elements of the next subgroups are copper ($Z = 29$) and zinc ($Z = 30$). The copper subgroup also includes silver ($Z = 47$) and gold ($Z = 79$); the zinc subgroup, cadmium ($Z = 48$) and mercury ($Z = 80$). With these elements, the sequence we have referred to as the transition elements is completed.

22.1 COPPER SUBGROUP

The elements of the copper subgroup, copper, silver, and gold, have been known to man since antiquity, for, unlike most of the preceding elements discussed, they are sometimes found in nature in the uncombined, or native, state. Originally decorative in function, they soon were adapted to use in coins because of their relative scarcity and resistance to corrosion. Originally, only silver and gold were used as coins, but then someone discovered the happy coincidence that copper could be added not only to make the coins cost less but also to increase their life in circulation because of increased hardness. Since then, copper, silver, and gold have been called the coinage metals, even though their principal uses are quite different.

Some of the important properties of these elements are shown in Figure 22.1. All these elements are typically metallic with rather high

Symbol	Z	Electronic configuration	Melting point, °C	Boiling point, °C	Ionization potential, ev	Oxidation potential (to M⁺), volts
Cu	29	$(18) 3d^{10}4s^1$	1083	2300	7.72	-0.52
Ag	47	$(36) 4d^{10}5s^1$	961	1950	7.57	-0.799
Au	79	$(68) 5d^{10}6s^1$	1063	2600	9.22	-1.7

22.1
Elements of copper subgroup

melting points and rather high boiling points. The low oxidation potentials indicate that they are not very reactive. According to the electronic configurations, there is, in the ground state of these atoms, one electron in the outermost energy level. When this electron is removed, the $+1$ ion results. This is all that we expect, since the second-outermost shell is filled and presumably is hard to break into. In this respect these elements resemble the alkali metals (Chapter 17) and consequently are sometimes classified as a group IB. However, the d electrons in the second-outermost shell are close in energy to the outermost electrons and can be removed with little additional energy, especially if there is some way to stabilize the resulting $+2$ or $+3$ ions. Apparently, this is exactly what happens. Copper forms $+1$ and $+2$ compounds; silver forms $+1$, $+2$, and $+3$ (although the $+2$ and $+3$ are rare); and gold forms $+1$ and $+3$ compounds. However, even with such a variable oxidation state, the chemistry of these elements is simpler than that of the preceding transition elements.

22.2 COPPER

Considering its usefulness and familiarity, it is surprising that copper is such a small fraction (0.0001%) of the earth's crust. Fortunately, its deposits are concentrated and easily worked. Besides native copper,

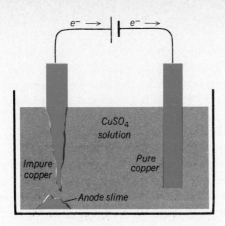

which is 99.9% pure, the element occurs as two principal classes of minerals: sulfide ores and oxide ores. The principal sulfide ores are chalcocite (Cu_2S), chalcopyrite, or copper pyrites ($CuFeS_2$), and covellite (CuS); the principal oxide ores are cuprite (Cu_2O), malachite [$CuCO_3 \cdot Cu(OH)_2$], and tenorite (CuO). About 80% of present copper production is from the sulfide ores. In order to make the metal, the minerals are first concentrated by flotation (Section 21.5), roasted in air, and then smelted. The roasting and smelting process, represented, for example, by the simplified overall equation

$$2CuFeS_2(s) + 5O_2(g) \longrightarrow 2Cu(s) + 2FeO(s) + 4SO_2(g)$$

produces tremendous quantities of sulfur dioxide, which are converted on the spot into sulfuric acid.

The copper product is about 97 to 99% pure and must be refined (purified) for most uses. This can be done best in a $CuSO_4$ electrolysis cell, like that sketched in Figure 22.2. In the electrolysis cell the impure copper is made the anode and pure copper the cathode. By careful control of the electrolysis voltage, the copper can be transferred from the anode to the cathode. The principle of operation can be seen from the following example, in which we consider the purification of a typical bar of copper containing iron and silver as impurities: The iron represents an impurity that is more easily oxidized than copper; the silver, an impurity that is less easily oxidized than copper. The pertinent half-reactions and their oxidation potentials are

$$Fe(s) \longrightarrow Fe^{++} + 2e^- \qquad +0.44 \text{ volt}$$

$$Cu(s) \longrightarrow Cu^{++} + 2e^- \qquad -0.34 \text{ volt}$$

$$Ag(s) \longrightarrow Ag^+ + e^- \qquad -0.80 \text{ volt}$$

By keeping the cell voltage at an appropriate value, only the Fe and Cu are oxidized and go into the solution as ions. The more difficultly oxidized Ag simply drops off to the bottom of the cell as the anode dissolves away. At the cathode, where reduction must occur, the high concentration of Cu^{++} and the fact that Cu^{++} is more readily reduced than Fe^{++}

lead to deposition of pure copper. The Fe^{++} remains in solution, and the solid silver stays at the bottom of the cell. Some common impurities in crude copper are iron, nickel, arsenic, antimony, and bismuth (all of which, like iron, are oxidized and remain oxidized) and silver, gold, and traces of platinum metals (all of which, like silver, are not oxidized and collect at the bottom of the cell). The residue at the bottom of the cell beneath the anode is called the *anode slime*. With efficient operation, the recovery of noble metals from the anode slime can pay for the whole refinery operation, leaving the copper as profit.

Metallic copper is malleable and ductile and a very good conductor of heat and electricity. Except for silver, it has the lowest electrical resistance of any metal (page 390) and is used extensively in wires and switches that carry current. It is a poorer reducing agent than hydrogen and does not dissolve in acids unless they contain oxidizing anions. When exposed to the air, it slowly tarnishes with the formation of a green hydroxy carbonate, but this adheres to the metal and protects it from further corrosion.

World production of copper is of the order of 3 million tons per year. Most of this goes into the electrical industry; the remainder is used to make alloys. There are over a thousand of these alloys ranging from simple *brasses* (copper plus zinc) and *bronzes* (copper plus tin) to more complex and specialized alloys such as monel metal (copper, nickel, iron, and manganese).

The compounds of copper correspond to oxidation states of $+1$ (*cuprous*) and $+2$ (*cupric*). The $+1$ state is easily oxidized and is stable only in very insoluble compounds or in complex ions. The $+2$ state is the one commonly observed in most copper compounds. The simple cuprous ion, Cu^+, cannot exist in aqueous solution, since it oxidizes and reduces itself by the reaction

$$2Cu^+ \longrightarrow Cu^{++} + Cu(s)$$

A comparison of the oxidation potentials

$$Cu^+ \longrightarrow Cu^{++} + e^- \qquad -0.15 \text{ volt}$$

$$Cu(s) \longrightarrow Cu^+ + e^- \qquad -0.52 \text{ volt}$$

indicates that Cu^+ is a better reducing agent than Cu. This means that, when Cu^+ ions are placed in aqueous solutions, some of the Cu^+ ions transfer electrons to other Cu^+ ions. Disproportionation (self-oxidation-reduction) occurs, with the formation of solid copper and cupric ion. This reaction takes place, for example, when cuprous oxide, Cu_2O, is placed in a solution of sulfuric acid. The net reaction

$$Cu_2O(s) + 2H^+ \longrightarrow Cu(s) + Cu^{++} + H_2O$$

can be considered to be the sum of two steps:

$$Cu_2O(s) + 2H^+ \longrightarrow 2Cu^+ + H_2O$$

$$2Cu^+ \longrightarrow Cu(s) + Cu^{++}$$

However, the cuprous condition can be stabilized by formation of insoluble substances or complex ions. For instance, in the presence of chloride ion, cuprous ion can form insoluble cuprous chloride.

$$CuCl(s) \rightleftharpoons Cu^+ + Cl^- \qquad K_{sp} = 3.2 \times 10^{-7}$$

The oxidation potentials then become

$$CuCl(s) \longrightarrow Cu^{++} + Cl^- + e^- \qquad -0.54 \text{ volt}$$

$$Cu(s) + Cl^- \longrightarrow CuCl(s) + e^- \qquad -0.14 \text{ volt}$$

which indicates that CuCl is not a good enough reducing agent to reduce itself (i.e., reverse the second half-reaction). Thus, cuprous chloride can be obtained as a stable white solid in contact with aqueous solutions. If there is a high concentration of chloride ion in the aqueous phase, then an additional complication appears in the formation of complex ions such as $CuCl_2^-$, called dichlorocuprate(I). The cuprous complex can be prepared by boiling $CuCl_2$ with copper turnings in concentrated hydrochloric acid. The deep brown color first formed is believed to be due to a complex containing both cuprous and cupric copper. As all the cupric state becomes reduced, the solution turns colorless. If the chloride-ion concentration of the colorless solution is decreased, as by dilution, white CuCl precipitates.

The cuprous state is also found in cuprous oxide, Cu_2O, a reddish, insoluble solid. It can be formed by addition of base to a solution of a cuprous complex (for example, $CuCl_2^-$), followed by dehydration. The reddish color observed on metallic copper that has been heated in air is apparently due to a surface coating of Cu_2O. In the classic test for reducing sugars (e.g., glucose, which, unlike sucrose, acts as a mild reducing agent), Cu_2O is formed as a red precipitate when a reducing sugar is heated with an alkaline solution of a cupric salt.

Although many anhydrous cupric salts are white, hydrated cupric salts and their aqueous solutions are blue, owing to the presence of hydrated cupric ion. In general, aqueous solutions of cupric salts are acidic because of hydrolysis

$$Cu^{++} + H_2O \rightleftharpoons CuOH^+ + H^+$$

but the hydrolysis is not very extensive ($K_h = 1 \times 10^{-8}$). When base is added to these solutions, light blue cupric hydroxide, $Cu(OH)_2$, is formed. The hydroxide is slightly soluble in excess base, and so it might be called slightly amphoteric. When treated with aqueous ammonia solution, $Cu(OH)_2$ dissolves to give a deep blue solution. The color is usually attributed to a copper-ammonia complex ion, $Cu(NH_3)_4^{++}$.

$$Cu(OH)_2(s) + 4NH_3 \longrightarrow Cu(NH_3)_4^{++} + 2OH^-$$

Like many other complexes of cupric ion, $Cu(NH_3)_4^{++}$ is paramagnetic owing to an unpaired electron. It has a planar structure (but with H_2O above and below the plane), and it can be destroyed by heat or by addition of acid. Heat is effective, because it boils the NH_3 out of the solution

$$Cu(NH_3)_4^{++} \longrightarrow Cu^{++} + 4NH_3(g)$$

and thus favors dissociation of the complex. Addition of acids results in neutralization of the NH_3 and similarly favors breakup of the complex.

$$Cu(NH_3)_4^{++} + 4H^+ \longrightarrow Cu^{++} + 4NH_4^+$$

It is interesting to note that addition of an acid to a basic solution containing $Cu(NH_3)_4^{++}$ can produce $Cu(OH)_2$ precipitation. As acid is added, the concentration of Cu^{++} rises to compensate for the gradual neutralization of NH_3, until eventually the K_{sp} of $Cu(OH)_2$, 1.6×10^{-19}, is exceeded.

One of the least soluble of cupric compounds is cupric sulfide, CuS. This is the black precipitate which is easily prepared by bubbling hydrogen sulfide through a solution of cupric salt. The very low K_{sp} of CuS (8×10^{-37}) indicates that not even very concentrated H^+ can dissolve appreciable amounts of it. For instance, in 10 M H^+ the relation $[H^+]^2[S^{--}] = 1 \times 10^{-22}$ indicates that the S^{--} concentration is $1 \times 10^{-22}/(10)^2$, or 1×10^{-24}, M. From the K_{sp} of CuS, the copper concentration would be $8 \times 10^{-37}/(1 \times 10^{-24})$, or 8×10^{-13}, M. Thus, not any appreciable amount of CuS can dissolve in this fashion. It is possible, however, to dissolve appreciable amounts of CuS by heating it with nitric acid. Dissolving occurs, not because H^+ reacts with the S^{--}, but because hot nitrate ion (especially in acid solution) is a very good oxidizing agent and oxidizes the sulfide ion to elementary sulfur. The net reaction is

$$3CuS(s) + 2NO_3^- + 8H^+ \longrightarrow 3Cu^{++} + 3S(s) + 2NO(g) + 4H_2O$$

Probably the best known cupric compound is copper sulfate pentahydrate, $Cu(H_2O)_4SO_4 \cdot H_2O$. In this material each cupric ion is surrounded by a distorted octahedron of oxygen atoms; four of these lie in a square and belong to four H_2O molecules, and the other two belong to neighboring sulfate groups. The odd H_2O molecule, the fifth one, is not directly bound to the cupric ion but forms a bridge between SO_4^{--} and other H_2O groups. The pentahydrate, or blue vitriol, as it is sometimes called, is used extensively as a germicide and fungicide, since the cupric ion is toxic to lower organisms. Its application to water supplies for controlling algae and its use on grapevines to control molds depend on this toxicity.

22.3 SILVER

Silver is a rather rare element ($10^{-8}\%$ of the earth's crust) occurring principally as native silver, argentite (Ag_2S), and horn silver (AgCl). Only about one-fifth of current silver production comes from silver ores; the rest is mainly a by-product of copper and lead production. The main problem in extracting silver from its ores is to get the rather inert silver (or the very insoluble silver compounds) to go into solution. This can be accomplished by blowing air for a week or two through a suspension of the ore in dilute aqueous sodium cyanide (NaCN) solution. With native silver, the reaction can be written

$$4Ag(s) + 8CN^- + 2H_2O + O_2(g) \longrightarrow 4Ag(CN)_2^- + 4OH^-$$

Were it not for the presence of cyanide ion, the oxygen would not oxidize the silver to a higher oxidation state. This can be seen from a comparison of the following oxidation potentials:

$$Ag(s) \longrightarrow Ag^+ + e^- \qquad\qquad -0.799 \text{ volt}$$

$$Ag(s) + 2CN^- \longrightarrow Ag(CN)_2^- + e^- \qquad +0.31 \text{ volt}$$

In the absence of cyanide ion, metallic silver is a rather poor reducing agent, and hence it is difficult to oxidize it to Ag^+. In the presence of cyanide ion, Ag^+ forms a strongly associated complex ion and is thus stabilized. What this means is that, when silver reacts to form the silver-cyanide complex ion, it acts as a fair reducing agent and is rather easily oxidized. Similar reasoning applies to the dissolving of argentite (Ag_2S). This sulfide is very insoluble ($K_{sp} = 5.5 \times 10^{-51}$), and air oxidation by itself is not sufficient to get it into solution. However, in the presence of cyanide ion, solution does occur. In fact, the stability of the complex $Ag(CN)_2^-$ is so great that with high concentrations of cyanide ion the reaction

$$Ag_2S(s) + 4CN^- \longrightarrow 2Ag(CN)_2^- + S^{--}$$

can be made to proceed to a useful extent without invoking air oxidation to oxidize the S^{--}. To recover the silver from the residual solutions, it is necessary to use a rather strong reducing agent, such as aluminum metal or zinc metal in basic solution. A possible reaction is

$$Zn(s) + 2Ag(CN)_2^- + 4OH^- \longrightarrow 2Ag(s) + 4CN^- + Zn(OH)_4^{--}$$

where some of the zinc in the final solution is also present as a cyanide complex, $Zn(CN)_4^{--}$.

Massive silver appears almost white because of its high luster. It is too soft to be used pure in jewelry and coinage and is usually alloyed with copper for these purposes. Because of expense it cannot be used much for its best property, its electrical and thermal conductivity, which is second to none. In the finely divided state silver appears black, because the haphazard arrangement of tiny crystalline faces reflects light in all directions with very little probability of sending it back to the eye of the observer. Also with smaller particles (of colloidal dimensions), metallic reflection of the type discussed in Section 17.1 cannot occur.

The compounds of silver are essentially all of the $+1$ state, although $+2$ and $+3$ compounds have been prepared under extreme oxidizing conditions. For example, an oxide believed to be AgO is formed when ozone is passed over elementary silver. The compound is not very stable toward decomposition to Ag and O_2 and, in general, behaves as a very strong oxidizing agent. In the $+1$ state silver forms the ion Ag^+, sometimes called argentous ion after the Latin word for silver, *argentum*. It does not hydrolyze appreciably in aqueous solution; it is a good oxidizing agent; and it forms many complex ions [for example, $Ag(NH_3)_2^+$, $Ag(CN)_2^-$, $AgCl_2^-$, all of which are linear]. When base is added to solutions of silver salts, a brown oxide, which shows little sign of being amphoteric, is formed:

$$2Ag^+ + 2OH^- \longrightarrow Ag_2O(s) + H_2O$$

However, the oxide does dissolve in an aqueous solution of ammonia because of formation of the colorless complex ion, $Ag(NH_3)_2^+$, diamminesilver(I).

$$Ag_2O(s) + 4NH_3 + H_2O \longrightarrow 2Ag(NH_3)_2^+ + 2OH^-$$

Solutions containing $Ag(NH_3)_2^+$ are frequently used as sources of silver for silver plating. They have the advantage of providing low concentrations of Ag^+, so that reduction by mild reducing agents, such as glucose, slowly deposits a compact silver plate. Evaporation of these solutions leaves dangerous solid residues which are violently explosive. Their composition is not known but has been described both as silver amide, $AgNH_2$, and as silver nitride, Ag_3N.

Probably the most interesting of all the silver compounds are the silver halides, AgF, AgCl, AgBr, and AgI. Except for silver fluoride, which is very soluble in water (up to 14.3 moles per 1000 g of H_2O), these halides are quite insoluble. The solubility products, 1.7×10^{-10} for AgCl, 5.0×10^{-13} for AgBr, and 8.5×10^{-17} for AgI, indicate a decrease in solubility from AgCl to AgI. The low solubility is rather surprising, because salts of $+1$ cations and -1 anions are usually soluble. In this respect AgF is normal; it dissolves much like NaF or KF. The abnormal insolubility of the other silver halides is attributed to the fact that their lattice energies (Section 16.6) are higher than expected. The principal reason for this is that there are strong van der Waals attractions between Ag^+ ions and the halide ions, and these attractions are superposed on the ordinary ionic attractions. Suppose we compare AgCl with KCl. Since Ag^+ (ionic radius, 1.26 Å) and K^+ (ionic radius, 1.33 Å) have about the same size, we would expect the ionic attractions in the solid to be about the same. However, the Ag^+ has 46 electrons, whereas K^+ has only 18. In general, the more electrons an atom has, the more easily it is deformed electrically, and hence the stronger its van der Waals attraction to neighboring atoms (Section 5.12). Consequently, the lattice of AgCl should be held together more strongly than that of KCl. In fact, the lattice energy of AgCl is 214 kcal; that of KCl, 168 kcal. Since more energy is required to break up the AgCl lattice than the KCl, AgCl should be less soluble. In support of this picture is the observed decrease in solubility from AgF to AgCl to AgBr to AgI. As the anion contains more electrons, the van der Waals attraction increases, and the lattice energy gets bigger.

Except for AgF, the silver halides are sensitive to light. For this reason, they find use in making photographic emulsions. The chemistry of the photographic process is not well understood and is complicated, because it apparently involves defect structures (see Section 6.7). However, the basic steps are usually described as follows: When photographic film, consisting essentially of a dispersion of silver bromide in gelatin, is exposed to light, grains of silver bromide are activated, depending on the intensity of the incident light. This is not a visible change and, according to one theory, simply involves migration of electrons in the silver bromide emulsion. Whatever the cause, the activated grains are more susceptible to chemical reduction by mild reducing agents (developers) than nonactivated grains. When the exposed photographic emulsion is developed, black metallic silver forms by the preferential reduction of exposed silver bromide grains. The result is that black areas appear on the film where the light was strongest. Since AgBr slowly turns black when exposed to light, the whole film would turn black eventually. However, the photographic image can be fixed by washing out unexposed AgBr grains. Although very insoluble ($K_{sp} = 5.0 \times 10^{-13}$), AgBr will dissolve in solutions containing high concentrations of thiosulfate ion, $S_2O_3^{--}$, by the reaction

$$AgBr(s) + 2S_2O_3^{--} \longrightarrow Ag(S_2O_3)_2^{-3} + Br^-$$

Thus, the final step involves soaking the film in a fixing bath, the essential component of which is $Na_2S_2O_3$, or hypo. The result is a fixed negative image of the exposure. By shining light through the negative onto another emulsion, developing, and then fixing it, the light and dark areas are inverted to produce a positive image.

In color photography the processes are much more involved. Fundamentally, they depend on having film coated with three emulsion layers, each of which is sensitive to one of three primary colors. On exposure and development, images are formed in each of the three layers. By appropriate choice of dyes and other chemicals, these three images can be colored separately to reproduce by superposition the original multicolored pattern.

22.4 GOLD

Gold is a very rare element, being about one-tenth as abundant as silver. It occurs naturally as *native gold* (where it is usually alloyed with silver) and less frequently as compounds of tellurium, such as $AuTe_2$ (gold telluride, or calaverite). The recovery is generally a mechanical process which makes use of the very high density (19.3 g cc^{-1}) of the metal. Chemical extraction is usually by a cyanide process like that used for silver:

$$4Au(s) + 8CN^- + O_2(g) + 2H_2O \longrightarrow 4Au(CN)_2^- + 4OH^-$$

Although gold is the most malleable and ductile of all metals and is a very good conductor of heat and electricity, its principal use is for currency and jewelry. As a reducing agent, it is rather inert.

The compounds of gold correspond to the $+1$ and $+3$ oxidation states; these are called aurous and auric, respectively, after the Latin word for gold, *aurum*. The aurous ion, Au^+, cannot exist in aqueous solution, because it is such a good oxidizing agent. The oxidation potential for $Au(s) \longrightarrow Au^+ + e^-$ is -1.7 volts, thus making Au^+ about as strong an oxidizing agent as permanganate ion. It will, in fact, oxidize itself to Au^{+3}. However, the $+1$ state of gold can be stabilized by complexing with cyanide ion to form $Au(CN)_2^-$. The oxidation potential for $Au(s) + 2CN^- \longrightarrow Au(CN)_2^- + e^-$ is $+0.60$ volt.

In the $+3$ state, gold exists as complex ions. The most common of these is the chloraurate ion, $AuCl_4^-$, which is obtained when gold is dissolved in aqua regia. Aqua regia, which consists of one part of concentrated nitric acid and about three parts of concentrated hydrochloric acid, can dissolve gold, whereas concentrated HNO_3 or concentrated HCl alone cannot. The reason for this is that HNO_3 cannot oxidize gold unless the chloride ion is present to complex the product. In other words, the half-reaction $Au(s) + 4Cl^- \longrightarrow AuCl_4^- + 3e^-$ with -1.0 volt is easier to carry out than the half-reaction $Au(s) \longrightarrow Au^{+3} + 3e^-$ with -1.42 volts.

The net equation for dissolving gold in aqua regia is usually written

$$Au(s) + 3NO_3^- + 4Cl^- + 6H^+ \longrightarrow AuCl_4^- + 3NO_2(g) + 3H_2O$$

22.5 ZINC SUBGROUP

The elements of the zinc subgroup are zinc, cadmium, and mercury. They are more active than the elements of the copper subgroup, but their chemistry is somewhat more simple. The zinc-subgroup elements have a characteristic oxidation state of $+2$, except for mercury, which also forms $+1$ compounds. Some of the more important properties are listed in Figure 22.3.

Symbol	Z	Electronic configuration	Melting point, °C	Boiling point, °C	Ionization potential, ev	Oxidation potential (to M^{++}), volts
Zn	30	$(18)\,3d^{10}4s^2$	419	907	9.39	$+0.76$
Cd	48	$(36)\,4d^{10}5s^2$	321	767	8.99	$+0.40$
Hg	80	$(68)\,5d^{10}6s^2$	-38.9	357	10.43	-0.85

22.3
Elements of zinc subgroup

As seen from the electronic configurations, each of these elements has two electrons in the outermost energy level. The situation is reminiscent of that found for the alkaline-earth elements (Section 18.1). The low melting points may at first sight be surprising, but they are not entirely unexpected. In progressing from left to right through the transition sequence, the low point in the atomic volume has been passed (see Figure 2.19), and the atoms get bigger from there on. As the atoms get bigger, they are farther apart, and forces of attraction are smaller. Thus, it becomes easier to melt the elements. Probably of greater importance is the fact that the d shells of the second-outermost shells are filled; therefore, there is little chance for the covalent binding between ions found in other transition elements. In mercury, the interatomic forces are so weak that the melting point is below room temperature.

There is a striking difference between these elements and the analogous group II elements. In Figure 22.4 the element zinc is compared with calcium, a typical element of group II. Although both of these elements have but two electrons in the outermost shell and have no partially filled shells, their properties are quite different. For example, as shown by the oxidation potentials, calcium is a very powerful reducing agent, whereas zinc is only moderately strong. The fundamental reason for the change in properties is the decreased size of the zinc atom. Since the nuclear charge has increased by 10 units in going from $Z = 20$ to $Z = 30$, there is a greater attraction for the electrons in zinc, and the shells are pulled in. The atom is thus smaller. The valence electrons are fourth-shell electrons in both cases and are held more tightly in the zinc atom.

Property	Calcium	Zinc
Atomic number	20	30
Electronic configuration	2, 8, 8, 2	2, 8, 18, 2
Atomic volume, cc	26	9
Size of M^{++} (radius), Å	0.94	0.70
First ionization potential, ev	6.11	9.39
Second ionization potential, ev	11.87	17.89
Third ionization potential, ev	51.21	40.0
Density, g cc^{-1}	1.55	7.14
Melting point, °C	810	419
Boiling point, °C	1300(?)	907
Oxidation potential, volts	+2.87	+0.76

22.4
Comparison of calcium
and zinc

22.6 ZINC

About a hundred times as abundant as copper, zinc occurs principally as the mineral sphalerite (ZnS), also called zinc blende. The metal is prepared by roasting the sulfide in air to convert it to oxide and then reducing the oxide with finely divided carbon. The reactions are

$$2ZnS(s) + 3O_2(g) \longrightarrow 2ZnO(s) + 2SO_2(g)$$

$$ZnO(s) + C(s) \longrightarrow Zn(g) + CO(g)$$

Since the second reaction is carried out at about 1200°C, above the boiling point of Zn, the metal forms as a vapor and must be condensed. Very rapid condensation produces the fine powder known as zinc dust.

Massive zinc has fairly good metallic properties except that it is rather brittle, especially at 200°C, where it can be ground up into a powder. It is a moderately active metal and can even reduce water to hydrogen, but only when heated. With acids, ordinary Zn gives the well-known evolution of H_2. Strangely enough, this is very rapid when the Zn is impure but almost too slow to be observed when the Zn is very pure. Apparently, the impurities (especially arsenic and antimony) speed dissolving by serving as centers from which hydrogen gas can evolve.

In air, zinc tarnishes but slightly, probably because it forms a self-protective coat of oxide or carbonate. Because it itself withstands corrosion so well and because it can give cathodic protection (Section 21.4) to iron, zinc is often used as a coating on iron to keep it from rusting. Iron protected in this way, called galvanized iron, can be made by dipping the iron into molten zinc or by plating zinc on it from an electrolytic bath. The other important use of zinc is in alloys such as the brasses, which are essentially copper-zinc alloys.

In all its compounds zinc shows only a $+2$ oxidation state. The zinc ion, Zn^{++}, is colorless and not paramagnetic. In aqueous solutions it hydrolyzes to give slightly acid solutions. The hydrolysis, usually written

$$Zn^{++} + H_2O \rightleftharpoons Zn(OH)^+ + H^+ \qquad K_h = 2.5 \times 10^{-10}$$

does not proceed so far toward the right as that of Cu^{++} ion. Thus, for equal concentrations, solutions of zinc salts are less acid than those of cupric salts. When base is added to solutions of zinc salts, white zinc hydroxide, $Zn(OH)_2$, is precipitated. This hydroxide is amphoteric, and therefore further addition of base dissolves it to give zincate ion, $Zn(OH)_4^{--}$. The concentration of Zn^{++} in equilibrium in basic solution is very small. This means that the half-reaction

$$Zn(s) \longrightarrow Zn^{++} + 2e^-$$

has greater tendency to go to the right in basic solution than in acid solution. Consequently, zinc metal is a stronger reducing agent (has higher oxidation potential) for basic solutions than for acid solutions. For basic solutions, the half-reaction can be written

$$Zn(s) + 4OH^- \longrightarrow Zn(OH)_4^{--} + 2e^-$$

and the oxidation potential is $+1.22$ volts. As indicated in Figure 22.3, the oxidation potential for acid solutions is $+0.76$ volt.

Like other transition elements, zinc has great tendency to form stable complex ions. For example, zinc hydroxide is easily dissolved in aqueous ammonia because of the formation of a complex, $Zn(NH_3)_4^{++}$, tetraamminezinc(II). The hydroxide can also be dissolved in cyanide solutions because of the formation of $Zn(CN)_4^{--}$, tetracyanozincate(II). As shown by the following equilibrium constants

$$Zn(NH_3)_4^{++} \rightleftharpoons Zn^{++} + 4NH_3 \qquad K = 3.4 \times 10^{-10}$$

$$Zn(CN)_4^{--} \rightleftharpoons Zn^{++} + 4CN^- \qquad K = 1.2 \times 10^{-18}$$

the cyanide complex is less dissociated than the ammonia complex. The greater stability of the cyanide complex is reflected in the fact that zinc metal is a stronger reducing agent in cyanide solutions than in ammonia solutions. The oxidation potentials are

$$Zn(s) + 4CN^- \longrightarrow Zn(CN)_4^{--} + 2e^- \qquad +1.26 \text{ volts}$$

$$Zn(s) + 4NH_3 \longrightarrow Zn(NH_3)_4^{++} + 2e^- \qquad +1.04 \text{ volts}$$

When hydrogen sulfide is passed through solutions of zinc salts which are not too acid, white zinc sulfide precipitates. Although the solubility product of ZnS (1×10^{-22}) is rather small, so that ZnS is essentially insoluble in neutral solutions, addition of acid lowers the sulfide-ion concentration sufficiently that ZnS becomes soluble. The enhanced solubility of ZnS in acid solution gives a method for separating it from other sulfides such as CuS, Ag_2S, and CdS.

Zinc sulfide is used extensively in the white pigment, lithopone, an approximately equimolar mixture of ZnS and $BaSO_4$. ZnS is also used in making fluorescent screens, because impure ZnS acts as a phosphor; i.e., it can convert energy such as that of an electron beam into visible light. The action of phosphors is very complex and is closely related to the properties of defects in solid-state structures (Section 6.7). The simplest view is that an electron beam impinging on impure ZnS uses its energy to remove electrons from impurity centers. An electron so removed moves through the crystal until it encounters some other center to which it can return by giving off a flash of light.

22.7 CADMIUM

The properties of cadmium are so similar to those of zinc that the two elements invariably occur together. There are no important minerals of cadmium, which is only about one-thousandth as abundant as zinc. The principal source of cadmium is the flue dust from the purification of zinc by distillation. Since Cd is more volatile than Zn, it evaporates first and concentrates in the first distillates. The principal use of Cd is as a protective plate on other metals, such as steel. It is particularly good for alkaline conditions because, unlike Zn, it is not amphoteric and does not dissolve in base. The other principal use of cadmium is in making low-melting alloys, such as Wood's metal (mp, 70°C).

In its compounds the usual oxidation state of cadmium is +2. It exists in aqueous solutions as colorless Cd^{++} ion. With H_2S, it forms insoluble, yellow CdS ($K_{sp} = 1.0 \times 10^{-28}$), which is used as the pigment "cadmium yellow." Like zinc, cadmium forms a variety of complex ions, including $Cd(NH_3)_4^{++}$, $Cd(CN)_4^{--}$, $CdCl_4^{--}$, and CdI_4^{--}. Some of the salts of cadmium are peculiar in the sense that they do not dissociate completely into ions in aqueous solution as practically all other salts do. Cadmium sulfate, for example, has a dissociation constant of 5×10^{-3} and so can be called a weak salt.

Transition elements IV: copper and zinc subgroups

455

The only common mineral of mercury is cinnabar (HgS), from which the element is produced by roasting in air:

$$HgS(s) + O_2(g) \longrightarrow Hg + SO_2(g)$$

Unlike any other metal,* mercury is a liquid at room temperature, and its symbol emphasizes this, since it comes from the Latin *hydrargyrum*, meaning liquid silver. The liquid is not very volatile (vapor pressure is 0.0018 torr at 25°C), but the vapor is very poisonous, and *prolonged exposure even to the liquid should be avoided.*

Liquid mercury has a high metallic luster, but it is not a very good metal in that it has a higher electrical resistance than any of the other transition metals. However, for some uses, as in making electrical contacts, its fluidity is such a great advantage that its mediocre conductivity can be tolerated. Furthermore, its inertness to air oxidation, its relatively high density, and its uniform expansion with temperature lead to special uses as in barometers and thermometers.

Liquid mercury dissolves many metals, especially the softer ones like copper, silver, gold, and the alkali elements. The resulting alloys, which may be solid as well as liquid, are called *amalgams*. Probably their most distinctive property is that the reactivity of the metal dissolved in the mercury is thereby lowered. For example, the reactivity of sodium in sodium amalgam is so low that the amalgam can be kept in water with only slow evolution of hydrogen.

In its compounds mercury shows both +1 (mercurous) and +2 (mercuric) oxidation states. In this respect, it is unlike the other members of the zinc subgroup. The mercurous compounds are unusual because they all contain two mercury atoms bound together. In aqueous solutions, the ion is a double ion corresponding to Hg_2^{++}, in which there is a covalent σ bond between the two mercury atoms. Experimental evidence for this is the lack of paramagnetism of mercurous compounds. The ion Hg^+ would have one unpaired electron in its $6s$ orbital and would be paramagnetic, whereas the ion Hg_2^{++} would have the two electrons paired in a σ-bonding molecular orbital and would not be paramagnetic. Further experimental evidence for Hg_2^{++} comes from a study of the equilibrium between liquid mercury, mercuric ion, and mercurous ion. There are two possible ways of writing this equilibrium, depending on whether mercurous mercury exists as Hg_2^{++} or Hg^+:

$$Hg(l) + Hg^{++} \rightleftharpoons Hg_2^{++} \qquad K = [Hg_2^{++}]/[Hg^{++}]$$

$$Hg(l) + Hg^{++} \rightleftharpoons 2Hg^+ \qquad K' = [Hg^+]^2/[Hg^{++}]$$

If the amounts of mercurous mercury and mercuric mercury in solution are determined for various equilibrium solutions, it is found that the ratio of mercurous to mercuric is constant, but the ratio of mercurous

* Cesium metal has a melting point of 28.5°C, or 83.3°F, and gallium metal has a melting point of 29.8°C, or 85.6°F. Thus, the uniqueness of mercury as a liquid metal disappears on hot days.

squared to mercuric is not. In other words, K is found to be a true constant (1.7×10^2) for all experiments, but K' is not. Apparently, there is little, if any, Hg^+ in solution.

Except for the doubling, mercurous ion behaves much like Ag^+; for example, it reacts with chloride ion to precipitate white mercurous chloride, Hg_2Cl_2, also known as calomel. When exposed to light, calomel darkens by partial disproportionation into Hg and $HgCl_2$. Just as the silver halides decrease in solubility in going from AgF to AgI, so do the mercurous halides. Mercurous fluoride, Hg_2F_2, is quite soluble in water, but the solution immediately decomposes to form HF and insoluble, black Hg_2O. For the other halides the solubility products are as follows:

$$Hg_2Cl_2(s) \rightleftharpoons Hg_2^{++} + 2Cl^- \qquad K_{sp} = 1.1 \times 10^{-18}$$

$$Hg_2Br_2(s) \rightleftharpoons Hg_2^{++} + 2Br^- \qquad K_{sp} = 1.3 \times 10^{-22}$$

$$Hg_2I_2(s) \rightleftharpoons Hg_2^{++} + 2I^- \qquad K_{sp} = 4.5 \times 10^{-29}$$

Unlike Ag^+, mercurous ion does not form an ammonia complex. When aqueous ammonia is added to Hg_2Cl_2, the solid turns black because of formation of finely divided mercury.

$$Hg_2Cl_2(s) + 2NH_3 \longrightarrow HgNH_2Cl(s) + Hg + NH_4^+ + Cl^-$$

The compound $HgNH_2Cl$, mercuric ammonobasic chloride, is white, but its color is obscured by the intense black. This difference in behavior toward NH_3 provides a simple test for distinguishing $AgCl$ from Hg_2Cl_2.

In the $+2$ state, mercury is frequently represented as the simple ion Hg^{++}, although it is usually found in the form of complex ions, insoluble solids, or weak salts. For example, in a solution of mercuric chloride, the concentration of Hg^{++} is much smaller than the concentration of undissociated $HgCl_2$ molecules. With excess chloride ion the complexes $HgCl_3^-$ and $HgCl_4^{--}$ are also formed. In ammonia solutions complex ions containing one, two, three, and four NH_3 molecules are known. For complete dissociation of $Hg(NH_3)_4^{++}$ the constant is 5.2×10^{-20}. The complex $Hg(CN)_4^{--}$ is even more stable ($K = 4 \times 10^{-42}$).

Although mercuric sulfide as found in nature is red, when H_2S is passed through a mercuric solution, a black precipitate of HgS is obtained. The color difference may be due to differences in crystal structure. The solubility product of black HgS is very low (1.6×10^{-54}), but not as low as that of platinum sulfide, PtS ($K_{sp} = 8 \times 10^{-73}$). In order to dissolve these very insoluble sulfides, drastic measures are required. HgS, for example, will not dissolve even in boiling nitric acid. Aqua regia, however, which supplies both nitrate for oxidizing the sulfide and chloride for complexing the mercuric, does take it into solution.

The oxidation potentials

$$2Hg(l) \longrightarrow Hg_2^{++} + 2e^- \qquad -0.79 \text{ volt}$$

$$Hg_2^{++} \longrightarrow 2Hg^{++} + 2e^- \qquad -0.92 \text{ volt}$$

are so close that practically any oxidizing agent which is able to oxidize mercury to mercurous ion is also able to oxidize mercurous ion to mercuric ion. Also, most any reducing agent that can reduce mercuric to mercurous can also reduce mercurous to mercury. If a limited amount of reducing agent such as Sn^{++} (stannous ion) is added to a mercuric solution, only Hg_2^{++} is formed; if Sn^{++} is added in excess, the reduction goes all the way to Hg.

22.9 QUALITATIVE ANALYSIS

Mercurous ion and silver ion can be separated from the other cations by adding HCl to precipitate white, insoluble Hg_2Cl_2 and AgCl. If NH_3 is added to a mixture of these chlorides, a black color appears, owing to formation of Hg and $HgNH_2Cl$. Since NH_3 converts AgCl into soluble $Ag(NH_3)_2^+$ and Cl^-, the filtrate contains the silver, and AgCl can be re-precipitated by addition of HNO_3.

If H_2S is added to an acidic solution containing Cd^{++}, Hg^{++}, Cu^{++}, and Zn^{++}, the first three precipitate as insoluble sulfides (yellow CdS, black HgS, and black CuS). If the solution is then made basic with NH_3, white ZnS is formed. A confirmatory test for ZnS would be to dissolve it in HCl plus HNO_3, evaporate to dryness, and reprecipitate by addition of H_2S in a SO_4^{--}-HSO_4^- buffer.

The separation of CdS, HgS, and CuS makes use of the fact that CdS and CuS are soluble in boiling HNO_3, whereas HgS is not. HgS can be confirmed by dissolving in aqua regia and reducing with $SnCl_2$ to Hg_2Cl_2 and Hg. Addition of NH_3 to a solution containing Cu^{++} and Cd^{++} gives the blue color characteristic of $Cu(NH_3)_4^{++}$. Cadmium can be detected by first precipitating out the Cu^{++} with H_2S in acid solution in the presence of high-concentration chloride ion (which keeps Cd^{++} in solution as $CdCl_4^{--}$) and then adding $NaC_2H_3O_2$ and H_2S. The added acetate ion serves to reduce the H^+ concentration, thereby raising the S^{--} concentration sufficiently to precipitate yellow CdS.

QUESTIONS

22.1 Magnetism What do you predict to be the magnetic moment for each of the following: Ag^{++}, Cd_2^{++}, $Cu(CN)_3^{--}$, $Au(CN)_4^-$, $Cu(NH_3)_4^{++}$?

22.2 Nomenclature Give systematic names for each of the following:

$Ag(NH_3)_2^+$, $Zn(CN)_4^{--}$, $HgCl_2Br_2^{--}$, $Au(CN)_2^-$, $Cu(NH_3)_4(H_2O)_2^{++}$.

22.3 Structure Tell which orbitals are probably used for bonding and what the expected geometry will be for each of the following:

$Au(CN)_2^-$, $AuCl_4^-$, $Zn(CN)_4^{--}$, CdI_4^{--}.

22.4 Oxidation potential From the oxidation potentials given in Section 22.4 calculate the $E°$ for $Au^+ \longrightarrow Au^{+3} + 2e^-$. Show that Au^+ should disproportionate.

22.5 Equations Write balanced equations for each of the following: (a) roasting of Cu_2S in air, (b) dissolving of copper in concentrated HNO_3 to form NO_2, (c) precipitation of AgCl by addition of nitric acid to a solution containing $Ag(NH_3)_2^+$ and Cl^-, (d) disproportionation of aqueous Au^+, (e) dissolution of zinc in base to liberate hydrogen, (f) precipitation of CdS by addition of H_2S to aqueous cadmium sulfate, (g) dissolving of HgS in aqua regia to form SO_2, NO_2, and $HgCl_4^{--}$.

22.6 Solubility product Show whether a precipitate should form when the following mixtures are prepared: (a) 10 ml of 1.0×10^{-6} M $AgNO_3$ plus 40 ml of 1.0×10^{-6} M NaCl, (b) 10 ml of 1.0×10^{-6} M $AgNO_3$ plus 40 ml of 1.0×10^{-6} M NaI, (c) 10 ml of 1.0×10^{-6} M $Hg_2(NO_3)_2$ plus 40 ml of 1.0×10^{-6} M NaCl.

22.7 Simultaneous equilibria (a) Given that K_{sp} of AgCl is 1.7×10^{-10} and $K_{diss} = 6.0 \times 10^{-8}$ for $Ag(NH_3)_2^+ \rightleftharpoons Ag^+ + 2NH_3$, calculate the K for $AgCl(s) + 2NH_3 \rightleftharpoons Ag(NH_3)_2^+ + Cl^-$. (b) What is the solubility, in moles per liter, of AgCl in 0.10 M NH_3?

22.8 Simultaneous equilibria Calculate the concentration of ZnS that can dissolve in each of the following solutions to give a solution saturated with respect to H_2S and ZnS: (a) solution maintained at pH = 0.0, (b) solution maintained at pH = 1.0, (c) solution maintained at pH = 2.0.

22.9 Nernst equation From the data given in this chapter calculate the oxidation potential for each of the following:

(a) $Ag(s) + Cl^- \longrightarrow AgCl(s) + e^-$
(b) $2Hg(l) + 2Cl^- \longrightarrow Hg_2Cl_2(s) + 2e^-$
(c) $Hg(l) + 4CN^- \longrightarrow Hg(CN)_4^{--} + 2e^-$

22.10 Preparations Starting with the appropriate common mineral, indicate the mode of preparation, including equations, for each of the following: (a) ZnO, (b) $Zn(NO_3)_2$, (c) $(NH_4)_2Zn(SO_4)_2 \cdot 6H_2O$, (d) Hg_2Cl_2, (e) $HgCrO_4$, (f) HgO.

22.11 Conversions Tell, with the use of balanced equations, how you would effect each of the following conversions: (a) $CuCO_3$ to $CuCl_2$, (b) CuS to $CuSO_4$, (c) AgCl to $AgNO_3$, (d) Ag-Au alloy to pure Au.

22.12 Alloys Copper-zinc alloys change structure discontinuously in going from copper-rich to zinc-rich compositions. As with many other alloy phase changes, the important factor is the average valence-electron-to-atom ratio. Discontinuities occur when this ratio equals 1.5000, 1.6154, and 1.7500. Writing the limiting compositions as Cu_xZn_y, where x and y are small whole numbers, what are the apparent compounds that correspond to the limiting ratios? Assume one valence electron for Cu and two valence electrons for Zn.

22.13 Structure Zinc blende, ZnS, has a diamond-like structure in which Zn and S atoms alternate. Given that the internuclear Zn-to-S distance is 2.35 Å, calculate the Zn-to-Zn distance.

22.14 Thermodynamics The heats of fusion at the melting points (in calories per gram) for Zn, Cd, and Hg are 28.13, 13.66, and 2.82, respectively. Calculate the molar entropies of fusion.

22.15 Stoichiometry Given a solution labeled "0.100 M Hg_2SO_4" that has been partially air oxidized to $HgSO_4$. If 40.0 ml of this solution requires 45.8 ml of 0.100 M SnSO$_4$ for complete reduction to Hg as Sn^{++} goes to Sn^{+4}, calculate the concentration of Hg$_2^{++}$ and of Hg^{++} in the original solution.

22.16 Mixing problem   Calculate the final concentration of each ion in a solution made by mixing equal volumes of 0.30 M solutions of each of the following: Hg$_2$(NO$_3$)$_2$, NaCl, NaI. Assume volumes of solution are additive.

ANSWERS

22.1 1.73; zero; zero; zero; 1.73 Bohr magnetons   22.7 (*a*) 2.8 × 10^{-3} (*b*) 4.8 × 10^{-3} 22.9 (*a*) −0.22 volt   (*b*) −0.26 volt (*c*) +0.37 volt   22.13 3.84 Å   22.15 0.0855 M Hg$_2^{++}$ and 0.029 M Hg^{++} 22.16 6.5 × 10^{-7} M Hg$_2^{++}$; 0.20 M NO$_3^-$; 0.20 M Na$^+$; 1.3 × 10^{-6} M Cl$^-$; 8.3 × 10^{-12} M I$^-$

23 group III elements

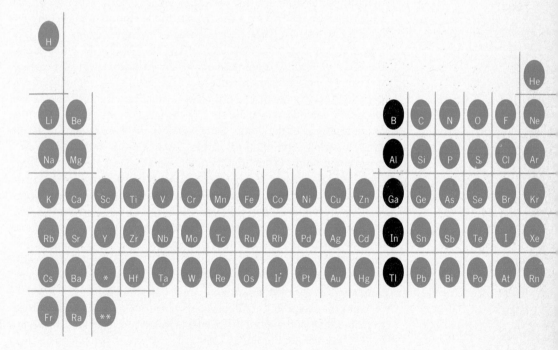

The peculiar electronic expansion responsible for the transition elements
is completed with the zinc subgroup. The next elements, of group III,
like those of groups I and II, are again main-group elements. Although
the insertion of transition elements between groups II and III can
modify the properties of later elements of group III, the early members,
boron and aluminum, follow the alkaline-earth elements directly. Therefore, it is not surprising that the group III elements have the same relationship to the alkaline-earth elements as the alkaline-earth elements
have to the alkali metals; i.e., the group properties are modified by a
third valence electron.

Symbol	Z	Electronic configuration	Melting point, °C	Boiling point, °C	Ionization potential, ev	Oxidation potential, volts
B	5	(2) $2s^22p^1$	2300	2550(?)	8.30	+0.87 (to H_3BO_3)
Al	13	(10) $3s^23p^1$	659.7	2300	5.98	+1.66 (to Al^{+3})
Ga	31	(28) $4s^24p^1$	29.8	2000	6.00	+0.53 (to Ga^{+3})
In	49	(46) $5s^25p^1$	155	1450	5.79	+0.34 (to In^{+3})
Tl	81	(78) $6s^26p^1$	304	1460	6.11	+0.34 (to Tl^{+})

23.1
Elements of group III

23.1 GROUP PROPERTIES

The elements of group III are boron, aluminum, gallium, indium, and thallium. Their properties are listed in Figure 23.1. Except for boron, which may be classed as a *semimetal,* these elements show typically metallic properties. The special character of boron stems principally from the small size of the boron atom. Like lithium of group I and beryllium of group II, boron has only the K shell underlying the valence electrons, whereas other members of the group have additional shells populated. Consequently, the B atom is smaller and, as shown by the ionization potentials in Figure 23.1, gives up electrons less readily than do other atoms of the group. Since, as previously discussed in Section 17.1, low ionization potential favors metallic properties, it is not surprising that boron is the least metallic of the group III elements. However, ionization potential is not the only factor which determines whether an element is metallic. For example, gold has a higher ionization potential than boron and yet is a typical metal. The detailed structure of the solid and the specific interactions are also important. Gold has a simple structure with 12 atoms as nearest-neighbors; boron has several complex structures in which B_{12} icosahedra (20-faced regular polyhedra) are linked together differently, giving some B atoms 6 nearest-neighbors and others fewer than 6.

From the electronic configurations given in Figure 23.1 it might be expected that all the group III elements would form +3 ions. However, as just mentioned, boron has such firm hold on its three valence electrons that it does not exist as B^{+3} cations in its compounds, but takes part in chemical combination only through covalent binding. Even so, in its compounds it is assigned oxidation state +3, because usually the compounds are formed with more electronegative elements. The other members of the group give up their electrons more readily; hence, formation of a +3 ion becomes progressively easier down the group. In the case of thallium, it is also possible to remove only one electron from the neutral atom, thus forming a +1 ion.

As discussed in Section 9.4, a highly charged cation in water can pull electrons to itself sufficiently to facilitate the rupture of O—H bonds in water. The larger the cation, the smaller is the effect, because a large cation exerts a smaller pull on the electrons. In going down group III

23.1 Group properties

462

the effect of this change is illustrated. Boron is so small that, if a B^{+3} ion were placed in water, it would pull electrons to itself from H_2O strongly enough to rupture the O—H bond and release H^+. In other words, $B(OH)_3$ and the corresponding oxide B_2O_3 are acidic. Al^{+3} and Ga^{+3} are larger than B^{+3}, and they hydrolyze less; $Al(OH)_3$, Al_2O_3, and the corresponding compounds of gallium are amphoteric. In^{+3} and Tl^{+3} are still larger. Their interactions with water are so small that the O—H bond of water is essentially unperturbed; i.e., the ions are but slightly hydrolyzed. Their hydroxides are basic. Thus, in going down group III there is a trend from acidic behavior to basic behavior of the oxides and hydroxides. Similar trends favoring the basic behavior for the larger atoms of a group are also found in later groups of the periodic table.

23.2 BORON

Both as an element and in its compounds boron differs markedly in properties from the other members of group III. In nature, it is moderately rare (0.0003% abundance) and occurs principally as the borates (oxyboron anions) of calcium and sodium, e.g., colemanite, $Ca_2B_6O_{11} \cdot 5H_2O$, and borax, $Na_2B_4O_7 \cdot 10H_2O$. The element may be produced by reducing the oxide, B_2O_3, with a metal such as Mg, electrolyzing fused borates, or reducing boron trichloride, BCl_3, with hydrogen at high temperature. Only the last method gives a reasonably pure product. The purest boron is made by thermal decomposition of $BI_3(g)$ on a heated tantalum filament at about 900°C.

Massive boron is very hard but brittle. It has a dull metallic luster but is a poor conductor of electricity and is not classified as a metal. When its temperature is raised, its conductivity increases. This is unlike metallic behavior; therefore, boron and substances like it (silicon and germanium) are called *semiconductors*. The explanation of semiconductivity is that, at room temperature, electrons are bound rather tightly to local centers, but as the temperature is raised, they are freed and are able to move through the crystal. The higher the temperature, the greater the number of electrons freed; hence, the conductivity increases even though lattice vibrations offer more resistance at the higher temperature (Section 13.1). The conductivity is proportional to n, the number of electric-charge carriers, times μ, the mobility of each; n increases with temperature by the exponential factor $e^{-E/kt}$, where E is a measure of the energy required to free the electron, while μ is generally affected much less by temperature and depends on some small power of T.

At room temperature, boron is inert to all except the most powerful oxidizing agents, such as fluorine and concentrated nitric acid. However, when fused with alkaline oxidizing mixtures, such as NaOH and $NaNO_3$, it reacts to form borates. Boron also dissolves in molten aluminum, from which there separates on cooling an aluminum boride, AlB_{12}. This same boride is formed when boron oxide is reduced with aluminum and for a long time was considered to be pure boron. In fact

AlB_{12} is still referred to as "crystalline boron." Other borides such as Mg_3B_2 are known and can be prepared by direct union of the elements.

When magnesium boride reacts with acids, several boron-hydrogen compounds are formed. They have puzzled chemists since their discovery. The simplest of these boron hydrides would be BH_3, formed by sharing the three valence electrons of boron with three H atoms. However, this compound is not known. Instead, boron forms a series of hydrides ranging from B_2H_6 (diborane) to $B_{18}H_{22}$ (octadecaborane). All of these compounds are surprising, since there seem to be too few electrons to hold them together. Diborane, for example, has only twelve valence electrons (three from each B and one from each H) for what appears to be seven bonds (three bonds in each BH_3 unit and one bond between them).

There is no simple valence-bond structure which can be written for diborane. A relatively simple molecular-orbital description has been worked out and is shown in Figure 23.2. Four of the H atoms of B_2H_6 are coplanar with the two B atoms; the other two H atoms are located one above and one below this plane, on a line through the midpoint of the molecule. Whereas the four outer hydrogens are bonded to boron by four conventional σ bonds, the other two hydrogens are bound by "three-center" molecular orbitals. These three-center bonds, sometimes called "banana bonds," each extend over three atoms, the two B's and a bridging H. One three-center molecular orbital is above the plane of the rest of the molecule, the other is below; each of these molecular orbitals accommodates one pair of electrons. Such a molecular-orbital scheme not only gives a proper electron count but also is consistent with the observed properties of B_2H_6, viz., no paramagnetism, two of the H atoms are structurally and chemically different from the other four.

All the boron hydrides, ranging from gaseous B_2H_6 to solid $B_{18}H_{22}$, inflame in air to give dark-colored products of unknown composition. In the absence of air, they decompose on heating to boron and hydrogen. They react with water to form hydrogen and boric acid.

The only important oxide of boron is B_2O_3, boric oxide. As already mentioned, it is acidic, dissolving in water to form H_3BO_3, boric acid. Boric acid is an extremely weak acid for which K_I is 6.0×10^{-10}. Because its acidity is so slight, it can safely be used as an eyewash to take advantage of its antiseptic properties.

The borates, formed either by neutralization of boric acid or reaction of B_2O_3 with basic oxides, are extremely complicated compounds. Although a few, such as $LaBO_3$, contain discrete BO_3^{-3} ions, most contain more complex anions in which boron atoms are joined together by oxygen bridges. As shown in Figure 23.3, the simple BO_3^{-3}, or orthoborate ion, is a planar ion with the three oxygen atoms at the corners of an equilateral triangle. In more complex anions such as the one shown, there are still three oxygen atoms about each boron atom, but some of these are joined to other boron atoms. An extended structure similar to this, containing $B_2O_4^{--}$ as a repeating unit, is found in CaB_2O_4. Other borates are even more complex and may have, in addition to triangular

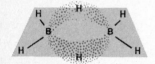

23.2
Molecular-orbital
representation of diborane

$$\left[\quad O-\overset{\overset{\displaystyle O}{|}}{B}-O \quad \right]^{-3}$$

SIMPLE

COMPLEX

BO$_3$ units, tetrahedral BO$_4$ units. This seems to be true of borax, which is the most common of the borates. It is extensively used in water soften-ing, partly because it reacts with Ca^{++} to form insoluble calcium borate and partly because it hydrolyzes to give an alkaline solution (Section 18.7). Because borax dissolves many metal oxides to form easily fusible borates, it is widely used as a flux in soldering operations. By removing oxides such as Cu$_2$O from the surface of hot brass, the flux allows fresh metal surfaces to fuse together.

The boron halides (BF$_3$, BCl$_3$, BBr$_3$, and BI$_3$) are also unusual in sev-eral respects. For one thing, unlike the halides formed by typical metals, these are molecular substances and do not contain ions in the solid state. For another thing, the boron atom in these molecules has only a sextet of electrons; hence, it can accommodate another pair of elec-trons. This occurs, for example, in the reaction

$$:\!\ddot{F}\!: \quad\; H \qquad\qquad :\!\ddot{F}\!: \;\; H$$
$$:\!\ddot{F}\!:\!B \;+\; :\!\ddot{N}\!:\!H \longrightarrow\; :\!\ddot{F}\!:\!B\!:\!\ddot{N}\!:\!H$$
$$:\!\ddot{F}\!: \quad\; H \qquad\qquad :\!\ddot{F}\!: \;\; H$$

where the product is sometimes called an *addition compound*. The action of BF$_3$ as a Lewis acid, i.e., its ability to draw a pair of electrons to itself, makes it useful as a catalyst for many reactions that are also catalyzed by H$^+$.

23.3 ALUMINUM

Although aluminum is the most abundant metal and, in fact, is the third most abundant element (8% of the earth's crust), it is of secondary im-portance to iron, partly because of the difficulties in its preparation. It occurs primarily as complex aluminum silicates, such as felspar (KAlSi$_3$O$_8$), from which it is economically unfeasible to separate pure aluminum. Further, unless the product Al is completely free of iron and silicon, its properties are practically useless. Fortunately, there are nat-ural deposits of oxide in the form of bauxite (Al$_2$O$_3 \cdot x$H$_2$O) from which pure Al can be obtained by electrolytic reduction. However, before elec-trolysis is carried out, it is necessary to remove iron and silicon impur-ities from the ore.

Purification of bauxite is accomplished by the Bayer process, which makes use of the amphoterism of aluminum. The crude oxide is treated with hot NaOH solution, in which the aluminum oxide dissolves because of the formation of aluminate ion [$Al(OH)_4^-$]. Silicon oxide also dissolves (to form silicate ions), but ferric oxide stays undissolved, since Fe_2O_3, unlike Al_2O_3, is not amphoteric. The solution is filtered to remove Fe_2O_3 and cooled. On agitation with air and addition of crystalline aluminum hydroxide as a seed, aluminum hydroxide precipitates, leaving the silicate in solution.

The production of metallic aluminum from purified bauxite is usually carried out by the Hall-Héroult process. Bauxite, dissolved in a molten mixture of fluorides, such as cryolite* (Na_3AlF_6), calcium fluoride, and sodium fluoride, is electrolyzed at about 1000°C in cells like that represented schematically in Figure 23.4. The anode consists of graphite (carbon) rods dipping into the molten mixture; the cathode, of a graphite lining supported by an iron box. The electrode reactions are very complicated and only imperfectly understood. At the cathode, oxyfluoaluminum complex ions (perhaps of the type $AlOF_5^{-4}$) are reduced to liquid aluminum (mp, 659.7°C). At the anode, a series of products is formed; they include oxygen, fluorine, and various carbon compounds of these elements. The carbon anodes gradually corrode away and must be replaced periodically. Continual addition of bauxite and recurrent draining off of the liquid aluminum allow uninterrupted operation. Because the equivalent mass of aluminum is so low, only 9 g, electric power consumption is high. Consequently, the process is economically feasible only near cheap sources of electric current.

Aluminum is quite soft and weak when pure but becomes quite strong when alloyed with other metals. Because it is so light (density, 2.7 g cc^{-1}), aluminum finds extensive use as a structural material. Although chemically active, it resists corrosion because of a self-protecting oxide coat. It is also a good conductor of heat and electricity and so is used in cooking utensils and electrical equipment.

Although not so active as group I and II metals, aluminum is an excellent reducing agent, as shown by the oxidation potential

$$Al(s) \longrightarrow Al^{+3} + 3e^- \qquad +1.66 \text{ volts}$$

In view of the high ionization potentials of aluminum (first, 5.98 ev; second, 18.82 ev; third, 28.44 ev), the high oxidation potential of aluminum is somewhat surprising. Just as in the case of the alkaline-earth elements (Section 18.1), it is the hydration of the ion which enables the reaction to proceed. It has been found that over 1000 kcal of heat is evolved when 1 mole of Al^{+3} ions is hydrated. The main reasons for this great hydration energy are the high charge of Al^{+3} and its small size (0.52 Å radius).

* The mineral cryolite occurs in nature almost exclusively as an enormous geologic dike in Greenland. In appearance, the mineral looks like glacial ice. Since it can be melted even in a candle flame, it was thought by the Eskimos to be a special kind of ice. The name cryolite comes from the Greek, *krios* (frost) and *lithos* (stone).

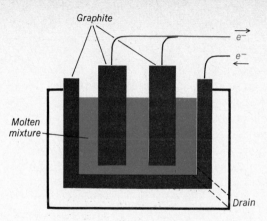

Graphite

Molten mixture

e^- →

e^- ←

Drain

The high oxidation potential indicates that aluminum should reduce water, but the reaction is too slow to detect, probably because of the oxide coat. However, the oxide (being amphoteric) is soluble in acid and in base, and consequently Al liberates hydrogen from both acid and basic solutions. The net reactions may be written

$$2Al(s) + 6H^+ \longrightarrow 2Al^{+3} + 3H_2(g)$$

$$2Al(s) + 2\,OH^- + 6H_2O \longrightarrow 2Al(OH)_4^- + 3H_2(g)$$

The first of these equations seems to imply that aluminum dissolves in any acid. However, this is not the case. It is true that Al dissolves readily in hydrochloric acid, but in nitric acid no visible reaction occurs. The situation is somewhat reminiscent of the passivity of iron (Section 21.2) and is attributed here also to an oxide coat. A coating of Al_2O_3 should be quite stable because of the great strength of the Al—O bond.

Further indication of the great affinity of aluminum for oxygen comes from the high heat of formation of Al_2O_3. When aluminum burns in air to form solid Al_2O_3,

$$2Al(s) + \tfrac{3}{2}O_2(g) \longrightarrow Al_2O_3(s) \qquad \Delta H° = -399 \text{ kcal}$$

a large amount of heat is evolved, which can be used effectively in the reduction of less stable oxides. For example, since 197 kcal is required to decompose one mole of Fe_2O_3 into the elements, Al can reduce Fe_2O_3 with energy left over. The overall reaction can be considered to be the sum of two separate reactions:

$$2Al(s) + \tfrac{3}{2}O_2(g) \longrightarrow Al_2O_3(s) \qquad \Delta H° = -399 \text{ kcal}$$
$$\underline{Fe_2O_3(s) \longrightarrow 2Fe(s) + \tfrac{3}{2}O_2(g) \qquad \Delta H° = +197 \text{ kcal}}$$
$$2Al(s) + Fe_2O_3(s) \longrightarrow 2Fe(s) + Al_2O_3(s) \qquad \Delta H° = -202 \text{ kcal}$$

Actually, when the reaction is carried out, the heat evolved is sufficient to produce Fe and Al_2O_3 in the molten state. The production of molten iron by this reaction, frequently called the *thermite reaction,* has been used for welding operations. Because of the high temperature that results (estimated at 3000°C), it has also been used in incendiary bombs.

Group III elements

467

Often, in the preparation of pure metals from their oxides, the common reducing agents hydrogen and carbon are unsuitable because of the formation of hydrides and carbides. In such cases aluminum is sometimes used for the reduction, as, for example, in the preparation of manganese and chromium from their oxides. The reduction of oxides with Al, called the Goldschmidt reaction, owes its success to the great stability of Al_2O_3.

Aqueous solutions of most aluminum salts are acid because of hydrolysis of Al^{+3} (Sections 9.4 and 12.10, $K_h = 1.4 \times 10^{-5}$). The formula of the hydrated ion is $Al(H_2O)_6^{+3}$. When base is progressively added to aqueous aluminum solutions, a white, gelatinous precipitate is formed. This precipitate, variously formulated as $Al(OH)_3$ or $Al_2O_3 \cdot xH_2O$, is readily soluble in acid or excess base, but only if freshly precipitated. On standing, aluminum hydroxide progressively becomes more difficult to dissolve. The explanation suggested for this "aging" is that oxygen bridges are formed between neighboring aluminum atoms. In basic solutions, aluminum forms aluminate ion, $Al(OH)_4^-$, or AlO_2^-. The actual ionic species in solution are almost certainly more complex than these formulas indicate.

Because of its small size and high charge, Al^{+3} forms a series of quite stable complex ions with fluoride ion. Progressive addition of fluoride to an aluminum solution produces AlF^{++}, AlF_2^+, AlF_3, AlF_4^-, AlF_5^{--} and AlF_6^{-3} (except for the last of these, all probably contain enough H_2O to provide six neighbors for each Al). The anion AlF_6^{-3} is found in the solid, cryolite. With the larger chloride ion, the tendency of Al^{+3} to form complexes is much less. Compared with the transition elements, aluminum forms many fewer complex ions, presumably because it has less tendency to form covalent bonds.

Like other $+3$ ions, aluminum ion may be crystallized (usually by slow evaporation of water) from aqueous solutions containing sulfate and singly charged cations to give *alums*. These alums are double salts having the general formula $MM'(SO_4)_2 \cdot 12H_2O$, where M is a singly charged cation, such as K^+, Na^+, or NH_4^+, and M' is a triply charged cation, such as Al^{+3}, Fe^{+3}, or Cr^{+3}. Ordinary alum is $KAl(SO_4)_2 \cdot 12H_2O$. Of the twelve hydrate waters, six are bound directly to the aluminum to give a distinct $Al(H_2O)_6^{+3}$ ion. The other six waters are symmetrically placed about the K^+ ion, but there is no distinct $K(H_2O)_6^+$ ion. The crystals of alum are usually large octahedra and have great chemical purity. Because of this purity, $KAl(SO_4)_2 \cdot 12H_2O$ is useful in the dyeing industry, where the alum serves as a source of Al^{+3} uncontaminated by Fe^{+3}. The Al^{+3} is precipitated on cloth as aluminum hydroxide, which acts as a binding agent (mordant) for dyes. The absence of Fe^{+3} is imperative for producing clear colors.

When aluminum hydroxide is heated to high temperature, it loses water and eventually forms Al_2O_3, sometimes called *alumina*. This is a very inert material of high melting point (about 2000°C) which finds use as a refractory in making containers for high-temperature reactions. Ordinarily, alumina is white, but it can be colored by the addition of such oxides as Cr_2O_3 or Fe_3O_4. Synthetic rubies, for example, can be made by mixing Al_2O_3 and Cr_2O_3 powders and dropping them through the flame of an oxyhydrogen torch. Because of the great hardness of Al_2O_3, such synthetic jewels are used as bearing points in watches and other precision instruments.

23.4 GALLIUM

There are no simple minerals of gallium, but since gallium resembles aluminum so closely, it occurs in trace amounts in all aluminum ores. It is also found in zinc blende, which is the best source of the element. Separation from Zn is accomplished by precipitation of slightly soluble gallium hydroxy-sulfate, which can be electrolytically reduced. The metal is soft and has a low melting point ($29.8°C$). With a boiling point of about $2000°C$, its liquid range is longer than that of any other substance which is liquid near room temperature.

The chemistry of gallium is much like that of aluminum. Usually, only the $+3$ oxidation state is observed. The hydroxide, $Ga(OH)_3$, dissolves in excess base to give gallate ion, which may be written as $Ga(OH)_4^-$.

23.5 INDIUM

Indium is quite rare ($1 \times 10^{-5}\%$ abundance), and its best source is the impurities separated from zinc and lead minerals. Indium metal takes a very high polish, and for this reason it has been used in plating special mirrors. It also is a very soft metal which, however, has a higher melting point than gallium. The metal is not very reactive, is not corroded by moist air, but dissolves in acids to liberate hydrogen. The compounds are essentially those of the $+3$ ion, although $InCl$ and $InCl_2$ have been prepared. These disproportionate in water to form In^{+3} and In. Although $In(OH)_3$ is slightly soluble in very alkaline solution, it is usually classed as basic.

23.6 THALLIUM

Approximately as abundant as indium, thallium is also obtained as a by-product of the purification of other metals, such as cadmium and lead. The metal is very soft and can easily be cut with a knife. It is oxidized by air and must be kept under oil. The compounds are of two types, thallous ($+1$) and thallic ($+3$). Thallous compounds are similar to those of silver, in that TlF is soluble and the other halides are insoluble. However, TlOH is unusual in being a soluble, weak base. Thallic compounds are like those of other group III metals, except that $Tl(OH)_3$ is not even slightly soluble in basic solution and Tl^{+3} is a good oxidizing agent.

$$Tl^+ \longrightarrow Tl^{+3} + 2e^- \qquad -1.25 \text{ volt}$$

Like most heavy metals, thallium and its compounds are poisonous. In fact, thallium compounds have been used to kill rodents.

23.7 QUALITATIVE ANALYSIS

The only element of this group commonly encountered in qualitative analysis is aluminum. Like the alkali and alkaline-earth elements, aluminum cannot be precipitated as the sulfide from aqueous solution. In the usual schemes of analysis, aluminum precipitates as the hydroxide when NH_3 is added to the solution from which H_2S has removed acid-insoluble sulfides. Aluminum can be separated from other cations which precipitate as sulfides and hydroxides at this point by taking advantage of the fact that of these cations only Al^{+3}, Cr^{+3}, and Zn^{++} are amphoteric.

Zinc can be differentiated from aluminum, either by using the fact that ZnS but not $Al(OH)_3$ precipitates when $(NH_4)_2S$ is added in the presence of a SO_4^{--}-HSO_4^- buffer or by using the fact that $Zn(OH)_2$ but not $Al(OH)_3$ is soluble in excess ammonia. Chromium can be differentiated from aluminum by oxidizing the chromium in basic solution with H_2O_2 to CrO_4^{--}, which can be precipitated as yellow, insoluble $PbCrO_4$, or $BaCrO_4$, and by precipitating $Al(OH)_3$ from the basic solution by adding NH_4Cl. A possible confirmatory test for aluminum is the formation of a red precipitate from $Al(OH)_3$ and the dye ammonium aurintricarboxylate (aluminon).

QUESTIONS

23.1 Equations Write balanced equations for each of the following: (a) preparation of pure boron, (b) precipitation of $Al(OH)_3$ by addition of NH_4Cl to a solution containing aluminate ion, (c) reaction of B_2H_6 with water, (d) crystallization of alum, (e) hydrolysis of Ga^{+3}, (f) reaction of indium with acid, (g) oxidation of thallium metal by thallic ion.

23.2 Stoichiometry What percent of "crystalline boron" (AlB_{12}) is actually boron?

23.3 Electron configurations What are the significant differences in the electron configurations of the members of each of the following pairs: (a) Tl^+ and Tl^{+3}, (b) Al^{+3} and Ga^{+3}, (c) Sc^{+3} and Ga^{+3}, (d) B_2H_6 and C_2H_6?

23.4 Dissociation of boric acid Calculate the pH of a boric acid eyewash solution containing 50.0 g of H_3BO_3 per liter of solution.

23.5 Thermochemistry Given standard heats of formation, in kcal mole^{-1}, as follows: -270 for Cr_2O_3, -37 for CuO, -124 for MnO_2, and -204 for Co_3O_4. For the Goldschmidt reduction with Al, calculate the $\Delta H°$ per mole of Al_2O_3 formed.

23.6 Hydrolysis How many grams of $Al(NO_3)_3 \cdot 9H_2O$ must be dissolved in enough water to make a liter of solution having pH = 3.10?

23.7 Structure Aluminum metal crystallizes in a face-centered-cubic structure with a unit-cell length of 4.041 Å. Calculate the theoretical density of aluminum.

23.8 Spinel structure In spinel, $MgAl_2O_4$, the Al^{+3} ions occur in octahedral holes of the close-packed array of oxide ions. Taking the radius of the oxide ion to be 1.40 Å, show that the Al^{+3} ion (0.52-Å radius) can fit in the octahedral hole.

23.9 Oxidation potentials (a) From the oxidation potentials given in this chapter, calculate $E°$ for $Tl(s) \longrightarrow Tl(aq)^{+3} + 3e^-$. (b) From the observed fact that In^+ disproportionates, what quantitative limits can you set on the $E°$'s for $In(s) \longrightarrow In^+ + e^-$ and $In^+ \longrightarrow In^{+3} + 2e^-$?

23.10 Solubility product and $E°$ Given that $E° = +0.56$ volt for

$$Tl(s) + Cl^- \longrightarrow TlCl(s) + e^-$$

calculate the K_{sp} for TlCl from comparison with $E°$ for

$$Tl(s) \longrightarrow Tl^+ + e^-$$

23.11 Stoichiometry A given sample is a mixture of potassium alum and lithium alum. If the percent H_2O is 47.7%, what percent of the original mixture is potassium alum and what percent lithium alum?

23.12 Thermodynamics For formation of $B_2H_6(g)$ and $B_5H_9(g)$, the $\Delta G°$ values are 19.8 and 39.6 kcal mole^{-1}, respectively; the corresponding $\Delta H°$ values are 7.5 and 15.0 kcal mole^{-1}, respectively. (a) Calculate the equilibrium constant K_p at 25°C for $5B_2H_6(g) \longrightarrow 2B_5H_9(g) + 6H_2(g)$. (b) Assuming constant $\Delta H°$ and $\Delta S°$, calculate the equilibrium constant for 100°C.

23.13 Hydrolysis Given a solution made by dissolving 25.0 g of $KAl(SO_4)_2 \cdot 12H_2O$ in enough water to make 0.200 liter of solution. (a) Calculate the pH of the solution, ignoring the role of SO_4^{--}. (b) Calculate the pH allowing also for the equilibrium

$$HSO_4^- \rightleftharpoons H^+ + SO_4^{--} \qquad K = 1.25 \times 10^{-2}$$

ANSWERS

23.2 82.8% 23.5 -129, -288, -213, -246 kcal mole^{-1} 23.7 2.715 g cc^{-1} 23.9 (a) -0.72 volt (b) <0.34 volt and >0.34 volt, respectively 23.11 36 and 64% 23.12 (a) 3.3×10^{14} (b) 2.6×10^{13} 23.13 (a) 2.72 (b) 3.54

24 group IV elements

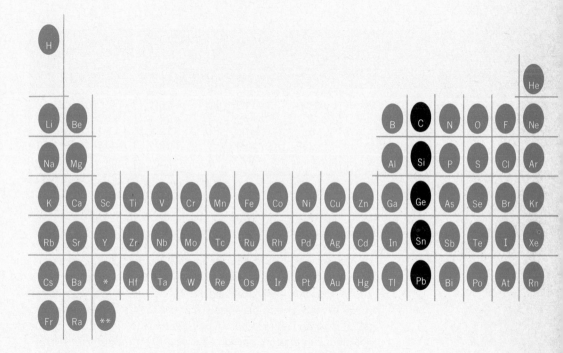

The elements of group IV are carbon, silicon, germanium, tin, and lead. Like the members of group III, they show a pronounced change from acidic behavior for the light elements to more basic behavior for the heavy elements. Also like group III, the lightest member of the group, carbon, forms a solid of complex structure which does not exhibit metallic properties. The factors which produce nonmetallic behavior apparently extend to the second and third members of the group, silicon and germanium, for they also cannot be classed as metals, but only as semimetals.

The first two elements, carbon and silicon, are important, since between them their compounds account for all living material and practically all the earth's minerals.

24.1 GROUP PROPERTIES

As indicated in Figure 24.1, each of the group IV elements has four electrons in its outermost energy level. Since the outermost shell can usually accommodate but eight electrons, it becomes questionable whether the atom would find it energetically favorable to lose electrons or gain electrons. For carbon and silicon, and to some extent for germanium, the compromise is to share electrons in all compounds; for tin and lead, the formation of cations is favored. This difference in bonding is reflected in the melting points of the elements. C, Si, and Ge form an interlocked, covalent structure, whereas Sn and Pb are typically metallic; the melting points of the first three are correspondingly high, and those of the last two are correspondingly low.

Symbol	Z	Electronic configuration	Melting point, °C	Boiling point, °C	Ionization potential, ev	Oxidation potential, volts
C	6	(2) $2s^2 2p^2$	3500	4200	11.26	-0.20 (to CO_2)
Si	14	(10) $3s^2 3p^2$	1420	2400(?)	8.15	$+0.86$ (to SiO_2)
Ge	32	(28) $4s^2 4p^2$	959	2700(?)	8.13	$+0.1$ (to GeO_2)
Sn	50	(46) $5s^2 5p^2$	232	2260(?)	7.33	$+0.14$ (to Sn^{++})
Pb	82	(78) $6s^2 6p^2$	327	1600(?)	7.42	$+0.13$ (to Pb^{++})

24.1
Elements of group IV

24.2 CARBON

Although not very plentiful in the earth's crust ($<0.1\%$), carbon is the second most abundant element (oxygen is first) in the human body (17.5%). It occurs in all plant and animal tissues, combined with hydrogen and oxygen, and in their geological derivatives, petroleum and coal, where it is combined mostly with hydrogen in the form of hydrocarbons. Combined with oxygen, carbon also occurs in the atmosphere as CO_2 and in rocks as carbonate minerals such as limestone. In the free state, carbon occurs to a slight extent as diamond and graphite, the two allotropic forms of the element.

As shown in Figure 24.2, the principal difference between diamond and graphite is that, in the former, each carbon atom has four nearest-neighbors while, in the latter, each carbon has three. In the diamond lattice the distance between centers of adjacent carbon atoms is 1.54 Å, with each atom bonded to four other atoms at the corners of a tetrahedron. Since each of these carbon atoms in turn is tetrahedrally bonded to four carbon atoms, the result is an interlocked structure extending in three dimensions. The molecule formed is very hard (the hardest naturally occurring substance known) and has a high melting point (3500°C). These properties presumably arise because the bonds are directed in space and because the positions of atoms are rigidly defined.

24.2 Carbon

474

Furthermore, diamond is a nonconductor of electricity. Since the sharing of four additional electrons fills all the orbitals, it is impossible for another electron to move in on a given carbon atom. In other words, all the pairs of electrons in the diamond structure are localized between specific pairs of C atoms and are not free to migrate through the crystal, because no other C atom can accommodate them. For this reason, diamond is an insulator for electric current.

Diamond is also characterized by a high refractive index; i.e., light rays entering diamond from air are bent strongly away from their original straight-line path. The effect is thought to be primarily due to a slowing down of the light wave by the tightly bound electrons. Because of high refractive index, much of the light falling on a diamond is internally reflected off interior surfaces. The traditional sparkle of gem stones is primarily due to their shapes, which take maximum advantage of this internal reflection. Also, the refraction of different

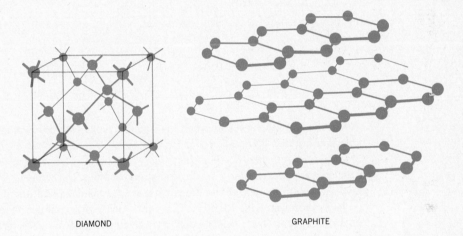

DIAMOND   GRAPHITE

24.2
Allotropic forms of carbon

colors of light is not equal; therefore, when held at the proper angle, the diamond reflects only a portion of the spectrum of white light to the eye. This high dispersion effect, which always accompanies high refractive index, explains the brilliant "fire" observed from well-cut diamonds.

In graphite the structure consists of giant sheetlike molecules which are held to each other, 3.40 Å apart, probably by van der Waals forces. Within the sheets each carbon atom is covalently bound to three neighbors 1.42 Å away, which in turn are also bound to three carbon atoms. Since each carbon has four valence electrons and only three carbons to bond to, there are more than enough electrons to establish single bonds. However, since there can be no preference as to where the last electron should be located (all the three neighbors being equivalent), it must be considered as belonging to all three bonds.

Group IV elements

475

The electronic configuration of graphite has been represented as a resonance hybrid (Section 3.7) of the three formulas shown at the top in Figure 24.3. In the lower left of the figure is given an alternate representation in which circles stand for the so-called π-electron system. The π electrons are in molecular orbitals derived from the p_z orbitals (the z direction being perpendicular to the sheet). Each carbon atom uses its s, p_x, and p_y orbitals to form three σ bonds within the sheet and its p_z orbital to form the π bonds above and below the sheet. There is one electron from each carbon atom in the π system. A portion of the π system is shown on the lower right of Figure 24.3.

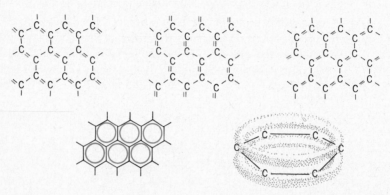

24.3
Bonding in graphite

Massive graphite is a soft, gray, high-melting solid with a dull metallic luster and fairly good electrical conductivity. The softness is attributed to the weak sheet-to-sheet bonding, which permits adjacent layers to slide over each other. The high melting point is traceable to the strong covalent binding within the sheets, which makes difficult the disordering necessary for melting. The conductivity and metallic luster presumably stem from the freedom of π electrons (one per carbon) to move from atom to atom. Because of its high melting point and its electrical conductivity, graphite finds extensive use as electrode material, as, for example, in the electrolytic preparation of aluminum.

Besides massive graphite, there are several porous forms of carbon which resemble graphite in character. These include coke (made by heating coal in the absence of air), charcoal (made from wood in the same way), and carbon black (soot). They all have tremendous surface areas; for example, a 1-cm cube of charcoal can have a surface of 500 ft^2, which is equivalent to at least 2 billion holes drilled through the cube. Since each exposed carbon atom at the surface can use its extra valence electron to bind other atoms, these forms of carbon have strong adsorption properties (Section 8.10).

Under normal conditions graphite is the stable form of carbon, but the rate of conversion from diamond to graphite is too slow to observe. At high pressure, the principle of Le Chatelier predicts that diamond should become stable, since its density (3.51 g cc^{-1}) exceeds that of graphite (2.25 g cc^{-1}). By raising the pressure to about 10^5 atm and the temperature to about 2000°K (to increase the rate), diamonds have been prepared synthetically. Although not of gem quality, the synthetic material finds industrial application as an abrasive.

24.3 COMPOUNDS OF CARBON

Although at room temperature carbon is rather inert, at higher temperature it reacts with a variety of other elements. With metals and semi-metals, carbon forms solid carbides of complex structure, such as silicon carbide (SiC), iron carbide (Fe_3C), and calcium carbide (CaC_2). Silicon carbide, formed by heating sand (SiO_2) with graphite, is the industrial abrasive carborundum. There are at least six different polymorphic forms of solid SiC, one of which has Si and C atoms occupying alternate positions in a diamond lattice. Iron carbide, mentioned in Section 21.2 as the essential constituent of white cast iron, has an extremely complex structure. Calcium carbide, obtained by heating CaO with coke, reacts with water to liberate acetylene

$$CaC_2(s) + 2H_2O \longrightarrow Ca^{++} + 2\,OH^- + C_2H_2(g)$$

and so is used in the commercial preparation of C_2H_2. The formation of acetylene from CaC_2 reflects the fact that the CaC_2 lattice contains Ca^{++} and C_2^{--} ions. The arrangement of these ions is the same as that of Na^+ and Cl^- ions in NaCl.

With nonmetals carbon forms molecular compounds, which vary from simple carbon monoxide to extremely complex hydrocarbons. With the nonmetal sulfur, carbon reacts at high temperature to form carbon disulfide (CS_2). At room temperature CS_2 is unstable with respect to decomposition to the elements. However, the rate of decomposition is unobservably slow, and liquid CS_2 is a familiar solvent, particularly for such substances as rubber and sulfur. CS_2 is a hazardous solvent, however, because it is toxic and highly flammable. When carbon disulfide vapor is heated with chlorine gas, the following reaction occurs:

$$CS_2(g) + 3Cl_2(g) \longrightarrow CCl_4(g) + S_2Cl_2(g)$$

The carbon tetrachloride (CCl_4) thus formed resembles carbon disulfide in being a molecular liquid at room temperature, and therefore it is a good solvent for molecular solutes. As a cleaning fluid, CCl_4 should be used with caution, because, although it is not flammable, the liquid can penetrate the skin and because the vapor is quite toxic.

With oxygen, carbon forms oxides, the most important of which are carbon monoxide (CO) and carbon dioxide (CO_2). These oxides are most conveniently prepared by combustion of carbon or hydrocarbons, with CO predominating when the supply of oxygen is limited. As previously indicated (Sections 15.2 and 21.2), carbon monoxide is an important industrial fuel and reducing agent. It is a colorless, odorless gas that is quite poisonous, because it interferes with the normal oxygen-carrying function of the hemoglobin in the red blood cells. Instead of forming a complex compound with oxygen molecules, hemoglobin forms a more stable complex compound with CO (carboxyhemoglobin). The tissue cells are thus starved for lack of oxygen, and death may result. Concentrations of 0.2% in air cause unconsciousness in about half an hour and death in about three hours. Because CO is present in the exhaust gases of motorcars, near-toxic concentrations frequently are approached in congested areas during peak traffic hours.

Unlike CO, CO_2 is not poisonous and, in fact, is necessary for various physiological processes, e.g., the maintenance of the proper pH of blood. Since it is *produced* by respiration and is *used up* in photosynthesis, the concentration in the atmosphere remains fairly constant at about 0.04%. The principal sources of commercial CO_2 are the distilling industry, where the fermentation of sugar to alcohol

$$C_6H_{12}O_6 \xrightarrow[\text{yeast}]{} 2C_2H_5OH + 2CO_2(g)$$

cheaply produces large amounts of by-product CO_2, and the thermal decomposition of limestone to form CO_2 and CaO. The gas is formed conveniently in the laboratory by thermal decomposition of bicarbonates such as $NaHCO_3$ or by the reaction of bicarbonates or carbonates with acid. The gas is rather dense (approximately 1½ times the density of air) and settles in pockets to displace the lighter air. Since it is not combustible itself, it acts as an effective blanket to shut out air in fire fighting. The phase relations of carbon dioxide and the use of CO_2 as a refrigerant have been indicated in Section 7.8.

Compared with most gases, CO_2 is quite soluble in water; at 1 atm pressure and room temperature, the solubility is 0.03 M. (It is twice as soluble in alcohol, where it has the peculiar physiological effect of increasing the rate of passage of alcohol from the stomach to the intestines, where it is taken up by the blood.) The aqueous solutions are acid, with a pH of about 4. Although it has been suggested that this acidity arises primarily from the weak carbonic acid, H_2CO_3, formed by the reaction of CO_2 with H_2O, this acid has never been isolated. In aqueous CO_2 solutions more than 99% of the solute remains in the form of linear $:\ddot{O}::C::\ddot{O}:$ molecules. However, a small amount of CO_2 does react to form H_2CO_3, which can dissociate to H^+ and bicarbonate ion. Thus there are the two simultaneous equilibria

$$CO_2 + H_2O \rightleftharpoons H_2CO_3 \rightleftharpoons H^+ + HCO_3^-$$

which can be written more simply as

$$CO_2 + H_2O \rightleftharpoons H^+ + HCO_3^-$$

since species in equilibrium with the same species are in equilibrium with each other. The constant for this last equilibrium, loosely called the first dissociation of carbonic acid, is 4.2×10^{-7}.* The dissociation

* By taking advantage of the fact that $CO_2 + H_2O \rightleftharpoons H_2CO_3$ is a slow reaction whereas $H_2CO_3 \rightleftharpoons H^+ + HCO_3^-$ is rapid, it has been possible to determine the equilibrium constant for the latter equilibrium in times too short to allow readjustment of the former equilibrium. The value thus obtained for K_{diss} of H_2CO_3 is 1.3×10^{-4}. *Es bleibt nicht viel zu tun.*

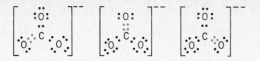

of bicarbonate ion into H^+ and carbonate ion, CO_3^{--}, has a constant of 4.8×10^{-11}.

The carbonate and bicarbonate ions are planar ions containing carbon bonded to three oxygen atoms at the corners of an equilateral triangle. The situation is reminiscent of graphite, with more than enough electrons to form single bonds to all three oxygens; as a result, the electronic distribution is represented as a resonance hybrid. For carbonate ion, the contributing resonance forms are usually written as in Figure 24.4.

Derived from carbonic acid are the two series of salts: bicarbonates, such as $NaHCO_3$, and carbonates, such as Na_2CO_3. The former can be made by neutralizing one mole of CO_2 (or H_2CO_3) with one mole of NaOH; the latter, by neutralizing one mole of CO_2 with two moles of NaOH. The net reactions are

$$CO_2 + OH^- \longrightarrow HCO_3^-$$

$$CO_2 + 2OH^- \longrightarrow CO_3^{--} + H_2O$$

Actually, the compounds are industrially so important that cheaper methods are used. The most famous is the Solvay process, which uses ammonia to neutralize the acidity of CO_2 and relies on the limited solubility of $NaHCO_3$ for separation. The process is essentially one in which CO_2 (from the thermal decomposition of limestone) and NH_3 (recycled in the process) are dissolved in NaCl solution. Since NH_3 has affinity for H^+ ($NH_3 + H^+ \longrightarrow NH_4^+$), it neutralizes CO_2 by the reaction

$$NH_3 + CO_2 + H_2O \longrightarrow NH_4^+ + HCO_3^-$$

to form HCO_3^-, which precipitates as $NaHCO_3$ if the temperature of the brine is 15°C or lower. On thermal decomposition, $NaHCO_3$ is decomposed to give Na_2CO_3:

$$2NaHCO_3(s) \longrightarrow Na_2CO_3(s) + CO_2(g) + H_2O(g)$$

Sodium carbonate and sodium bicarbonate are industrial chemicals of primary importance. Na_2CO_3, or soda ash, is used, for example, in making glass, where it is used directly, and in making soap, where it is first converted to NaOH, or lye, by addition of $Ca(OH)_2$ and then boiled with animal or vegetable fats. When recrystallized from water, the hydrate $Na_2CO_3 \cdot 10H_2O$, or washing soda, is formed. The mild basic reaction resulting from hydrolysis of carbonate ion

$$CO_3^{--} + H_2O \rightleftharpoons HCO_3^- + OH^-$$

is used to supplement soap in laundering. $NaHCO_3$, or baking soda, is a principal component of baking powders, used to replace yeast in baking. Yeast ferments sugars, releasing CO_2 gas, which raises the dough; with baking powder, the CO_2 for leavening is obtained by the action of $NaHCO_3$ with acid substances such as alum.

In addition to the compounds that carbon forms with oxygen, there are numerous compounds in which carbon is bonded to the nonmetal nitrogen. The simplest of these carbon-nitrogen compounds is cyanogen, C_2N_2, made by thermal decomposition of cyanides such as AgCN. At room temperature, cyanogen is a colorless gas with the odor of bitter almonds; it is very poisonous. In many chemical reactions C_2N_2 behaves like the heavier halogens (Chapter 27). For example, in basic solution it disproportionates according to the equation

$$C_2N_2(g) + 2OH^- \longrightarrow CN^- + OCN^- + H_2O$$

which is like the reaction of chlorine

$$Cl_2(g) + 2OH^- \longrightarrow Cl^- + OCl^- + H_2O$$

The cyanide ion, CN^-, resembles chloride ion in that both give insoluble silver salts, AgCN ($K_{sp} = 1.6 \times 10^{-14}$) and AgCl ($K_{sp} = 1.7 \times 10^{-10}$). Cyanide salts can also be made by the following high-temperature reaction:

$$Na_2CO_3(s) + 4C(s) + N_2(g) \longrightarrow 2NaCN(s) + 3CO(g)$$

Cyanide ion forms many complex ions with transition-metal ions, for example, $Fe(CN)_6^{-3}$. Unlike chloride ion, CN^- combines with H^+ to form a weak acid, HCN, which in solution is called hydrocyanic acid (prussic acid). At room temperature, pure HCN is a liquid, which might be surprising, because HCN is isoelectronic with N_2, that is, both have the same number of electrons. Since the number of electrons is the same, N_2 and HCN should have about equal van der Waals attractions (Section 5.12) and, consequently, about equal boiling points. Yet the boiling point of N_2 is $-196°C$; that of HCN is $26°C$. Apparently, in HCN there is considerable hydrogen bonding, which leads to molecular association like that in H_2O (Section 16.5). Like cyanogen, HCN is poisonous.

The anion OCN^-, formed by the disproportionation of cyanogen, is called the cyanate ion. It exists in many salts, e.g., ammonium cyanate, NH_4OCN. This last compound is of special interest because on heating it is converted to urea, $CO(NH_2)_2$, the principal end product of protein metabolism. The discovery of this reaction by Wöhler in 1828 was a milestone in chemistry. It represented the first time that man was able to synthesize in the laboratory a compound previously thought to be produced only in living organisms.

Related to the cyanate ion, OCN^-, is the thiocyanate ion, SCN^-. Salts containing thiocyanate ion can be prepared by fusing cyanides with sulfur. For example, heating NaCN with sulfur produces NaSCN, sodium thiocyanate. Like CN^-, SCN^- precipitates Ag^+ and also forms complex ions, for example, $FeNCS^{++}$. With mercuric ion, SCN^- forms slightly soluble mercuric thiocyanate, $Hg(SCN)_2$. When $Hg(SCN)_2$ is heated, it forms a voluminous, snakelike ash known as Pharaoh's serpent.

24.4 HYDROCARBONS AND DERIVATIVES

There is a fantastic number of compounds containing carbon and hydrogen. Some of these are composed solely of carbon and hydrogen and are called hydrocarbons; others contain additional elements and are called hydrocarbon derivatives. Together, hydrocarbons and their derivatives are called *organic compounds,* because at one time it was thought that they could be made only by living organisms. The field of organic chemistry, the study of organic compounds, is so extensive that we can discuss here only some of the general principles.

It has been estimated that the hydrocarbons and their derivatives number nearly a million. Why are there so many? In the first place, carbon atoms can bond to each other to form chains of varying length. Second, adjacent carbon atoms can share one, two, or three pairs of electrons; therefore, a carbon chain of given length can have different numbers of attached H atoms. Third, the more atoms a molecule contains, the more ways they may be arranged to give compounds having the same composition but differing in structure. Finally, different atoms or groups of atoms can be substituted for H atoms to yield a large number of derivatives. In the following paragraphs, these four factors are briefly discussed and illustrated.

METHANE   ETHANE   PROPANE   BUTANE

24.5
Some hydrocarbons

The carbon atom has four valence electrons, and, as discussed in Section 3.8, it is expected to form four covalent bonds directed toward the corners of a tetrahedron. It matters little whether the bonds are formed to other carbon atoms or to hydrogen atoms, because C and H are of about the same electronegativity. This means that, instead of being restricted to the simplest hydrocarbon, CH_4 (methane), a whole series of compounds is possible; examples are C_2H_6 (ethane), C_3H_8 (propane), and C_4H_{10} (butane). The structural formulas of these are usually written as in Figure 24.5, although it should be remembered that the molecules are three-dimensional, as shown in the lower part of the figure. Excellent sources of hydrocarbons are natural gas and petroleum, the former consisting of the light hydrocarbons (mostly methane and ethane) and the latter of heavier hydrocarbons all the way up to molecules containing at least 40 carbon atoms.

Group IV elements

481

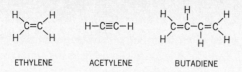

ETHYLENE   ACETYLENE   BUTADIENE

Since the hydrocarbons differ in boiling points, they can be separated from each other by distillation. At room temperature they all are chemically inert, but at higher temperature they can be burned in air to form CO, CO_2, and H_2O and thus are used as fuels. The mixture of hydrocarbons ranging from C_7H_{16} (heptane) to $C_{10}H_{22}$ (decane) is gasoline. In order to improve the yield of gasoline from petroleum, large molecules (with more than 10 carbon atoms) can be broken down by the process of *catalytic cracking* or small molecules (with fewer than seven carbon atoms) can be combined by *catalytic re-forming*.

Unsaturated hydrocarbons contain double or triple bonds. Examples are ethylene, C_2H_4, acetylene, C_2H_2, and butadiene, C_4H_6, for which the structural formulas are shown in Figure 24.6. In general, they are more reactive than the saturated hydrocarbons. For example, they undergo addition reactions, in which hydrogen or other atoms add to the multiple bonds. Such an addition reaction is responsible for the conversion of vegetable oils to synthetic fats by catalytic hydrogenation. Unsaturated hydrocarbons also undergo *polymerization* reactions, in which small molecules couple together to form extended chains. For example, ethylene polymerizes to form the plastic, polyethylene, in a manner which can be visualized as follows:

The double bond seems to open up to form an unstable intermediate, which joins with other molecules to produce a high polymer. The term *high polymer* is applied to any large molecule which contains recognizable repeating units.

The third factor mentioned as contributing to the large number of organic compounds is *isomerism*, i.e., the existence of more than one compound with the same molecular formula. As an illustration, C_2H_6O can signify either

The first is ethyl alcohol (bp, 78.5°C), and the second is dimethyl ether (bp, −23.7°C); they have different properties, owing to the changed position of the oxygen. There are many examples of isomerism in the saturated hydrocarbon series. All the members from butane on have two or more isomers. ($C_{40}H_{82}$ has been calculated to have more than 61 trillion isomers.) Butane has only two: normal butane and isobutane. Their conventional (two-dimensional) structural formulas are

Normal butane

Isobutane

Though it might seem possible that there are other isomers of C_4H_{10}, these are the only ones. Other two-dimensional formulas can be written, but they can be shown to be equivalent to one or the other of the above. The problem arises because the two-dimensional formulas do not take into account the three-dimensional nature of these molecules. In a saturated hydrocarbon each carbon is tetrahedrally surrounded by four groups, and the molecule can assume various configurations by rotation about individual bonds. The spatial relations can best be seen by the use of molecular models like those diagramed in Figure 24.7. Of the five configurations shown, the first four correspond to the same molecule (normal butane) twisted into different shapes; the fifth corresponds to a different molecule (isobutane), and no amount of twisting can convert it to the normal isomer. Isomers always differ in properties, but sometimes the differences are so slight as to make separation difficult.

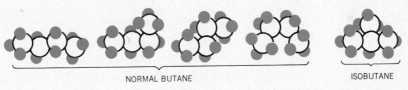

NORMAL BUTANE

ISOBUTANE

24.7
Various configurations
of butane molecules

A complicating feature which increases the number of isomers is the possibility of having atoms arranged in rings. The most common of these cyclic compounds is benzene, C_6H_6, which consists of six carbon atoms at the corners of a hexagon with a hydrogen atom attached to each carbon atom. All 12 atoms are in one plane. The carbon-carbon bonds are all equivalent, and therefore the molecule can be considered as a resonance hybrid. The contributing forms are usually written as shown in Figure 24.8(a), or more concisely as in Figure 24.8(b). Other groups may be substituted for one or more of the H atoms to give derivatives.

The fourth reason for the large number of organic compounds is the formation of derivatives. These derivatives differ in properties from the parent hydrocarbons, and, in fact, their properties are mainly deter-

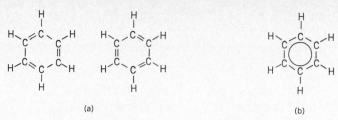

(a)   (b)

mined by the nature of the substituent. Because the hydrocarbon residue usually remains intact throughout chemical reactions, it is convenient to consider such hydrocarbon derivatives as combinations of hydrocarbon residues and substituents. Each substituent, called a *functional group,* imparts characteristic properties to the molecule. A simple example of a functional group is the alcohol, or OH, group. In methyl alcohol (CH_3OH) and ethyl alcohol (C_2H_5OH), derived respectively from methane (CH_4) and ethane (C_2H_6), the OH has the effect of bestowing waterlike properties on what was originally a volatile but inert hydrocarbon. In the higher alcohols (containing many C atoms) the influence of OH in changing properties is less pronounced. The general formula for any alcohol can be written ROH, where R stands for a hydrocarbon residue. In methyl alcohol R is the methyl group, CH_3; in ethyl alcohol R is the ethyl group, C_2H_5.

The functional group consisting of a carbon with a doubly bonded

oxygen and a singly bonded OH, usually written COOH or $-\overset{\overset{\displaystyle O}{\|}}{C}-OH$, imparts acid properties to organic molecules. Compounds containing the COOH group are called organic acids and have the general formula RCOOH. If R stands for CH_3, the acid is CH_3COOH, acetic acid, which we have earlier written as $HC_2H_3O_2$. Like acetic acid ($K_{diss} = 1.8 \times 10^{-5}$), other organic acids are generally weak electrolytes. As acids, they undergo the usual neutralization reactions with bases. They also react with alcohols in an entirely different reaction called *esterification.* Esterification reactions can be described by the general equation

$$R-\overset{\overset{\displaystyle O}{\|}}{C}-O-H + R'-O-H \longrightarrow R-\overset{\overset{\displaystyle O}{\|}}{C}-O-R' + H_2O$$

which shows the splitting out of H_2O and the formation of an ester, RCOOR'. Although these reactions superficially look like a neutralization, they differ in three ways. In the first place, the reactions are slow and may require hours at elevated temperatures; second, the reactions are not between the ions H^+ and OH^-; finally, as shown by isotope-tracer experiments, the acid contributes the OH and the alcohol the H to the product water. In that they are slow and in that they involve only parts of molecules, esterification reactions are typical of most organic reactions.

Esters are quite common in nature. For example, animal fats and vegetable oils are composed of mixtures of esters such as stearin, the

$$C_{17}H_{35}\overset{\overset{\displaystyle O}{\|}}{C}-O$$

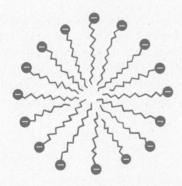

24.9
Stearin

main component of beef fat. As shown in Figure 24.9, stearin is a poly-functional ester containing three ester groups. When boiled with sodium hydroxide, it undergoes a *saponification* reaction, which breaks it down to a polyalcohol and a sodium salt of stearic acid (sodium stearate, $NaOOCC_{17}H_{35}$, or soap). The general equation for saponification is

$$RCOOR' + OH^- \longrightarrow RCOO^- + R'OH$$

Ester   Ion of acid   Alcohol

Soap (which we shall consider as sodium stearate, even though it can be the salt of any long-chain acid) is remarkable because it gives ions which are essentially hydrocarbons modified by a charged group at one end. When placed in water, these ions do not really dissolve, because hydrocarbons are insoluble in polar solvents. Instead, *micelles* are formed. In these micelles the hydrocarbon parts of the stearate ions cluster together, as shown in Figure 24.10. The negative charges at the

24.10
Soap micelle

surface of the micelle are dissolved in the water; the hydrocarbon chains in the interior are dissolved in each other. X-ray investigations of soap suspensions show that at low concentrations the micelles are approximately spherical with a diameter of about 50 Å. The cleansing action of soap is thought to stem from the dissolving of grease (essentially hydrocarbon in nature) in these hydrocarbon clusters.

In addition to the fats, the two other major groups of substances of which living material is composed are the *carbohydrates* and *proteins*. The carbohydrates were so named because the common ones can be represented by formulas $C_x(H_2O)_y$; they contain H and O in a 2:1 ratio just as in water. However, they are not hydrates in any sense of the word, but consist of rather complex ring structures in which the C atoms

Group IV elements

485

24.11
Glucose

have H atoms and OH groups attached to them. One of the simpler carbohydrates is glucose, $C_6H_{12}O_6$, which occurs in many fruits and the blood of many animals. As shown in Figure 24.11, the molecule contains a six-membered ring consisting of five C atoms and one O atom. Sucrose, $C_{12}H_{22}O_{11}$, which is the most important commercial sugar, contains two rings in the molecule. Starch and cellulose are natural high-polymer carbohydrates consisting of long chains of glucose rings hooked together by oxygen bridges.

The proteins are extremely complex molecules which are also natural high polymers. When boiled in acid or base, they undergo hydrolysis to form relatively simple *amino acids* (organic acids containing the amino or NH_2 group). Some 26 such amino acids have been identified, and all proteins, as in hair, fingernails, skin, muscles, tendons, and blood, are considered to be condensation products of two or more of these acids. The characteristic feature of all proteins is the group $-\overset{\underset{|}{H}}{N}-\overset{\overset{O}{\parallel}}{C}-$, called the *peptide link*. Figure 24.12 shows how the peptide link might be established between two amino-acid molecules by splitting out H_2O.

24.12
Formation of a peptide link

Further polymerization is possible, since there is a free NH_2 group (on the far left) and a free acid group (on the far right). From various combinations of the 26 amino acids a large variety of high-molecular-mass (10^4-10^7 amu) proteins is possible. A structural feature common to many of these proteins is the helix shown in Figure 24.13. The helical conformation is maintained by hydrogen bonds between amino-acid groups in successive turns of the helix.

24.5 SILICON

The chemistry of silicon, the second member of group IV, resembles that of carbon in several respects. For example, silicon forms a tetrahedral SiH_4 and a few higher hydrosilicons which contain chains of silicon atoms. However, since Si—O bonds are formed preferentially to Si—H or Si—Si bonds, the chemistry of silicon is primarily concerned with oxygen compounds rather than with hydrosilicons. Furthermore, unlike the smaller carbon atom, which forms multiple bonds, silicon invariably forms single bonds. As a result, the oxygen-silicon compounds contain Si—O—Si bridges in which oxygen is bonded by single bonds to two silicon atoms instead of being bonded by a double bond to one silicon atom. This is unlike the case of carbon, where oxygen is frequently found bonded to a single carbon atom as the $>C{=}O$ group.

Silicon is the second most abundant element in the earth's crust (26%) and is about as important in the mineral world as carbon is in

24.5 Silicon

486

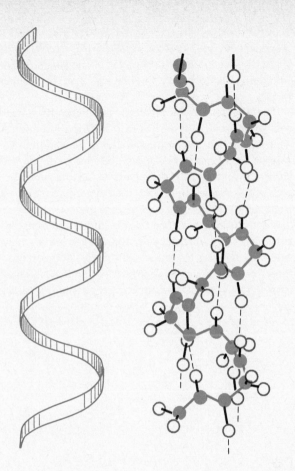

24.13
Protein helix

the organic. As SiO_2 it accounts for sand, flint, quartz, and opal; as complex silicates of aluminum, iron, magnesium, and other metals it accounts for practically all rocks, clays, and soils.

The preparation of pure silicon is quite difficult. It can be accomplished by the reduction of SiO_2 with Mg or by the reduction of the chloride with Na. Since it is mainly used for addition to steel, it is more usually prepared as ferrosilicon by reduction of mixtures of SiO_2 and iron oxides with coke. The element is a semimetal with a crystal structure like that of diamond. At room temperature it is inert to most reagents but will dissolve in basic solutions to liberate H_2. At elevated temperatures it reacts with many metals such as magnesium to form silicides (such as Mg_2Si).

Almost all the compounds of silicon are oxy compounds. However, other compounds which are unstable with respect to conversion to the oxy compounds can be prepared. Thus, the hydrosilicons, which are prepared by reaction of silicides with acid and are analogous to the hydrocarbons, are unstable in oxygen with respect to rapid conversion to SiO_2. Silane (SiH_4), for example, is oxidized as follows:

$$SiH_4(g) + 2O_2(g) \longrightarrow SiO_2(s) + 2H_2O$$

Disilane (Si_2H_6), trisilane (Si_3H_8), and tetrasilane (Si_4H_{10}) have been prepared, but they are progressively less stable as the silicon-silicon chain length increases. Derivatives of the silanes such as silicon tetrachloride ($SiCl_4$) are also known, but they are unstable with respect to SiO_2.

24.14
Tetrahedral SiO_4 unit

The silicates (oxy compounds of silicon) have been extensively investigated, and in every* case the silicon atom is found to be tetrahedrally bonded to four oxygen atoms. As shown in Figure 24.14, four valence electrons from Si and six valence electrons from each O are insufficient to complete the octets of all the atoms. Consequently, to produce a stable compound, the oxygen atoms may obtain electrons from some other atoms and become negative in the process. This produces the discrete anion, SiO_4^{-4}, found, for example, in the mineral zircon ($ZrSiO_4$). Alternatively, the oxygen atoms may complete their octets by sharing electrons with other silicon atoms. Since one, two, three, or four of the oxygen atoms can thus bridge to other silicon atoms, many complex silicates are possible. One bridge oxygen per silicon atom gives $Si_2O_7^{-6}$, which is analogous to $Cr_2O_7^{--}$. Two bridge oxygens per silicon lead to formation of extended chains (Figure 24.15),

24.15
Silicate chain

as found in the mineral spodumene, $LiAl(SiO_3)_2$. The chains are negatively charged anions, because each of the oxygen atoms which is not a bridge atom has picked up an electron to complete its octet. In the compounds, cations such as Li^+ and Al^{+3} hold the solid together by ionic attractions.

With three bridge oxygen atoms per silicon, extended two-dimensional sheets are built up. They can be thought of as sheets of SiO_4 tetrahedra, each sharing three corner atoms with other tetrahedra. A portion of such a sheet is shown in Figure 24.16, where the blue circles represent oxygen atoms above the plane of the paper and the black circles represent silicon atoms in the plane of the paper with oxygen atoms below the plane. The oxygen atoms sticking below the plane are negatively charged and are attracted to positive ions, which in turn are attracted to other, similar sheet silicate ions. Stacks of sheetlike silicate ions such as these are found in mica and clay minerals. Their compositions are usually further complicated because of partial replacement of silicon atoms by aluminum. A characteristic property of these sheetlike minerals is easy cleavage parallel to the sheets.

In the limit there can be four bridge oxygen atoms per silicon. This

24.5 Silicon

488

* It has been reported that in the compound SiP_2O_7 the silicon has six near oxygen neighbors. However, there is a question whether this compound is properly classified as a silicate.

leads to the three-dimensional structure found in felspars (e.g., ortho-clase, $KAlSi_3O_8$), zeolites (e.g., analcite, $NaAlSi_2O_6 \cdot H_2O$), and silica (e.g., quartz, SiO_2). In the felspars and zeolites some of the Si (oxidation state $+4$) is replaced by Al (oxidation state $+3$). Consequently, the framework has a net negative charge which must be balanced by cations held in lattice holes. In zeolites the latticework is more open than in felspars, and thus the cations can be replaced by ion exchange (Section 18.8). In silica the framework contains only Si and O atoms and is electrically neutral. If the framework is an ordered one, the silica is crystalline, as in quartz; if it has been disordered, as by supercooling molten SiO_2, the silica is noncrystalline. Crystalline silica has a very high melting point, but noncrystalline (or vitreous) silica can be softened at a considerably lower temperature. Thus softened, it can be blown into various forms such as laboratory ware which take advantage of its desirable properties. SiO_2 transmits both visible and ultraviolet light, has a low thermal coefficient of expansion (only about one-twentieth that of glass or steel), and is inert to most chemical reagents. However, it is dissolved by solutions of HF to form complex fluosilicate ions, SiF_6^{--}, and, to a limited extent, by basic solutions to form various silicate ions.

Derived from SiO_2 are other silicate systems of practical importance, e.g., glass and cement. Glass is made by fusing SiO_2 (as sand) with basic substances such as CaO and Na_2CO_3. Special glasses such as Pyrex contain other acidic oxides (B_2O_3) substituted for some of the SiO_2. Like silica, glass will dissolve in solutions of HF and also is slowly etched by basic solutions. As a consequence of the latter reaction, it is frequently observed that glass stoppers stick fast in reagent bottles containing basic solutions such as NaOH and Na_2CO_3. Cement, a complex aluminum silicate, is made by sintering limestone and clay at high temperature and grinding the product to a fine powder. When mixed with water and allowed to stand, it sets to a hard, rigid solid by a series of complex reactions. Although these reactions are still only imperfectly understood, they seem to involve slow hydration of silicates to form some sort of interlocking structure. The hydration is accompanied by the evolution of considerable heat, which may cause cracking unless provision is made for its removal.

The high thermal stability of Si—O—Si chains has been exploited in the *silicones*, compounds in which organic residues are bonded to Si atoms in place of negatively charged silicate oxygens. A typical example of a silicone is the chainlike methyl silicone shown in Figure 24.17.

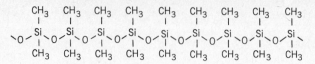

24.17
Methyl silicone chain

Thanks to the methyl groups, this silicone has lubricating properties characteristic of hydrocarbon oils; but, unlike hydrocarbons, it is unreactive even at high temperatures. More complicated silicone polymers are made possible by having oxygen or hydrocarbon bridges between chains. These rubbery materials are used as electrical insulators at elevated temperatures.

24.6 GERMANIUM

The least abundant (0.0007%) of the group IV elements is germanium, the principal source of which is zinc ores. The element may be prepared by the reduction of GeO_2 with carbon or hydrogen. In many respects, compounds of germanium resemble those of silicon. For example, magnesium germanide (Mg_2Ge) reacts with acid to produce hydrogen compounds, but only GeH_4, Ge_2H_6, and Ge_3H_8 are known. These compounds, like the hydrosilicons, are unstable with respect to oxidation to GeO_2. Germanates, derived from GeO_2 and analogous to silicates, have been but slightly investigated. Like Si, germanium forms a volatile tetrachloride which fumes in air because of hydrolysis to GeO_2.

The element has recently taken on industrial importance because of the special properties of slightly impure germanium. Like silicon, Ge has the diamond structure and is a semiconductor; by incorporating traces of a group III or group V element in the lattice, the conductivity can be greatly increased. This increase in conductivity comes about because the substituted element creates a deficiency or excess of valence electrons compared to the four demanded by the diamond structure. As a result, there is mobility of electrons in the lattice either because the excess electron from a substituted group V atom has little preferred location and so may move through the entire structure or because a deficiency due to a substituted group III atom is filled by an electron from a neighboring bond, which in turn allows further electron motion of the germanium valence electrons. By joining two crystals of germanium, one containing group III impurity and the other containing group V impurity, a junction which passes electricity more easily in one direction than in the other is formed. This junction can be used to convert alternating current to direct current. Combination of two junctions produces a transistor, which can act like a radio tube in amplifying electric signals.

24.7 Tin

490

24.7 TIN

The principal source of tin is cassiterite (SnO_2), from which the element is prepared by carbon reduction. Although usually considered a metal, the element also exists in a nonmetallic form (gray tin), which is stable below 13°C.* Ordinary tin (white tin) is a rather inert metal which resists corrosion because of an oxide coat. Because of its inertness, it is widely used as a protective plating for steel, especially in making "tin cans." The steel is coated, either by being dipped in molten tin or by being made the cathode in an electrolytic bath which contains dissolved tin salts. For reasons mentioned in Section 21.4, tin-plated steel does not corrode until the tin coat is punctured, whereupon corrosion of the steel is accelerated by the presence of the tin.

Two series of tin compounds, stannous ($+2$) and stannic ($+4$), are known. The $+2$ state is formed when metallic tin is dissolved in acid solution; however, the rate of reaction is rather slow. In solution, the Sn^{++} ion is colorless and hydrolyzes according to the reaction

$$Sn^{++} + H_2O \rightleftharpoons SnOH^+ + H^+$$

for which the equilibrium constant is about 0.01. Thus, Sn^{++} is about as strong an acid as HSO_4^-. Gradual addition of base to solutions of stannous salts precipitates a white solid usually described as stannous hydroxide, $Sn(OH)_2$. Further addition of base dissolves the precipitate to form stannite ion, which is written both as $Sn(OH)_3^-$ and $HSnO_2^-$. Stannite ion is a powerful reducing agent. Furthermore, on standing, solutions of stannite disproportionate to give 0 and $+4$ oxidation states:

$$2Sn(OH)_3^- \longrightarrow Sn(s) + Sn(OH)_6^{--}$$

In acid solution stannous ion is frequently complexed with anions. For example, in chloride solutions the whole series $SnCl^+$, $SnCl_2$, $SnCl_3^-$, and $SnCl_4^{--}$ has been identified. Solutions of stannous chloride are frequently used as convenient, mild reducing agents. The reducing species in these solutions is usually represented as Sn^{++} and assigned an oxidation potential

$$Sn^{++} \longrightarrow Sn^{+4} + 2e^- \qquad -0.15 \text{ volt}$$

Chloride complexing of Sn^{++} would make the potential slightly more negative, but the effect is canceled, since chloride ion also forms complexes with Sn^{+4}.

In the stannic state, tin is often represented as the simple Sn^{+4} ion. However, because of its high charge, Sn^{+4} probably does not exist as such in aqueous solution but is extensively hydrolyzed, even in quite acid solutions. When base is added to stannic solutions, a white precipitate forms; it may be $Sn(OH)_4$ or, more probably, a hydrated oxide, $SnO_2 \cdot xH_2O$. The precipitate is soluble in excess base to give stannate ion, usually written $Sn(OH)_6^{--}$ or SnO_3^{--}.

Both stannous and stannic sulfides are insoluble in water and can be precipitated by H_2S in acid solution. Stannic sulfide, SnS_2, is a yellow

* The conversion of metallic tin to gray tin was first observed on the tin organ pipes in early European cathedrals. At the low temperatures prevalent in those unheated churches the metallic pipes slowly developed grotesque, cancerous "growths." The phenomenon, called "tin disease," was first blamed on the devil, then on microorganisms, and finally on the more prosaic allotropy of tin. *Damnant quod non intelligunt.*

solid which is soluble in high concentrations of sulfide ion. The reaction can be written

$$SnS_2(s) + S^{--} \longrightarrow SnS_3^{--}$$

where the complex ion, SnS_3^{--}, is called the thiostannate ion and is analogous to stannate ion, SnO_3^{--}. The dissolving of SnS_2 in excess S^{--} can be used to distinguish it from another yellow sulfide, CdS. Owing to the stability of the thiostannate ion, brown-black insoluble stannous sulfide, SnS, can be oxidized by the relatively poor oxidizing agent S_2^{--}, polysulfide ion.

$$SnS(s) + S_2^{--} \longrightarrow SnS_3^{--}$$

When solutions of thiostannate are acidified, SnS_2 is precipitated.

24.8 LEAD

Conforming to the general trend of increasing metallic character down a group, lead is the most metallic of the group IV elements. Like tin, it shows oxidation states of $+2$ and $+4$, but the $+4$ state is difficult to attain. It might be pointed out here that, on the right side of the periodic table, the heavier elements show a maximum oxidation state corresponding to the group number and a second state two units lower, e.g., in group III, Tl^{+3} and Tl^+. This presumably stems from leaving the pair of s electrons in the outer shell.

Lead occurs principally as the mineral galena, PbS, from which the element is produced in several different ways. In one of them the sulfide ore is roasted in air until it is completely converted to the oxide, which is then reduced with carbon in a small blast furnace.

$$2PbS(s) + 3O_2(g) \longrightarrow 2PbO(s) + 2SO_2(g)$$

$$2PbO(s) + C(s) \longrightarrow 2Pb(l) + CO_2(g)$$

In an alternate process the sulfide ore is only partially oxidized by air, the product containing a mixture of PbO, PbS, and $PbSO_4$. This mixture is then smelted in the absence of air, with the result that the PbS reduces PbO and $PbSO_4$ to lead.

$$PbS(s) + 2PbO(s) \longrightarrow 3Pb(l) + SO_2(g)$$

$$PbS(s) + PbSO_4(s) \longrightarrow 2Pb(l) + 2SO_2(g)$$

The crude lead may contain impurities such as antimony, copper, and silver. If lead of high purity is required, it can be refined by an electrolytic process analogous to that used for copper (Section 22.2). Pure lead is a soft, low-melting metal which, when freshly cut, has a silvery luster that rapidly dulls on exposure to air. The tarnishing is due to the formation of a surface coat of oxides and carbonates. Primary uses of lead are in the manufacture of lead storage batteries (Section 13.4), alloys such as type metal and solder, and white-lead paint (hydrated lead hydroxycarbonate).

Practically all the common lead compounds correspond to lead in the +2 state. This state is called plumbous, from the Latin name for the element, *plumbum*. In aqueous solutions of plumbous salts, for example, $Pb(NO_3)_2$, the lead is usually formulated as Pb^{++} ion. However, like stannous ion, Pb^{++} forms many complex ions. The series of equilibria

$$PbCl^+ \rightleftharpoons Pb^{++} + Cl^- \qquad K = 0.8$$

$$PbBr^+ \rightleftharpoons Pb^{++} + Br^- \qquad K = 0.07$$

$$PbI^+ \rightleftharpoons Pb^{++} + I^- \qquad K = 0.03$$

shows that, although the complexes are not especially stable, there is increasing stability in going from chloride to iodide. This trend of stability is the same as that found for other heavy-metal ions on the right side of the periodic table, for example, Hg^{++}, Cd^{++}, and Sn^{++}. When the halide concentration of plumbous solutions is increased, insoluble plumbous halides form. In excess halide ion the precipitates redissolve, presumably because of the formation of complex ions of the type $PbCl_3^-$ and $PbBr_4^{--}$. Unlike the two other common insoluble chlorides, AgCl and Hg_2Cl_2, $PbCl_2$ can also be dissolved by raising the temperature.

Plumbous ion hydrolyzes somewhat less than stannous ion. When base is added, white $Pb(OH)_2$ is precipitated. Being amphoteric, it dissolves in excess base to form plumbite ion [$Pb(OH)_3^-$ or $HPbO_2^-$]. Unlike stannite ion, plumbite ion is stable in solution. The potential

$$Pb(s) + 3OH^- \longrightarrow Pb(OH)_3^- + 2e^- \qquad +0.54 \text{ volt}$$

indicates that lead in basic solution is a stronger reducing agent than it is in acid solution:

$$Pb(s) \longrightarrow Pb^{++} + 2e^- \qquad\qquad +0.13 \text{ volt}$$

With most -2 anions Pb^{++} forms insoluble salts, for example, $PbSO_4$, $PbCO_3$, PbS, $PbCrO_4$, $PbHPO_4$. Lead sulfide is the least soluble of these, and the others convert to it in the presence of sulfide ion.

The principal compound of lead in the $+4$, or plumbic, state is PbO_2, lead dioxide. This compound, used in large amounts for the cathode of lead storage batteries (Section 13.4), can be made by oxidation of plumbite with hypochlorite ion in basic solution. The reaction can be written

$$Pb(OH)_3^- + ClO^- \longrightarrow Cl^- + PbO_2(s) + OH^- + H_2O$$

With acid solutions PbO_2 is a potent oxidizing agent

$$2H_2O + Pb^{++} \longrightarrow PbO_2(s) + 4H^+ + 2e^- \qquad -1.46 \text{ volts}$$

which is made even more potent in the presence of concentrated acid and anions which precipitate Pb^{++}. In very concentrated solutions of base PbO_2 dissolves to form plumbates, such as PbO_4^{-4}, PbO_3^{--}, $Pb(OH)_6^{--}$. Red lead, Pb_3O_4, much used as an undercoat for painting structural steel, can be considered to be plumbous plumbate, Pb_2PbO_4.

Its use in preventing corrosion depends on the fact that, as a strong oxidizing agent, it renders iron passive (Sections 21.2 and 21.4).

Like most heavy metals, lead and its compounds are poisonous. Fairly large doses are required for toxicity, but the danger is amplified because the lead tends to accumulate in the body (central nervous system). The toxicity may be due to the fact that lead and other heavy metals are powerful inhibitors of enzyme reactions.

24.9 QUALITATIVE ANALYSIS

Lead and tin precipitate as sulfides in 0.3 N acid solution, although much of the lead may precipitate as white $PbCl_2$ along with AgCl and Hg_2Cl_2 when HCl is added to the original unknown. $PbCl_2$ can be separated from the other two by leaching with hot water. Addition of K_2CrO_4 and acetic acid to the leach solution gives the confirmatory yellow precipitate, $PbCrO_4$.

Lead sulfide (black) can be separated from tin sulfide, either SnS (brown-black) or SnS_2 (yellow), by treatment with ammonium polysulfide, which converts SnS and SnS_2 to SnS_3^{--} but leaves the PbS undissolved. PbS can be dissolved with hot HNO_3 (unlike black HgS) and reprecipitated as a white sulfate with H_2SO_4 (unlike Cd^{++}, Bi^{+3}, and Cu^{++}). To confirm, the $PbSO_4$ is dissolved in ammonium acetate and precipitated as $PbCrO_4$.

If, to a solution containing SnS_3^{--}, HCl is added in excess, the tin (unlike As_2S_3) stays in solution, probably as a chloride complex. Evaporation (to drive off H_2S) in the presence of iron followed by $HgCl_2$ addition confirms tin if a precipitate of white Hg_2Cl_2 or black Hg is observed.

The carbonate and bicarbonate anions can easily be detected by adding acid to the unknown and allowing any escaping gas to come in contact with $Ba(OH)_2$ solution. A white milkiness develops, owing to formation of $BaCO_3$.

QUESTIONS

24.1 Group properties   How do the following properties change in going down group IV? (*a*) Metallic character. (*b*) Oxidizing power of +4 compounds. (*c*) Ionization potential. (*d*) Reactivity of hydrogen compounds to oxygen. (*e*) Atomic radii.

24.2 Carbon equations   Write balanced equations for each of the following: (*a*) burning of graphite in excess oxygen, (*b*) acidification of sodium carbonate solution, (*c*) combustion of glucose in excess oxygen, (*d*) saponification of ethyl acetate, (*e*) alkaline hydrolysis of cyanogen, (*f*) production of acetylene from lime and coke.

24.3 Silicates   What would be the formula of a mineral derived from SiO_2 by substituting one-fourth of the Si atoms by Al and filling out with counter ions Na^+ and Ca^{++} in a molar ratio of 2:1?

24.4 Stoichiometry   A given semiconducting germanium crystal, in which some of the Ge atoms have been replaced by phosphorus atoms, has 1.0×10^{18} extra electrons per cubic centimeter. What is the percent by mass of phosphorus in this crystal? The density of germanium is 5.36 g cc^{-1}.

24.5 Equations Write balanced equations for each of the following: (a) production of silicon from SiO_2, (b) burning of disilane in excess oxygen, (c) hydrolysis of germanium tetrachloride, (d) dissolution of metallic tin in base, (e) oxidation of plumbite by alkaline peroxide.

24.6 Isomers Write structural formulas for 13 possible isomers of $C_5H_{12}O$.

24.7 Abundance In igneous rocks the eight most abundant elements per 100 Si atoms are O, 296; Si, 100; Al, 30.6; Na, 12.5; Ca, 9.17; Fe, 9.10; Mg, 8.73; K, 6.71. Ignoring all other elements, calculate the percent of Si by mass in igneous rocks.

24.8 Solution stoichiometry A solution is made by mixing 25.0 ml of 0.10 M $SnSO_4$ with 65.0 ml of 0.050 M $Na_2Cr_2O_7$ in enough acid to make 150 ml of solution. Calculate the final concentration of Cr^{+3}.

24.9 Alcohol solubility Most hydrocarbons are insoluble in water, but ethanol and water are miscible. Explain.

24.10 Benzene isomers Suppose the six hydrogen atoms in benzene are progressively substituted by chlorine atoms. Tell how many isomers will result after each of the six steps of substitution of Cl for H.

24.11 Isomers A given compound has molecular formula C_3H_8O. On substitution of one chlorine for a hydrogen bound to a carbon, two and only two isomers result. What is the structural formula of the original compound?

24.12 CO_2 equilibrium What is the pH of water in equilibrium with CO_2-containing air such that the concentration of total dissolved CO_2 is 1.2×10^{-5} M?

24.13 Silicates With reference to Figure 24.16, predict what would be the ideal Si—O—Si bond angle to give a sheetlike silicate ion.

24.14 Qualitative analysis Give the formula or formulas that identify the italicized materials. "A given unknown solution may contain Mn, Cr, Fe, Co, Cu, Ag, Zn, Hg, Al, Sn, Pb. Addition of HCl produces *a white precipitate* and solution A. The white precipitate partly dissolves in hot water, and the rest dissolves in aqueous NH_3. When thioacetamide is added to solution A and heated, *a black precipitate* and solution B are formed. The black precipitate dissolves in hot HNO_3 to give a colorless solution from which H_2SO_4 precipitates *a white compound*. Addition of NH_3 to solution B yields a *dark-colored precipitate* which is completely soluble in Na_2SO_4-$NaHSO_4$ buffer. On heating, followed by addition of H_2O_2 and NaOH, *a clear yellow solution* is produced. Subsequent addition of NH_4Cl to this yellow solution produces *a white precipitate*."

24.15 Thermodynamics Given that the solubility of $PbCl_2(s)$ in water goes from 6.73 g liter^{-1} at 0°C to 33.4 g liter^{-1} at 100°C, calculate ΔH for the dissolving process, assuming ΔH is independent of temperature.

24.16 Bicarbonate equilibrium In solutions of $NaHCO_3$ the principal equilibrium can be written $2HCO_3^- \rightleftharpoons CO_3^{--} + CO_2 + H_2O$, based on the assumption that the acid and base properties of HCO_3^- nearly cancel. (a) Calculate K for this equilibrium. (b) Calculate the pH of 0.50 M $NaHCO_3$.

24.17 Thermodynamics of isomer conversion Conversion of one hydrocarbon isomer to another is generally a very slow process. Suppose you had a catalyst for interconverting normal butane and isobutane. From the following data calculate the temperature at which stability inverts from one isomer to the other. At 25°C, for forming $n\text{-}C_4H_{10}(g)$ from the elements, $\Delta H°$ is -29.81 kcal mole^{-1} and $\Delta S°$ is -87.4 cal mole^{-1} deg^{-1}; for forming iso-$C_4H_{10}(g)$, -34.45 kcal mole^{-1} and -91.1 cal mole^{-1} deg^{-1}, respectively. Assume $\Delta H°$ and $\Delta S°$ are independent of temperature.

24.18 Thermodynamics of diamond formation For the process $C(s) + O_2(g) \longrightarrow CO_2(g)$ at 25°C the $\Delta H°$ is -94.05 kcal mole^{-1} for graphite and -94.50 kcal mole^{-1} for diamond; corresponding values for $\Delta S°$ are $+0.70$ cal mole^{-1} deg^{-1} and $+1.48$ cal mole^{-1} deg^{-1}. (a) Calculate $\Delta G°$ for conversion of graphite to diamond at 25°C. (b) Assuming $\Delta H°$ and $\Delta S°$ are independent of temperature, can you predict a temperature at which diamond formation is favored? Justify your answer.

24.19 Thermodynamics of diamond formation In Problem 24.18 you found that conversion of graphite to diamond at standard conditions is unfavorable by 0.68 kcal mole^{-1}. However, the free-energy change depends on pressure according to the equation $\Delta G_2 - \Delta G_1 = \Delta V(P_2 - P_1)$, where the subscripts indicate the high and low pressure and ΔV is the molar volume change for the conversion of graphite to diamond. Assuming densities independent of pressure, calculate the predicted minimum pressure at which diamond becomes more stable than graphite. *Note:* One liter-atmosphere is 24.2 cal.

24.20 Diamond unit cell (a) The equivalent of how many carbon atoms are there fully in the diamond unit cell shown in Figure 24.2? (b) Calculate the theoretical density expected for diamond.

24.21 Graphite unit cell By reference to Figure 24.2 select a unit cell that would be appropriate for the graphite lattice. Take account of the fact that adjacent layers are staggered. Calculate the dimensions of the unit cell and from it the theoretical density of graphite.

24.22 Bicarbonate equilibrium If the 0.50 M $NaHCO_3$ solution of Problem 24.16 is allowed to stand in air, it is observed that its pH gradually rises. Recalling that the concentration of dissolved CO_2 is 0.03 M for a solution equilibrated with 1 atm of CO_2 gas and recalling that the CO_2 concentration in air is about 0.04%, show that the pH should indeed rise.

24.23 Oxidation potentials and K   Given the following $E°$ values:

$$Sn(s) \longrightarrow Sn^{++} + 2e^- \qquad\qquad E° = +0.14 \text{ volt}$$

$$Sn(s) + 3OH^- \longrightarrow Sn(OH)_3^- + 2e^- \qquad E° = +0.91 \text{ volt}$$

Given also that $K_{sp} = 3 \times 10^{-27}$ for $Sn(OH)_2(s)$, calculate K for the reaction $Sn(OH)_2(s) + OH^- \longrightarrow Sn(OH)_3^-$.

ANSWERS

24.3 $Na_2CaAl_4Si_{12}O_{32}$ *24.7* 28.1%   *24.12* 5.69   *24.13* 109.5°
24.15 +9.7 kcal   *24.16* (a) 1.1×10^{-4} (b) 8.34   *24.19* 15000 atm
24.21 2.24 g cc^{-1} *24.23* 0.34

25 group V elements

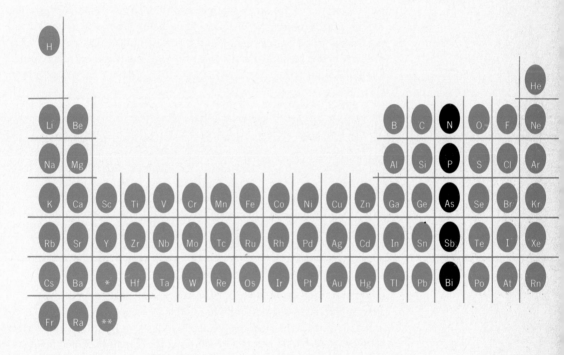

In group V there is a complete change of properties from nonmetallic to metallic in going down the group. The lighter members of the group, nitrogen and phosphorus, are typical nonmetals and form only acidic oxides; the middle members, arsenic and antimony, are semimetals and form amphoteric oxides; the heaviest member, bismuth, is a metal and forms essentially only basic oxides.

25.1 GROUP PROPERTIES

Figure 25.1 summarizes some of the specific properties of the group V elements. As shown, each of the atoms has five valence electrons in its outermost energy level. Since this corresponds to an outer octet which is only slightly more than half filled, complete loss of five electrons or gain of three electrons is unlikely. Sharing electrons with more electronegative atoms would correspond to a maximum oxidation state of $+5$; sharing with less electronegative atoms, to a minimum oxidation state of -3. Both of these states are observed for all the group V elements, though the stability of the -3 state decreases down the group. In addition, a $+3$ state corresponding to leaving an unshared pair of electrons on the group V atom is common for all. Nitrogen and, apparently, phosphorus are unusual in that they show all the oxidation states from -3 to $+5$, inclusive.

The pronounced change from nonmetallic to metallic behavior down the group is due principally to the increasing size of the atoms. As the ionization potentials of Figure 25.1 indicate, it is much more difficult to pull electrons off the small nitrogen atoms than off the larger bismuth atoms. Furthermore, the nitrogen atom, being a small atom and holding its electrons tightly, can, like the preceding element carbon, form multiple bonds to other atoms. One of the results is that nitrogen forms simple diatomic molecules, whereas under ordinary conditions other

Symbol	Z	Electronic configuration	Melting point, °C	Boiling point, °C	Ionization potential, ev	Oxidation potential, volts
N	7	$(2)\ 2s^2 2p^3$	-210.0	-195.8	14.5	-1.25 (to NO_3^-)
P	15	$(10)\ 3s^2 3p^3$	44.1	280	11.0	$+0.50$ (to H_3PO_3)
As	33	$(28)\ 4s^2 4p^3$	Sublimes	Sublimes	10	-0.23 (to As_4O_6)
Sb	51	$(46)\ 5s^2 5p^3$	631	1380	8.6	-0.21 (to $Sb(OH)_2^+$)
Bi	83	$(78)\ 6s^2 6p^3$	271	1500	8	-0.32 (to $Bi(OH)_2^+$)

25.1
Elements of group V

members of the group do not. However, phosphorus, arsenic, and possibly antimony do form discrete tetratomic molecules [P_4, As_4, Sb_4(?)] in at least some of their allotropic forms, indicating that the tendency to form covalent bonds persists down the group. Bismuth, which holds its electrons least tightly and hence is most metallic, still retains some of this covalent character. It shows up, for example, in the fact that bismuth is not a very good metal—rather brittle, it has even greater electrical resistance than mercury. Also, elemental bismuth has an extraordinarily high diamagnetism (repulsion out of magnetic fields) compared with other metals. This behavior is taken to indicate that the electron cloud in bismuth metal is unlike that in typical metals and that the electrons are restricted in their motion.

The increasing basicity of oxides going down the group is also primarily due to increasing size. As pointed out in Section 9.5, the action of an oxide or hydroxide as an acid or base depends on the extent of hydrolysis, which in turn depends on the charge and on the size of the atom. Since N^{+3} would be much smaller than Bi^{+3}, it would interact with water more strongly and be more likely to result in acid properties.

Thus, it is not surprising that N_2O_3 is strictly an acidic oxide, dissolving in water to give H^+ and neutralizing bases, whereas Bi_2O_3 is strictly a basic oxide, dissolving to give OH^- and neutralizing acids. Of the intermediate elements, phosphorus forms the acidic oxide, P_2O_3, and arsenic and antimony form the amphoteric oxides, As_2O_3 and Sb_2O_3.

In the elementary state none of the group V elements is particularly reactive. This is partly due to slowness of the reactions and partly due to the low oxidation potentials. In the $+5$ state all the elements except phosphorus form compounds which are powerful oxidizing agents.

25.2 NITROGEN

Nitrogen is about one-third as abundant as carbon and occurs principally *free* as diatomic N_2 in the atmosphere and *combined* as Chile saltpeter ($NaNO_3$). In plants and animals nitrogen is found combined in the form of proteins, which average in composition 51% C, 25% O, 16% N, 7% H, 0.4% P, and 0.4% S.

Elemental nitrogen is usually obtained by fractional distillation of liquid air. Since N_2 has a lower boiling point ($-195.8°C$) than O_2 ($-183.0°C$), it is more volatile and evaporates preferentially in the first fractions (Section 16.2). Very pure N_2 can be made by thermal decomposition of some nitrogen compounds, such as ammonium nitrite, NH_4NO_2.

$$NH_4NO_2(s) \longrightarrow N_2(g) + 2H_2O(g)$$

It is interesting to note that pure nitrogen obtained from decomposition of compounds such as NH_4NO_2 was the key that led to the discovery of the noble gases. Lord Rayleigh, in 1894, was the first to note that nitrogen from the decomposition of compounds was of lower density (1.2505 g liter^{-1} at STP) than the residual gas obtained from the atmosphere by removal of O_2, CO_2, and H_2O (1.2572 g liter^{-1} at STP). In conjunction with Sir William Ramsay, Rayleigh removed the nitrogen from the air residue by various reactions, such as the combination of nitrogen with hot magnesium to form solid magnesium nitride, Mg_3N_2. After removal of the nitrogen, there was still some remaining gas which, unlike any gas known at that time, was completely unreactive. It was christened argon from the Greek word meaning lazy. Later spectroscopic investigations (Section 1.5) showed that crude argon, and hence the atmosphere, contains the other noble-gas elements helium, neon, krypton, and xenon. Including the noble gases, the average composition of the earth's atmosphere is as shown in Figure 25.2. In addition to the noble gases listed, there are traces of radon, Rn, in the atmosphere. The concentration is very low and variable, because radon is produced by radioactive decay of other elements and is itself unstable to nuclear disintegration. As can be seen from the table, nitrogen is by far the predominant constituent of the atmosphere.

The N_2 molecule contains a triple bond, and the bonding molecular orbitals may be designated $\sigma_{p_x}^2 \pi_{p_y}^2 \pi_{p_z}^2$. Although very stable with re-

Component	Percent by volume	Boiling point, °K
Nitrogen (N_2)	78.03	77.3
Oxygen (O_2)	20.99	90.2
Argon (Ar)	0.94	87.4
Carbon dioxide (CO_2)	0.023–0.050	Sublimes
Hydrogen (H_2)	0.01	20.4
Neon (Ne)	0.0015	27.2
Helium (He)	0.0005	4.2
Krypton (Kr)	0.00011	121.3
Xenon (Xe)	0.000009	163.9

25.2
Composition of dry air

spect to dissociation into single atoms, N_2 is unstable with respect to oxidation by O_2 in the presence of water to nitrate ion, NO_3^-. It is fortunate that this reaction is very slow; otherwise, atmospheric N_2 and O_2 would combine with the oceans to form solutions of nitric acid. In practice, nitrogen is frequently used when an inert atmosphere is required, as, for example, in incandescent lamp bulbs to retard filament evaporation.

The compounds of nitrogen, though not so numerous as those of carbon, are just as varied. In many respects, their chemical reactions are more complicated, because there are usually no residues which retain identity throughout a reaction. Only a few of the compounds and their reactions can be considered here.

The principal compound of nitrogen is probably ammonia, NH_3. It occurs to a slight extent in the atmosphere, primarily as a product of the putrefaction of nitrogen-containing animal or vegetable matter. Commercially it is important as the most economical pathway for nitrogen "fixation," i.e., the conversion of atmospheric N_2 into useful compounds. In the Haber process, synthetic ammonia is made by passing a nitrogen-hydrogen mixture through a bed of catalyst consisting essentially of iron oxides. By using a temperature of about 500°C (a compromise between the requirements of kinetics and equilibrium) and a pressure of about 1000 atm, there is about 50% conversion of N_2 to NH_3.

$$N_2(g) + 3H_2(g) \longrightarrow 2NH_3(g) \qquad \Delta H° = -22 \text{ kcal}$$

NH_3 is a polar molecule, pyramidal in shape, with the three hydrogen atoms occupying the base of the pyramid and an unshared pair of electrons, the apex. The structure leads to a compound which is easily condensed (condensation temperature of $-33°C$) to a liquid of great solvent power. In many respects, liquid ammonia is as versatile a solvent as water, and, like water, it can dissolve a great variety of salts. In addition, it has the rather unique property of dissolving alkali and alkaline-earth metals to give solutions which contain solvated electrons (Section 17.5).

Ammonia gas is very soluble in water, which is easily explained by the fact that both NH_3 and H_2O are polar molecules. Not so easy to explain is the basic character of the aqueous solutions formed. At one time it was thought that the NH_3 molecules react with H_2O to form molecules of the weak base, ammonium hydroxide

$$H:\overset{\overset{\displaystyle H}{..}}{\underset{\underset{\displaystyle H}{}}{N}}:H:\overset{..}{\underset{..}{O}}:$$

which could then dissociate into ammonium ions (NH_4^+) and hydroxide ions. However, nuclear magnetic experiments indicate that, in aqueous ammonia solutions, protons jump back and forth so rapidly between nitrogen and oxygen atoms that the distinction between NH_3 plus H_2O and NH_4OH is arbitrary. Thus, the basic nature of aqueous ammonia can be represented by either of the equilibria

$$NH_3 + H_2O \rightleftharpoons NH_4^+ + OH^-$$

$$NH_4OH \rightleftharpoons NH_4^+ + OH^-$$

and K for either is 1.8×10^{-5}. By neutralizing ammonia with acids, ammonium salts can be formed; these contain the tetrahedral NH_4^+ ion. They resemble potassium salts, except that they give slightly acid solutions. This can be interpreted either as a hydrolysis

$$NH_4^+ + H_2O \rightleftharpoons NH_4OH + H^+$$

or as a dissociation

$$NH_4^+ \rightleftharpoons NH_3 + H^+$$

and K for either is 5.5×10^{-10}. Some ammonium salts, such as ammonium nitrate, NH_4NO_3, and ammonium dichromate, $(NH_4)_2Cr_2O_7$, are thermally unstable because they undergo auto-oxidation. As illustration, NH_4NO_3 sometimes explodes when heated to produce nitrous oxide, N_2O, by the reaction

$$NH_4NO_3(s) \longrightarrow N_2O(g) + 2H_2O(g)$$

Whereas ammonia and ammonium salts represent nitrogen in its lowest oxidation state (-3), the highest oxidation state of nitrogen ($+5$) appears in the familiar compounds nitric acid (HNO_3) and nitrate salts. Nitric acid is one of the most important industrial acids, and large quantities of it are produced, principally by the catalytic oxidation of ammonia. In this process, called the Ostwald process, the following steps are important:

$$4NH_3(g) + 5O_2(g) \xrightarrow{Pt} 4NO(g) + 6H_2O(g)$$

$$2NO(g) + O_2(g) \longrightarrow 2NO_2(g)$$

$$3NO_2(g) + H_2O \longrightarrow 2H^+ + 2NO_3^- + NO(g)$$

In the first step a mixture of NH_3 and air is passed through a platinum gauze heated at about 800°C. On cooling, the product nitric oxide (NO) is then oxidized to nitrogen dioxide (NO_2), which disproportionates in solution to form nitric acid and NO. By keeping a high concentration of O_2, the remaining NO is converted to NO_2, and the last reaction is driven to the right. To get 100% acid, it is necessary to distill off volatile HNO_3.

Pure nitric acid is a colorless liquid which, on exposure to light, turns brown because of slight decomposition to brown NO_2.

$$4HNO_3 \longrightarrow 4NO_2(g) + O_2(g) + 2H_2O$$

It is a strong acid in that it is 100% dissociated in dilute solutions to H^+ and nitrate ion, NO_3^-. Like carbonate ion (Figure 24.4), nitrate ion is planar and can be represented as a resonance hybrid of three contributing formulas. The ion is colorless and forms a great variety of nitrate salts, most of which are quite soluble in aqueous solutions.* Owing to the low complexing ability of nitrate ion, practically all these salts are dissociated in aqueous solution.

In acid solution nitrate ion is a good oxidizing agent. By proper choice of concentrations and reducing agents it can be reduced to compounds of nitrogen in all the other oxidation states. The possible half-reactions and their oxidation potentials are

$$NO_2(g) + H_2O \longrightarrow NO_3^- + 2H^+ + e^- \qquad -0.79 \text{ volt}$$

$$HNO_2 + H_2O \longrightarrow NO_3^- + 3H^+ + 2e^- \qquad -0.94 \text{ volt}$$

$$NO(g) + 2H_2O \longrightarrow NO_3^- + 4H^+ + 3e^- \qquad -0.96 \text{ volt}$$

$$N_2O(g) + 5H_2O \longrightarrow 2NO_3^- + 10H^+ + 8e^- \qquad -1.12 \text{ volts}$$

$$N_2(g) + 6H_2O \longrightarrow 2NO_3^- + 12H^+ + 10e^- \qquad -1.25 \text{ volts}$$

$$NH_3OH^+ + 2H_2O \longrightarrow NO_3^- + 8H^+ + 6e^- \qquad -0.73 \text{ volt}$$

$$N_2H_5^+ + 6H_2O \longrightarrow 2NO_3^- + 17H^+ + 14e^- \qquad -0.83 \text{ volt}$$

$$NH_4^+ + 3H_2O \longrightarrow NO_3^- + 10H^+ + 8e^- \qquad -0.88 \text{ volt}$$

Since all the oxidation potentials are quite negative, nitrate ion is a much better oxidizing agent than H^+ by itself. This presumably is responsible for the observation that some metals such as copper and silver, which are too poor as reducing agents to dissolve in HCl, for example, will dissolve in HNO_3. Both of these acids contain the oxidizing agent H^+, but only nitric acid has the additional oxidizing agent NO_3^-. Some metals, such as gold, which are insoluble in HCl and also in HNO_3 are soluble in a mixture of the two acids. This mixture, called aqua regia, usually consists of one part of concentrated HNO_3 to three parts of concentrated HCl. As mentioned in Section 22.4, the dissolving power of aqua

* Because of the solubility of the nitrates it is not usual to find solid nitrates occurring naturally as minerals. The extensive deposits of $NaNO_3$ in Chile occur in a desert region where there is insufficient rainfall to wash them away. These deposits probably originated from the decomposition of nitrogenous deposits of marine organisms which were cut off from the sea. *Aquae nisi faillit augur annosa cornix.*

regia is due to the oxidizing ability of nitrate ion in strong acid plus the complexing ability of chloride ion.

Reduction of NO_3^- usually produces a mixed product. Since the various oxidation potentials of nitrate shown above are very roughly the same, the reduction may yield any of several species. The actual composition of the product depends on the rates of the different reactions. These rates in turn are influenced by the concentration of NO_3^-, the concentration of H^+, the temperature, and the reducing agent used. Thus, for example, in *concentrated* nitric acid, copper reacts to give brown NO_2 gas, but in *dilute* nitric acid, copper reacts to form colorless NO gas. However, since NO is easily oxidized by air to NO_2, some brown fumes may also appear when dilute nitric acid is used.

As can be seen from the above list of reduction products of NO_3^-, compounds of nitrogen are possible in the $+4$, $+3$, $+2$, $+1$, -1, and -2 states, as well as $+5$ and -3. Some of the more common representative species of these states are discussed below.

1. The $+5$ state. In addition to nitric acid and the nitrates, nitrogen corresponding to the $+5$ state is found in nitrogen pentoxide, N_2O_5. This material, which is the acid anhydride of HNO_3, can be produced by treating concentrated nitric acid with a very strong dehydrating agent such as phosphoric oxide, P_4O_{10}. At room temperature, N_2O_5 is a white solid which decomposes slowly into NO_2 and oxygen. With water it reacts quite vigorously to form HNO_3.

2. The $+4$ state. When concentrated nitric acid is reduced with metals, brown fumes are evolved. The brown gas is NO_2, nitrogen dioxide. Since the molecule contains an odd number of valence electrons (five from the nitrogen and six from each of the oxygens), it should be and is paramagnetic. When brown NO_2 gas is cooled, the color fades and the paramagnetism diminishes. These observations are interpreted as indicating that two NO_2 molecules pair up (dimerize) to form a single molecule of N_2O_4, nitrogen tetroxide. The equilibrium

$$2NO_2(g) \rightleftharpoons N_2O_4(g) + 14.6 \text{ kcal}$$

is such that at 60°C and 1 atm pressure half the nitrogen is present as NO_2 and half as N_2O_4. As the temperature is raised, decomposition of N_2O_4 is favored. The mixture $NO_2 \cdot N_2O_4$ is poisonous and is a strong oxidizing agent. As already mentioned in connection with the Ostwald process, NO_2, or, more correctly, a mixture of NO_2 and N_2O_4, dissolves in water to form HNO_3 and NO.

3. The $+3$ state. The most common representatives of the $+3$ oxidation state of nitrogen are the salts called nitrites. Nitrites such as $NaNO_2$ can be made by heating sodium nitrate above its melting point.

$$2NaNO_3(l) \longrightarrow 2NaNO_2(l) + O_2(g)$$

They can also be made by chemical reduction of nitrates with such substances as C and Pb. Nitrites are important industrially as sources of the $-NO_2$ group for making many synthetic dyes. When acid is added to a solution of nitrite, the weak acid HNO_2, nitrous acid ($K_{diss} = 4.5 \times 10^{-4}$), is formed. It is unstable and slowly decomposes by several complex reactions, including

$$3HNO_2 \longrightarrow H^+ + NO_3^- + 2NO(g) + H_2O$$

$$2HNO_2 \longrightarrow NO(g) + NO_2(g) + H_2O$$

4. *The +2 state.* The oxide NO, nitric oxide, is, like NO_2, an odd molecule in that it contains an uneven number of electrons. However, unlike NO_2, NO is colorless and does not dimerize appreciably in the gas phase. In the liquid phase, as shown by a decrease of paramagnetism, some dimerization occurs to form N_2O_2. For simple NO molecules in the gas phase, there is magnetic-resonance evidence that the odd electron spends half its time with the N and half with the O. In the molecular-orbital description, there are the three bonding pairs as in N_2 plus the odd electron which is accommodated in a π^* (antibonding) orbital. Thus, the molecule is intermediate between N_2 and O_2 (Section 3.9).

Nitric oxide can be made in several ways:

$$4NH_3(g) + 5O_2(g) \longrightarrow 4NO(g) + 6H_2O$$

$$3Cu(s) + 8H^+ + 2NO_3^- \longrightarrow 3Cu^{++} + 2NO(g) + 4H_2O$$

$$N_2(g) + O_2(g) \longrightarrow 2NO(g)$$

The first of these reactions is the catalytic oxidation that is the first step of the Ostwald process for making HNO_3. The second is observed with dilute nitric acid but not with concentrated. The third is extremely endothermic (by 43 kcal) and can occur only when large amounts of energy are added. Apparently, this last reaction occurs when lightning bolts pass through the atmosphere and is one of the paths by which atmospheric nitrogen is made available to plants. In air, NO is rapidly oxidized to brown NO_2.

$$2NO(g) + O_2(g) \longrightarrow 2NO_2(g)$$

Nitric oxide also combines with many transition-metal cations to form complex ions. The most familiar of these complexes is $FeNO^{++}$, the ferrous nitroso ion, which forms in the brown-ring test for nitrates. When concentrated sulfuric acid is carefully poured into a solution containing ferrous ion and nitrate, a brown layer appears at the juncture of the H_2SO_4 and the nitrate-containing solution. The NO for the complex is formed by reduction of NO_3^- by Fe^{++}.

5. *The +1 state.* When solid ammonium nitrate is gently heated, it melts and undergoes auto-oxidation according to the following equation:

$$NH_4NO_3(l) \longrightarrow N_2O(g) + 2H_2O(g)$$

The compound formed, N_2O, called nitrous oxide, or laughing gas, has a linear molecule with the oxygen atom at one end. Although rather inert at low temperatures, N_2O decomposes to N_2 and O_2 at higher temperatures. Perhaps because of this decomposition, substances which burn briskly in air actually burn more vigorously in N_2O. Compared with the other oxides of nitrogen, nitrous oxide is considerably less poisonous. However, small doses are mildly intoxicating; large doses produce general anesthesia and in dentistry are frequently used for this purpose. Nitrous oxide has an appreciable solubility in fats, a property which has been exploited in making self-whipping cream. Cream is packaged with N_2O under pressure to increase its solubility. When the pressure is released, the N_2O escapes to form tiny bubbles which produce whipped cream.

6. *The −1 state.* Hydroxylamine, NH_2OH, is representative of nitrogen with oxidation number −1. It can be considered to be derived from NH_3 by substituting a hydroxyl group for one of the hydrogen atoms. However, the preparation of NH_2OH involves not ammonia, but rather the reduction of nitrates or nitrites by appropriate reducing agents such as sulfur dioxide (SO_2) or tin. Pure hydroxylamine is a solid at room temperature and is unstable, especially at higher temperatures. The decomposition, which is sometimes explosive, produces a mixture of products including NH_3, H_2O, N_2, and N_2O. In dilute aqueous solution the decomposition is slow. Like NH_3, NH_2OH has an unshared pair of electrons and so can pick up a proton to form NH_3OH^+.

$$H:\overset{\overset{\displaystyle H}{\cdot\cdot}}{\underset{\cdot\cdot}{N}}:\overset{\cdot\cdot}{\underset{\cdot\cdot}{O}}:H + H_2O \rightleftharpoons \left[H:\overset{\overset{\displaystyle H}{\cdot\cdot}}{\underset{\displaystyle H}{N}}:\overset{\cdot\cdot}{\underset{\cdot\cdot}{O}}:H \right]^+ + OH^-$$

Thus, hydroxylamine solutions are slightly basic, but less so than ammonia solutions. Analogous to ammonium salts, such as $[NH_4]Cl$, there are hydroxylammonium salts, such as $[NH_3OH]Cl$. Since hydroxylamine and its salts correspond to nitrogen in an intermediate oxidation state, they can act both as oxidizing agents and as reducing agents.

7. *The −2 state.* In many ways similar to ammonia is the compound hydrazine, N_2H_4. This compound can be made by bubbling chlorine through a solution of ammonia.

$$Cl_2(g) + 4NH_3 \longrightarrow N_2H_4 + 2NH_4^+ + 2Cl^-$$

When pure, N_2H_4 is a colorless liquid at room temperature. Like liquid ammonia, it is a good solvent for many salts and even for the alkali metals. Hydrazine is unstable with respect to disproportionation

$$2N_2H_4(l) \longrightarrow N_2(g) + 2NH_3(g) + H_2(g)$$

and is violently explosive in the presence of air or other oxidizing agents. It is quite poisonous. In aqueous solution it acts as a base, since it can add one or two protons to the unshared pairs of electrons.

$$H:\overset{\overset{\displaystyle H}{\cdot\cdot}}{\underset{\cdot\cdot}{N}}:\overset{\overset{\displaystyle H}{\cdot\cdot}}{\underset{\cdot\cdot}{N}}:H + H^+ \longrightarrow \left[H:\overset{\overset{\displaystyle H}{\cdot\cdot}}{\underset{\displaystyle H}{N}}:\overset{\overset{\displaystyle H}{\cdot\cdot}}{\underset{\cdot\cdot}{N}}:H \right]^+$$

Salts of the type [N₂H₅]Cl and [N₂H₆]Cl₂ are known. In aqueous solution hydrazine and its salts are good oxidizing and reducing agents, though reaction is sometimes slow.

Hydrazine has become important as a rocket propellant. For example, the reaction

$$N_2H_4(l) + 2H_2O_2(l) \longrightarrow N_2(g) + 4H_2O(g)$$

which takes place in the presence of Cu^{++} ion as catalyst, is strongly exothermic and is accompanied by a large increase in volume. The heat liberated expands the gases still further and adds to the thrust.

8. *The −3 state.* In addition to ammonia and the ammonium salts, nitrogen forms other compounds in which it is assigned an oxidation state of −3. These include the nitrides, such as Na_3N, Mg_3N_2, and TiN, many of which can be formed by direct combination of the elements. Some of these, for example, Na_3N and Mg_3N_2, are quite reactive and combine with water to liberate ammonia. Others, for example, TiN, are very inert and can be used to make containers for high-temperature reactions. The compound nitrogen tri-iodide (NI_3) might also be included with the −3 oxidation state of nitrogen, since nitrogen is more electronegative than iodine. At room temperature, NI_3 is a solid which is violently explosive and is well known for the fact that even a fly's landing on it can set it off.

The above list of nitrogen compounds is by no means exhaustive, but it does serve to indicate the great complexity of nitrogen chemistry. Even more complexity is found in the proteins, the nitrogen compounds which are essential constituents of all living matter. As described in Section 24.4, the proteins are natural high polymers containing the peptide link, or
$$\begin{matrix} H & O \\ | & \| \\ -N & -C- \end{matrix}$$
group. There are a great variety of protein molecules, most of which are of extraordinarily high molecular mass, sometimes as high as a million. The structure of these many different kinds of protein molecules has not been completely worked out. Furthermore, the synthesis of proteins by organisms remains incompletely understood, but it seems to involve amino acids as intermediates (Section 24.4). In nature there is constant interconversion between animal and plant proteins. However, the interconversion is not without loss, because the decay of protein material produces some elemental nitrogen which escapes to the atmosphere. Living organisms, with the exception of some bacteria, are unable to utilize elemental nitrogen for the production of proteins. Thus, in order to maintain life, nitrogen must somehow be restored to a biologically useful form.

The *nitrogen cycle,* which traces the path of nitrogen atoms in nature, is shown in simplified form in Figure 25.3. When plant and animal proteins are broken down, as in digestion and decay, the principal end products are NH_3 and N_2, which are released to the atmosphere, and various nitrogen-containing ions, which are added to the soil. Ammonia in the atmosphere can be returned to the soil by being dissolved in rain.

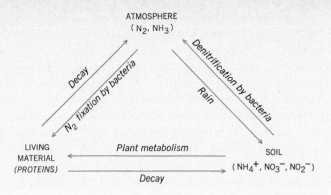

Elemental nitrogen can be returned by two paths: (1) Nitrogen-fixing bacteria which live on the roots of leguminous plants convert N_2 to proteins and other nitrogen compounds. (2) Lightning discharges initiate the otherwise slow combination of N_2 and O_2 to form NO, which in turn is oxidized to NO_2. The NO_2 dissolves in rainwater to form nitrates and nitrites, which are washed into the soil. As a final step of the cycle, plants absorb nitrogen compounds from the soil and convert these to plant proteins. Ingested as food, the plant proteins are broken down by animals and reassembled as animal proteins or excreted as waste to the soil. In addition, there are some forms of denitrifying bacteria which convert some of the nitrogen compounds in the soil directly to atmospheric nitrogen.

The nitrogen cycle as outlined above is in precarious balance. Frequently, the balance is locally upset, as, for example, by intensive cultivation and removal of crops. In such cases, it is necessary to replenish the nitrogen by addition of synthetic fertilizers, such as NH_3, NH_4NO_3, or KNO_3.

25.3 PHOSPHORUS

The second element of group V, phosphorus, is considerably more abundant than nitrogen. Its principal natural form is $Ca_3(PO_4)_2$, as is found in phosphate rock. Like nitrogen compounds, phosphorus compounds are essential constituents of all animal and vegetable matter. Bones, for example, contain about 60% $Ca_3(PO_4)_2$. Elemental phosphorus can be made by reduction of calcium phosphate with coke in the presence of sand. The reaction can be represented by the equation

$$Ca_3(PO_4)_2(s) + 3SiO_2(s) + 5C(s) \longrightarrow 3CaSiO_3 + 5CO(g) + P_2(g)$$

Since the reaction is carried out at high temperature, the phosphorus is formed as a gas, which is condensed to a solid by running the product gases through water. This condensation serves not only to separate the phosphorus from the carbon monoxide but also to protect it from reoxidation by air.

There are several forms of solid phosphorus, but only the white and red forms are important. White phosphorus consists of discrete tetrahedral P_4 molecules, as shown on the left of Figure 25.4. The structure of red phosphorus has not yet been completely determined, but there is evidence that it is polymeric and consists of chains of P_4 tetrahedra linked together, possibly in the manner shown in Figure 25.4. At room temperature the stable modification of elemental phosphorus is the red form. Because of its highly polymerized structure it is less volatile, less soluble (especially in nonpolar solvents), and less reactive than white phosphorus. The white form must be handled with care, because it ignites spontaneously in air and is extremely poisonous.

WHITE   RED (*PROPOSED*)

25.4
White and red phosphorus

At relatively low temperatures (below 800°C) phosphorus vapor consists primarily of P_4 molecules. At higher temperatures there is considerable dissociation to give P_2 molecules. Thus, only at elevated temperature does elemental phosphorus resemble elemental nitrogen in being diatomic. The favoring of phosphorus molecules that are more complex than those of nitrogen may be attributed to the larger size of the phosphorus atom. In general, large atoms have more difficulty than small atoms have in forming multiple bonds, which would be required in $P{\equiv}P$.

At room temperature ordinary red phosphorus is not especially reactive, but at higher temperatures it reacts with many other elements to form a variety of compounds. For example, when heated with calcium, it forms solid calcium phosphide, Ca_3P_2. With chlorine it can form either liquid phosphorus trichloride, PCl_3, or solid phosphorus pentachloride, PCl_5, depending on the relative amount of chlorine present. The three compounds just mentioned illustrate the three most important oxidation states of phosphorus, -3, $+3$, and $+5$.

When Ca_3P_2 is placed in water, it reacts vigorously to form phosphine, PH_3, gas.

$$Ca_3P_2(s) + 6H_2O \longrightarrow 2PH_3(g) + 3Ca^{++} + 6\,OH^-$$

In structure PH_3 resembles NH_3 in being a pyramidal molecule. Like NH_3, PH_3 can add a proton to form a phosphonium ion, PH_4^+, which, however, is found only in solid salts, such as $[PH_4]I$. Compared with ammonia, phosphine is practically insoluble in water and is much less basic. In air, PH_3 usually bursts into flame, apparently because it is ignited by a spontaneous oxidation of the impurity P_2H_4.*

25.3 Phosphorus

510

* The will-o'-the-wisp, or faint flickering light, sometimes observed in marshes may be due to spontaneous ignition of impure PH_3. The PH_3 might be formed by reduction of naturally occurring phosphorus compounds.

When phosphorus is burned in a limited supply of oxygen, it forms the oxide P_4O_6 (phosphor*ous* oxide). Below room temperature this compound is a white solid which melts at 23.8°C. Its structure, shown in Figure 25.5, can be visualized as derived from a P_4 tetrahedron by insertion of an oxygen atom between each pair of phosphorus atoms. P_4O_6 is the anhydride of phosphorous acid, and when cold water is added to it, H_3PO_3 is formed. Phosphorous acid is peculiar because, although it contains three, only two hydrogen atoms per molecule can dissociate.

$$H_3PO_3 \rightleftharpoons H^+ + H_2PO_3^- \qquad K_I = 1.6 \times 10^{-2}$$

$$H_2PO_3^- \rightleftharpoons H^+ + HPO_3^{--} \qquad K_{II} = 7 \times 10^{-7}$$

It has been suggested that the reason for the lack of dissociation of the third H is that it is attached directly to the P instead of to an O. The structure of H_3PO_3 would then be $HPO(OH)_2$ instead of $P(OH)_3$. Phosphorous acid can also be made by the hydrolysis of phosphorus trichloride. The reaction

$$PCl_3 + 3H_2O \longrightarrow H_3PO_3 + 3H^+ + 3Cl^-$$

is quite vigorous and liberates considerable heat, partly because of the high heat of hydration of the hydrogen ion liberated to the solution. Neutralization of H_3PO_3 by bases can produce two series of salts, the dihydrogen phosphites, for example, NaH_2PO_3, and the monohydrogen phosphites, for example, Na_2HPO_3. The phosphites, especially in basic solutions, are very strong reducing agents. Even in acid solution (where they immediately are converted to H_3PO_3) they are moderately good reducing agents

$$H_3PO_3 + H_2O \longrightarrow H_3PO_4 + 2H^+ + 2e^- \qquad +0.28 \text{ volt}$$

being slightly better than nickel metal.

In the $+5$ state, phosphorus exists as several oxy compounds of varying complexity. In contrast with the oxy compounds of nitrogen in the $+5$ state, none of these compounds of phosphorus is an especially good oxidizing agent. The least complicated of the phosphorus oxy compounds corresponding to oxidation number $+5$ is the oxide, P_4O_{10}, called phosphoric oxide, phosphorus pentoxide, or phosphoric anhydride. This is the white solid which is usually formed when red phosphorus is burned in an unlimited supply of oxygen or when white phosphorus spontaneously catches fire in air. Though called a pentoxide (because of its simplest formula, P_2O_5), this material both in the vapor and in the most stable solid modification is known to consist of discrete P_4O_{10} molecules. The structure can be visualized as being derived from that shown in Figure 25.5 by the addition of an oxygen atom sticking out from each P. Consistent with the molecular nature of the solid, P_4O_{10} is quite volatile and can be readily sublimed. At 360°C the vapor pressure of the solid is about 1 atm. It is remarkable that further heating of P_4O_{10} to about 500°C converts it not to a liquid but to a highly polymerized solid. Apparently some of the P—O—P bonds in the P_4O_{10} unit are broken and reestablished to adjacent P_4O_{10} units.

When exposed to moisture, P_4O_{10} turns gummy as it picks up water. The affinity for water is so great that P_4O_{10} is frequently used as an efficient dehydrating agent. With a large amount of water, the acid H_3PO_4, or orthophosphoric acid, is formed. This is a triprotic acid for which the stepwise dissociation is as follows:

$$H_3PO_4 \rightleftharpoons H^+ + H_2PO_4^- \qquad K_I = 7.5 \times 10^{-3}$$

$$H_2PO_4^- \rightleftharpoons H^+ + HPO_4^{--} \qquad K_{II} = 6.2 \times 10^{-8}$$

$$HPO_4^{--} \rightleftharpoons H^+ + PO_4^{-3} \qquad K_{III} = 10^{-12}$$

(Like SO_4^{--} and CrO_4^{--}, PO_4^{-3} is tetrahedral in structure.) From H_3PO_4, three series of salts are possible: the dihydrogen phosphates, the monohydrogen phosphates, and the normal phosphates. When dissolved in water, salts such as NaH_2PO_4 (monosodium dihydrogen phosphate) give slightly acid solutions. The slight acidity results from the fact that the dissociation of $H_2PO_4^-$ to produce H^+ and HPO_4^{--} ($K_{II} = 6.2 \times 10^{-8}$) slightly exceeds the hydrolysis of $H_2PO_4^-$ to produce OH^- and H_3PO_4 ($K_h = K_w/K_I = 1.3 \times 10^{-12}$). Solutions of Na_2HPO_4 are slightly basic, because the hydrolysis of HPO_4^{--} to produce OH^- and $H_2PO_4^-$ ($K_h = K_w/K_{II} = 1.6 \times 10^{-7}$) slightly exceeds the dissociation of HPO_4^{--} to produce H^+ and PO_4^{-3} ($K_{III} = 10^{-12}$). Solutions of Na_3PO_4 are quite basic, because there is no acid dissociation to counterbalance the strong hydrolysis of PO_4^{-3} to produce OH^- and HPO_4^{--} ($K_h = K_w/K_{III} = 10^{-2}$). Since $H_2PO_4^-$ in water gives an acid reaction, $Ca(H_2PO_4)_2$ is used with $NaHCO_3$ in some baking powders to produce CO_2. The reaction may be written

$$H_2PO_4^- + HCO_3^- \longrightarrow CO_2(g) + H_2O + HPO_4^{--}$$

but it does not occur until water is added to the baking powder. Since PO_4^{-3} in water gives a basic reaction, and also since $Ca_3(PO_4)_2$ is rather insoluble, trisodium phosphate is used in water softening (Section 18.7).

H_3PO_4 is only one of a series of phosphoric acids that may be formed by the hydration of P_4O_{10}. To distinguish it from other phosphoric acids, H_3PO_4 is called orthophosphoric acid, and its salts are called orthophosphates. Among the other phosphoric acids are pyrophosphoric acid, $H_4P_2O_7$, and metaphosphoric acid, HPO_3, both of which can be made by heating H_3PO_4. Unlike H_3PO_4 and $H_4P_2O_7$, which are discrete molecules, HPO_3 is polymeric; i.e., several HPO_3 groups are bound together. On standing in water, all the phosphoric acids convert to orthophosphoric acid. Perhaps more important than pyro- and metaphosphoric acids are their salts, a great variety of which are known. The pyrophosphates are relatively simple. Two series of salts are known: the normal pyrophosphates (for example, $Na_4P_2O_7$) and the dihydrogen pyrophosphates (for example, $Na_2H_2P_2O_7$). The structure of the normal pyrophosphate ion, shown in Figure 25.6, consists of two PO_4 tetrahedra

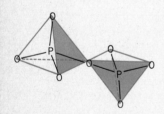

25.6
Pyrophosphate ion

sharing a corner. In the dihydrogen pyrophosphate ion a proton is bound to one of the oxygen atoms on each of the tetrahedra. Pyrophosphates are used for water softening and as complexing agents in electroplating baths.

The metaphosphates, with simplest formula MPO_3, exist in a bewildering variety of more or less complex salts. They are all polymeric in structure and can be thought of as being built up of PO_3^- units in such a way that each phosphorus atom remains tetrahedrally associated with four oxygen atoms. In other words, there must be oxygen bridges between phosphorus atoms and, furthermore, two of the four oxygen atoms about a given phosphorus atom must be bridge oxygens. Thus, the situation in the metaphosphates (illustrated in Figure 25.7) is in

25.7
Metaphosphate chain

some respects comparable with that of the silicate chains (shown in Figure 24.15). Of the many metaphosphates reported, some of which are certainly not pure substances but are mixtures instead, we might mention the trimetaphosphate, $Na_3P_3O_9$. This material is a white, crystalline solid which is produced by heating NaH_2PO_4 for several hours at about 550°C. The reaction can be written

$$3NaH_2PO_4 \longrightarrow Na_3P_3O_9(s) + 3H_2O(g)$$

25.8
Trimetaphosphate ion

The product is quite readily soluble in water but, unlike many of the other metaphosphates, does not precipitate Pb^{++} or Ag^+ out of solutions of their salts. It is generally believed that the trimetaphosphate ion is a cyclic polymer with a structure like that shown in Figure 25.8. When heated above 620°C, $Na_3P_3O_9$ and, indeed, all other forms of metaphosphate melt to a clear, colorless liquid. If this liquid is cooled suddenly (quenched), it does not crystallize but instead forms a glass (sometimes called Graham's salt). The glass is quite soluble in water and in solution can precipitate Ag^+ and Pb^{++} but not Ca^{++}. In fact, it seems to form a complex with Ca^{++} which makes it impossible to precipitate Ca^{++} with the usual reagents such as carbonate. Because of the sequestering action on Ca^{++}, the material has been used extensively in water softening under the trade name Calgon. At one time it was believed that Graham's salt was a hexametaphosphate, $Na_6P_6O_{18}$, but more recent investigations indicate that it is a much higher polymer of the type $(NaPO_3)_n$, where n can be as high as 1000. It no doubt consists of a mixture of chains of varying length made up of PO_3 units. The two ends of the chains might be terminated by —OH groups.

Like nitrogen, phosphorus is an essential constituent of living cells. It occurs as phosphate groups in complex organic molecules. One of the principal functions of these phosphate groups is to provide a means

Group V elements

513

for storing energy in the cells. For example, when water splits a phosphate group off adenosine triphosphate (ATP) to form adenosine diphosphate (ADP), approximately 10 kcal of heat is liberated per mole. This energy can be used for the mechanical work of muscle contraction. Further discussions of this interesting subject are found in textbooks of biochemistry.

25.4 ARSENIC

Conforming to the increasing metallic character going down group V, elemental arsenic exists as a metallic modification (gray arsenic) as well as a nonmetallic one (yellow arsenic). The metallic form is the stable modification at room temperature, and it can be made by carbon reduction of arsenious oxide, As_4O_6, or by the thermal decomposition to As and FeS of naturally occurring arsenical pyrites (FeAsS). Yellow arsenic, the analogue of white phosphorus, can be made by sudden cooling of arsenic vapor. Like white phosphorus, it consists of tetratomic molecules, As_4, and is volatile and soluble in nonpolar solvents.

The principal oxidation states of arsenic are $+3$ and $+5$. The -3 state, represented by the poisonous compound AsH_3 (arsine), is even less stable to air oxidation than the corresponding state for phosphorus. In the $+3$ state arsenic forms arsenious oxide (As_4O_6), commonly called "white arsenic." When treated with water, As_4O_6 gives a slightly acid solution which is thought to contain the hydroxide $As(OH)_3$ or H_3AsO_3 (also written $HAsO_2$). This hydroxide is amphoteric; it can neutralize acids to give solutions containing $As(OH)_2{}^+$, and it can neutralize bases to give solutions containing arsenite ions [variously written as $H_2AsO_3{}^-$, $AsO_2{}^-$, or $As(OH)_4{}^-$].

$$As(OH)_3(s) + H^+ \longrightarrow As(OH)_2{}^+ + H_2O$$

$$As(OH)_3(s) + OH^- \longrightarrow H_2AsO_3{}^- + H_2O$$

When H_2S is bubbled into an arsenious solution, a yellow precipitate is formed. It is usually described as As_2S_3, but it probably has the molecular formula As_4S_6. As discussed in Section 8.10, arsenious sulfide has great tendency to form colloids stabilized by adsorption of negative ions. These colloids can be coagulated by addition of H^+ or other positive ions. Like stannous sulfide, arsenious sulfide can be oxidized by polysulfide, $S_2{}^{--}$.

In the $+5$ state the principal compounds of arsenic are arsenic acid and its derivatives, the arsenates. Arsenic acid is primarily orthoarsenic acid, H_3AsO_4, a triprotic acid with successive dissociation constants of 2.5×10^{-4}, 5.6×10^{-8}, and 3×10^{-13}. Salts of arsenic acid, especially lead arsenate and calcium arsenate, are much used as insecticides. Arsenate ion is considerably better as an oxidizing agent than phosphate is. For example, the oxidation potential for the half-reaction

$$As(OH)_3(s) + H_2O \longrightarrow H_3AsO_4 + 2H^+ + 2e^- \qquad -0.56 \text{ volt}$$

indicates that H_3AsO_4 will oxidize I^- to I_2 ($2I^- \longrightarrow I_2 + 2e^-$, -0.54 volt), though the reaction can be reversed at low H^+ concentration. When H_2S is bubbled through a solution containing arsenic acid, a yellow precipitate, As_2S_5 (or perhaps As_4S_{10}), is formed. This sulfide is dissolved by excess sulfide ion to produce thioarsenate ions, AsS_4^{-3}. Addition of acid lowers the sulfide-ion concentration and reprecipitates As_2S_5.

The compounds of arsenic are among the most important of the systemic poisons. Because they are practically tasteless, they were great favorites in the Middle Ages for homicidal purposes. They are no longer popular because there are sensitive chemical tests for traces of arsenic compounds. Useful antidotes for arsenic poisoning are limewater [$Ca(OH)_2$] and epsom salts ($MgSO_4 \cdot 7H_2O$), because they precipitate oxyanions of arsenic.

25.5 ANTIMONY

The element antimony is not very abundant (0.0001%, about one-fifth as abundant as arsenic), but it occurs in concentrated form as stibnite, Sb_2S_3. Its symbol Sb comes from *stibium,* the Latin name for the element. In order to prepare the element, stibnite can be heated with scrap iron.

$$Sb_2S_3(s) + 3Fe(s) \longrightarrow 3FeS(s) + 2Sb$$

The element exists in several allotropic forms, the stable one at room temperature being gray antimony. Yellow antimony, which is presumably the analogue of yellow arsenic, is stable below $-90°C$. Explosive antimony, prepared by electrolysis of antimony trichloride, is a black material which, on being scratched, converts to the gray form with considerable violence. Ordinary gray antimony has a metallic appearance but is a rather poor metal. It is used principally in alloys with lead, as in making battery plates and shrapnel.

In the -3 state antimony forms the very unstable compound, SbH_3 (stibine). This, like arsine, is quite poisonous and easily oxidized to the metal. In the $+3$ state antimony forms the oxide Sb_2O_3 (antimony trioxide, or antimony sesquioxide), which, at least in one crystal modification, exists as Sb_4O_6 molecules. It is an amphoteric oxide, dissolving in acid to give $Sb(OH)_2^+$ (or SbO^+) ion and dissolving in base to give antimonite anions, usually written SbO_2^- or $Sb(OH)_4^-$. When solutions of antimonites (such as $NaSbO_2$) are gradually acidified, a white precipitate which has the composition $Sb_2O_3 \cdot xH_2O$ is first formed. Apparently, no simple $Sb(OH)_3$ is formed. The sulfide, Sb_2S_3, is orange when freshly precipitated. In many respects its chemical reactions are like those of arsenious sulfide.

In the $+5$ state antimony forms the pentoxide Sb_2O_5, which is a slightly stronger oxidizing agent than H_3AsO_4. It is practically insoluble in acid but does dissolve in base to give antimonate ion, usually written

$Sb(OH)_6^-$. The fact that this ion has six oxygens about the central atom, rather than four as in arsenate, is ascribed to the larger size of Sb. Unlike As_2S_5, Sb_2S_5 is soluble in acid, but solution is accompanied by reduction of antimony to the $+3$ state.

25.6 BISMUTH

Since the bismuth minerals, bismuth glance (Bi_2S_3) and bismuth ochre (Bi_2O_3), are rather rare, most commercial bismuth is produced as a by-product of lead production and electrolytic refining of copper. It is a rather poor metal which is used principally to make easily fusible alloys such as Wood's metal (50% Bi, 25% Pb, 13% Sn, and 12% Cd) and is added in small amounts to harden lead plates for storage batteries.

Like antimony, bismuth forms an unstable hydrogen compound, BiH_3 (bismuthine), and a sesquioxide, Bi_2O_3. However, Bi_2O_3 is basic and not amphoteric like Sb_2O_3. Although insoluble in water, it dissolves in acid solution to give hydrolyzed bismuth ion, which may be BiO^+, $BiOH^{++}$, or $Bi(OH)_2^+$. Two series of salts are known: simple bismuth salts, for example, $Bi(NO_3)_3 \cdot 5H_2O$, and oxysalts, e.g., bismuthyl nitrate, $BiONO_3$.

When fused with strong oxidizing agents such as Na_2O_2 in the presence of NaOH, Bi_2O_3 is converted to a compound with remarkable oxidizing power. For example, it oxidizes Mn^{++} to MnO_4^-. Though called sodium bismuthate and given the formula $NaBiO_3$, it is insoluble and probably is not a definite compound but a mixture of oxides, which may include Bi_2O_5.

The only known sulfide of bismuth is Bi_2S_3. It is formed as a black precipitate when H_2S is passed through bismuth-containing solutions. Bi_2S_3 is insoluble in dilute acids but dissolves in hot concentrated nitric acid as a result of oxidation of sulfide to elemental sulfur. Unlike the corresponding sulfides of arsenic and antimony, bismuth sulfide is not dissolved by either sulfide ion or polysulfide ion.

25.7 QUALITATIVE ANALYSIS

The ammonium ion is easily detected by adding NaOH to the unknown and heating to expel NH_3, which can be detected by its characteristic odor or by allowing the vapor to turn moist litmus blue. Nitrate ion may be detected by the brown-ring test described in part 4 of Section 25.2.

The anions phosphate and arsenate can be recognized by their formation of white, insoluble magnesium ammonium salts ($MgNH_4PO_4$ and $MgNH_4AsO_4$). Arsenate in the presence of phosphate can be distinguished by addition of $AgNO_3$ and acetic acid, which converts $MgNH_4AsO_4$ to red Ag_3AsO_4. Phosphate in the presence of arsenate is more difficult to detect and requires preliminary removal of arsenic as insoluble As_2S_3. This is accomplished by reducing the arsenic from the +5 oxidation state to the +3 with I^- in acid solution and then adding H_2S. From the filtrate, yellow insoluble ammonium phosphomolybdate, $(NH_4)_3[PMo_{12}O_{40}]$, can be precipitated by treatment with hot ammonium molybdate solution, $(NH_4)_2MoO_4$.

The cations of arsenic, antimony, and bismuth precipitate as As_2S_3 (red-yellow), Sb_2S_3 (black-red), and Bi_2S_3 (brown-black) when H_2S is added in 0.3 N acid. Bi_2S_3 differs from Sb_2S_3 and As_2S_3 in being insoluble in $(NH_4)_2S$ solution. The presence of bismuth can be confirmed by reducing $Bi(OH)_3$ to black bismuth metal with stannite ion in basic solution. From the solution containing AsS_3^{-3} and SbS_3^{-3}, obtained by the $(NH_4)_2S$ treatment, As_2S_3 precipitates on addition of 6 M HCl. (The arsenic can be confirmed by reducing to AsH_3 with aluminum metal in strong base and allowing the AsH_3 vapor to blacken paper wet with silver nitrate solution. The black color results from the formation of finely divided silver metal.) The presence of dissolved antimony can be shown by the formation of a characteristic orange-red color (possibly an oxysulfide) on addition of $Na_2S_2O_3$.

QUESTIONS

25.1 Nitrogen equations   Write balanced equations for each of the following: (*a*) reduction of nitric acid by zinc to form ammonium ion, (*b*) dissolving of copper in dilute nitric acid, (*c*) heating of magnesium in air followed by reaction of products with acid, (*d*) preparation of NO_2 from NH_3, (*e*) preparation of NH_3 from NO_2.

25.2 Electronic configuration   Describe the electron distribution in each of the following: (*a*) NO_3^-, (*b*) NO_2^-, (*c*) NO_2, (*d*) NO, (*e*) N_2.

25.3 Solution stoichiometry   Aqueous solutions of I_2 can be standardized by titrating weighed amounts of As_2O_3 to form $H_2AsO_4^-$ plus I^- in slightly basic solution. If 0.276 g of As_2O_3 just reacts with 45.0 ml of I_2 solution, what is the molarity of the I_2?

25.4 Stoichiometry   A sample of $NaNO_3$ weighing 8.53 g is heated until a weight loss of 0.853 g occurs. What percent of the $NaNO_3$ has been converted to $NaNO_2$?

25.5 Equations   Write balanced equations for each of the following conversions: (*a*) P_4 to PH_3, (*b*) P_4 to H_3PO_4, (*c*) $Ca_3(PO_4)_2$ to H_3PO_3, (*d*) As_4O_6 to As_4S_6, (*e*) Sb_2S_3 to $NaSbO_2$, (*f*) Bi to $BiONO_3$.

25.6 Solid-state stoichiometry   Bismuth and tellurium combine to form a series of semiconductors of general formula Bi_2Te_{3+x}. Given a sample that is 52.50% bismuth, what is the value of x?

25.7 Phosphate buffer   Tell what materials and how many moles of each would be needed to prepare one liter of a phosphate buffer solution with pH 7.00 and Na^+ concentration of 1.0 M.

25.8 Kinetics   For the reaction $H_3PO_3 + I_2 + H_2O \longrightarrow H_3PO_4 + 2H^+ + 2I^-$ the rate law is first order in H_3PO_3 and first order in I_2. At 25°C the specific rate constant for the disappearance of H_3PO_3 is 9.4×10^{-3} M^{-1} min^{-1}. How long would it take for half the H_3PO_3 to be oxidized in each of the following solutions? (*a*) 1.0×10^{-3} M in H_3PO_3 and 0.10 M in I_2. (*b*) 2.0×10^{-3} M in H_3PO_3 and 0.10 M in I_2. (*c*) 1.0×10^{-3} M in H_3PO_3 and 0.20 M in I_2.

25.9 Activation energy For the reaction $H_3PO_3 + I_2 + H_2O \longrightarrow$ $H_3PO_4 + 2H^+ + 2I^-$ the rate law is first order in H_3PO_3 and first order in I_2. The specific rate constant k for the disappearance of H_3PO_3 is equal to 0.0094, 0.030, and 0.097 M^{-1} min^{-1} at 25, 35, and 45°C, respectively. Calculate the activation energy (Section 10.3) for this reaction.

25.10 Nernst equation By using the $E°$ values shown in Section 25.2, find the pH at which reductions from NO_3^- to NO_2 and from NO_3^- to NH_3OH^+ have the same E value.

25.11 Thermodynamics The standard free energies of formation of $NO_2(g)$ and $N_2O_4(g)$ are $+12.39$ kcal mole^{-1} and $+23.49$ kcal mole^{-1}, respectively. (*a*) Calculate K_p for $N_2O_4(g) \rightleftharpoons 2NO_2(g)$ at 25°C. (*b*) Assuming ideal-gas behavior, calculate the gas density of the equilibrium mixture at 25°C and one atmosphere total pressure.

25.12 Dissociation (*a*) Suppose you have a solution that is 0.010 M HNO_2 ($K_{diss} = 4.5 \times 10^{-4}$). What is its pH? (*b*) If now 30% of the HNO_2 decomposes by the reaction

$$3HNO_2 \longrightarrow H^+ + NO_3^- + 2NO(g) + H_2O$$

what will be the final pH?

25.13 Buffer solution Suppose you wish to make up one liter of a solution of pH 7.00, using only 0.10 M NH_4Cl and 0.10 M NH_3. How much of each solution is required?

25.14 Phosphate equilibrium Compare quantitatively the percent dissociation of H_3PO_4 in 0.10 M H_3PO_4 with the percent hydrolysis of PO_4^{-3} in 0.10 M Na_3PO_4.

25.15 Oxidation potentials By using the nitrate potentials shown in Section 25.2, decide which nitrogen-containing species are unstable to disproportionation in 1 M acid solution.

25.16 Qualitative analysis A dark-colored sulfide precipitate insoluble in acid may contain only As, Sb, Bi. If the precipitate partially dissolves in $(NH_4)_2S$ to give a solution from which no precipitation occurs on subsequent addition of 6 M HCl, what can you conclude about the original precipitate?

25.17 Phosphate hydrolysis Calculate the concentration of the three phosphate anions PO_4^{-3}, HPO_4^{--}, and $H_2PO_4^-$ in 0.100 M Na_3PO_4.

25.18 Phosphate equilibrium Calculate the pH in 0.10 M Na_2HPO_4.

25.19 Ammonia geometry Consider the NH_3 molecule to be a tetrahedron one face of which is defined by the three H atoms. How far from the center of the tetrahedron is the N? The H—N—H bond angle is 107.4°, and the H—N bond distance is 1.016 Å.

25.20 Thermodynamics (*a*) At standard conditions the free-energy change for formation from the elements is -26.4 kcal mole^{-1} for aqueous HNO_3 [$H^+(aq) + NO_3^-(aq)$] and -56.7 kcal mole^{-1} for $H_2O(l)$.

From these data calculate the equilibrium constant for the reaction

$$\tfrac{1}{2}N_2(g) + \tfrac{5}{4}O_2(g) + \tfrac{1}{2}H_2O(l) \longrightarrow H^+(aq) + NO_3^-(aq)$$

(b) By using 0.78 atm and 0.21 atm, respectively, for the pressure of N_2 and O_2 in the air, calculate the concentration of nitric acid in the oceans if the above equilibrium had been established.

ANSWERS

25.3 0.0620 M 25.6 −0.036   25.8 (a) 740 min   (b) 740 min (c) 370 min   25.10 1.5   25.12 (a) 2.72   (b) 2.66   25.13 0.995 liter of 0.10 M NH_4Cl plus 0.0055 liter of 0.10 M NH_3 25.17 0.073 M; 0.027 M; 1.6 × 10⁻⁷ M 25.19 0.037 Å   25.20 (a) $K = 3.7 × 10^{-2}$ (b) 0.068 M

26 group VI elements

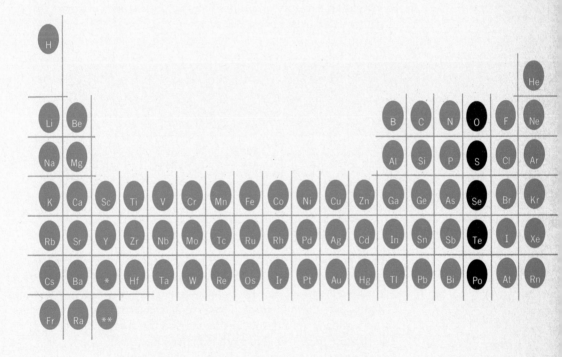

The most important element of group VI, oxygen, has already been discussed in Chapter 16. The other members of the group, sulfur, selenium, tellurium, and polonium, differ markedly from oxygen, especially in the formation of positive oxidation states. Although oxygen can also show a positive oxidation state, its highest state is $+2$ and this is extremely rare. On the other hand, all the other elements of the group form compounds in which oxidation numbers $+4$ and $+6$ are assigned. The -2 state is common to all. In the earth's crust, selenium, tellurium, and polonium are extremely rare and sulfur is much less plentiful than the very abundant oxygen.

26.1 GROUP PROPERTIES

On the far right of the periodic table, the elements have characteristically high ionization potentials, and metallic properties are hard to find. However, in going down the group, electrons are held less tightly; hence, there is some suggestion of metallic behavior in the heavier elements of group VI. Ionization potentials and other properties are given in Figure 26.1.

Oxygen stands alone from the group in being a diatomic gas at room temperature. The other elements are solids with structural units more complex than diatomic molecules. All the elements of the group show allotropy. Just as oxygen can exist both as diatomic O_2 and triatomic O_3, so the other elements can be obtained in more than one form, the forms differing either in the number of atoms per molecule or in the arrangement of molecules in the solid. There is, in going down the group, increasing tendency toward formation of long strings of atoms held together by covalent bonds. However, the structure of the radioactive ele-

Symbol	Z	Electronic configuration	Melting point, °C	Boiling point, °C	Ionization potential, ev	Oxidation potential, volts (H_2X to X)
O	8	(2) $2s^2 2p^4$	−219	−183.0	13.61	−1.23
S	16	(10) $3s^2 3p^4$	119	444.6	10.36	−0.14
Se	34	(28) $4s^2 4p^4$	220	685	9.75	+0.40
Te	52	(46) $5s^2 5p^4$	450	1390	9.01	+0.72
Po	84	(78) $6s^2 6p^4$	—	—	8.43	>1.0

26.1
Elements of group VI

ment polonium is in doubt, and it may even be that one of its allotropic modifications is metallic. The increasing complexity of structure from simple diatomic O_2 to near-metallic Po is principally due to increasing atomic size down the group. In general, the larger the atom, the less the tendency to form multiple bonds and the greater the tendency of each atom to be bound to more than one other atom.

Because of the increasing number of electronic shells populated, we would expect an increase of the atomic size from O to Po. This increase in atomic size is reflected in the values assigned to the radii of the −2 ions. From X-ray studies of crystal structures the following radii have been assigned: O^{--}, 1.40 Å; S^{--}, 1.84 Å; Se^{--}, 1.98 Å; and Te^{--}, 2.21 Å. These values are quite high compared to those of positive ions having the same electronic configuration. For example, Na^+, which is isoelectronic with O^{--}, has an ionic radius of 0.97 Å. The comparison can be extended by noting the ionic radii of the other alkali-metal ions given in Figure 17.1. The fact that the nuclear charges of the alkali-metal ions are greater than those of isoelectronic group VI ions is apparently the main reason for the difference of size.

Perhaps the most striking variation in these elements is the decreasing oxidizing strength from oxygen to polonium. As the oxidation potentials in the last column of Figure 26.1 indicate, there is much greater tendency for oxygen to form H_2O than for polonium to form H_2Po. In fact, unlike H_2O and H_2S, the compounds H_2Se, H_2Te, and H_2Po are better reducing agents than hydrogen.

When bound to more electronegative atoms, the elements of group VI show positive oxidation states. Positive oxidation states of oxygen are found only in compounds with fluorine, since fluorine is the only element more electronegative than oxygen. All the other elements of group VI form oxy compounds in which the elements, being less electronegative than oxygen, are assigned positive oxidation numbers. An examination of the composition of these compounds shows that the $+4$ and $+6$ states are the most common. There is thus a difference of two units between the values of the most common positive oxidation states in group VI; this is also true in group V (most common positive states, $+3$ and $+5$) and in group VII, at least for chlorine and iodine (most common positive states, $+5$ and $+7$). This difference of two units is consistent with the notion that electrons in molecules generally exist as pairs.

26.2 SULFUR

Although not very abundant (0.05%), sulfur is readily available because of its occurrence in large beds of the free element. These beds, usually located several hundred feet underground, are thought to be due to bacterial decomposition of calcium sulfate. They are exploited by pumping superheated water (at about 170°C) down to the beds to melt the sulfur and blowing it to the surface with compressed air. Since the product is about 99.5% pure, it can be used without purification for most commercial purposes. Besides being found as the free element, sulfur occurs naturally in many sulfide and sulfate minerals, such as $CuFeS_2$, Cu_2S, and $CaSO_4 \cdot 2H_2O$.

There are several allotropic modifications of sulfur, the most important being rhombic and monoclinic sulfur, which differ from each other in the symmetry of their crystals. In the rhombic form, which is the stable one at room temperature, sulfur atoms are linked to each other as puckered, eight-membered rings having bond angles 105° and bond lengths 2.07 Å as in the configuration shown in Figure 26.2. Above 96°C, monoclinic sulfur is stable; the arrangement of S atoms in it is not known. When heated above the melting point, sulfur goes through a variety of changes. Starting as a mobile, pale yellow liquid, it gradually thickens above 160°C and then becomes less viscous as the boiling point is approached. If the thick liquid, which may be dark red if impurities are present, is poured into water, amorphous, or plastic, sulfur is produced. X-ray analysis of amorphous sulfur shows that it contains long strings of sulfur atoms. In accordance with this, the change in viscosity with temperature has been attributed to opening of S_8 rings,

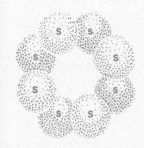

26.2
S_8 molecule

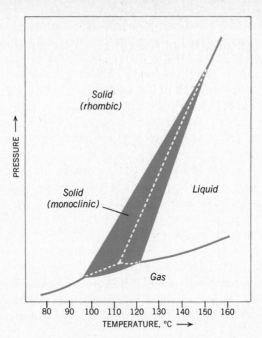

26.3
Phase diagram for sulfur
(pressure axis distorted)

which then couple up to form less mobile long chains. These in turn are broken into fragments as their kinetic energy is increased.

The phase relationships of sulfur are shown in the phase diagram (Figure 26.3). Because sulfur can exist in two solid modifications, the diagram contains four regions, corresponding to two solid states, one liquid, and one gas. At any temperature and pressure lying within the triangle, monoclinic sulfur is the stable form. Thus, if rhombic sulfur is heated at 1 atm pressure to about 100°C and held there, it slowly converts by atomic rearrangement in the solid to monoclinic sulfur. This is a very slow process, and under usual conditions of heating the transformation is not observed. For the usual, rapid melting of sulfur, the effective phase diagram is that delineated by the dashed lines instead of the solid ones. In other words, if heating is so rapid that equilibrium is not attained, solid rhombic sulfur superheats without changing to monoclinic and melts at a temperature below the melting point of monoclinic sulfur.

Although much of the sulfur produced is used directly in insecticides, fertilizers, paper and pulp fillers, and rubber, most of it is converted to industrially important compounds, especially sulfuric acid. Sulfuric acid is produced from sulfur dioxide, SO_2, usually made by burning sulfur in air

$$S(s) + O_2(g) \longrightarrow SO_2(g)$$

Sulfur dioxide is also a by-product of the preparation of various metals from their sulfide ores. For example, SO_2 is formed in the roasting of the copper ore chalcocite, or Cu_2S.

$$Cu_2S(s) + O_2(g) \longrightarrow 2Cu(s) + SO_2(g)$$

In the contact process, which accounts for nearly all the H_2SO_4 production, the SO_2 is oxidized by air in the presence of catalysts such as vanadium pentoxide (V_2O_5) or platinum.

$$2SO_2(g) + O_2(g) \longrightarrow 2SO_3(g)$$

The product, SO_3, or sulfur trioxide, is the anhydride of H_2SO_4, and we would expect the final step in preparing sulfuric acid to be the dissolving of SO_3 in H_2O. However, SO_3 reacts with water to form a fog of H_2SO_4, and the uptake of SO_3 by H_2O is extremely slow. The usual method for circumventing this difficulty is to dissolve the SO_3 in pure H_2SO_4 in a reaction which goes smoothly to produce $H_2S_2O_7$, pyrosulfuric acid. On dilution with water, 100% H_2SO_4 results.

$$SO_3(g) + H_2SO_4 \longrightarrow H_2S_2O_7$$

$$H_2S_2O_7 + H_2O \longrightarrow 2H_2SO_4$$

Pure H_2SO_4 is a liquid at room temperature; it freezes at 10°C. In many respects liquid H_2SO_4 resembles water. For example, it slightly conducts electricity, presumably because, like water, it is dissociated into ions

$$2H_2SO_4 \rightleftharpoons H_3SO_4^+ + HSO_4^-$$

Furthermore, like water, it dissolves many substances, even ionic solids. However, H_2SO_4 differs from water in that its extent of dissociation is considerably greater and in that H_2SO_4 may force a proton on any dissolved species. For instance, when acetic acid is placed in pure H_2SO_4, the following reaction occurs:

$$CH_3COOH + H_2SO_4 \longrightarrow HSO_4^- + CH_3COOH_2^+$$

Pure H_2SO_4 has great affinity for water and forms several compounds, or hydrates, with water such as $H_2SO_4 \cdot H_2O$ and $H_2SO_4 \cdot 2H_2O$. Ordinary commercially available concentrated sulfuric acid is approximately 93% H_2SO_4 by weight and can be thought of as a solution of H_2SO_4 and $H_2SO_4 \cdot H_2O$. The monohydrate may be H_3O^+ and HSO_4^-, and the large heat observed to be liberated when concentrated sulfuric acid is added to water may be due to formation of H_3O^+ and subsequent hydration of it and of HSO_4^-. Frequently, concentrated H_2SO_4 is used as a dehydrating agent, as for example, in desiccators to keep substances dry. It is also used in reactions to favor splitting off of water. As an example of the latter, H_2SO_4 is used in the manufacture of ethers from alcohols.

$$2C_2H_5OH \xrightarrow[H_2SO_4]{} C_2H_5OC_2H_5 + H_2O$$

In aqueous solutions, H_2SO_4 is a strong acid, but only for dissociation of one proton. The dissociation constant for the second proton is 1.3×10^{-2}. Because of the dissociation

$$HSO_4^- \longrightarrow H^+ + SO_4^{--}$$

solutions of HSO_4^-, such as solutions of sodium hydrogen sulfate ($NaHSO_4$), are acid. Because of the reverse reaction, solutions of SO_4^{--}, such as solutions of sodium sulfate (Na_2SO_4), are slightly basic. However, the extent of hydrolysis is extremely small ($K_h = 7.7 \times 10^{-13}$), and these solutions of sulfate salts are essentially neutral.

For the half-reaction

$$SO_2 + 2H_2O \longrightarrow HSO_4^- + 3H^+ + 2e^-$$

the oxidation potential is -0.11 volt. This means that HSO_4^- at 1 m concentration is a mild oxidizing agent. However, its action as an oxidizing agent in dilute solution at room temperature is not observed because reaction is so slow. With hot, concentrated solutions of sulfuric acid, oxidation is observed. For example, sodium bromide plus hot H_2SO_4 produces some bromine by oxidation of Br^- to Br_2. Furthermore, some of the less active metals such as copper are soluble in hot, concentrated sulfuric acid, presumably because of oxidation by sulfate.

Although sulfate is not an especially good oxidizing agent, there is a closely related derivative which is an extremely powerful oxidizing agent. This derivative is produced by electrolytic oxidation of cold, concentrated sulfuric acid and has been assigned the formula $H_2S_2O_8$. The acid is called peroxydisulfuric acid, and its salts are peroxy compounds, since they contain an oxygen-oxygen bond. The structural relation between H_2SO_4 and $H_2S_2O_8$ is shown in the following half-reaction:

$$2H-O-\overset{\displaystyle O}{\underset{\displaystyle O}{S}}-O-H \rightleftharpoons H-O-\overset{\displaystyle O}{\underset{\displaystyle O}{S}}-O-O-\overset{\displaystyle O}{\underset{\displaystyle O}{S}}-O-H + 2H^+ + 2e^-$$

The forward reaction applies to the electrolytic preparation; the reverse reaction, to the action of $H_2S_2O_8$ as an oxidizing agent. Both the acid and its salts, such as ammonium peroxydisulfate, $(NH_4)_2S_2O_8$, are very strong oxidizing agents and can, for example, oxidize manganous salts to permanganate. On a relative scale, the peroxydisulfates ($E° = -2.01$ volts) are about as good oxidizing agents as ozone ($E° = -2.07$ volts). In addition to their use as oxidizing agents, the peroxydisulfates are important as intermediates in the preparation of hydrogen peroxide.

$$K_2S_2O_8(s) + 2H^+ + 2H_2O \longrightarrow 2H_2SO_4 + H_2O_2 + 2K^+$$

In addition to the oxy compounds that sulfur forms in the +6 oxidation state, there are important oxy compounds corresponding to the +4 state of sulfur. The simplest of these is the dioxide, SO_2, which is formed either by burning sulfur in air or by reducing sulfates. At room temperature, SO_2 is a gas, but it is quite easily liquefied (bp, $-10°C$). The easy liquefaction reflects the fact that the molecule is polar because it has a nonlinear arrangement of atoms (shown in Section 3.7). Sulfur dioxide has a disagreeable, choking odor and is somewhat poisonous. It is especially toxic to lower organisms such as fungi and for this reason is used for sterilizing dried fruit and wine barrels. With water, SO_2 dissolves to give acid solutions, which contain about 5% sulfurous acid, H_2SO_3. The compound H_2SO_3 has never been isolated pure; any attempt to concentrate the solution, as by heating, simply expels SO_2. H_2SO_3 is a weak diprotic acid for which the principal equilibria are

$$SO_2 + H_2O \rightleftharpoons H_2SO_3 \qquad K = 0.05$$

$$SO_2 + H_2O \rightleftharpoons H^+ + HSO_3^- \qquad K = 1.3 \times 10^{-2}$$

$$HSO_3^- \rightleftharpoons H^+ + SO_3^{--} \qquad K = 5.6 \times 10^{-8}$$

It forms two series of salts. The sulfites, for example, Na_2SO_3, give slightly basic solutions owing to hydrolysis of SO_3^{--}; the hydrogen sulfites, for example, $NaHSO_3$, give slightly acid solutions, because the dissociation of HSO_3^- outweighs its hydrolysis. Addition of concentrated acids to either solid sulfites or solid hydrogen sulfites liberates SO_2 and is a convenient way of making sulfur dioxide in the laboratory. Sulfites, hydrogen sulfites, and sulfurous acid are mild reducing agents and are relatively easily oxidized to sulfates, though sometimes the reaction is quite slow.

When solutions containing sulfite ion are boiled with elemental sulfur, the solid sulfur dissolves in a reaction

$$S(s) + SO_3^{--} \rightleftharpoons S_2O_3^{--}$$

which is easily reversed by addition of acid. The ion formed, $S_2O_3^{--}$, is called thiosulfate ion, where the prefix *thio-* indicates substitution of a sulfur atom for an oxygen atom. Apparently, $S_2O_3^{--}$ contains two different kinds of sulfur atoms, as found by the following experiment: Solid sulfur containing a radioactive isotope of sulfur was boiled with a solution containing nonradioactive sulfite ions. The thiosulfate ions formed were found to be radioactive, but after acid was added so as to reverse the above reaction, all the radioactivity was recovered as precipitated solid sulfur. The implication is that the same S atom which adds on to SO_3^{--} to form $S_2O_3^{--}$ is dropped off when acid is added. This can be true only if the added S atom is bound in $S_2O_3^{--}$ in a way that is unlike the binding of the S atom already in SO_3^{--}. Otherwise, the two S atoms in $S_2O_3^{--}$ would be identical, and the addition of acid would not preferentially drop off the added radioactive S atom but would have a 50-50 chance of retaining it and its activity in the complex SO_3^{--}. The structure proposed for $S_2O_3^{--}$ has one sulfur atom at the center of a tetrahedron with the other sulfur atom and the three oxygen atoms at the four corners of the tetrahedron. The reverse reaction is brought about by acid, because H^+ unites with SO_3^{--}, and thus, by the principle of Le Chatelier, acid should favor the back reaction. This reaction is quite slow, at least so far as formation of visible solid sulfur is concerned. Indeed, when acid is added to thiosulfate solutions, nothing is observed at first. Then a white milkiness develops as colloidal sulfur is produced by gradual agglomeration of S atoms. In another reaction besides the above, thiosulfate ion acts as a mild reducing agent

$$2S_2O_3^{--} \longrightarrow S_4O_6^{--} + 2e^- \qquad -0.08 \text{ volt}$$

and has, for example, the ability of reducing iodine, I_2, to iodide ion, I^-. The reaction, which produces tetrathionate ion, $S_4O_6{}^{--}$, is frequently used to determine the amount of iodine in a solution. It also makes possible the quantitative analysis of many oxidizing agents. The unknown oxidizing agent is reduced with an excess of I^-, and the liberated I_2 is titrated with a thiosulfate solution. Thiosulfate ion also has the ability to form complex ions with the ions of some metals, especially Ag^+. The silver-thiosulfate complex ion is so stable

$$Ag^+ + 2S_2O_3{}^{--} \longrightarrow Ag(S_2O_3)_2{}^{-3} \qquad K = 1.6 \times 10^{13}$$

that thiosulfate solutions can dissolve the insoluble silver halides (see Section 22.3 for the use of thiosulfate in the photographic fixing process).

Besides occurring in the positive oxidation states, sulfur forms compounds corresponding to negative oxidation states, especially -2. The most familiar of these compounds is probably hydrogen sulfide, H_2S, notorious for its rotten-egg odor. Not so well known is the fact that hydrogen sulfide is as poisonous as hydrogen cyanide and four times as poisonous as carbon monoxide. The presence of H_2S in sewer gas is due to putrefaction of sulfur-containing organic material. The pure compound can be made by bubbling hydrogen gas through molten sulfur. In the laboratory, it is conveniently prepared by interaction of some sulfide such as FeS with acid

$$FeS(s) + 2H^+ \longrightarrow Fe^{++} + H_2S(g)$$

or by the warming of a solution of thioacetamide

Thioacetamide   Acetamide

This latter reaction is frequently used as an easily controlled laboratory source of hydrogen sulfide for qualitative analysis. Like H_2O, H_2S has a bent molecule and is polar; however, it is considerably harder to liquefy (bp, $-61°C$), presumably because of the lack of hydrogen bonding (Section 15.5) in the liquid. Gaseous H_2S burns to produce H_2O and either sulfur or sulfur dioxide, depending on the temperature and the oxygen supply. It is a mild reducing agent and can, for example, reduce ferric ion to ferrous ion

$$2Fe^{+3} + H_2S(g) \longrightarrow 2Fe^{++} + S(s) + 2H^+$$

During the course of the reaction, the solution becomes milky from the production of colloidal sulfur. In aqueous solution H_2S is a weak diprotic acid for which the dissociation constants are $K_I = 1.1 \times 10^{-7}$ and $K_{II} = 1 \times 10^{-14}$. A detailed consideration of the equilibria in aqueous H_2S solutions is given in Section 12.9.

Derived from H_2S are the sulfides, such as Na_2S and HgS. In regard to their solubility in water, the sulfides vary widely from those which,

Soluble in water	Na_2S, K_2S, $(NH_4)_2S$, BaS
Soluble in 0.3 M H^+	ZnS, FeS, MnS, CoS
Soluble in hot HNO_3	CuS, Ag_2S, PbS, SnS
Soluble in aqua regia	HgS

26.4
Solubilities of sulfides

like Na_2S, are quite soluble in water to those which, like HgS, require drastic treatment to be brought into solution.* In Figure 26.4 are listed various representative sulfides and methods required to dissolve them. The alkali-metal and alkaline-earth-metal sulfides dissolve readily in water to give basic solutions, with extensive hydrolysis of sulfide ion.

$$Na_2S(s) + H_2O \longrightarrow 2Na^+ + HS^- + OH^-$$

This equation represents the principal net reaction; about 10% of the sulfide ion remains unhydrolyzed. Because the sulfides of the group I and group II metals are so soluble, they cannot be precipitated by bubbling H_2S through solutions of their salts. As already discussed in Section 12.9, some sulfides that are insoluble in water can be dissolved simply by raising the H^+ concentration. ZnS, for example, is soluble in 0.3 M H^+, because the H^+ serves to lower the concentration of sulfide ion (in equilibrium with solid ZnS) by combining with it to form H_2S. The net equation can be represented as

$$ZnS(s) + 2H^+ \longrightarrow Zn^{++} + H_2S$$

The sulfides in the third row of Figure 26.4 are so insoluble that they cannot be dissolved by H^+ alone. However, hot nitric acid oxidizes sulfide to sulfur and hence lowers the sulfide-ion concentration sufficiently to permit solubility. For CuS, the net reaction can be written

$$3CuS(s) + 8H^+ + 2NO_3^- \longrightarrow 3Cu^{++} + 3S(s) + 2NO(g) + 4H_2O$$

The least soluble of the sulfides shown in Figure 26.4, mercuric sulfide, is not appreciably soluble in hot HNO_3. In order to "dissolve" it, aqua regia must be used in order that oxidation of the sulfide ion may be accompanied by complexing of the mercuric ion. The net reaction might be written

$$HgS(s) + 2NO_3^- + 4Cl^- + 4H^+ \longrightarrow$$
$$HgCl_4^{--} + 2NO_2(g) + S(s) + 2H_2O$$

although the reduction product of nitrate is probably a mixture rather than just NO_2. The differences in solubility behavior of metal sulfides can be used to great advantage in the separation and identification of various elements, as in qualitative analysis.

In addition to sulfides, sulfur forms polysulfides, in which two or more sulfur atoms are bound together in a chain. These polysulfides

Group VI elements

529

* HgS can be "dissolved" by heating it with aqua regia, but it is questionable whether this is a good description of the process. Although the mercury dissolves as $HgCl_4^{--}$, the sulfur does not dissolve but is oxidized to insoluble elemental sulfur.

can be made, for example, by boiling a solution of a soluble sulfide with elemental sulfur. With Na_2S and sulfur, the product is usually described as Na_2S_x and is thought to consist of Na^+ ions and $[S_x]^{--}$ ions. The polysulfide chains are of varying length and can be considered as being formed by progressive addition of sulfur atoms to sulfide ion.

$$[:\ddot{S}:]^{--} + \ddot{S}: \longrightarrow [:\ddot{S}:\ddot{S}:]^{--}$$

$$[:\ddot{S}:\ddot{S}:]^{--} + \ddot{S}: \longrightarrow [:\ddot{S}:\ddot{S}:\ddot{S}:]^{--} \text{ etc.}$$

The simplest of the polysulfide chains is the disulfide, S_2^{--}; it is found in the mineral FeS_2, iron pyrites, or fool's gold. Solid FeS_2 has a NaCl-like structure (Figure 6.6) consisting of an array of alternating Fe^{++} and S_2^{--} ions. In acid solution disulfides (and other polysulfides) break down to form solid sulfur and H_2S. In some respects, disulfides resemble peroxides. They are, for example, oxidizing agents, especially for metal sulfides. Thus, a solution of Na_2S_2 can oxidize stannous sulfide, SnS ($+2$ state of tin), to SnS_3^{--} ($+4$ state of tin).

$$SnS(s) + S_2^{--} \longrightarrow SnS_3^{--}$$

Tin is assigned oxidation number $+4$ in the thiostannate ion, SnS_3^{--}, because acidification produces stannic sulfide, SnS_2. The SnS_2 is identical with that precipitated from stannic solutions by H_2S.

26.3 SELENIUM

Selenium is about as rare as gold. It occurs principally along with sulfur, both as elemental selenium in native sulfur and as selenides in various sulfide minerals. Most commercial selenium is obtained as a by-product of the electrolytic refining of copper. The element exists in several allotropic forms, the most stable of which at room temperature is hexagonal, or "metallic," selenium. In this form, selenium atoms are joined in infinitely long spiral chains arranged parallel to each other. When dissolved in molten sulfur, these chains form Se_8 molecules, as is indicated by the freezing-point depression of the sulfur.

"Metallic" selenium is a poor conductor of electricity in the dark, but its conductivity increases proportionally to its illumination; i.e., it is a photoconductor. This property is utilized in the selenium photocell, used in exposure meters for measuring light intensity. The basic feature of the cell is a sandwich consisting of a copper plate, a selenium coating, and a thin, translucent gold film. Electrical leads go to the copper and to the gold film, but the circuit is not complete until light falls on the selenium. In the selenium rectifier, for converting alternating current to direct current, a similar cell is used; it differs in that the gold film of the photocell is replaced by an alloy such as Wood's metal. The selenium-to-alloy junction acts as a barrier to current, but in only one direction. In spite of these interesting properties, most selenium goes to the glass industry, where it is added in small amounts to molten glass to counteract the objectionable green color due to iron impurities. In large amounts it gives red glass.

The chemistry of selenium is similar to that of sulfur. It reacts with metals to form selenides, for example, Al_2Se_3, which decompose in acid to give gaseous hydrogen selenide, H_2Se. This, like H_2S, is toxic and burns to give Se or SeO_2, but it is a stronger reducing agent than H_2S. Selenium dioxide, SeO_2, is a colorless solid which dissolves in water to give the weak selenious acid, H_2SeO_3 ($K_I = 2.7 \times 10^{-3}$ and $K_{II} = 2.5 \times 10^{-7}$). Selenic acid, H_2SeO_4, the analogue of sulfuric acid, can be formed by oxidation of selenious acid with hydrogen peroxide or chlorine. It is a colorless solid which is not so strong an acid as H_2SO_4 but is a stronger oxidizing agent.

26.4 TELLURIUM

Nearly as abundant as selenium, tellurium is the only element with which gold occurs chemically combined in nature. It is also present as tellurides in copper and lead minerals and, in fact, is obtained principally as a by-product of their refining. The most stable modification of the element is hexagonal, or "metallic," tellurium. Its structure is much like that of selenium, but its photoconductivity is only slight. Because it is a semiconductor, its principal but limited use is in making rectifiers.

Hydrogen telluride, H_2Te, is a vile-smelling gas, unstable with respect to decomposition to the elements. In water it acts as a moderately weak acid ($K_I = 2.3 \times 10^{-3}$), slightly stronger than H_2Se ($K_I = 1.9 \times 10^{-4}$), which in turn is stronger than H_2S. Bi_2Te_3 is an important solid-state material for direct conversion of heat to electric current. Tellurium dioxide (TeO_2) and tellurous acid (H_2TeO_3) resemble the corresponding selenium compounds. Unlike selenic acid, telluric acid (H_6TeO_6) contains six oxygen atoms bound to the central tellurium atom, presumably because of the larger size of the tellurium atom. It is a very weak acid but a strong oxidizing agent.

Investigation of the chemical behavior of tellurium compounds, and to some extent of selenium compounds, has been retarded because of the foul-smelling nature of the compounds. These are taken up by the body and given off in the perspiration and breath. Elimination is slow, and the stench of "tellurium breath" may linger for months.

26.5 POLONIUM

Work on polonium has been retarded because of its high radioactivity. The nucleus is unstable and, like the radium nucleus, decomposes with the emission of alpha particles. Since alpha radiation is damaging to the human body, the element is extremely dangerous. Amounts greater than 0.000000000004 g cannot be tolerated in the body.

Polonium occurs naturally in uranium minerals such as pitchblende, but only to the extent of $5 \times 10^{-9}\%$ of the mineral. It is constantly being produced by the radioactive decay of other elements, but since it itself decays, the concentration stays constant.

X-ray studies of trace amounts indicate that the element exists in two forms which may be metallic, one of which seems to resemble lead. Little is known of its compounds, but it appears to form PoH_2, Po^{++}, PoO_2, and PoO_3.

26.6 QUALITATIVE ANALYSIS

An unknown solution might contain sulfur as sulfide, sulfate, or sulfite. The sulfide, on addition of acid, generates H_2S gas which can be detected either by its odor or by its blackening (due to PbS formation) of filter paper wet with a solution of lead acetate. Sulfate, on addition of barium nitrate and acid, produces white insoluble $BaSO_4$. If sulfite is present, it will not precipitate with Ba^{++} in acid solution; however, if Br_2 is added, the sulfite will be oxidized to sulfate and $BaSO_4$ forms.

QUESTIONS

26.1 Oxidation potentials By reference to Appendix 6, predict which of the following should be reduced by SO_2 in acid solution: I_2, Fe^{+3}, H_3PO_4, Cr^{+3}, Ag^+, Mn^{++}.

26.2 Sulfuric acid Commercially available "concentrated" H_2SO_4 is generally about 93% H_2SO_4 by weight with a density of 1.83 g cc^{-1}. Calculate the molarity of this solution.

26.3 Bisulfite You need a solution of HSO_3^- for a particular reaction. The chemical supply catalogs do not list any solid bisulfites. Which of the following could you dissolve in water to give the desired solution: Na_2SO_3, $Na_2S_2O_3$, $Na_2S_2O_5$, $Na_2S_2O_8$?

26.4 S equations Write balanced equations for each of the following: (*a*) FeS_2 is burned in O_2 to give Fe_2O_3, (*b*) chalcocite is dissolved in nitric acid to form S and NO, (*c*) generation of white fumes of SO_3 by thermal decomposition of $NaHSO_4$, (*d*) formation of white cloudiness from acidification of thiosulfate solution, (*e*) oxidation of H_2S to S by $Cr_2O_7^{--}$ in acid solution.

26.5 Group trends In the simplest approximation the energy required to ionize an atom is directly proportional to the effective nuclear charge and inversely proportional to the atomic radius. From the atomic radii of Figure 2.19 and the ionization potentials of Figure 26.1, calculate the effective nuclear charge for each group VI atom referred to $+6$ for oxygen.

26.6 Equations Write balanced equations for each of the following: (*a*) reaction of Al_2Se_3 with acid, (*b*) oxidation of selenious acid by chlorine, (*c*) reduction of telluric acid to the element by zinc, (*d*) dissolving of Na_2TeO_4 in water to form $H_5TeO_6^-$, (*e*) radioactive decay of $_{84}Po^{210}$.

26.7 Dissociation constant From the data given in Section 26.2, calculate the true K_I for H_2SO_3.

26.8 Mixing problem Assuming a net reaction involving oxidation of SO_3^{--} to SO_4^{--} by BrO^- going to Br^-, calculate the concentrations of

Na^+, OH^-, SO_3^{--}, SO_4^{--}, and Br^- in 0.100 liter of solution made by mixing 60.0 ml of 1.0 M NaOH with 10.0 ml of 0.20 M NaBrO and 30.0 ml of 0.10 M Na_2SO_3.

26.9 Thiosulfate equilibrium   Calculate K for the reaction

$$AgCl(s) + 2S_2O_3^{--} \longrightarrow Ag(S_2O_3)_2^{-3} + Cl^-$$

26.10 Structure   Calculate for the S_8 molecule the distance from one sulfur nucleus to the sulfur nucleus directly across the ring.

26.11 Thermodynamics   One hypothesis for the generation of gypsum deposits ($CaSO_4 \cdot 2H_2O$) involves the following reaction:

$$CaCO_3(s) + S(s) + \tfrac{3}{2}O_2(g) + 2H_2O(l) \longrightarrow CaSO_4 \cdot 2H_2O(s) + CO_2(g)$$

(a) Given that the standard free energies of formation are -429.2 kcal mole^{-1} for $CaSO_4 \cdot 2H_2O(s)$, -269.8 kcal mole^{-1} for $CaCO_3(s)$, -56.7 kcal mole^{-1} for $H_2O(l)$, and -94.3 kcal mole^{-1} for $CO_2(g)$, calculate the standard free-energy change for the conversion. (b) Supposing the CO_2 pressure generated by this reaction to be 1.0 atm, what O_2 pressure would be in equilibrium with the system?

26.12 Stoichiometry   You are given a mixture of Na_2SO_3 and Na_2SO_4. Half of the mixture, after oxidation, gives 2.86 g of $BaSO_4$ on addition of Ba^{++} in acid. The other half of the mixture gives 1.62 g of $BaSO_4$ on addition of Ba^{++} in acid. Calculate the weight percent of Na_2SO_4 in the original sample.

26.13 Buffer   (a) Calculate the concentrations of H^+, SO_3^{--}, and HSO_3^- in a solution made by mixing equal volumes of 0.010 M $NaHSO_3$ and 0.010 M Na_2SO_3. (b) What are the concentrations of SO_2 and of H_2SO_3 in the mixture of part (a)?

26.14 Solution reactions   Calculate the concentration of each ion in the final solution made by mixing 40.0 ml of 1.0 M Na_2SO_3, 40.0 ml of 0.50 M NaOH, and 20.0 ml of 1.0 M $KMnO_4$. The reduction product in basic solution is MnO_2. K_{diss} for HSO_4^- is 1.3×10^{-2}, and K_{diss} for HSO_3^- is 5.6×10^{-8}. Calculate also the pH of the final solution.

26.15 Sulfide precipitation   What is the maximum K_{sp} a sulfide MS can have to precipitate when H_2S is added to 0.10 M solution of M^{++} in (a) 0.30 M H^+, (b) equimolar acetate-acetic acid buffer, (c) equimolar ammonia-ammonium buffer?

26.16 Bisulfate   A solution is made by mixing ½ ml of saturated Na_2SO_4 (containing 24.4 g of Na_2SO_4 per 100 ml of solution) and ½ ml of 2 M $NaHSO_4$. What is the pH in the final mixture? For HSO_4^-, K_{diss} is 1.3×10^{-2}.

26.17 Kinetics   For the decomposition of peroxydisulfate

$$S_2O_8^{--} + H_2O \longrightarrow 2HSO_4^- + \tfrac{1}{2}O_2$$

the reaction is first order in $S_2O_8^{--}$ with a specific rate constant of 0.0016 min^{-1} at 70°C and 0.016 min^{-1} at 90°C. How long would it take for 25% decomposition of a peroxydisulfate solution at 25°C?

26.2 17 M 26.5 (+6); +6.4; +6.8; +7.4; +7.7   26.8 0.68 M Na^+; 0.60 M OH^-; 0.010 M SO_3^{--}; 0.020 M SO_4^{--}; 0.020 M Br^- 26.10 4.64 Å   26.11 (a) -140.3 kcal   (b) 2.7×10^{-69} atm   26.13 (a) 5.6×10^{-8} M; 0.0050 M; 0.0050 M (b) 2.2×10^{-8} M; 1×10^{-9} M 26.15 (a) 1×10^{-22} (b) 3×10^{-14} (c) 3×10^{-5} 26.17 68 days

27 halogens

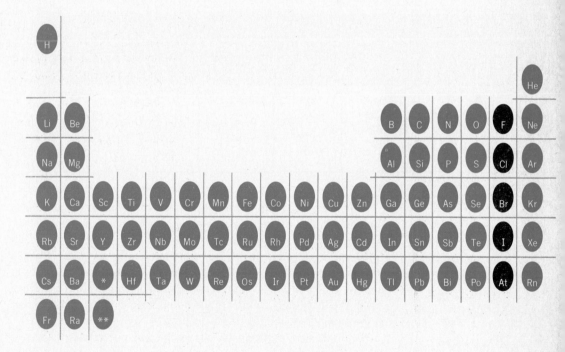

Although the chemistry of the group VII elements is somewhat complex, similarities within the group are more pronounced than in any of the other groups except I and II. The elements, fluorine, chlorine, bromine, iodine, and astatine, are collectively called halogens (from the Greek *halos,* salt, and *genes,* born), or salt producers, because they all have high electronegativity and form negative halide ions such as are found in ionic salts. Except for fluorine, they also show positive oxidation states.

27.1 GROUP PROPERTIES

Because of their high electronegativity, the halogens show practically no metallic properties, though solid iodine has a somewhat metallic appearance. Astatine, the heaviest member of the group, may also have some metal properties, but it is a short-lived radioactive element and not enough of it has been prepared to see whether the solid is metallic. Other properties of the group are shown in Figure 27.1. Although the bond between the halogen atoms in the X_2 molecules is fairly strong (see Figure 27.2), the attraction between X_2 molecules is quite weak and due only to van der Waals forces. In going down the group there is an increasing number of electrons per X_2 molecule, and we would expect van der Waals attraction to increase. Thus, it is not surprising that the boiling points increase in going from F_2 to I_2. At room temperature fluorine and chlorine are gases, bromine is a liquid, and iodine is a solid.

Symbol	Z	Electronic configuration	Melting point, °C	Boiling point, °C	Ionization potential, ev	Oxidation potential, volts (X^- to X_2)
F	9	(2) $2s^22p^5$	−223	−187	17.42	−2.87
Cl	17	(10) $3s^23p^5$	−102	−34.6	13.01	−1.36
Br	35	(28) $4s^24p^5$	−7.3	58.78	11.84	−1.09
I	53	(46) $5s^25p^5$	114	183	10.44	−0.54
At	85	(78) $6s^26p^5$	—	—	—	−0.2

27.1
Elements of group VII

As indicated by the relatively high values of the ionization potentials, it is fairly difficult to remove an electron from a halogen atom. In fact, more energy is required to remove an electron from a halogen atom than from any other atom in the same period except for the noble gas (compare values in Figure 2.23.) Within the group itself there is, of course, a decrease in the ionization potential; the larger the halogen atom, the less firmly bound are the outermost electrons and the lower is the energy required to remove an electron from the neutral atom.

Of greater significance chemically are the oxidation potentials, given in the last column of Figure 27.1. The potentials show that fluorine gas is the best oxidizing agent of the group. The reason for this, however, is not so simple as it appears. The overall half-reaction

$$X^-(aq) \longrightarrow \tfrac{1}{2}X_2(g) + e^-$$

can be constructed from the alternate path

27.1 Group properties
536

$$X^-(aq) \xrightarrow{\text{I}} X^-(g) \xrightarrow{\text{II}} X(g) + e^- \xrightarrow{\text{III}} \tfrac{1}{2}X_2(g) + e^-$$

Step I corresponds to removing the anions from the aqueous phase to the gas; step II, to the removal of electrons from the gaseous ions to give neutral atoms; step III, to the combining of neutral atoms to give the diatomic molecule. The free-energy changes for the various steps are listed in Figure 27.2. In the case of fluorine, for example, the sum of the three processes shown has a net free-energy change of $+182$ kcal for $X^-(aq) \longrightarrow \frac{1}{2}X_2(g) + e^-$. The electron, however, as discussed in Section 18.1, is referred to a hydrogen-electrode standard, which amounts to having a change of -115 kcal in the free energy:

$$X^-(aq) \longrightarrow \frac{1}{2}X_2(g) + e^- \qquad \Delta G^\circ = +182 \text{ kcal}$$

$$\underline{e^- + H^+(aq) \longrightarrow \frac{1}{2}H_2(g) \qquad \Delta G^\circ = -115 \text{ kcal}}$$

$$X^-(aq) + H^+(aq) \longrightarrow \frac{1}{2}X_2(g) + \frac{1}{2}H_2(g) \qquad \Delta G^\circ = +67 \text{ kcal}$$

By using the relation $\Delta G^\circ = -n\mathcal{F}E^\circ$, we see that the final ΔG° corresponds to a voltage of -2.9 volts. In other words, the calculated oxidation potential for fluorine is -2.9 volts. Similar calculations for chlorine, bromine, and iodine give E° values of -1.3, -1.1, and -0.55 volts, respectively. For the case of bromine and especially for the case of iodine, it is necessary to correct for the fact that the final state of X_2 is not gaseous but liquid and solid, respectively. This correction amounts to -0.4 kcal for bromine and -2.3 kcal for iodine.

Step	Fluorine	Chlorine	Bromine	Iodine
$X^-(aq) \longrightarrow X^-(g)$	$+114$	$+84$	$+78$	$+70$
$X^-(g) \longrightarrow X(g) + e^-$	$+83$	$+86$	$+81$	$+74$
$X(g) \longrightarrow \frac{1}{2}X_2(g)$	-15	-25	-19	-14

27.2
Free-energy data for halogens, kcal mole^{-1}

Comparing the halogens with each other, we see from Figure 27.2 that the most significant difference between the elements is the hydration step. It is about equally difficult to remove an electron from any gaseous halide ion [actually, most difficult in the case of $Cl^-(g)$]. Except for chlorine, there is about equal tendency for the atoms to pair up to form the X_2 molecule. In fact, if only the sum of the last two steps were considered, there would not be much difference between the various halogens and the E°'s would be within 0.3 volt of each other. The biggest single factor in making the E°'s differ greatly from each other is the hydration free energy. In going from F^- to I^- there is a large increase in ionic radius (1.33 Å for F^-, 1.81 Å for Cl^-, 1.96 Å for Br^-, and 2.20 Å for I^-) which makes for a large decrease in affinity for water. The reason why F_2 is such a good oxidizing agent [and $F^-(aq)$ is such a poor reducing agent] is that the fluoride ion is so strongly hydrated.*

* Although this discussion has been confined to aqueous solution, the uniquely great oxidizing strength of fluorine shows up even when water solutions are not involved. Thus, for example, dry F_2 can oxidize solid NaCl to Cl_2 and NaF. In these cases oxidation results because the smaller size of the fluoride ion leads to more favorable lattice energies.

Fluorine is the most electronegative of all the elements; therefore, it can show only a negative oxidation state. The other halogens, however, also show positive oxidation states in compounds with more electronegative elements. Most of these compounds contain oxygen, which has electronegativity between that of fluorine and chlorine. In their oxy compounds chlorine and iodine show a maximum oxidation number of $+7$, but the corresponding $+7$ bromine compounds have not been prepared. In addition, Cl, Br, and I form compounds in which the halogen atom is assigned oxidation numbers $+1$ and $+5$.

27.2 FLUORINE

Fluorine is about half as abundant as chlorine and is widely distributed in nature. It occurs principally as the minerals fluorspar, CaF_2; cryolite, Na_3AlF_6; and fluorapatite, $Ca_5F(PO_4)_3$. Because none of the ordinary chemical oxidizing agents is capable of extracting electrons from fluoride ions, elemental fluorine is prepared only by electrolytic oxidation of molten fluorides, such as KF-HF mixtures. At room temperature fluorine is a pale yellow gas which is extremely corrosive and reactive. With hydrogen it forms violently explosive mixtures because of the reaction

$$H_2(g) + F_2(g) \longrightarrow 2HF(g) \qquad \Delta H^\circ = -128 \text{ kcal}$$

On the skin it causes severe burns which are quite slow to heal.

Hydrogen fluoride is usually made by the action of sulfuric acid on fluorspar. Because of hydrogen bonding (Section 15.5), liquid HF has a higher boiling point (19.5°C) than any of the other hydrogen halides. Hydrogen bonding is also present in the gas phase and accounts for polymeric species, $(HF)_x$, where x is some small number such as 6 or less. In aqueous solutions HF is called hydrofluoric acid and is unique among the hydrogen halides in being a weak, rather than a strong, acid ($K_{\text{diss}} = 6.7 \times 10^{-4}$) and in being able to dissolve glass. The latter reaction is attributed to the formation of fluosilicate ions as in the equation

$$SiO_2(s) + 6HF \longrightarrow SiF_6^{--} + 2H_2O + 2H^+$$

where glass is represented for simplicity as SiO_2. Other complex ions of fluorine are known, for example, AlF_6^{-3}, ZrF_7^{-3}, TaF_8^{-3}, in which the small size of fluoride ion permits relatively large numbers of them to be attached to another atom.

In general, most simple fluoride salts formed with $+1$ cations are soluble (for example, KF and AgF) and give slightly basic solutions because of the hydrolysis of F^- to HF. With $+2$ cations, however, the fluorides are usually insoluble (for example, CaF_2 and PbF_2), but their solubility is somewhat increased in acid solution. The formation of insoluble, inert fluorides as surface coatings is apparently the reason why fluorine and its compounds can be stored in metal containers such as copper.

With oxygen fluorine forms two compounds, oxygen difluoride (OF_2) and dioxygen difluoride (O_2F_2). The first can be prepared by passing fluorine very rapidly through dilute NaOH solution.

$$2F_2(g) + 2OH^- \longrightarrow 2F^- + OF_2(g) + H_2O$$

It is somewhat less reactive than F_2 and slowly reacts with water to form HF and O_2. O_2F_2 results as a red liquid when an electric discharge is passed through a mixture of fluorine and oxygen below $-100°C$. It is unstable with respect to decomposition to the elements.

Most amazing of the fluorine compounds are the fluorocarbons. These are materials which can be considered to be derived from the hydrocarbons (Section 24.4) by substitution of fluorine atoms for hydrogen atoms. Thus, the fluorocarbon corresponding to methane, CH_4, is tetrafluoromethane, CF_4. This compound is typical of the saturated (i.e., containing no double bonds) fluorocarbons in being extremely inert. For example, unlike methane, it can be heated in air without burning. Furthermore, it can be treated with boiling nitric acid, concentrated sulfuric acid, and strong oxidizing agents such as potassium permanganate with no change. Reducing agents such as hydrogen and carbon do not affect it even at temperatures as high as $1000°C$. Because of their inertness, the fluorocarbons find application for special uses. For example, $C_{12}F_{26}$ is an ideal insulating liquid for heavy-duty transformers that operate at high temperature. Just as ethylene, C_2H_4, can polymerize to form polyethylene (Section 24.4), so tetrafluoroethylene, C_2F_4, can polymerize to form polytetrafluoroethylene. The polymerization can be imagined to proceed by the opening up of the double bond to form an unstable intermediate which joins with other molecules to produce a high polymer.

The high polymer is a plastic known commercially as Teflon, and, like the other saturated fluorocarbons, it is inert to chemical attack. It is unaffected even by boiling aqua regia or ozone. Though still rather expensive, fluorocarbon polymers find use as structural materials where corrosive conditions are extreme, as in chemical plants. They are also familiar for coating "greaseless" frying pans—a boon to brides, bachelors, and calorie counters.

27.3 CHLORINE

Chlorine is the most abundant (0.2%) of the halogens and occurs as chloride ion in seawater, salt wells, and salt beds, where it is combined with Na^+, K^+, Mg^{++}, and Ca^{++}. On a small scale, the element can be made by chemical oxidation as with MnO_2:

$$MnO_2(s) + 2Cl^- + 4H^+ \longrightarrow Mn^{++} + Cl_2(g) + 2H_2O$$

On a commercial scale, chlorine is more economically prepared by electrolytic oxidation of either aqueous or molten NaCl (see Section 13.2). The element is a greenish-yellow gas (in fact, it gets its name from the Greek *chloros*, green) and has a choking odor. Although not so reactive as fluorine, it is a good oxidizing agent and explodes with hydrogen when mixtures of H_2 and Cl_2 are exposed to ultraviolet light. In fact, chlorine has such great affinity for hydrogen that it reacts with hydrogen-containing compounds such as turpentine ($C_{10}H_{18}$) to form HCl and carbon. Most of the commercial chlorine is used as a bleach for paper and wood pulp and for large-scale disinfecting of public water supplies. Both of these uses depend on its oxidizing action.

The most important compounds of chlorine are those which correspond to the oxidation states -1, $+1$, $+5$, and $+7$, although there also are compounds of chlorine in the other positive states, $+3$, $+4$, and $+6$. The -1 state is familiar as the one assigned to chlorine in HCl and chloride salts. Although HCl can be produced by direct combination of the elements, a more convenient method of preparation is the heating of NaCl with concentrated H_2SO_4.

$$NaCl(s) + H_2SO_4 \longrightarrow NaHSO_4(s) + HCl(g)$$

Hydrogen chloride gas is very soluble in water, and it is the aqueous solutions that are properly referred to as hydrochloric acid. Commercially available concentrated hydrochloric acid is 37% HCl by mass, or 12 M. Unlike HF, HCl is a strong acid and is essentially completely dissociated into ions in 1 M solution. Why is HCl so much stronger as an acid than HF? The higher hydration energy of the fluoride ion would tend to favor the dissociation of HF. The fact that HCl is more highly dissociated apparently arises because the bond in HCl is weaker than that in HF. Inasmuch as HCl is a strong acid, there is no appreciable tendency for chloride ion to hydrolyze in aqueous solution. Thus, solutions of NaCl and KCl, for example, are neutral. Of the common chlorides, silver chloride (AgCl), mercurous chloride (Hg_2Cl_2), and lead chloride ($PbCl_2$) are rather insoluble.

The $+1$ oxidation state of chlorine is represented by hypochlorous acid, HOCl, and its salts, the hypochlorites. Hypochlorous acid is produced to a slight extent when chlorine gas is dissolved in water. Disproportionation of the dissolved chlorine occurs according to the equation

$$Cl_2 + H_2O \rightleftharpoons Cl^- + H^+ + HOCl \qquad K = 4.7 \times 10^{-4}$$

The yield of products can be greatly increased by tying up the Cl^- and H^+, as by adding silver oxide (Ag^+ to precipitate AgCl and oxide to neutralize H^+). The formula of hypochlorous acid is usually written HOCl, instead of HClO, to emphasize the fact that the proton is bonded to the oxygen and not directly to the chlorine. The acid is weak, with a dissociation constant of 3.2×10^{-8}, and exists only in aqueous solution. Even in solution it slowly decomposes with evolution of oxygen.

$$2HOCl \longrightarrow 2H^+ + 2Cl^- + O_2(g)$$

HOCl is a powerful oxidizing agent, as shown by the oxidation potential for the half-reaction

$$Cl_2(g) + 2H_2O \longrightarrow 2HOCl + 2H^+ + 2e^- \qquad -1.63 \text{ volts}$$

The value is more negative than that for permanganate ion in acid solution (-1.51 volts), indicating that HOCl is a stronger oxidizing agent than MnO_4^-. Hypochlorites, such as NaClO, can be made by neutralization of HOCl solutions, but they are produced more economically by the disproportionation of chlorine in basic solution:

$$Cl_2 + 2OH^- \longrightarrow Cl^- + ClO^- + H_2O$$

Commercially, the process is efficiently carried out by electrolyzing cold aqueous NaCl solutions and stirring vigorously. The stirring serves to mix chlorine produced at the anode

$$2Cl^- \longrightarrow Cl_2 + 2e^-$$

with hydroxide ion produced at the cathode

$$2e^- + 2H_2O \longrightarrow H_2(g) + 2OH^-$$

so that reaction can occur. Solutions of hypochlorite ion so produced are sold as laundry bleaches, e.g., Clorox. Another common household bleach which owes its action to the oxidizing power of hypochlorite ion is bleaching powder, or chlorinated lime. It is largely $4Ca(ClO)_2 \cdot Ca(OH)_2$, and is prepared by treating calcium hydroxide with chlorine.

In aqueous solution, hypochlorite ion is unstable with respect to self-oxidation and, when warmed, disproportionates by the equation

$$3ClO^- \longrightarrow 2Cl^- + ClO_3^-$$

to produce chloride ion and chlorate ion (ClO_3^-). Chlorate ion contains chlorine in oxidation state $+5$. Its structure is pyramidal, with the three oxygen atoms forming the base of the pyramid and the chlorine atom the apex. Probably the most important chlorate salt is $KClO_3$, used as an oxidizing agent in matches, fireworks, and some explosives. Since $KClO_3$ is only moderately soluble in water, it can be precipitated by addition of KCl to chlorate-containing solutions. The chlorate solutions can be produced by electrolyzing hot chloride solutions that are vigorously stirred. Steps in the production can be summarized as follows:

$$2Cl^- + 2H_2O \xrightarrow{\text{electrolyze}} Cl_2 + 2OH^- + H_2(g)$$

$$3Cl_2 + 6OH^- \xrightarrow{\text{stir, heat}} 5Cl^- + ClO_3^- + 3H_2O$$

$$K^+ + ClO_3^- \longrightarrow KClO_3(s)$$

As seen from the equation for the second step, only one-sixth of the chlorine is converted to ClO_3^-, which makes the process seem rather inefficient. However, on continued electrolysis the chloride produced in the second step is reoxidized in the first step.

Unlike hypochlorite ion, chlorate ion is the anion of a strong acid.

The parent acid, $HClO_3$, chloric acid, has not been prepared in the pure state, since it is unstable. When attempts are made to concentrate chloric acid solutions, as by evaporation, violent explosions occur. The principal reaction is

$$4HClO_3 \longrightarrow 4ClO_2(g) + O_2(g) + 2H_2O(g)$$

but the chlorine dioxide, ClO_2, produced may decompose further. In acid aqueous solutions, chlorate ion, like hypochlorite ion, is a good oxidizing agent. The oxidation potential for the half-reaction

$$Cl_2(g) + 6H_2O \longrightarrow 2ClO_3^- + 12H^+ + 10e^- \qquad -1.47 \text{ volts}$$

indicates that ClO_3^- is almost the equal of MnO_4^-.

When $KClO_3$ is heated, it can decompose by two reactions

$$2KClO_3(s) \longrightarrow 2KCl(s) + 3O_2(g)$$

$$4KClO_3(s) \longrightarrow 3KClO_4(s) + KCl(s)$$

the first of which is catalyzed by surfaces, such as powdered glass or MnO_2, from which oxygen can readily escape. In the absence of such catalysts, especially at lower temperatures, the formation of potassium perchlorate ($KClO_4$) is favored. A more efficient method of preparing perchlorates is to use electrolytic oxidation of chlorate solutions. Since $KClO_4$ is only sparingly soluble in water (less than $KClO_3$), it can be made by addition of K^+ to perchlorate solutions. The perchlorate ion has a tetrahedral configuration with the chlorine atom at the center of the tetrahedron and the four oxygen atoms at the corners. In aqueous solutions perchlorate ion is potentially a good oxidizing agent

$$Cl_2(g) + 8H_2O \longrightarrow 2ClO_4^- + 16H^+ + 14e^- \qquad -1.39 \text{ volts}$$

especially in acid solution, but its reactions are so very slow that they are usually not observed. For example, a solution containing ClO_4^- and the very strong reducing agent Cr^{++} (chromous ion) can be kept for weeks without any appreciable oxidation to Cr^{+3} (chromic ion).

Like chlorate ion, perchlorate ion is an anion of a strong acid. Consequently, in aqueous solution there is practically no association of ClO_4^- with H^+. However, when perchlorate salts are treated with sulfuric acid, pure hydrogen perchlorate ($HClO_4$) may be distilled off under reduced pressure. The anhydrous compound is a liquid at room temperature and is extremely dangerous, because it may explode spontaneously. With water, $HClO_4$ forms a series of hydrates. The monohydrate, $HClO_4 \cdot H_2O$, is a crystalline solid which actually contains H_3O^+ and ClO_4^- at the lattice points. Like the anhydrous material, the hydrate should be treated with respect because of the possibility of explosions. The danger is especially great in the presence of reducing agents such as organic material (e.g., wood, cloth, etc.). Dilute aqueous solutions of $HClO_4$ are safe and are useful reagents for the chemist. For one thing, perchlorate ion has less tendency to form complex ions with metal cations than any other anion. For another thing, perchloric acid is probably the strongest of all common acids and in aqueous solution is more completely dissociated than the usual strong acids, hydrochloric, sulfuric, and nitric.

Why is perchloric a stronger acid than the other oxyacids of chlorine? The dissociation of an oxyacid involves breaking a hydrogen-oxygen bond to form a hydrated hydronium ion and a hydrated anion. The bigger the anion, the less its hydration energy. Consequently, since ClO_4^- is obviously bigger than ClO^-, for example, we might expect $HClO_4$ to be less dissociated than $HOCl$. Since the reverse is true, the bond holding the proton to OCl^- must be stronger than the bond holding H^+ to ClO_4^-. That this is reasonable can be seen by noting that oxygen is more electronegative than chlorine; therefore, addition of oxygen atoms to the $HOCl$ molecule pulls electrons away from the H—O bond and tends to weaken it. This picture is supported by observing that the intermediate oxyacid $HOClO$ (chlorous acid) has a dissociation constant, $K_{diss} = 1.1 \times 10^{-2}$, larger than that of $HOCl$, $K_{diss} = 3.2 \times 10^{-8}$. In general, for any series of oxyacids the acid corresponding to highest oxidation number is the most highly dissociated.

The above discussion of the oxy compounds of chlorine primarily concerned the oxidation states $+1$, $+5$, and $+7$. Brief mention was made of two compounds which represent two other states, ClO_2 ($+4$ state) and $HClO_2$ ($+3$ state). The first of these compounds, chlorine dioxide, is produced when $HClO_3$ explodes, but a safer method of preparing it involves reduction of acid chlorate solutions with sulfur dioxide, SO_2, or oxalic acid, $H_2C_2O_4$. Pertinent equations are

$$2ClO_3^- + SO_2(g) + H^+ \longrightarrow 2ClO_2(g) + HSO_4^-$$

$$2ClO_3^- + H_2C_2O_4 + 2H^+ \longrightarrow 2ClO_2(g) + 2CO_2(g) + 2H_2O$$

Chlorine dioxide is a yellow gas at room temperature but is easily condensed to a red liquid (bp, 11°C). The gas is paramagnetic, indicating that the molecule contains an unpaired electron. Despite the fact that ClO_2 is explosive, it is produced in large quantities for bleaching flour, paper, etc. Its use depends on the fact that it is both a strong and a rapid oxidizing agent. When placed in basic solution, chlorine dioxide disproportionates thus:

$$2ClO_2(g) + 2OH^- \longrightarrow ClO_2^- + ClO_3^- + H_2O$$

One product is chlorate ion, previously discussed; the other is chlorite ion, ClO_2^-, which is frequently prepared commercially by this reaction. Chlorite ion is the anion of the moderately weak acid, $HClO_2$, or chlorous acid. Like $HOCl$, it exists only in solution, and even in solution it decomposes. The principal reaction seems to be

$$5HClO_2 \longrightarrow 4ClO_2(g) + H^+ + Cl^- + 2H_2O$$

Chlorites are important industrial bleaching agents because they can bleach without appreciably affecting other properties of the substance bleached. Like other oxy compounds of chlorine, they must be used with caution, because the dry salts may explode when in contact with organic material.

27.4 BROMINE

Bromine, from the Greek word *bromos* for stink, occurs as bromide ion in seawater, brine wells, and salt beds and is less than a hundredth as abundant as chlorine. The element is usually prepared by chlorine oxidation of bromide solutions, as by sweeping chlorine gas through seawater. Since chlorine is a stronger oxidizing agent than bromine, the reaction

$$Cl_2(g) + 2Br^- \longrightarrow Br_2 + 2Cl^-$$

occurs as indicated. Removal of the bromine from the resulting solution can be accomplished by sweeping the solution with air, because bromine is quite volatile. At room temperature pure bromine is a mobile, but dense, red liquid of pungent odor. It is a dangerous substance, since it attacks the skin to form slow-healing sores.

Although less powerful an oxidizing agent than chlorine, bromine readily reacts with other elements to form bromides. Hydrogen bromide, like HCl, is a strong acid but is more easily oxidized than HCl is. Whereas HCl can be made by heating the sodium salt with H_2SO_4, HBr cannot. The hot H_2SO_4 oxidizes HBr to Br_2, and a nonoxidizing acid such as H_3PO_4 must be used instead.

In basic solution, bromine disproportionates to give bromide ion and hypobromite ion (BrO^-). The reaction is quickly followed by further disproportionation

$$3BrO^- \longrightarrow 2Br^- + BrO_3^-$$

to give bromate ion, BrO_3^-. Bromic acid, $HBrO_3$, has never been prepared pure. In aqueous solution, it is a strong acid and a good oxidizing agent. The oxidation potential

$$Br_2 + 6H_2O \longrightarrow 2BrO_3^- + 12H^+ + 10e^- \qquad -1.50 \text{ volts}$$

indicates that bromate is a slightly stronger oxidizing agent than chlorate. It has the added virtue of being faster in its action. No compounds corresponding to bromine in the $+7$ state are known at present, although many attempts have been made to prepare them. This is somewhat surprising, considering that both chlorine and iodine form such compounds.

One of the important uses of bromine is in making silver bromide for photographic emulsions (Section 22.3). However, the principal use of bromine is in making dibromoethane ($C_2H_4Br_2$) for addition to gasolines which contain tetraethyllead. Tetraethyllead, $(C_2H_5)_4Pb$, added to gasoline as an antiknock agent, decomposes on burning to form lead deposits. The dibromoethane prevents accumulation of lead deposits in the engine.

27.5 IODINE

Of the halogens, iodine is the only one which occurs naturally in a positive oxidation state. In addition to its occurrence as I^- in seawater and salt wells, it is found as sodium iodate ($NaIO_3$), small amounts of which are mixed with $NaNO_3$ in Chile saltpeter. The Chilean ore is processed by the reduction of $NaIO_3$ with controlled amounts of $NaHSO_3$. The principal reaction is

$$5HSO_3^- + 2IO_3^- \longrightarrow I_2 + 5SO_4^{--} + 3H^+ + H_2O$$

Excess hydrogen sulfite must be avoided, for it would reduce I_2 to I^-. In the United States most of the iodine is produced by chlorine oxidation of I^- from salt wells.

At room temperature iodine crystallizes as black leaflets with metallic luster. Although, as shown by X-ray analysis, the solid consists of discrete I_2 molecules, its properties are different from those of usual molecular solids. For example, its electrical conductivity, though small, increases with increasing temperature like that of a semiconductor. Furthermore, liquid iodine also has perceptible conductivity, which decreases with increasing temperature like that of a metal. Thus, feeble as they are, metallic properties do appear even in the halogen group.

When heated, solid iodine readily sublimes to give a violet vapor, which consists of I_2 molecules. The violet color is the same as that observed in many iodine solutions, such as those in CCl_4 and in hydrocarbons. However, in water and in alcohol the solutions are brown, presumably because of unusual interactions between I_2 and the solvent. When iodine is brought in contact with starch, a characteristic deep blue color results; the color has been attributed to a starch-I_2 complex. The formation of the blue color is the basis for using starch–potassium iodide mixtures as a qualitative test for the presence of oxidizing agents. Oxidizing agents convert I^- to I_2, which with starch forms the colored complex. With very strong oxidizing agents the color may fade with oxidation of I_2 to a higher oxidation state.

Iodine is only slightly soluble in water (0.001 M), but the solubility is vastly increased by the presence of iodide ion. The color changes from brown to deep red because of the formation of the triiodide ion, I_3^-. The triiodide ion is also known in solids such as NH_4I_3, X-ray investigations of which indicate that the I_3^- ion is linear. No electronic formula conforming to the octet rule can be written for this ion. Apparently an iodine atom, perhaps because of its large size, can accommodate more than eight electrons in its valence shell. In basic solutions, I_2 disproportionates to form iodide ion and hypoiodite ion (IO^-).

$$I_2 + 2OH^- \longrightarrow I^- + IO^- + H_2O$$

Further disproportionation to give iodate ion (IO_3^-) is hastened by heating or by addition of acid. Iodate ion in acid solution is a weaker oxidizing agent than either bromate ion or chlorate ion. This is shown by the oxidation potential

$$I_2 + 6H_2O \longrightarrow 2IO_3^- + 12H^+ + 10e^- \qquad -1.20 \text{ volts}$$

Since IO_3^- is a weaker oxidizing agent than ClO_3^-, iodates can be made by oxidizing I_2 with ClO_3^-. Furthermore, iodate salts are not quite so explosive as chlorates or bromates. The greater stability of iodates also is evident in the fact that HIO_3, unlike $HClO_3$ and $HBrO_3$, can be isolated pure (as a white solid). The latter acids detonate when attempts are made to concentrate them.

Whereas bromate cannot be oxidized to the $+7$ state, iodate can be; however, it takes a very strong oxidizing agent to accomplish the oxidation. In the $+7$ state, the oxysalts of iodine are called periodates, but there are several kinds of periodates. There are those derived from HIO_4 (metaperiodic acid), those derived from H_5IO_6 (paraperiodic acid), and possibly others. In the metaperiodates the iodine is bonded tetrahedrally to four oxygen atoms (this ion is analogous to ClO_4^-); in the paraperiodates there are six oxygen atoms bound octahedrally to the iodine atom. The fact that there are paraperiodates but no paraperchlorates is apparently due to the larger size of the iodine atom. As in I_3^-, it is necessary to assume that in the paraperiodates the valence shell of iodine is expanded to contain more than eight electrons. Paraperiodic acid, H_5IO_6, is moderately weak ($K_I = 5.1 \times 10^{-4}$), but metaperiodic acid, HIO_4, seems to be strong.

In going down the halogen group the atoms of the elements get progressively larger, and it becomes easier to oxidize the halide ion to the free halogen. This shows up in the instability of iodide solutions to air oxidation. The oxidation is slow for basic and neutral solutions but becomes appreciably faster for acid solutions.

So far as uses are concerned, iodine is less widely used than other halogens. It finds limited use for its antiseptic properties, both as tincture of iodine (solution of I_2 in alcohol) and as iodoform (CHI_3). Since small amounts of iodine are required in the human diet, traces of sodium iodide (1 part per 10^5) are frequently added to table salt.

27.6 ASTATINE

Since astatine does not occur to an appreciable extent in nature, all that is known about it is based on experiments done with trace amounts of artificially produced element. It can be made by bombarding bismuth nuclei with alpha particles, and its chemistry is studied by observing whether radioactive astatine is carried along with iodine through the course of chemical reactions. On the basis of such tracer studies, it is concluded that astatine forms an astatide ion (At^-) and compounds in two positive oxidation states, probably $+1$ and $+5$.

27.7 INTERHALOGEN COMPOUNDS

In view of the fact that halogen atoms combine with each other to form diatomic molecules, it is not surprising that an atom of one halogen can combine with an atom of another halogen. Thus, we have compounds such as ICl, iodine monochloride, which can be prepared by direct union of the elements. ICl can also be made by reaction of iodate with iodide in concentrated HCl.

$$6H^+ + IO_3^- + 2I^- + 3Cl^- \longrightarrow 3ICl + 3H_2O$$

Pure ICl exists as a low-melting red solid (mp, 27°C) which, when melted, can be electrolyzed to produce I_2 at the cathode and Cl_2 at the anode. Since molten ICl conducts electric current and since iodine is discharged at the cathode, it has been assumed that the liquid contains I^+ ions. In dilute acid solution, ICl hydrolyzes to give chloride ion and probably hypoiodous acid (HOI), but the latter disproportionates, giving the net reaction

$$5ICl + 3H_2O \longrightarrow 5Cl^- + IO_3^- + 2I_2 + 6H^+$$

ICl is sometimes used for adding iodine to organic molecules.

In addition to ICl there are other interhalogen compounds of the type XY. In fact, all combinations except IF are known. More surprising than these compounds of type XY is the existence of more complex interhalogens of types XY_3, XY_5, and XY_7. Although there are three examples of XY_3 (ClF_3, BrF_3, and ICl_3) and two of XY_5 (BrF_5 and IF_5), there is only one XY_7 (IF_7). All of these compounds are of interest as examples of failure of the octet rule.

27.8 QUALITATIVE ANALYSIS

Fluoride differs from Cl^-, Br^-, and I^- in forming an insoluble magnesium salt but a soluble silver salt.

Iodide can be distinguished from Br^- and Cl^- in that its silver salt is insoluble in excess NH_3. Its presence can be confirmed by oxidizing I^- to I_2, which imparts a violet color to CCl_4.

Both Br^- and Cl^- form insoluble silver salts, but AgBr is more yellowish than the pure white of AgCl. Furthermore, AgBr dissolves with greater difficulty in excess NH_3 than does AgCl. Finally, when Br^- is oxidized to Br_2 in the presence of CCl_4, the CCl_4 solution is brown whereas Cl_2 in CCl_4 is yellow.

The oxyanions ClO_3^-, BrO_3^-, and IO_3^- can be detected by reducing them in acid (by adding sulfite or nitrite) and then analyzing for the corresponding halide ions as above.

Perchlorate ion, once encountered only rarely but now becoming increasingly common, can be recognized easily because it is one of the few anions that forms a white, sparingly soluble potassium salt.

QUESTIONS

27.1 *Equations* Write balanced equations for each of the following changes: (*a*) dissolving of bromine in basic solution, (*b*) oxidation of chloride by chlorate in acid, (*c*) reaction of OF_2 with water, (*d*) reduction of paraperiodate by SO_2 in acid to give I^-, (*e*) reduction of triiodide ion by H_3AsO_3 to form H_3AsO_4.

27.2 Buffer   What pH change should occur when 10.0 ml of 0.010 M NaOH is mixed with 10.0 ml of a buffer that is 0.50 M in NaOCl and 0.50 M in HOCl?

27.3 Solid-state oxidation   The lattice energies of NaCl(s) and NaF(s) are 184 and 216 kcal mole^{-1}, respectively. By using the data of Figure 27.2, show quantitatively that F$_2$(g) should oxidize NaCl(s) to form Cl$_2$(g) and NaF(s).

27.4 Triiodide equilibrium   The solubility of I$_2$ in water is 1.1×10^{-3} mole I$_2$ per liter of solution. In a solution that is originally 0.10 M KI, it is possible to dissolve 0.045 mole I$_2$ per liter. Calculate K for the reaction I$_2$ + I$^-$ $\rightleftharpoons$ I$_3^-$.

27.5 Preparations   Use balanced equations to show how the following conversions can be made: (a) NaCl to HCl, (b) NaCl to NaClO$_3$, (c) KClO$_3$ to Cl$_2$, (d) NaBr to IBr, (e) HF to F$_2$.

27.6 Thermodynamics   From the $E°$ values calculate K for

$$2ClO_3^- + Br_2 \longrightarrow Cl_2 + 2BrO_3^-$$

27.7 Solution stoichiometry   Calculate the final concentrations of IO$_3^-$ and Cl$^-$ in a solution made by mixing 0.0030 mole I$_2$ with 0.100 liter of 0.040 M ClO$_3^-$ and enough acid to make 0.250 liter of final solution.

27.8 Solution stoichiometry   To 25.0 ml of a solution labeled 0.00100 M I$_2$ it is necessary to add 4.90 ml of 0.00500 M Na$_2$S$_2$O$_3$ for complete reaction according to the equation

$$2S_2O_3^{--} + I_2 \longrightarrow S_4O_6^{--} + 2I^-$$

What fraction of the original I$_2$ must have evaporated from the original solution?

27.9 Thermodynamics   For the reaction Cl$_2$(g) $\longrightarrow$ Cl$_2$(aq) the standard free-energy change is +1.65 kcal mole^{-1}. By using this value and assuming ideal behavior, calculate (a) the solubility of chlorine in water in equilibrium with 1.0-atm chlorine and (b) the value of the equilibrium constant for the disproportionation of aqueous chlorine in contact with 1.0-atm chlorine gas. (*Hint:* Use the concentration K given in Section 27.3.)

27.10 Oxidation potentials   (a) By using the potentials given in Section 27.3, show that HOCl and ClO$_3^-$ should disproportionate in 1 M H$^+$ solution. (b) Given that the oxidation potential for HOCl $\longrightarrow$ HClO$_2$ is -1.64 volts, show that HClO$_2$ should also disproportionate in 1 M H$^+$ solution.

27.11 Solid-state structure   Given that KF has the NaCl structure and a density of 2.48 g cc^{-1}. Assuming that K$^+$ and F$^-$ have the same radius, calculate what it is from this datum.

27.12 Dissociation equilibria   Calculate the pH of a solution that is simultaneously 0.10 M HF and 0.10 M HOCl.

27.13 Oxidation-reduction   What will be the principal final products in each of the following mixtures? (a) 25 ml of 0.10 M I$^-$ plus 75 ml of

0.5 M BrO_3^- (acid). (b) 25 ml of 0.10 M BrO_3^- plus 75 ml of 0.5 M I^- (acid). (c) 25 ml of 0.10 M I^- plus 0.075 mole Cl_2 (acid). (d) 25 ml of 0.10 M Br^- plus 0.075 mole HOCl (acid).

ANSWERS

27.2 From 7.49 to 7.51   27.4 710   27.6 $K = 8.5 \times 10^{-6}$ 27.7 0.019 M IO_3^- and 0.016 M Cl^- 27.9 (a) 0.062 M (b) 2.9×10^{-5} 27.11 1.35 Å

28 noble gases

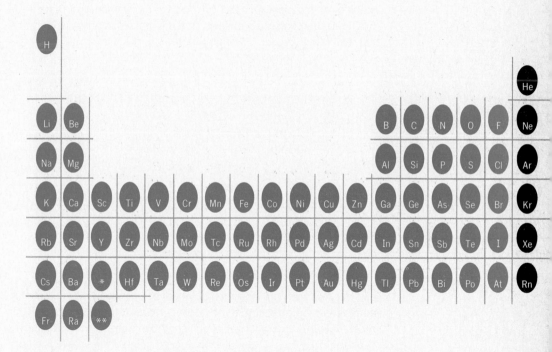

The last group of elements in the periodic table consists of six gases which, until recently, were believed to be completely unreactive chemically. Therefore, there was little to be said about the chemistry. When it was discovered in 1962 that compound formation could indeed occur, a flood of investigations both theoretical and experimental surged through the scientific community. A concerted effort was made to elucidate the principles and properties involved in forming these previously unexpected compounds. At present, our knowledge of these compounds is probably out of proportion to their technological value; however, the effort is justified in disclosing fundamentals of chemical bonding in compound formation.

As soon as the first compounds of these elements were prepared, there was a rush to drop the name "inert gases," which had traditionally been applied to group 0. Actually, the name "inert gases" is not bad, since admittedly the elements are not especially reactive. However, common usage seems to favor "noble gases" in analogy to the "noble metals," which also are not especially reactive. Another common name for group 0 elements is "rare gases."

28.1 THE ELEMENTS

The noble-gas group consists of the elements helium, neon, argon, krypton, xenon, and radon. Some of the atomic properties are listed in Figure 28.1. The ionization potentials are the largest of any element in the corresponding period of the periodic table, reflecting the special stability of the electron octet (or pair for $1s$). Xenon and radon have first ionization potentials smaller than the ionization potential of hydrogen (13.6 ev); except for helium and neon, the first ionization poten-

Element	Symbol	Z	Electronic configuration	Ionization potentials, ev		Effective gas radii, Å
				First	Second	
Helium	He	2	$1s^2$	24.6	54.4	1.40
Neon	Ne	10	(2) $2s^2 2p^6$	21.6	41.1	1.54
Argon	Ar	18	(10) $3s^2 3p^6$	15.8	27.6	1.88
Krypton	Kr	36	(28) $4s^2 4p^6$	14.0	24.6	2.02
Xenon	Xe	54	(46) $5s^2 5p^6$	12.1	21.2	2.16
Radon	Rn	86	(78) $6s^2 6p^6$	10.7	—	—

28.1
Properties of noble-gas atoms

tials are less than the ionization potential of fluorine (17.4 ev). There is nothing remarkable about the second ionization potentials; as with most elements, the removal of a second electron from the same subshell requires roughly double the energy needed to remove the first. The radii in the last column, showing the expected increase down the group, are derived from gas dynamics. They are not directly comparable with the kind of atomic radii discussed earlier for the other elements (Figure 2.19), which are deduced from observed bond distances. Only in the case of xenon do we know the conventional atomic radius. From the 1.9 to 2.0 Å values observed for the Xe-F distance in xenon compounds and the atomic radius 0.7 for fluorine, we can deduce that the xenon bonding radius is about 1.2 to 1.3 Å. This radius is markedly less than the gas radius listed in the table, in agreement with the usual result for other atoms.

Figure 28.2 lists some macroscopic properties of the noble gases. Only argon has appreciable abundance in the earth's atmosphere, from which it is extracted by liquefaction followed by fractional distillation. Helium, although rare in the earth's atmosphere, is quite abundant in the sun and on the heavier planets, where gravitational attraction can retain it in spite of its low mass. Because it is the product of radioactive decay (i.e., alpha particle, or $_2He^4$), helium occurs in some natural-gas deposits. Radon occurs in only trace amounts, because its nucleus is very unstable (longest half-life is 3.8 days for $_{86}Rn^{222}$); however, that it is found at all is the result of its being produced constantly from the decay of radium, coming ultimately from uranium.

As to physical properties, Figure 28.2 shows the not unexpected increase in melting point, boiling point, critical temperature, and heat of vaporization in going down the group. All are in line with increasing van der Waals attractions between the atoms as the number of electrons per atom increases. Helium, having the lowest boiling point of any substance known, finds extensive use as a cryogenic liquid, i.e., for producing extremely low temperatures. Helium is extraordinarily difficult to solidify, but it can be solidified under pressure at temperatures very near absolute zero.

Element	Vol. percent in dry air	Melting point, °K	Boiling point, °K	Critical temp, °K	Heat of vaporization, kcal mole^{-1}
He	5.2×10^{-4}	ca. 1 (26 atm)	4.2	5.2	0.022
Ne	1.8×10^{-3}	24.4	27.1	44.4	0.44
Ar	0.93	83.9	87.3	150.6	1.50
Kr	1.1×10^{-4}	ca. 110	120.3	210.5	2.31
Xe	8.7×10^{-6}	160	166.1	289.6	3.27
Rn	Trace	ca. 200	208.2	377.5	4.3

28.2
Properties of noble gases

Most remarkable of all is a peculiar transformation that liquid helium (He^4, but not He^3) undergoes below 2.2°K, where it converts from a normal liquid to a *superfluid*. Visually, this conversion appears with decreasing temperature as an abrupt transition from a violently bubbling liquid to a quiescent state, which nevertheless continues to disappear from the container. The superfluid has remarkable ability to flow through the tiniest of pinholes (too small even for most gases to penetrate) and apparently to defy gravity by climbing over edges of containers to reach a lower level. Its ability to conduct heat is nearly a thousand times as good as that of room-temperature copper.

Strange and wondrous as these properties are, it is only recently that they are becoming understandable and then only by a complex theory which treats a collection of particles as one giant entity instead of as individual particles. A closely related phenomenon is superconductivity, which appears in some metals below characteristic critical temperatures where electrical resistance completely vanishes.

Noble gases

28.2 COMPOUNDS

The search for compounds of the group 0 elements has been carried on for many years. Until recently, the best that could be done were the so-called *clathrate,* or "enclosure," compounds, in which noble-gas atoms were trapped in cagelike holes in a crystal lattice. The synthetic breakthrough came as a result of an observation by N. Bartlett that O_2 reacted with PtF_6 to form a solid compound, O_2PtF_6. X-ray diffraction data indicated that the compound consisted of O_2^+ and PtF_6^-. Recognizing that the ionization potential of the O_2 molecule (12.2 ev) is very close to that of xenon (12.1 ev), Bartlett tried the reaction between Xe and PtF_6. Reaction occurred readily at room temperature to produce a red solid, $XePtF_6$, the first real compound of a noble-gas element.

Since this discovery in 1962, a number of other compounds have been prepared. These are principally compounds of xenon (with fluorine or oxygen), but a few compounds of krypton and radon have also been prepared. Some of the compounds are complex. For example, xenon reacts with PtF_6, PuF_6, and RhF_6 to form compounds of the type $XePuF_6$, but not with the more stable hexafluorides such as UF_6. This observation, coupled with the fact that RuF_6 reacts with Xe to produce $Xe(RuF_6)_2$, suggests that the MF_6 may act as a fluoridating agent and not just as an electron acceptor.

Formula	Melting point, °C	Vapor pressure at 20°C, torr	ΔH_{evap}, kcal mole^{-1}	Bond energy, kcal mole^{-1}
XeF_2	*ca.* 130	3	12.3	39
XeF_4	100	3	15.3	32
XeF_6	46	27	9.0	32

28.3
Properties of xenon
fluorides

The most striking example of simple compound formation is the reaction of xenon with fluorine. For instance, heating of a 1:5 mixture of Xe and F_2 gases in a nickel container at 400°C followed by quenching produces a colorless solid product corresponding to XeF_4. Variation in the initial Xe-to-F_2 ratio leads to the compounds XeF_2 and XeF_6, also colorless solids. Some properties of these compounds are shown in Figure 28.3. Chemically, they all react with H_2 to produce HF and xenon. All dissolve in liquid HF and, in the case of XeF_6, there is about 30% conversion to ions, presumably XeF_5^+ and HF_2^-. In water, a variety of reactions occurs. XeF_2 oxidizes H_2O to O_2.

$$2XeF_2 + 2H_2O \longrightarrow O_2(g) + 2Xe(g) + 4HF$$

XeF_4 disproportionates to give Xe gas and some Xe(VI) species. After evaporation of the solution, the compound XeO_3 is obtained. This is a white, nonvolatile compound that is tremendously explosive (about like

TNT). It can be detonated by simple rubbing, pressing, or slight heating. Because XeO_3 is a frequent product of xenon-compound reactions, there is an element of added excitement in the work with xenon compounds. XeF_6 hydrolyzes in aqueous solutions to produce various products depending on the pH of the solution. In acid solution, Xe(VI) species are most stable [such as $XeOF_4$ and perhaps $Xe(OH)_6$*]; in base, Xe(VIII) species predominate. From NaOH solution, a solid of the formula $Na_4XeO_6 \cdot 8H_2O$ precipitates. X-ray studies show it to contain the octahedral ion XeO_6^{-4}, called the perxenate ion.

28.3 STRUCTURES AND BONDING

Because the noble-gas compounds were so late in arriving, there was awaiting an impressive array of elegant instruments for structural studies. Within one year of their preparation, many of the compounds became among the best characterized compounds in chemistry. Among the techniques brought to bear on the problem were X-ray, electron, and neutron diffraction as well as all types of spectroscopy including nuclear magnetic resonance, infrared, ultraviolet, and microwave (radar).

The shapes of the various molecules (shown in Figures 28.4 and 28.5) are as follows: XeF_2 is linear, XeF_4 is square-planar, XeO_3 is a pyramid, $XeOF_4$ is a square pyramid. As already noted, the Xe—F bond length is about 2 Å and the bond energy is about 35 kcal mole^{-1}. For Xe—O the bond length is about 1.8 Å. None of these values is unusual. Hence,

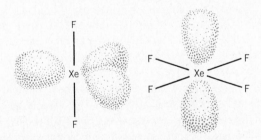

28.4
Xenon fluorides

xenon forms normal chemical bonds. The bonding can be accounted for by a valence-bond scheme which utilizes the $5d$ orbitals of xenon. In XeF_2, for example, one of the $5d$ orbitals can be hybridized with the $5s$ and the three $5p$ orbitals to form a set of five sp^3d hybrids. These are directed, as in Figure 28.4 (left), toward the corners of a trigonal bipyramid. (This can be visualized as two triangular pyramids sharing a common base.) Within the five sp^3d orbitals there are ten electrons (one from each of the bound fluorine atoms plus eight from Xe) to give

* This can also be written H_6XeO_6 and has been called xenic acid. It is hoped that the corresponding krypton compound can be formed so we can have "cryptic acid."

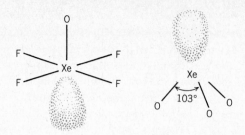

two ordinary covalent bonds and three unshared pairs. If the two F atoms are as far apart as possible, we get the structure shown on the left in Figure 28.4. For XeF_4 we need to use two of the $5d$ orbitals of Xe. The combination (two $5d$, one $5s$, and three $5p$) leads to six sp^3d^2 hybrid orbitals directed toward the corners of an octahedron. The twelve electrons (one from each of four F and eight from Xe) are disposed as four covalent bonds and two unshared pairs. With the four fluorine atoms in a plane, the structure is square-planar, as is shown on the right in Figure 28.4.

In $XeOF_4$, shown on the left in Figure 28.5, sp^3d^2 hybrid orbitals again lead to a basically octahedral disposition of twelve electrons (four from four F atoms, eight from Xe, and none from the O atom). The oxygen atom, two short of a full subshell, can be thought of as adding on to an unshared pair of the XeF_4 structure. In similar fashion, we can rationalize XeO_3. The three oxygen atoms of XeO_3 can be imagined to accept a share of three of the four electron pairs in the outer shell of a xenon atom. If the four pairs constitute an sp^3 set, the geometry is nearly tetrahedral, with three bonding pairs directed toward three vertices and the unshared pair going to a fourth. The observed O—Xe—O bond angle of 103° is reasonably close to the value of 109° expected for the tetrahedral angle.

For XeF_6 the simple valence-bond theory would lead to a prediction of a distorted octahedral structure. The reasoning goes as follows: Each of the six fluorine atoms makes available one electron to give a total of six. The xenon atom has eight valence electrons. Thus, the hybrid orbitals need to accommodate fourteen electrons, or seven pairs. Using the $5s$ and three $5p$ orbitals of the xenon, we need three more orbitals from the $5d$ set of Xe. This would give us the hybrid set sp^3d^3. As we have repeatedly seen, sp^3d^2 leads to an octahedron. The use of an additional d orbital for a pair of unshared electrons introduces a distortion the nature of which depends on which d orbital is used. The reason why the prediction of the expected structure is less definite for XeF_6 than for the other compounds is that in the case of XeF_6 the structure has not yet been experimentally determined. At first, the data suggested XeF_6 was a regular octahedron; later experiments showed it to be not so simple.

Finally, it might be noted that molecular-orbital methods provide alternate descriptions for the xenon compounds without using d orbitals. This is appealing because in Xe the $5d$ orbitals are considerably higher in energy than are the $5p$. (Note that in previously discussed transition-metal complexes the octahedral orbitals were d^2sp^3 instead of sp^3d^2; i.e., the d orbital used was one lower in principal quantum number than the s and p.)

To account for XeF_2, for example, molecular-orbital theory forms molecular orbitals by combining p orbitals of Xe with p orbitals of the two fluorines. The result is a linear three-center orbital somewhat analogous to the three-center banana bonds used for B_2H_6 (Section 23.2).

Figure 28.6 is a schematic version of how one of the molecular orbitals can be set up. With the three atoms being brought together along the x axis, the $2p_x$ orbitals of the F atoms can be considered to coalesce with the $5p_x$ orbital of Xe to give the bonding orbital shown. This orbital accommodates two electrons; it is bonding because of the relatively high electron density in the two Xe—F internuclear regions.

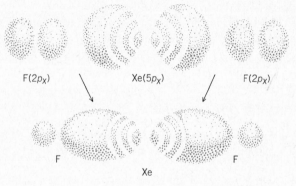

$F(2p_X)$ $Xe(5p_X)$ $F(2p_X)$

F   F
     Xe

28.6
Molecular orbital for XeF_2
(Xe $5p$ orbital is shown
schematically, since it is
much more complex than
$2p$ orbital of F.)

Actually, from three atomic orbitals three molecular orbitals must result. Figure 28.6 shows only the lowest-energy one of the three. Of the other two, one is nonbonding and corresponds to high electron density on the two F atoms, with little contribution from the xenon. This orbital also accommodates two electrons. The third molecular orbital, of very high energy, corresponds to considerable depletion of electron density from the internuclear region; hence, it is antibonding.

In the above set of molecular orbitals for XeF_2, we have four electrons to accommodate—one from each of the fluorine atoms and two that were originally in the $5p_x$ orbital of Xe. Of these four electrons, two can be placed in the bonding orbital and the remaining two in the nonbonding one. Since the antibonding orbital is unused, the net result is a bonding situation.

The above molecular-orbital construction can be extended by using successively the $5p_y$ and the $5p_z$ orbitals of the Xe to form additional molecular orbitals perpendicular to the set discussed above. In such fashion, XeF_4 and XeF_6 have been rationalized. However, there are seri-

Noble gases

557

ous difficulties, and the actual situation must be more complex than implied by successively combining the p orbitals as above. The final solution of the theoretical problems posed by the bonding in noble-gas compounds may be different from either of the above descriptions, but in any case, the final solution should have general applicability beyond these particular compounds.

QUESTIONS

28.1 *Stoichiometry*　Suppose you carry out a reaction in which 50.0 cc of F_2 gas at one atmosphere and 25°C is mixed with 10.0 cc of Xe gas at one atmosphere and 25°C in a nickel container of volume 2.5 cc. After heating to 400°C, the container is quenched at 0°C. Assuming complete reaction to give XeF_4 and ideal-gas behavior, calculate the final pressure.

28.2 *Equations*　Write balanced equations for each of the following reactions: (*a*) $XeF_4(g)$ with $H_2(g)$, (*b*) $XeF_6(g)$ with H_2O to give $XeOF_4$, (*c*) $XeF_6(g)$ plus base to give XeO_6^{-4} and Xe, (*d*) $XeF_4(g)$ plus H_2O to give XeO_3 on evaporation, (*e*) Xe plus RuF_6.

28.3 *Thermodynamics*　By using the data of Figures 3.8 and 28.3, estimate ΔH for the following processes:

$$Xe(g) + F_2(g) \longrightarrow XeF_2(s)$$

$$Xe(g) + 2F_2(g) \longrightarrow XeF_4(s)$$

$$Xe(g) + 3F_2(g) \longrightarrow XeF_6(s)$$

28.4 *Clausius-Clapeyron*　By using the data of Figure 28.3, estimate the temperature at which the vapor pressure of $XeF_2(s)$ becomes 15 torr.

28.5 *Oxidations*　It is observed that the addition of three moles of Xe(IV) species to water produces two moles of Xe, one mole of O_2, and one mole of dissolved Xe species. What might be the oxidation state of the xenon in solution, assuming no peroxide formation?

28.6 *Structure*　How could a magnetic experiment help to decide whether $XePtF_6$ exists as $Xe^+PtF_6^-$ or $Xe + PtF_6$?

28.7 *General*　Suggest reasons why most of the noble-gas compounds involve xenon and why most of them involve fluorine or oxygen.

28.8 *Structure*　(*a*) Imagine a structure for XeF_6 based on an octahedron of F atoms about Xe and a lone pair of electrons directed out either through the middle of an octahedral face or through the middle of an edge. By using only nearest-neighbor repulsions for the lone pair of electrons and its neighboring F^-, decide whether the repulsion energy should be greater for the electron pair in the face or on the edge. (*b*) Based on (*a*), how would you expect the octahedron to distort?

28.9 *Solution stoichiometry*　Suppose that 24.5 mg of a Xe compound has been dissolved in acid solution and titrated with potassium iodide to liberate I_2 and Xe(g). If complete reaction requires 15.0 ml of 0.040 M KI and liberates 2.45 cc of Xe gas at one atmosphere and 25°C, what is the apparent oxidation number of Xe in the original compound?

28.10 Structure   By using the valence-bond scheme of Section 28.3, predict the geometry for each of the following: ICl_2^-, ICl_4^-, IF_4, IO_3^-.

ANSWERS

28.1 11 atm   28.3 -54, -71, -93 kcal   28.5 $+8$ 28.9 $+6$

29 nuclear structure and radioactivity

In the preceding chapters the emphasis has been on interpretation of chemical behavior in terms of the electronic aspects of atoms. Little has been said of the nucleus because, except for its charge, which controls the electronic arrangement, it has essentially no influence on chemical behavior. In this final chapter some of the aspects of nuclear behavior are considered.

29.1 NUCLEAR STABILITY

As discussed in Section 1.4, the nucleus is thought to contain Z protons, where Z is the atomic number, and $(A - Z)$ neutrons, where A is the mass number, in a region which is about 10^{-13} cm in radius

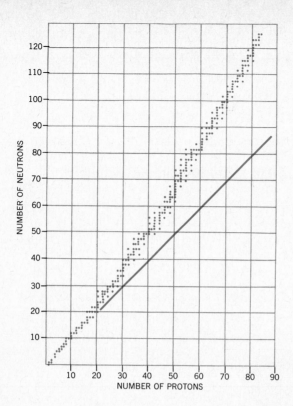

($r \cong 1 \times 10^{-13} A^{1/3}$ cm). The difficult thing to understand is how positive charges can be packed together into such a small space without flying
apart as a result of electrical repulsion. Neutrons must be at least partly
responsible for the binding, because, first, there is no nucleus consisting
solely of protons (plural!) and, second, the more protons there are in a
nucleus, the more neutrons required per proton for stability. This latter
point is demonstrated by the "belt of stability" shown in Figure 29.1,
where a plot is made of the stable (nonradioactive) nuclei. Each point
corresponds to a known nucleus containing a given number of protons
and a given number of neutrons. The straight line represents the line
along which nuclei would lie if they all contained an equal number of
neutrons and protons. It is evident that, whereas for the light elements,
nonradioactive nuclei contain approximately equal numbers of neutrons
and protons, for the heavier elements, nonradioactive nuclei contain considerably more neutrons than protons. Furthermore, it is observed that
nuclei which do not fall within this belt of stability are radioactive; i.e.,
their neutron-to-proton ratios are either too high or too low for stability,
and some kind of radioactive process (such as the processes discussed
in the following section) must occur in order to bring the nucleus back
to stability. The bigger question as to how neutrons act to bind the protons is still essentially unanswered.

At the present time there are two models used for the nucleus: the liquid-drop model and the shell model. The two are not mutually exclusive but emphasize different aspects of the nucleus. The liquid-drop model, first proposed by Bohr (1936), imagines the nucleus as consisting of neutrons and protons aggregated in a random, disordered fashion reminiscent of molecules in a drop of liquid. The strongest support for the model comes from the fact that the nuclear density is approximately constant at about 10^{14} g cc^{-1} for all atoms of the periodic table. The nuclear-shell model, due mainly to Mayer (1950), considers nuclear particles to be arranged in energy levels in the nucleus just as are electrons outside the nucleus. There are special complications arising from the fact that two kinds of particles (neutrons and protons) must be accommodated, but the model gains considerable support from the special stability of certain nuclei.* These especially stable nuclei occur whenever the number of neutrons or the number of protons equals one of the so-called "magic numbers," 2, 8, 20, 50, 82, or 126, a situation reminiscent of closed shells of electrons. Nuclei which contain simultaneously a magic number of protons and a magic number of neutrons are the most stable, for example, $_2He^4$, $_8O^{16}$, $_{20}Ca^{40}$, and $_{82}Pb^{208}$.

29.2 TYPES OF RADIOACTIVITY

If a nucleus lies outside the belt of stability, it tends to reach a stable configuration by a radioactive process which changes the number of neutrons and/or protons to a more favorable value. How does a nucleus get outside the belt of stability? There are two general cases which might be distinguished: *induced radioactivity* and *natural radioactivity*. Induced radioactivity results when stable nuclei are subjected to bombardment by other particles. If the energy of the incoming particles is of the proper magnitude, bombarded nuclei combine with incident particles to form new nuclei which, if unstable, undergo radioactive decay. An example of such a process occurs when $_6C^{12}$ nuclei are bombarded with protons which have been accelerated to high energies in a cyclotron. The process can be described by the nuclear equation

$$_6C^{12} + _1H^1 \longrightarrow _7N^{13} + \text{energy}$$

The equation is balanced in that it shows conservation of charge, denoted by the subscripts, and of mass, denoted by the superscripts. The nucleus produced, $_7N^{13}$, is unstable and lies below the belt of stability, with too few neutrons (six) for the number of protons (seven). Nuclear rearrangement occurs so as to give emission of a *positron*, a positive electron. This has the effect of decreasing the number of protons to six,

* One of the ways to indicate the relative stability of nonradioactive nuclei is to specify the amount of energy required to break the nuclei into isolated protons and neutrons. This amount of energy can be calculated by comparing the experimentally determined mass of a given nucleus with the total mass expected for the corresponding number of neutrons and protons. In the case of helium, as described more fully in Section 29.5, 629 million kcal is required to break up a mole of helium into protons and neutrons.

making the new nucleus a carbon nucleus, and increasing the number of neutrons to seven. The decay process can be written

$$_7N^{13} \longrightarrow {}_1e^0 + {}_6C^{13}$$

where $_1e^0$ represents the positron, a particle of $+1$ charge and essentially zero mass (like the electron), and $_6C^{13}$ is the resulting stable nucleus.

The rate at which radioactive disintegration occurs gives a measure of the stability of a nucleus and is usually expressed in terms of the *half-life* of the nucleus, the time required for half of a given number of atoms to disintegrate. For the above decay of $_7N^{13}$, the half-life, usually designated as $t_{1/2}$, is 10.1 min. This means that, of any aggregation of $_7N^{13}$ nuclei, half will have disintegrated in 10.1 min; in another 10.1 min, half of the remainder will have disintegrated, etc. Since radioactive decay is a statistical process essentially unaffected by changes in temperature or chemical binding, no one can predict which specific $_7N^{13}$ nucleus of a collection will disintegrate next. Only the probability of decay can be stated, and this is done by specifying the half-life. The shorter the half-life, the more probable the decay.

Radioactive decay is a first-order rate process (Section 10.2), which means that the rate of decay—i.e., the number of nuclear disintegrations per unit time—is proportional to the number of unstable nuclei present. This can be written

$$\frac{dN}{dt} = -kN$$

At any time t the number of nuclei present can be found by solving the above equation to give

$$\log \frac{N_0}{N} = \frac{kt}{2.303}$$

where N_0 is the number of nuclei at zero time. To solve for the half-life, we set N_0/N equal to 2, getting

$$t_{1/2} = \frac{2.303}{k} \log 2 = \frac{0.693}{k}$$

As with chemical reactions, k and hence $t_{1/2}$ can be determined from experiment by plotting $\log N$ versus t. Since the disintegration rate dN/dt is directly proportional to N, it is usual to plot log of the disintegration rate against time.

Natural radioactivity, as the name implies, refers to the decay of naturally occurring unstable isotopes. These unstable natural species are of long half-life, or else they are the result of other radioactive disintegrations and can be traced back to some long-lived isotope. For example, although there are no stable nuclei with atomic numbers higher than 83, still there are appreciable amounts of $_{90}Th^{234}$ in nature even though it has a half-life of only 24.1 days. With such a half-life, it would be expected that after a couple of years the $_{90}Th^{234}$ in nature would have disintegrated. The fact is, however, that $_{90}Th^{234}$ is constantly being regenerated by the decay of $_{92}U^{238}$. This disintegration

$$_{92}U^{238} \longrightarrow {}_{90}Th^{234} + {}_2He^4$$

has a half-life of 4.5×10^9 years. If we take the age of the earth as roughly 5 billion years, then approximately half the $_{92}U^{238}$ originally present at the creation is still with us and continues to replenish the $_{90}Th^{234}$ supply.

Although consideration of radioactivity as artificially induced or natural is convenient, it is sometimes more useful to classify radioactive reactions according to the types of particles which unstable nuclei eject. In terms of the belt of stability shown in Figure 29.1, three cases can be considered: (1) the unstable nucleus is above the belt of stability; (2) the unstable nucleus is below the belt of stability; or (3) the unstable nucleus lies beyond ($Z > 83$) the belt of stability.

In case 1 the nucleus has too high a neutron-proton ratio and can remedy matters either by ejecting a neutron or by forming and ejecting a beta particle (electron). Simple neutron ejection is rarely observed, because it usually occurs so rapidly. For example, the decay

$$_2He^5 \longrightarrow {}_2He^4 + {}_0n^1$$

to produce an alpha particle and a neutron ($_0n^1$) has been calculated to have a half-life of 2×10^{-21} sec, much too short to be observed.*

Beta emission is much more common. It corrects a neutron-proton ratio that is too high by removing one unit of negative charge and thereby increasing the positive charge of the nucleus. Since a β particle (or electron, designated $_{-1}e^0$) has very little mass, its emission does not change the mass of a nucleus appreciably. A few examples of β decay are:

$$_6C^{14} \longrightarrow {}_7N^{14} + {}_{-1}e^0 \qquad\qquad t_{1/2} = 5570 \text{ years}$$

$$_{11}Na^{24} \longrightarrow {}_{12}Mg^{24} + {}_{-1}e^0 \qquad\qquad t_{1/2} = 15.0 \text{ hr}$$

$$_{53}I^{136} \longrightarrow {}_{54}Xe^{136} + {}_{-1}e^0 \qquad\qquad t_{1/2} = 86 \text{ sec}$$

If, as in case 2, an unstable nucleus lies below the belt of stability, it has too low a neutron-proton ratio and must increase the number of neutrons, decrease the number of protons, or do both simultaneously. For such nuclei, one of the common devices leading to a gain in stability is to absorb into the nucleus one of the orbital electrons, usually one of the electrons from the K shell. Such K capture reduces the nuclear

---

* However, there are some neutron emissions which are delayed long enough that they are observable. These occur, for instance, in some of the products resulting from the fission of $_{92}U^{235}$ nuclei. A specific case of this is found in the decay of high-energy $_{36}Kr^{87}$ by the reaction

$$_{36}Kr^{87} \longrightarrow {}_{36}Kr^{86} + {}_0n^1$$

for which the half-life appears to be about 1 min.

charge by one unit, leaving the nuclear mass essentially unchanged, as in the following example:

$$_{18}Ar^{37} \xrightarrow[K \text{ capture}]{} {}_{17}Cl^{37} \qquad t_{1/2} = 35 \text{ days}$$

Invariably, when a K electron is captured, an outer-shell electron of the atom drops into the K shell to fill the vacancy, thus liberating energy, usually as an X ray.

Another device to raise a neutron-proton ratio that is too low is for the nucleus to emit a positron ($_1e^0$, a positive electron). This process, typified by

$$_{15}P^{30} \longrightarrow {}_{14}Si^{30} + {}_1e^0 \qquad t_{1/2} = 2.5 \text{ min}$$

decreases the nuclear charge by one unit and leaves the mass essentially unchanged.

In case 3 the nuclei lie beyond the belt of stability; they have too many protons crammed into one nucleus for stability, no matter how many neutrons are present. For nuclei with 84 or more protons, no one of the above steps by itself can lead to a stable nucleus. Instead, it is necessary to split off larger pieces, and even then a series of steps may be required. Most commonly, the piece split off is an alpha particle, symbol $_2He^4$ (two protons plus two neutrons), and, in fact, most of the heavy nuclei are alpha emitters. With $_{84}Po^{212}$ a single step is sufficient to reach stability.

$$_{84}Po^{212} \longrightarrow {}_{82}Pb^{208} + {}_2He^4 \qquad t_{1/2} = 0.3 \times 10^{-6} \text{ sec}$$

With $_{92}U^{234}$ many steps involving a combination of α and β decays are required, as in the following:

$$_{92}U^{234} \xrightarrow{\alpha} {}_{90}Th^{230} \xrightarrow{\alpha} {}_{88}Ra^{226} \xrightarrow{\alpha} {}_{86}Rn^{222} \xrightarrow{\alpha}$$

$$_{84}Po^{218} \xrightarrow{\alpha} {}_{82}Pb^{214} \xrightarrow{\beta} {}_{83}Bi^{214} \xrightarrow{\alpha} {}_{81}Tl^{210} \xrightarrow{\beta}$$

$$_{82}Pb^{210} \xrightarrow{\beta} {}_{83}Bi^{210} \xrightarrow{\beta} {}_{84}Po^{210} \xrightarrow{\alpha} {}_{82}Pb^{206}$$

Other steps leading to the same stable nucleus, $_{82}Pb^{206}$, are also possible.

Finally, to complete the discussion of the types of radioactive decay, mention must be made of γ rays (gamma rays). These are essentially bundles of energy, much like very high-energy X rays, which frequently accompany beta emission and positron emission. They represent the principal way in which excited nuclei can get rid of excess energy.

29.3 TRANSURANIUM ELEMENTS

Until recently it was thought that there were only 92 elements in the periodic table. However, as radioactive processes were studied in greater detail, it was observed that atoms of atomic number higher than 92 could be produced. These transuranium elements have now been extended up to $Z = 103$ and will probably go even higher (but not much).

The first transuranium element to be prepared (1940) was neptunium, made by irradiation of $_{92}U^{238}$ with neutrons. The nucleus formed, $_{92}U^{239}$, decays by beta emission

$$_{92}U^{239} \longrightarrow {_{93}}Np^{239} + {_{-1}}e^0 \qquad t_{1/2} = 23.5 \text{ min}$$

to produce $_{93}Np^{239}$, which is also beta active. It decays

$$_{93}Np^{239} \longrightarrow {_{94}}Pu^{239} + {_{-1}}e^0 \qquad t_{1/2} = 2.3 \text{ days}$$

to produce plutonium, the second transuranium element, which is alpha-active. Higher elements have been produced by similar irradiation of transuranium elements with neutrons or even with nuclei of a lighter element such as helium or carbon. The transuranium elements have different chemical properties and can be separated from each other by chemical means. The isolation of plutonium is important, because the element is used as a source of nuclear energy.

29.4 RADIOCHEMISTRY

In chemistry, radioactive nuclei are useful because they are easy to follow. Their presence can be detected even in trace amounts by the darkening of photographic plates or by the use of various devices such as the Geiger counter, which can count individual particles because of ionization of gases by the particles. These counters operate because an alpha particle, for example, in passing through a gas-filled chamber, produces ions which can conduct an electric pulse between charged plates.

One of the most useful applications of radioactive tracers to chemistry has been in the elucidation of the mechanism of complex organic reactions. For example, by feeding radioactive carbon dioxide (labeled with $_6C^{14}$) to plants, it has been shown that, in the photosynthetic conversion of CO_2 to carbohydrates, the CO_2 is first converted to an organic phosphate and then stepwise to sugar.

The fact that $_6C^{14}$ is radioactive has led to the development of a rather novel method for dating archaeological discoveries. The basic ideas of the method are as follows: Carbon dioxide in the atmosphere contains mostly $_6C^{12}$ and a little $_6C^{13}$, both of which are nonradioactive. In addition, there is a small amount of $_6C^{14}$ which, even though it is constantly decaying, remains rather uniform in abundance, apparently because cosmic rays act on $_7N^{14}$ of the atmosphere to form $_6C^{14}$. Because the rate of decay balances the rate of production, the ratio of $C^{14}O_2$ to $C^{12}O_2$ in the atmosphere does not change with time. Now, it is well known that plants absorb CO_2 from the atmosphere in the process of photosynthesis. So long as the plant is alive and growing, the ratio of $_6C^{14}$ to $_6C^{12}$ atoms in the plant carbohydrates will be the same as that in the atmosphere. However, once the plant has been removed from the life cycle, as, for instance, when a tree is chopped down, the ratio of $_6C^{14}$ to $_6C^{12}$ begins to diminish as the $_6C^{14}$ atoms undergo radioactive decay. The half-life of $_6C^{14}$ is 5570 years; therefore, at the end of 5570 years the ratio of $_6C^{14}$ to $_6C^{12}$ in the wood becomes half as great as it is in the atmosphere. To determine the age of a wooden relic or, for that matter, of any once-living material, a sample is burned to CO_2 and the ratio of $_6C^{14}$ to $_6C^{12}$ is measured.

Another application of radioactivity has been made in determining the rate at which an electron can be transferred between two similar species in aqueous solution. Such a transfer between MnO_4^{--} and MnO_4^- has been found to be very rapid; that between $Co(NH_3)_6^{++}$ and $Co(NH_3)_6^{+3}$, very slow. In the latter case one of the complexes is made with radioactive cobalt and mixed with the other, which is originally nonradioactive. From time to time the solution is sampled and the cobalt species separated to see how fast radioactive cobalt appears in the originally nonradioactive species. Since the loss of an electron by radioactive $Co(NH_3)_6^{++}$ produces radioactive $Co(NH_3)_6^{+3}$, the rate of appearance of radioactivity in $Co(NH_3)_6^{+3}$ measures the rate of electron transfer.

Perhaps the most spectacular application of tracer techniques has been the elucidation of chemical properties of artificially produced elements. In the case of mendelevium, element 101, with a sample of only 17 atoms it was possible to decide that its properties are somewhat similar to those of thulium ($Z = 69$).

29.5 NUCLEAR ENERGY

In the preceding sections of this chapter we have considered stability of nuclei with respect to radioactive decay. In this section we consider stability of nuclei with respect to conversion of mass to energy. That such a conversion can exist is seen by considering the helium nucleus. A helium nucleus is believed to contain two neutrons and two protons. Since the mass of a neutron is 1.00867 amu and since the mass of a proton is 1.00728 amu, we might expect that the mass of a helium nucleus would be

$$2(1.00867) + 2(1.00728) = 4.03190 \text{ amu}$$

However, the experimentally observed mass of the helium nucleus is 4.0026 amu. What has happened to the missing mass of 0.0293 amu? At present it is believed that, in forming a helium nucleus from protons and neutrons, mass is converted to energy. The amount of energy equivalent to the lost mass can be calculated from the Einstein relation

$$E = mc^2$$

where E is the energy equivalent in ergs (one erg is 2.390×10^{-8} cal) of the mass m in grams and c is the velocity of light, 2.998×10^{10} cm sec^{-1}. For the helium nucleus, the loss of 0.0293 amu of mass corresponds to the liberation of 629 million kcal per mole of helium. Conversely, the same amount of energy is required to break up one mole of helium nuclei into protons and neutrons and so gives a measure of the binding energy of the nucleus.

Similar calculations for other nuclei show that different nuclei have different binding energies. The binding energy per nuclear particle—i.e., the total binding energy of one nucleus divided by the number of protons plus neutrons in the nucleus—is plotted in Figure 29.2 for each of the different elements. As can be seen, intermediate elements of mass number about 60 have the highest binding energies per particle and are the most stable. The other elements are unstable with respect to conversion to them. This means, for example, that, if a heavy element such as uranium is converted to iron, energy should be liberated. Similarly, if a light element such as hydrogen is converted to iron, energy should also be liberated. Such conversions are the bases for utilization of nuclear energy.

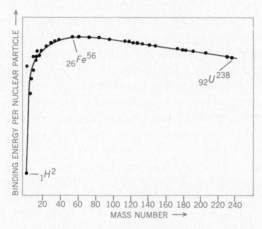

29.2
Binding energies of the elements (energy per nuclear particle)

One method by which nuclear binding energy is made available is *nuclear fission,* the process in which a heavy nucleus breaks down to two approximately equal nuclei of intermediate mass. A typical fission process is shown in Figure 29.3, where a neutron impinging on a U^{235} nucleus produces an unstable U^{236} nucleus that cleaves into a Te^{137} nucleus, a Zr^{97} nucleus, and two neutrons. Both the product nuclei have very high neutron-to-proton ratios and subsequently decay with the emission of beta particles. Actually, the fission shown is just one of the many ways in which a U^{236} nucleus can split. Some of the ways of splitting result in nuclei which undergo decay by neutron emission. Since in any fission more neutrons are produced than are needed to initiate the fission, once started, fission can become self-sustaining as a chain reaction.

29.3
A typical fission

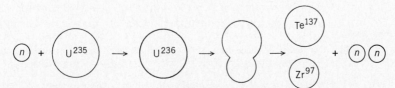

For the very heaviest transuranium elements, fission is spontaneous, but for others, for example, $_{92}U^{235}$ and $_{94}Pu^{239}$, fission can be initiated by exposure to neutrons. No matter how fission occurs, there is a change from a less stable nucleus (lower binding energy per nuclear particle) to more stable nuclei (higher binding energies per nuclear particle). In going from the less stable state to the more stable state, energy is liberated in large amounts. This release of energy by nuclear fission is the basis of nuclear reactors and atomic bombs. In nuclear reactors fissionable material* such as U^{235} or Pu^{239} is stacked together with some "moderator" material (heavy water or graphite) which can remove energy from the neutrons produced in fission so that they can be captured to initiate new fission. The rate of the chain reaction is controlled by the insertion of cadmium rods, which have the ability to absorb neutrons. The energy released by the controlled chain reaction appears principally as heat and can be removed from the reactor by a circulating coolant to provide power for steam turbines. In atomic bombs fissionable material is concentrated in a small region, so that the chain reaction builds up rapidly and tremendous explosions result. It has been estimated that the fission of 1 lb of U^{235} liberates the heat equivalent of more than 1000 tons of coal.

Another method by which nuclear binding energy can be made available is *nuclear fusion,* the process in which two or more light nuclei combine to produce a single nucleus of heavier mass. Because of the steepness of the binding-energy curve (Figure 29.2) at the low end, greater energy can be liberated per nuclear particle by nuclear fusion than by nuclear fission. However, the process has a much higher activation energy and so requires enormous temperatures (of the order of a million degrees) in order to occur. In the sun, temperatures are high enough that nuclear fusion can take place to produce the energy that the sun pours out into space. It has been proposed that the chief source of this energy is the conversion of hydrogen to helium. The following steps have been suggested:

$$2 \times (_1H^1 + {}_1H^1 \longrightarrow {}_1H^2 + {}_1e^0)$$

$$2 \times (_1H^2 + {}_1H^1 \longrightarrow {}_2He^3)$$

$$_2He^3 + {}_2He^3 \longrightarrow {}_2He^4 + {}_1H^1 + {}_1H^1$$

Net change:

$$_1H^1 + {}_1H^1 + {}_1H^1 + {}_1H^1 \longrightarrow {}_2He^4 + {}_1e^0 + {}_1e^0$$

For the consumption of 1 lb of hydrogen by the overall reaction, the energy liberated is equivalent to the burning of about 10000 tons of coal. Since the mass of the sun is so large and since it is mostly hydrogen, it would take a conversion of only 1% of the sun's mass from hydrogen to helium to keep the sun shining at its present rate for another billion years.

* Natural uranium is 99.3% U^{238} and 0.7% U^{235}. The more abundant isotope requires high-energy neutrons to initiate fission; the less abundant one undergoes fission with readily available low-energy neutrons. Therefore, in practice it is desirable to have uranium enriched in U^{235}. Separation can be achieved by the diffusion process described in Section 5.9.

Nuclear fusion, or thermonuclear reaction, as it is sometimes called, would seem impossible on the earth because of the high temperatures required. However, with new techniques, e.g., the release of energy by nuclear fission, temperatures high enough that thermonuclear reactions can occur have been produced on the earth. Hydrogen bombs are a spectacular illustration of the destructive violence that can be achieved when nuclear energy is rapidly released through nuclear fusion. The slow, controlled release of nuclear energy by nuclear fusion opens to man a source of energy that dwarfs any supply hitherto available.

QUESTIONS

29.1 Radioactive decay series   What will be the identity of the nuclei formed in the decay series starting with U^{235} and giving off successively, α, β^-, α, α, β^-, α, α, α, β^-, β^-, α?

29.2 Equations   Write balanced nuclear equations for each of the following processes: (*a*) alpha, beta decay of Th^{228}, (*b*) beta decay of K^{40}, (*c*) K capture by Cr^{51}, (*d*) positron emission by Ga^{58}, (*e*) gamma emission by Nb^{93}.

29.3 Half-life   The nucleus Na^{24} undergoes β decay with a half-life of 15.0 hr. How long would it take for the activity of a given sample containing Na^{24} to diminish to 1.0% of its initial value?

29.4 Half-life   You wish to carry out some experiments with F^{18} ($t_{1/2} = 1.87$ hr). Using scheduled airlines, the quickest delivery time from the nuclear reactor to your laboratory is 12.5 hr. How much F^{18} should you order in order to get one milligram of F^{18} into your laboratory?

29.5 Binding energy   Which nucleus has higher binding energy per nuclear particle: $_{28}Ni^{58}$ (57.941 amu) or $_{25}Mn^{55}$ (54.939 amu)?

29.6 Nuclear energy   How many kilocalories of energy will be released when two moles of $_1H^2$ (2.0141 amu) are converted to $_2He^4$?

29.7 Half-life   A given sample of a radioactive isotope shows an activity of 8640 counts per minute at one time and 7620 counts per minute one hour later. What is its half-life?

29.8 Transuranium elements   What isotope will result from the following nuclear processes? (*a*) $_{92}U^{238}$ absorbs a neutron and the product decomposes by two subsequent β^- emissions. (*b*) The product of (*a*) absorbs two neutrons and emits one β^-. (*c*) The product of (*b*) absorbs a neutron and emits one β^-. (*d*) The product of (*c*) is irradiated in a cyclotron so as to absorb an α and emit two neutrons. (*e*) The product of (*d*) is bombarded with boron nuclei ($_5B^{11}$).

29.9 Sr^{90} decay   You are given a sample of pure Sr^{90} ($t_{1/2} = 28$ years). The disintegration rate of the sample is 18000 disintegrations min^{-1}. What is the mass of the given sample?

29.10 Solar energy   (*a*) The sun presently radiates energy at the rate of 4.0×10^{33} ergs sec^{-1}. Its present mass is 2.0×10^{33} kg. Assume that all the solar radiation can be attributed to the process $4_1H^1 \longrightarrow$

$_2$He^4 + 2β^+, which liberates 27 million ev per helium nucleus formed. Assume also that in the beginning the sun was entirely hydrogen. What percent of the original hydrogen remains after the intervening time, estimated to be 4.5×10^9 years? (*b*) How long would be required for half of the present hydrogen to be used up?

ANSWERS

29.4 102 mg   *29.7* 5.52 hr   *29.9* 5.71×10^{-11} g   *29.10* (*a*) 99.9956% (*b*) 7.1×10^{13} years

appendix 1
nomenclature of inorganic chemistry

The names of the elements are listed inside the back cover of the book. Some of the elements also have Latin names (argentum for silver, aurum for gold, cuprum for copper, ferrum for iron, plumbum for lead, and stannum for tin) which appear in the names of compounds of these elements.

Compounds composed of but two elements have names derived directly from the elements. Usually the more electropositive element is named first and the other element is given an *-ide* ending. Thus, we have sodium chloride (NaCl), calcium oxide (CaO), and aluminum nitride (AlN). If more than one atom of an element is involved, prefixes such as *di-* (for 2), *tri-* (3), *tetra-* (4), *penta-* (5), and *sesqui-* (1½) are used. For example, AlF_3 is aluminum trifluoride, Na_3P is trisodium phosphide, and

N_2O_4 is dinitrogen tetroxide. When the same two elements form more than one compound, the compounds can be distinguished as in the following example:

	FeCl$_2$	**FeCl$_3$**
(a)	Iron dichloride	Iron trichloride
(b)	Ferrous chloride	Ferric chloride
(c)	Iron(II) chloride	Iron(III) chloride

In (a) distinction is made through use of prefixes; in (b) the endings -ous and -ic denote the lower and higher oxidation states, respectively, of iron; in (c), the Stock system, Roman numerals in parentheses indicate the oxidation states. In a given series of compounds, the suffixes -ous and -ic may not be sufficient for complete designation but may need to be supplemented by one of the other methods of nomenclature. For example, the oxides of nitrogen are usually named as follows:

N_2O	Nitrous oxide
NO	Nitric oxide
N_2O_3	Dinitrogen trioxide, or nitrogen sesquioxide
NO_2	Nitrogen dioxide
N_2O_4	Dinitrogen tetroxide, or nitrogen tetroxide
N_2O_5	Dinitrogen pentoxide, or nitrogen pentoxide

Compounds containing more than two elements are named differently depending on whether they are bases, acids, or salts. Since most bases contain hydroxide ion (OH^-), they are generally called hydroxides, e.g., sodium hydroxide (NaOH), calcium hydroxide [Ca(OH)$_2$], arsenic trihydroxide [As(OH)$_3$]. The naming of acids and of salts derived from them is more complicated, as can be seen from the following series:

ACID	SODIUM SALT
HClO, hypochlorous acid	NaClO, sodium hypochlorite
HClO$_2$, chlorous acid	NaClO$_2$, sodium chlorite
HClO$_3$, chloric acid	NaClO$_3$, sodium chlorate
HClO$_4$, perchloric acid	NaClO$_4$, sodium perchlorate
H$_2$SO$_3$, sulfurous acid	Na$_2$SO$_3$, sodium sulfite
H$_2$SO$_4$, sulfuric acid	Na$_2$SO$_4$, sodium sulfate

When there are only two common oxyacids of a given element, the one corresponding to lower oxidation state is given the -ous ending and the other the -ic ending. If there are more than two oxyacids, of different oxidation states, the prefixes *hypo-* and *per-* may also be used. As indicated in the above example, the prefix *hypo-* indicates an oxidation state lower than that of an -ous acid, and the prefix *per-* an oxidation state higher than that of an -ic acid. For salts derived from oxyacids the names are formed by replacing the ending -*ous* by -*ite* and -*ic* by -*ate*. Salts derived from polyprotic acids (for example, H_3PO_4) are best named so as to indicate the number of hydrogen atoms left unneutralized. For example, NaH_2PO_4 is monosodium dihydrogen phosphate and Na_2HPO_4 is disodium monohydrogen phosphate. Frequently, the prefix *mono-* is left off. For monohydrogen salts of diprotic acids, such as $NaHSO_4$, the presence of hydrogen may also be indicated by the prefix *bi-*. Thus, $NaHSO_4$ is sometimes called sodium bisulfate, though the name sodium hydrogen sulfate is preferred.

Complex cations, such as $Cr(H_2O)_6{}^{+3}$, are named by giving the number and name of the groups attached to the central atom followed by the name of the central atom, with its oxidation number indicated by Roman numerals in parentheses. Thus, $Cr(H_2O)_6{}^{+3}$ is hexaaquochromium(III). Complex anions, such as $PtCl_6{}^{--}$, are named by giving the number and name of attached groups followed by the name of the element with an -*ate* ending and its oxidation number in parentheses. Thus, $PtCl_6{}^{--}$ is hexachloroplatinate(IV). If the attached groups (*ligands*) are not all alike, it is customary to name the ligands in the same order in which they should be written in the formula—i.e., anion ligands generally precede neutral ligands. If more than one kind of anion ligand is present, the order is H^- (hydrido), O^{--} (oxo), OH^- (hydroxo), other monoatomic anions (in order of increasing electronegativity of the elements— for example, F^-, fluoro, last), polyatomic anions (in order of increasing number of atoms), organic anions (in alphabetical order). If more than one kind of neutral ligand is present, the order is H_2O (aquo), NH_3 (ammine), other inorganic ligands (in order of increasing electronegativity of their central atom—for example, CO, carbonyl, precedes NO, nitrosyl), organic ligands (in alphabetical order). To indicate the numbers of each kind of ligand, Greek prefixes are used: mono (usually can be omitted), di, tri, tetra, penta, hexa, hepta, octa. Instead of these prefixes, bis (twice), tris (thrice), tetrakis (four times), etc. may be used, especially when the name of the ligand itself contains a numerical designation (e.g., ethylenediamine, frequently abbreviated *en*). Some examples of the application of the above rules follow:

$CrCl_2(H_2O)_4{}^+$	dichlorotetraaquochromium(III)
$CrCl_4(H_2O)_2{}^-$	tetrachlorodiaquochromate(III)
$Cr(H_2O)(NH_3)_5{}^{+3}$	aquopentaamminechromium(III)
$Ga(OH)Cl_3{}^-$	hydroxotrichlorogallate(III)
cis-$PtBrCl(NO_2)_2{}^{--}$	*cis*-bromochlorodinitroplatinate(II)
trans-$Co(OH)Clen_2{}^+$	*trans*-hydroxochlorobisethylenediamine-cobalt(III)
$Mn(CO)_3(C_6H_6)^+$	tricarbonylbenzenemanganese(I)

In the case of complex-ion isomerism, the names cis or trans may precede the formula or the complex-ion name to indicate the spatial arrangement of the ligands. Cis means the ligands occupy adjacent coordination positions; trans means opposite positions.

appendix 2
mathematical operations

2.1 EXPONENTIAL NUMBERS

Multiplication by a positive power of 10 corresponds to moving the decimal point to the right; multiplication by a negative power of 10 corresponds to moving the decimal point to the left.

1.23×10^4 is 12300

1.23×10^{-4} is 0.000123

Numbers expressed with powers of 10 can be added or subtracted directly only if the powers of 10 are the same.

577

$$1.23 \times 10^4 + 1.23 \times 10^5 = 1.23 \times 10^4 + 12.3 \times 10^4$$

$$= 13.5 \times 10^4$$

$$1.23 \times 10^{-4} - 1.23 \times 10^{-5} = 1.23 \times 10^{-4} - 0.123 \times 10^{-4}$$

$$= 1.11 \times 10^{-4}$$

When powers of 10 are multiplied, exponents are added; when divided, exponents are subtracted.

$$(1.23 \times 10^4) \times (1.23 \times 10^5) = (1.23 \times 1.23) \times (10^4 \times 10^5)$$

$$= 1.51 \times 10^9$$

$$\frac{1.23 \times 10^{-4}}{1.23 \times 10^{-5}} = \frac{1.23}{1.23} \times \frac{10^{-4}}{10^{-5}} = 1.00 \times 10$$

In taking square roots of powers of 10, the exponent is divided by 2; in taking cube roots, by 3.

Square root of 9×10^4 is 3×10^2

Cube root of 8×10^{-12} is 2×10^{-4}

2.2 LOGARITHMS

A logarithm of a given number is the power to which a base number must be raised to equal the given number. There are in common usage two bases for logarithms: the base 10 and the base e ($e = 2.71828 \cdots$). These can be distinguished by writing "log" for the base 10 system and "ln" for the base e system. The latter is derived from the name "natural logarithm" for reference to base e. The two systems are related by the equality

$$2.303 \log x = \ln x$$

For numerical calculations it is usually more convenient to use the base 10 logarithms because of the decimal nature of our number system. However, when dealing with equations from calculus, natural logarithms arise because of relations such as $dx/x = d \ln x$. This relation between derivatives is true only for the case of natural logarithms. For numbers in the decimal system, tables of natural logarithms are quite extensive because each multiplication by a power of 10 does not simply add 1 to the natural logarithm. When needed, natural logarithms can be derived from a table of base 10 logarithms by use of the multiplier 2.303. The table on pages 580–581 gives the base 10 logarithms.

One principal use of logarithms in this text is in connection with pH, defined as the negative of the logarithm of the hydrogen-ion concentration. For a hydrogen-ion concentration of 0.00036 M the pH is found as follows:

$$\log (0.00036) = \log (3.6 \times 10^{-4})$$

$$= \log 3.6 + \log (10^{-4})$$

$$= 0.556 - 4$$

$$= -3.444$$

$$\text{pH} = +3.444$$

Sometimes, the reverse procedure is required. For example, if a solution has a pH of 8.50, its hydrogen-ion concentration can be found as follows:

$$\text{pH} = 8.50$$

$$\log [\text{H}^+] = -8.50 = 0.50 - 9$$

$$[\text{H}^+] = 3.2 \times 10^{-9}$$

The number 3.2 is the antilog of 0.50 (the number whose log is 0.50). Antilogs are obtained by using the table in reverse, i.e., by looking up the logarithm in the body of the table and then finding the number which corresponds to it.

2.3 QUADRATIC EQUATIONS

A quadratic equation is an algebraic equation in which a variable is raised to the second power but no higher and which can be written in the form

$$ax^2 + bx + c = 0$$

The solution of such an equation is

$$x = \frac{-b \pm \sqrt{b^2 - 4ac}}{2a}$$

where the $\pm$ sign indicates that there are two roots. Thus, the equation obtained in Example 2 of Section 12.2,

$$1.8 \times 10^{-5} = \frac{(1.00 + y)(1.00 - y)}{y}$$

when rewritten gives

$$y^2 + (-2.00 - 1.8 \times 10^{-5})y + 1.00 = 0$$

for which the roots are

$$y = \frac{-(-2.000018) \pm \sqrt{(2.000018)^2 - (4)(1)(1.00)}}{(2)(1)}$$

$$= +1.004 \text{ or } 0.996$$

The first root ($y = 1.004$) is inadmissible from the nature of the problem (y cannot be greater than 1.00, which represents all the acid present). The second root ($y = 0.996$) must be the correct one. It might be noted that the usual rules for carrying through significant figures do not apply when we operate with the quadratic formula.

Logarithms

	0	1	2	3	4	5	6	7	8	9
10	0000	0043	0086	0128	0170	0212	0253	0294	0334	0374
11	0414	0453	0492	0531	0569	0607	0645	0682	0719	0755
12	0792	0828	0864	0899	0934	0969	1004	1038	1072	1106
13	1139	1173	1206	1239	1271	1303	1335	1367	1399	1430
14	1461	1492	1523	1553	1584	1614	1644	1673	1703	1732
15	1761	1790	1818	1847	1875	1903	1931	1959	1987	2014
16	2041	2068	2095	2122	2148	2175	2201	2227	2253	2279
17	2304	2330	2355	2380	2405	2430	2455	2480	2504	2529
18	2553	2577	2601	2625	2648	2672	2695	2718	2742	2765
19	2788	2810	2833	2856	2878	2900	2923	2945	2967	2989
20	3010	3032	3054	3075	3096	3118	3139	3160	3181	3201
21	3222	3243	3263	3284	3304	3324	3345	3365	3385	3404
22	3424	3444	3464	3483	3502	3522	3541	3560	3579	3598
23	3617	3636	3655	3674	3692	3711	3729	3747	3766	3784
24	3802	3820	3838	3856	3874	3892	3909	3927	3945	3962
25	3979	3997	4014	4031	4048	4065	4082	4099	4116	4133
26	4150	4166	4183	4200	4216	4232	4249	4265	4281	4298
27	4314	4330	4346	4362	4378	4393	4409	4425	4440	4456
28	4472	4487	4502	4518	4533	4548	4564	4579	4594	4609
29	4624	4639	4654	4669	4683	4698	4713	4728	4742	4757
30	4771	4786	4800	4814	4829	4843	4857	4871	4886	4900
31	4914	4928	4942	4955	4969	4983	4997	5011	5024	5038
32	5051	5065	5079	5092	5105	5119	5132	5145	5159	5172
33	5185	5198	5211	5224	5237	5250	5263	5276	5289	5302
34	5315	5328	5340	5353	5366	5378	5391	5403	5416	5428
35	5441	5453	5465	5478	5490	5502	5514	5527	5539	5551
36	5563	5575	5587	5599	5611	5623	5635	5647	5658	5670
37	5682	5694	5705	5717	5729	5740	5752	5763	5775	5786
38	5798	5809	5821	5832	5843	5855	5866	5877	5888	5899
39	5911	5922	5933	5944	5955	5966	5977	5988	5999	6010
40	6021	6031	6042	6053	6064	6075	6085	6096	6107	6117
41	6128	6138	6149	6160	6170	6180	6191	6201	6212	6222
42	6232	6243	6253	6263	6274	6284	6294	6304	6314	6325
43	6335	6345	6355	6365	6375	6385	6395	6405	6415	6425
44	6435	6444	6454	6464	6474	6484	6493	6503	6513	6522
45	6532	6542	6551	6561	6571	6580	6590	6599	6609	6618
46	6628	6637	6646	6656	6665	6675	6684	6693	6702	6712
47	6721	6730	6739	6749	6758	6767	6776	6785	6794	6803
48	6812	6821	6830	6839	6848	6857	6866	6875	6884	6893
49	6902	6911	6920	6928	6937	6946	6955	6964	6972	6981
50	6990	6998	7007	7016	7024	7033	7042	7050	7059	7067
51	7076	7084	7093	7101	7110	7118	7126	7135	7143	7152
52	7160	7168	7177	7185	7193	7202	7210	7218	7226	7235
53	7243	7251	7259	7267	7275	7284	7292	7300	7308	7316
54	7324	7332	7340	7348	7356	7364	7372	7380	7388	7396

	0	1	2	3	4	5	6	7	8	9
55	7404	7412	7419	7427	7435	7443	7451	7459	7466	7474
56	7482	7490	7497	7505	7513	7520	7528	7536	7543	7551
57	7559	7566	7574	7582	7589	7597	7604	7612	7619	7627
58	7634	7642	7649	7657	7664	7672	7679	7686	7694	7701
59	7709	7716	7723	7731	7738	7745	7752	7760	7767	7774
60	7782	7789	7796	7803	7810	7818	7825	7832	7839	7846
61	7853	7860	7868	7875	7882	7889	7896	7903	7910	7917
62	7924	7931	7938	7945	7952	7959	7966	7973	7980	7987
63	7993	8000	8007	8014	8021	8028	8035	8041	8048	8055
64	8062	8069	8075	8082	8089	8096	8102	8109	8116	8122
65	8129	8136	8142	8149	8156	8162	8169	8176	8182	8189
66	8195	8202	8209	8215	8222	8228	8235	8241	8248	8254
67	8261	8267	8274	8280	8287	8293	8299	8306	8312	8319
68	8325	8331	8338	8344	8351	8357	8363	8370	8376	8382
69	8388	8395	8401	8407	8414	8420	8426	8432	8439	8445
70	8451	8457	8463	8470	8476	8482	8488	8494	8500	8506
71	8513	8519	8525	8531	8537	8543	8549	8555	8561	8567
72	8573	8579	8585	8591	8597	8603	8609	8615	8621	8627
73	8633	8639	8645	8651	8657	8663	8669	8675	8681	8686
74	8692	8698	8704	8710	8716	8722	8727	8733	8739	8745
75	8751	8756	8762	8768	8774	8779	8785	8791	8797	8802
76	8808	8814	8820	8825	8831	8837	8842	8848	8854	8859
77	8865	8871	8876	8882	8887	8893	8899	8904	8910	8915
78	8921	8927	8932	8938	8943	8949	8954	8960	8965	8971
79	8976	8982	8987	8993	8998	9004	9009	9015	9020	9025
80	9031	9036	9042	9047	9053	9058	9063	9069	9074	9079
81	9085	9090	9096	9101	9106	9112	9117	9122	9128	9133
82	9138	9143	9149	9154	9159	9165	9170	9175	9180	9186
83	9191	9196	9201	9206	9212	9217	9222	9227	9232	9238
84	9243	9248	9253	9258	9263	9269	9274	9279	9284	9289
85	9294	9299	9304	9309	9315	9320	9325	9330	9335	9340
86	9345	9350	9355	9360	9365	9370	9375	9380	9385	9390
87	9395	9400	9405	9410	9415	9420	9425	9430	9435	9440
88	9445	9450	9455	9460	9465	9469	9474	9479	9484	9489
89	9494	9499	9504	9509	9513	9518	9523	9528	9533	9538
90	9542	9547	9552	9557	9562	9566	9571	9576	9581	9586
91	9590	9595	9600	9605	9609	9614	9619	9624	9628	9633
92	9638	9643	9647	9652	9657	9661	9666	9671	9675	9680
93	9685	9689	9694	9699	9703	9708	9713	9717	9722	9727
94	9731	9736	9741	9745	9750	9754	9759	9763	9768	9773
95	9777	9782	9786	9791	9795	9800	9805	9809	9814	9818
96	9823	9827	9832	9836	9841	9845	9850	9854	9859	9863
97	9868	9872	9877	9881	9886	9890	9894	9899	9903	9908
98	9912	9917	9921	9926	9930	9934	9939	9943	9948	9952
99	9956	9961	9965	9969	9974	9978	9983	9987	9991	9996

appendix 3
definitions from physics

3.1 VELOCITY AND ACCELERATION

When an object changes its position, it is said to undergo a *displacement*. The rate at which displacement changes with time is called the *velocity* and has the dimensions of distance divided by time (e.g., centimeters per second). *Acceleration* is the rate at which velocity changes with time and has the dimensions of velocity divided by time (e.g., centimeters per second per second, or cm sec^{-2}).

3.2 FORCE AND MASS

Force can be thought of as a push or pull on an object which tends to change its motion, to speed it up or slow it down or to cause it to deviate from its path. Mass is a quantitative measure of the inertia of an object to having its motion changed. Thus, mass determines how difficult it is to accelerate an object. Quantitatively, force and mass are related by the equation

$$F = ma$$

where F is the force which produces acceleration a in mass m. If m is in grams and a is in centimeters per second per second, then F is in gram-centimeters per second per second, or dynes. Weight is an expression of force and arises because every object has mass and is being accelerated by gravity. Pounds weight is therefore a measure of force.

3.3 MOMENTUM AND IMPULSE

In dealing with collision problems it is useful to have terms for describing the combined effect of mass and velocity and its change with time. *Mass times velocity, mv,* called the *momentum,* determines the length of time required to bring a moving body to rest when decelerated by a constant force. Thus, for a particle of momentum mv to be stopped by a constant force F, the time required t is mv/F.

The *impulse* is defined for the case of a constant force as Ft, where t is the time during which the force F acts. Thus, for the stopping of a particle originally of momentum mv by force F in time t, the impulse is just

$$Ft = F\frac{mv}{F} = mv$$

This is true if the particle comes to a complete rest. If, however, the particle bounces back, as it would on collision with a rigid wall, the particle is reflected from the wall with momentum—mv (the minus sign indicating that the velocity is now in the opposite direction). The total impulse, counting the time for deceleration to zero and acceleration to $-mv$, is twice what it was before, or $2mv$.

In considering the pressure exerted by a gas, impulse comes in as follows. The pressure, or force per unit area, is the rate of collision per unit area times the effect of each collision.

$$\text{Pressure} = \frac{\text{force}}{\text{area}} = \frac{\text{number of collisions}}{\text{(time)(area)}} \times \text{?}$$

$$\text{?} = \frac{\text{(force)(time)}}{\text{number of collisions}} = \text{impulse per collision}$$

3.4 WORK AND ENERGY

When a force F operates on (e.g., pushes) an object through a distance d, work W is done:

$$W = Fd$$

If force is expressed in dynes (gram-centimeters per second per second) and distance in centimeters, then work has the dimensions dyne-centimeters ($g \cdot cm^2 sec^{-2}$), or ergs. One erg is thus the work done in moving one gram through one centimeter so as to increase its velocity by one centimeter per second all in one second. (For reference, 1 erg is approximately the work a fly does in one push-up.)

Energy is the ability to do work, and the dimensions of energy are the same as those of work. Kinetic energy is the energy a body possesses because of its motion and mass. It is equal to one-half the mass times the square of its velocity. Potential energy is the energy a body possesses because of its position or arrangement with respect to other bodies.

3.5 ELECTRIC CHARGE AND ELECTRIC FIELD

Electric charge is a property assigned to objects to account for certain observed attractions or repulsions which cannot be explained in terms of gravitational attraction between masses. Electric charge can be of two types, positive and negative. Objects which have the same type of electric charge repel each other; objects with opposite charges attract each other. A unit of charge can be defined as the quantity of electric charge which at a distance of one centimeter from another identical charge produces a repulsive force of one dyne in a vacuum. This unit of charge is called the electrostatic unit (esu). An electron has a negative charge of 4.80×10^{-10} esu. The practical unit of electric charge is the coulomb, which is almost exactly 3×10^9 esu. In coulombs, the charge of an electron is 1.60×10^{-19} coulomb.

An electric field is said to exist at a point if a force of electrical origin is exerted on any charged body placed at that point. The intensity of an electric field is defined as the magnitude of the electric force exerted on a unit charge. Any electrically charged body placed in an electric field moves unless otherwise constrained. The direction of a field is usually defined as the direction in which a positive charge would move.

3.6 VOLTAGE AND CAPACITY

An electric condenser is a device for storing electric charge. In its simplest form a condenser consists of two parallel, electrically conducting plates separated by some distance. The condenser can be charged by making one plate positive and the other plate negative. In order to transfer a unit positive charge from the negative plate to the positive plate, work must be done against the electric field which exists between the charged plates. Therefore, the potential energy of the unit charge is increased in the process. In other words, there is a change in potential energy in going from one plate to the other. This difference in potential energy for a unit charge moved from one plate to the other is called the potential difference, or the voltage, of the condenser. Voltage, or potential difference, is not restricted to condensers but may exist between any two points so long as work must be done in transferring an electric charge from one point to the other. The potential difference between two points is said to be one volt if 10^7 ergs is required to move one coulomb of charge from one point to the other. To move an electron through a potential difference of one volt requires an amount of energy, called the electron volt, equal to 1.6×10^{-12} erg.

Capacity is the term used to describe quantitatively the amount of charge that can be stored on a condenser. It is equal to the amount of charge that can be stored on the plates when the voltage difference between the plates is one volt. In general, the amount of charge a condenser can hold is directly proportional to the voltage; the capacity is simply the proportionality constant.

$$Q = CV$$

If Q, the charge, is one coulomb and if V, the voltage, is one volt, then C, the capacity, is one farad. The capacity of a condenser depends on the condenser design (area of the plates, distance between them) and on the nature of the material between the plates. For a parallel-plate condenser the capacity is given approximately by the following equation:

$$C = \frac{KA}{4\pi d}$$

where A is the area of the plates, d is the distance between the plates, and K is the dielectric constant of the material between the plates. For a vacuum the dielectric constant K is exactly equal to 1; for all other substances K is greater than 1. Some typical dielectric constants are 1.00059 for air at STP, 1.00026 for hydrogen gas at STP, 1.0046 for HCl gas at STP, 80 for liquid water at 20°C, 28.4 for ethyl alcohol at 0°C, 2 for petroleum, 4 for solid sulfur.

3.7 ELECTRIC CURRENT

A collection of moving charges is called an electric current. The unit of current is the ampere, which corresponds to a flow of one coulomb of charge past a point in one second. Since current specifies the rate at which charge is transferred, the product of current multiplied by time gives the total amount of charge transferred.

$$Q = It$$

If the current I is in amperes (coulombs per second) and the time t is in seconds, the charge Q is in coulombs.

The current that a wire carries is directly proportional to the voltage difference between the ends of the wire. The proportionality constant, called the conductance of the wire, is equal to the reciprocal of the resistance of the wire:

$$I = \frac{1}{R} V \qquad \text{or} \qquad V = IR$$

If V is the potential difference, in volts, and I is the current, in amperes, R is the resistance, in ohms.

There are two important kinds of current, direct and alternating. Direct current implies that the charge is constantly moving in the same direction along the wire. Alternating current implies that the current reverses its direction at regular intervals of time. The usual house current is 60-cycle alternating current, i.e., it goes through 60 complete back-and-forth oscillations per second.

appendix 4

FUNDAMENTAL CONSTANTS

Avogadro number, N	6.0225×10^{23} molecules mole^{-1}
Boltzmann constant, k	1.3805×10^{-16} erg deg^{-1}
Electron charge, e	1.6021×10^{-19} coulomb
Electron mass, m	9.1091×10^{-28} g
Faraday constant, $\mathscr{F}$	9.6487×10^4 coulombs equiv^{-1}
Gas constant, R	8.2057×10^{-2} liter-atm mole^{-1} deg^{-1}
Planck constant, h	6.6256×10^{-27} erg-sec
Speed of light, c	2.9979×10^{10} cm sec^{-1}

CONVERSION FACTORS

1 kilometer (km) = 1000 meters = 0.62137 mile
1 meter (m) = 100 centimeters = 39.370 inches
1 centimeter (cm) = 10 millimeters (mm) = 0.39370 inch

1 kilogram (kg) = 1000 grams = 2.2046 pounds
1 gram (g) = 1000 milligrams (mg) = 0.035274 ounce

1 liter (l) = 1000 milliliters (ml) = 1.0567 quarts

1 atomic mass unit (amu) = 1.6604×10^{-24} g
1 angstrom (Å) = 1×10^{-8} cm

1 electron volt (ev) = 1.6021×10^{-12} erg = 23.061 kcal mole^{-1}
1 calorie (cal) = 4.1840×10^7 ergs
1 liter-atmosphere = 24.217 cal

appendix 5
vapor pressure of water

Temp, °C	Pressure, torr	Temp, °C	Pressure, torr
0	4.6	23	21.1
1	4.9	24	22.4
2	5.3	25	23.8
3	5.7	26	25.2
4	6.1	27	26.7
5	6.5	28	28.3
6	7.0	29	30.0
7	7.5	30	31.8
8	8.0	35	42.2
9	8.6	40	55.3
10	9.2	45	71.9
11	9.8	50	92.5
12	10.5	55	118.0
13	11.2	60	149.4
14	12.0	65	187.5
15	12.8	70	233.7
16	13.6	75	289.1
17	14.5	80	355.1
18	15.5	85	433.6
19	16.5	90	525.8
20	17.5	95	633.9
21	18.7	100	760.0
22	19.8	105	906.1

appendix 6
oxidation potentials

HALF-REACTION	$E°$, VOLTS
$Li(s) \longrightarrow Li^+ + e^-$	+3.05
$K(s) \longrightarrow K^+ + e^-$	+2.93
$Rb(s) \longrightarrow Rb^+ + e^-$	+2.93
$Cs(s) \longrightarrow Cs^+ + e^-$	+2.92
$Ra(s) \longrightarrow Ra^{++} + 2e^-$	+2.92
$Ba(s) \longrightarrow Ba^{++} + 2e^-$	+2.90
$Sr(s) \longrightarrow Sr^{++} + 2e^-$	+2.89
$Ca(s) \longrightarrow Ca^{++} + 2e^-$	+2.87
$Na(s) \longrightarrow Na^+ + e^-$	+2.71
$La(s) \longrightarrow La^{+3} + 3e^-$	+2.52

Half-reaction	$E°$, Volts
$Ce(s) \longrightarrow Ce^{+3} + 3e^-$	$+2.48$
$Mg(s) \longrightarrow Mg^{++} + 2e^-$	$+2.37$
$Y(s) \longrightarrow Y^{+3} + 3e^-$	$+2.37$
$H^- \longrightarrow \frac{1}{2}H_2(g) + e^-$	$+2.25$
$Sc(s) \longrightarrow Sc^{+3} + 3e^-$	$+2.08$
$Pu(s) \longrightarrow Pu^{+3} + 3e^-$	$+2.07$
$Th(s) \longrightarrow Th^{+4} + 4e^-$	$+1.90$
$Be(s) \longrightarrow Be^{++} + 2e^-$	$+1.85$
$U(s) \longrightarrow U^{+3} + 3e^-$	$+1.80$
$Hf(s) \longrightarrow Hf^{+4} + 4e^-$	$+1.70$
$Al(s) \longrightarrow Al^{+3} + 3e^-$	$+1.66$
$Zr(s) \longrightarrow Zr^{+4} + 4e^-$	$+1.53$
$Mn(s) \longrightarrow Mn^{++} + 2e^-$	$+1.18$
$V(s) \longrightarrow V^{++} + 2e^-$	$ca.\ 1.2$
$Ti(s) + H_2O \longrightarrow TiO^{++} + 2H^+ + 4e^-$	$ca.\ 0.9$
$Zn(s) \longrightarrow Zn^{++} + 2e^-$	$+0.76$
$Cr(s) \longrightarrow Cr^{+3} + 3e^-$	$+0.74$
$U^{+3} \longrightarrow U^{+4} + e^-$	$+0.61$
$Ga(s) \longrightarrow Ga^{+3} + 3e^-$	$+0.53$
$Fe(s) \longrightarrow Fe^{++} + 2e^-$	$+0.44$
$Eu^{++} \longrightarrow Eu^{+3} + e^-$	$+0.43$
$Cr^{++} \longrightarrow Cr^{+3} + e^-$	$+0.41$
$Cd(s) \longrightarrow Cd^{++} + 2e^-$	$+0.40$
$In(s) \longrightarrow In^{+3} + 3e^-$	$+0.34$
$Tl(s) \longrightarrow Tl^+ + e^-$	$+0.34$
$Co(s) \longrightarrow Co^{++} + 2e^-$	$+0.28$
$H_3PO_3 + H_2O \longrightarrow H_3PO_4 + 2H^+ + 2e^-$	$+0.28$
$V^{++} \longrightarrow V^{+3} + e^-$	$+0.26$
$Ni(s) \longrightarrow Ni^{++} + 2e^-$	$+0.25$
$Mo(s) \longrightarrow Mo^{+3} + 3e^-$	$ca.\ 0.2$
$Sn(s) \longrightarrow Sn^{++} + 2e^-$	$+0.14$
$Pb(s) \longrightarrow Pb^{++} + 2e^-$	$+0.13$
$H_2(g) \longrightarrow 2H^+ + 2e^-$	Zero
$UO_2^+ \longrightarrow UO_2^{++} + e^-$	-0.05
$PH_3(g) \longrightarrow P(s) + 3H^+ + 3e^-$	-0.06
$SO_2 + 2H_2O \longrightarrow HSO_4^- + 3H^+ + 2e^-$	-0.11
$H_2S(g) \longrightarrow S(s) + 2H^+ + 2e^-$	-0.14
$Sn^{++} \longrightarrow Sn^{+4} + 2e^-$	-0.15
$Cu^+ \longrightarrow Cu^{++} + e^-$	-0.15
$U^{+4} + 2H_2O \longrightarrow UO_2^{++} + 4H^+ + 2e^-$	-0.33
$Cu(s) \longrightarrow Cu^{++} + 2e^-$	-0.34
$Fe(CN)_6^{-4} \longrightarrow Fe(CN)_6^{-3} + e^-$	-0.36
$V^{+3} + H_2O \longrightarrow VO^{++} + 2H^+ + e^-$	-0.36
$Cu(s) \longrightarrow Cu^+ + e^-$	-0.52
$2I^- \longrightarrow I_2 + 2e^-$	-0.54
$HAsO_2 + 2H_2O \longrightarrow H_3AsO_4 + 2H^+ + 2e^-$	-0.56
$MnO_4^{--} \longrightarrow MnO_4^- + e^-$	-0.56
$U^{+4} + 2H_2O \longrightarrow UO_2^+ + 4H^+ + e^-$	-0.62

Appendix 6

HALF-REACTION	$E°$, VOLTS
$H_2O_2 \longrightarrow O_2(g) + 2H^+ + 2e^-$	-0.68
$Fe^{++} \longrightarrow Fe^{+3} + e^-$	-0.77
$2Hg(l) \longrightarrow Hg_2^{++} + 2e^-$	-0.79
$Ag(s) \longrightarrow Ag^+ + e^-$	-0.80
$N_2O_4(g) + 2H_2O \longrightarrow 2NO_3^- + 4H^+ + 2e^-$	-0.80
$Hg_2^{++} \longrightarrow 2Hg^{++} + 2e^-$	-0.92
$NO(g) + 2H_2O \longrightarrow NO_3^- + 4H^+ + 3e^-$	-0.96
$Pu^{+3} \longrightarrow Pu^{+4} + e^-$	-0.97
$NO(g) + H_2O \longrightarrow HNO_2 + H^+ + e^-$	-1.00
$VO^{++} + 3H_2O \longrightarrow V(OH)_4^+ + 2H^+ + e^-$	-1.00
$NO(g) + 2H_2O \longrightarrow N_2O_4(g) + 4H^+ + 4e^-$	-1.03
$Pu^{+4} + 2H_2O \longrightarrow PuO_2^{++} + 4H^+ + 2e^-$	-1.04
$2Br^- \longrightarrow Br_2(l) + 2e^-$	-1.07
$2HNO_2 \longrightarrow N_2O_4(g) + 2H^+ + 2e^-$	-1.07
$2Br^- \longrightarrow Br_2 + 2e^-$	-1.09
$Pu^{+4} + 2H_2O \longrightarrow PuO_2^+ + 4H^+ + e^-$	-1.15
$ClO_3^- + H_2O \longrightarrow ClO_4^- + 2H^+ + 2e^-$	-1.19
$\frac{1}{2}I_2 + 3H_2O \longrightarrow IO_3^- + 6H^+ + 5e^-$	-1.20
$HClO_2 + H_2O \longrightarrow ClO_3^- + 3H^+ + 2e^-$	-1.21
$2H_2O \longrightarrow O_2(g) + 4H^+ + 4e^-$	-1.23
$Mn^{++} + 2H_2O \longrightarrow MnO_2(s) + 4H^+ + 2e^-$	-1.23
$Tl^+ \longrightarrow Tl^{+3} + 2e^-$	-1.25
$N_2O(g) + 3H_2O \longrightarrow 2HNO_2 + 4H^+ + 4e^-$	-1.29
$2Cr^{+3} + 7H_2O \longrightarrow Cr_2O_7^{--} + 14H^+ + 6e^-$	-1.33
$NH_4^+ + H_2O \longrightarrow NH_3OH^+ + 2H^+ + 2e^-$	-1.35
$2Cl^- \longrightarrow Cl_2(g) + 2e^-$	-1.36
$Au(s) \longrightarrow Au^{+3} + 3e^-$	-1.50
$\frac{1}{2}Br_2 + 3H_2O \longrightarrow BrO_3^- + 6H^+ + 5e^-$	-1.50
$Mn^{++} \longrightarrow Mn^{+3} + e^-$	-1.51
$Mn^{++} + 4H_2O \longrightarrow MnO_4^- + 8H^+ + 5e^-$	-1.51
$IO_3^- + 3H_2O \longrightarrow H_5IO_6 + H^+ + 2e^-$	-1.6
$Ce^{+3} \longrightarrow Ce^{+4} + e^-$	-1.61
$\frac{1}{2}Cl_2(g) + H_2O \longrightarrow HClO + H^+ + e^-$	-1.63
$HClO + H_2O \longrightarrow HClO_2 + 2H^+ + 2e^-$	-1.64
$Au(s) \longrightarrow Au^+ + e^-$	$ca.\ -1.7$
$MnO_2(s) + 2H_2O \longrightarrow MnO_4^- + 4H^+ + 3e^-$	-1.70
$2H_2O \longrightarrow H_2O_2 + 2H^+ + 2e^-$	-1.77
$Co^{++} \longrightarrow Co^{+3} + e^-$	-1.82
$Ag^+ \longrightarrow Ag^{++} + e^-$	-1.98
$O_2(g) + H_2O \longrightarrow O_3(g) + 2H^+ + 2e^-$	-2.07
$2F^- \longrightarrow F_2(g) + 2e^-$	-2.87
$2HF \longrightarrow F_2(g) + 2H^+ + 2e^-$	-3.06

After W. M. Latimer, *Oxidation Potentials*, 2d ed., Prentice-Hall, Englewood Cliffs, N.J., 1952.

appendix 7
equilibrium constants, K_C

DISSOCIATION CONSTANTS (first step only)

$CrOH^{++}$	5×10^{-11}	$H_2AsO_4^-$	5.6×10^{-8}
$CuOH^+$	1×10^{-8}	$HAsO_4^{--}$	3×10^{-13}
$ZnOH^+$	4×10^{-5}	H_2O	1.0×10^{-14}
H_3BO_3	6.0×10^{-10}	H_2S	1.1×10^{-7}
$CO_2 + H_2O$	4.2×10^{-7}	HS^-	1×10^{-14}
HCO_3^-	4.8×10^{-11}	H_2SO_3	1.3×10^{-2}
$HC_2H_3O_2$	1.8×10^{-5}	HSO_3^-	5.6×10^{-8}
HCN	4.0×10^{-10}	HSO_4^-	1.3×10^{-2}
$NH_3 + H_2O$	1.8×10^{-5}	H_2Se	1.9×10^{-4}
HNO_2	4.5×10^{-4}	H_2SeO_3	2.7×10^{-3}
H_3PO_3	1.6×10^{-2}	$HSeO_3^-$	2.5×10^{-7}
$H_2PO_3^-$	7×10^{-7}	H_2Te	2.3×10^{-3}
H_3PO_4	7.5×10^{-3}	HF	6.7×10^{-4}
$H_2PO_4^-$	6.2×10^{-8}	$HOCl$	3.2×10^{-8}
HPO_4^{--}	10^{-12}	$HClO_2$	1.1×10^{-2}
H_3AsO_4	2.5×10^{-4}		

SOLUBILITY PRODUCTS

$Mg(OH)_2$	8.9×10^{-12}	NiS	3×10^{-21}
MgF_2	8×10^{-8}	PtS	8×10^{-73}
MgC_2O_4	8.6×10^{-5}	$Cu(OH)_2$	1.6×10^{-19}
$Ca(OH)_2$	1.3×10^{-6}	CuS	8×10^{-37}
CaF_2	1.7×10^{-10}	$AgCl$	1.7×10^{-10}
$CaCO_3$	4.7×10^{-9}	$AgBr$	5.0×10^{-13}
$CaSO_4$	2.4×10^{-5}	AgI	8.5×10^{-17}
CaC_2O_4	1.3×10^{-9}	$AgCN$	1.6×10^{-14}
$Sr(OH)_2$	3.2×10^{-4}	Ag_2S	5.5×10^{-51}
$SrSO_4$	7.6×10^{-7}	ZnS	1×10^{-22}
$SrCrO_4$	3.6×10^{-5}	CdS	1.0×10^{-28}
$Ba(OH)_2$	5.0×10^{-3}	Hg_2Cl_2	1.1×10^{-18}
$BaSO_4$	1.5×10^{-9}	Hg_2Br_2	1.3×10^{-22}
$BaCrO_4$	8.5×10^{-11}	Hg_2I_2	4.5×10^{-29}
$Cr(OH)_3$	6.7×10^{-31}	HgS	1.6×10^{-54}
$Mn(OH)_2$	2×10^{-13}	$Al(OH)_3$	5×10^{-33}
MnS	7×10^{-16}	SnS	1×10^{-26}
FeS	4×10^{-19}	$Pb(OH)_2$	4.2×10^{-15}
$Fe(OH)_3$	6×10^{-38}	$PbCl_2$	1.6×10^{-5}
CoS	5×10^{-22}	PbS	7×10^{-29}

appendix 8
atomic and ionic radii

Ac^{+3}	1.18 Å	Au$^+$	1.37 Å	Br^0	1.14 Å
Ag^0	1.34	Au^{+3}	*ca.* 0.9	Br$^-$	1.96
Ag$^+$	1.26			Br^{+5}	0.47
Ag^{++}	0.89	B^0	0.81		
Al^0	1.25	B^{+3}	0.23	C^0	0.77
Al^{+3}	0.51	Ba^0	1.98	C^{+4}	0.16
Am^{+3}	1.07	Ba^{++}	1.34	Ca^0	1.74
Am^{+4}	0.92	Be^0	0.89	Ca^{++}	0.99
As^0	1.21	Be^{++}	0.35	Cd^0	1.41
As^{+3}	0.58	Bi^0	*ca.* 1.5	Cd^{++}	0.97
As^{+5}	0.46	Bi^{+3}	0.96	Ce^0	1.65
Au^0	1.34	Bi^{+5}	0.74	Ce^{+3}	1.07

Ion	Radius	Ion	Radius	Ion	Radius
Ce^{+4}	0.94 Å	La^0	1.69 Å	Ra^{++}	1.43 Å
Cl^0	0.99	La^{+3}	1.14	Rb^0	2.16
Cl^-	1.81	Li^0	1.23	Rb^+	1.47
Cl^{+5}	0.34	Li^+	0.68	Re^0	1.28
Cl^{+7}	0.27	Lu^0	1.56	Re^{+4}	*ca.* 0.7
Co^0	1.16	Lu^{+3}	0.85	Re^{+7}	0.56
Co^{++}	0.72			Rh^0	1.25
Co^{+3}	0.63	Mg^0	1.36	Rh^{+3}	0.68
Cr^0	1.18	Mg^{++}	0.66	Ru^0	1.25
Cr^{+3}	0.63	Mn^0	1.17	Ru^{+4}	0.67
Cr^{+6}	0.52	Mn^{++}	0.80		
Cs^0	2.35	Mn^{+3}	0.66		
Cs^+	1.67	Mn^{+4}	0.60		
Cu^0	1.17	Mn^{+7}	0.46	S^0	1.04
Cu^+	0.96	Mo^0	1.30	S^{--}	1.84
Cu^{++}	0.72	Mo^{+4}	0.70	S^{+4}	0.37
		Mo^{+6}	0.62	S^{+6}	0.30
Dy^0	1.60			Sb^0	1.41
Dy^{+3}	0.92	N^0	0.70	Sb^{+3}	0.76
		N^{+3}	0.16	Sb^{+5}	0.62
		N^{+5}	0.13	Sc^0	1.44
Er^0	1.58	Na^0	1.57	Sc^{+3}	0.81
Er^{+3}	0.89	Na^+	0.97	Se^0	1.17
Eu^0	1.85	Nb^0	1.34	Se^{--}	1.98
Eu^{+3}	0.98	Nb^{+4}	0.74	Se^{+4}	0.50
		Nb^{+5}	0.69	Se^{+6}	0.42
F^0	0.64	Nd^{+3}	1.04	Si^0	1.17
F^-	1.33	Ni^0	1.15	Si^{+4}	0.42
Fe^0	1.17	Ni^{++}	0.69	Sm^0	1.62
Fe^{++}	0.74	Np^{+3}	1.10	Sm^{+3}	1.00
Fe^{+3}	0.64	Np^{+4}	0.95	Sn^0	1.40
				Sn^{++}	0.93
Ga^0	1.25	O^{--}	1.40	Sn^{+4}	0.71
Ga^{+3}	0.62	O^0	0.66	Sr^0	1.91
Gd^0	1.62	Os^0	1.26	Sr^{++}	1.12
Gd^{+3}	0.97	Os^{+4}	0.69		
Ge^0	1.22				
Ge^{++}	0.73	P^0	1.10	Ta^0	1.34
Ge^{+4}	0.53	P^{+3}	0.44	Ta^{+5}	0.68
		P^{+5}	0.35	Tb^0	1.61
Hf^0	1.44	Pa^{+4}	0.98	Tb^{+3}	0.93
Hf^{+4}	0.78	Pb^0	1.54	Tb^{+4}	0.81
Hg^0	1.44	Pb^{++}	1.20	Tc^0	1.27
Hg^{++}	1.10	Pb^{+4}	0.84	Tc^{+7}	0.56
Ho^0	1.58	Pd^0	1.28	Te^0	1.37
Ho^{+3}	0.91	Pd^{++}	0.80	Te^{--}	2.21
		Pd^{+4}	0.65	Te^{+4}	*ca.* 0.7
I^0	1.33	Pm^0	1.63	Te^{+6}	0.56
I^-	2.20	Pm^{+3}	1.06	Th^0	1.65
I^{+5}	0.62	Po^0	1.53	Th^{+4}	1.02
I^{+7}	0.50	Pr^0	1.64	Ti^0	1.32
In^0	1.50	Pr^{+3}	1.06	Ti^{+3}	0.76
In^{+3}	0.81	Pr^{+4}	0.92	Ti^{+4}	0.68
Ir^0	1.27	Pt^0	1.30	Tl^0	1.55
Ir^{+4}	0.68	Pt^{++}	0.80	Tl^+	1.47
		Pt^{+4}	0.65	Tl^{+3}	0.95
K^0	2.03	Pu^{+3}	1.08	Tm^0	1.58
K^+	1.33	Pu^{+4}	0.93	Tm^{+3}	0.87

U^0	1.42 Å	V^{+4}	0.63 Å	Y^0	1.62 Å
U^{+4}	0.97	V^{+5}	0.59	Y^{+3}	0.92
U^{+6}	0.80				
				Zn^0	1.25
V^0	1.22	W^0	1.30	Zn^{++}	0.74
V^{++}	0.88	W^{+4}	0.70	Zr^0	1.45
V^{+3}	0.74	W^{+6}	0.62	Zr^{+4}	0.79

appendix 9
references

References of general utility covering many of the topics in this text are *Inorganic Chemistry: Principles and Elements* by M. J. Sienko, R. A. Plane, and R. E. Hester (Benjamin), *Introduction to Physical Inorganic Chemistry* by K. B. Harvey and G. B. Porter (Addison-Wesley), and *Advanced Inorganic Chemistry* by F. A. Cotton and G. Wilkinson (Interscience).

Additional information and background material can be found in the following books, which are listed by the chapters to which they most apply:

1   *Atomic Spectra and Atomic Structure* by G. Herzberg (Dover), *Modern Physics* by J. C. Slater (McGraw-Hill), and *Modern Physics* by R. L. Sproull (Wiley).

2, 3   *Electronic Structure and Chemical Binding* by O. K. Rice (McGraw-Hill), *Nature of the Chemical Bond* by L. Pauling (Cornell), *Electrons and Chemical Bonding* by H. B. Gray (Benjamin), *Chemical Bonding* by A. L. Companion (McGraw-Hill), and *Valence* by C. A. Coulson (Oxford).

4   *Stoichiometry and Structure* by M. J. Sienko (Benjamin).

5, 7   *Physical Chemistry* by G. M. Barrow (McGraw-Hill) and *An Introduction to Molecular Kinetic Theory* by J. H. Hildebrand (Reinhold).

6   *Introduction to Solids* by L. V. Azároff (McGraw-Hill).

8, 9   *Metal Ions in Solution* by J. P. Hunt (Benjamin) and *Electrolyte Solutions* by R. A. Robinson and R. H. Stokes (Butterworth).

10   *How Chemical Reactions Occur* by E. L. King (Benjamin) and *Inorganic Reaction Mechanisms* by J. O. Edwards (Benjamin).

11, 12   *Equilibrium* by M. J. Sienko (Benjamin).

13   *The Principles of Electrochemistry* by D. A. MacInnes (Reinhold) and *Oxidation Potentials* by W. M. Latimer (Prentice-Hall).

14   *Elementary Chemical Thermodynamics* by B. H. Mahan (Benjamin) and *Thermodynamics* by G. N. Lewis, M. Randall, K. S. Pitzer, and L. Brewer (McGraw-Hill).

15–27   *Reference Book of Inorganic Chemistry* by W. M. Latimer and J. H. Hildebrand (Macmillan), *Structural Inorganic Chemistry* by A. F. Wells (Oxford), *Inorganic Chemistry* by T. Moeller (Wiley), *Inorganic Chemistry* by J. Kleinberg, W. J. Argersinger, Jr., and E. Griswold (Heath).

19   *Transition-metal Chemistry* by L. E. Orgel (Methuen) and *Coordination Chemistry* by F. Basolo and R. C. Johnson (Benjamin).

28   *Noble-gas Compounds* edited by H. H. Hyman (Chicago).

29   *Nuclear and Radiochemistry* by G. Friedlander and J. W. Kennedy (Wiley).

Footnotes   *New Latin Grammar* by C. E. Bennett (Allyn and Bacon), *Odes and Epodes by Horace* edited by C. E. Bennett (Allyn and Bacon).

index

Page numbers followed by *n.* refer to footnotes, by *t.* to tables.

606

E° (standard emf), for alkaline-earth elements, 373–375
standard free-energy change and, 322–323
table of, 593–595
e, electron change, 589
e, log base, 578
e_g orbitals, 393
ΔE, 310–311
"earth," 371
Earth's crust, 332
Edison cell, 298, 436
Edge dislocation, 145
EDTA, 399
Einstein relation, 568
Einsteinium, 409
Electric charge, 585
Electric conductivity, 288–290
Electric current, 586
Electric field, 288, 585
Electric resistance, transition elements, 389–390
Electrochemistry, 287–308
Electrolysis, 290–295
aqueous sodium chloride, 292–293
aqueous sodium sulfate, 293
laws of, 294–295
molten sodium chloride, 290–291
Electrolytes, 180–186
strong, 181
weak, 181
Electrolytic cells, 290–295
Electrolytic conduction, 288
Electrolytic current, 289
Electrolytic hydrogen, 332
Electromagnetic radiation, 7–8
Electromotive force series, 302
Electron, 2–6
valence, 51
Electron affinity, 43–45
Electron charge, 4, 589
Electron configuration, 28–29
transition elements, 388–389
Electron mass, 11, 589
Electron shell, 33
Electron spin, 35–36
Electron volt, 42, 589
Electronegativity, 59–62
table, 60
Electrophoresis, 194–195
Electrorefining, 445–446

Electrovalent bond, 51
Element abundance in crust, 332
Elements, rare-earth, 406–408
transition, 387–460
(See also Group)
e/m, 3
Embrittlement by hydrogen, 336
Emerald, 377
emf series, 302
Emulsions, 192–193
en, 400, 575
Enantiomers, 402
Enantiomorphs, 402
Energy, 585
activation, 227, 230
bond, 61
crystal, 144–145
free, 166–169
lattice, 144
mass conversion to, 568–571
unavailable, 168
Energy distribution in gas, 121
Energy levels, 22–30
Enthalpy, 167, 311
Entropy, 166–169, 316
Enzymes, 229
Epsom salt, 380
Equation balancing, 90–95
Equation, chemical, calculations, 95–98
net, 90
Equation of state, 117–118
van der Waals, 118
Equilibrium, 239–286
aqueous solution, 259–286
change with temperature, 324–326
chemical kinetics and, 242
and free energy, 318
heterogeneous, 247–248
hydrogen-iodine, 244–247
law of, 242
simultaneous, 277–283
temperature effect on, 252–253
Equilibrium calculations, 244–247
Equilibrium constant, 241, 243–244
standard free-energy change and, 320–321
table of, 597–598
Equilibrium state, 240
Equilibrium vapor pressure, 153–157
Equivalence point, 269
Equivalents, 98–100, 215–216

ATOMIC MASSES REFERRED TO C^{12} = 12.0000

ELEMENT	SYMBOL	ATOMIC NUMBER	ATOMIC MASS	ELEMENT	SYMBOL	ATOMIC NUMBER	ATOMIC MASS
Actinium	Ac	89	[227]	Erbium	Er	68	167.26
Aluminum	Al	13	26.9815	Europium	Eu	63	151.96
Americium	Am	95	[243]	Fermium	Fm	100	[253]
Antimony	Sb	51	121.75	Fluorine	F	9	18.9984
Argon	Ar	18	39.948	Francium	Fr	87	[223]
Arsenic	As	33	74.9216	Gadolinium	Gd	64	157.25
Astatine	At	85	[210]	Gallium	Ga	31	69.72
Barium	Ba	56	137.34	Germanium	Ge	32	72.59
Berkelium	Bk	97	[249]	Gold	Au	79	196.967
Beryllium	Be	4	9.0122	Hafnium	Hf	72	178.49
Bismuth	Bi	83	208.980	Helium	He	2	4.0026
Boron	B	5	10.811	Holmium	Ho	67	164.930
Bromine	Br	35	79.904	Hydrogen	H	1	1.00797
Cadmium	Cd	48	112.40	Indium	In	49	114.82
Calcium	Ca	20	40.08	Iodine	I	53	126.9044
Californium	Cf	98	[251]	Iridium	Ir	77	192.2
Carbon	C	6	12.01115	Iron	Fe	26	55.847
Cerium	Ce	58	140.12	Krypton	Kr	36	83.80
Cesium	Cs	55	132.905	Lanthanum	La	57	138.91
Chlorine	Cl	17	35.453	Lawrencium	Lw	103	[257]
Chromium	Cr	24	51.996	Lead	Pb	82	207.19
Cobalt	Co	27	58.9332	Lithium	Li	3	6.939
Copper	Cu	29	63.546	Lutetium	Lu	71	174.97
Curium	Cm	96	[247]	Magnesium	Mg	12	24.312
Dysprosium	Dy	66	162.50	Manganese	Mn	25	54.9380
Einsteinium	Es	99	[254]	Mendelevium	Md	101	[256]